Introduction to Quantitative
Methods and Finance

PEARSON CUSTOM PUBLISHING

Introduction to Quantitative Methods and Finance

Compiled from:

Mathematics for Economics and Business
Sixth Edition
by Ian Jacques

Statistics for Economics, Accounting and Business Studies
Fifth Edition
by Michael Barrow

Fundamentals of Investments
by Haim Levy

ALWAYS LEARNING

PEARSON

Harlow, England • London • New York • Boston • San Francisco • Toronto • Sydney • Auckland • Singapore • Hong Kong
Tokyo • Seoul • Taipei • New Delhi • Cape Town • Sao Paulo • Mexico City • Madrid • Amsterdam • Munich • Paris • Milan

Pearson Education Limited
Edinburgh Gate
Harlow
Essex CM20 2JE

And associated companies throughout the world

Visit us on the World Wide Web at:
www.pearsoned.co.uk

ISBN 978 1 78086 532 4

Printed and bound in Italy

Contents

CHAPTER 1
Linear Equations

The main aim of this chapter is to introduce the mathematics of linear equations. This is an obvious first choice in an introductory text, since it is an easy topic which has many applications. There are seven sections, which are intended to be read in the order that they appear.

Sections 1.1, 1.2, 1.3, 1.4 and 1.6 are devoted to mathematical methods. They serve to revise the rules of arithmetic and algebra, which you probably met at school but may have forgotten. In particular, the properties of negative numbers and fractions are considered. A reminder is given on how to multiply out brackets and how to manipulate mathematical expressions. You are also shown how to solve simultaneous linear equations. Systems of two equations in two unknowns can be solved using graphs, which are described in Section 1.3. However, the preferred method uses elimination, which is considered in Section 1.4. This algebraic approach has the advantage that it always gives an exact solution and it extends readily to larger systems of equations.

The remaining two sections are reserved for applications in microeconomics and macroeconomics. You may be pleasantly surprised by how much economic theory you can analyse using just the basic mathematical tools considered here. Section 1.5 introduces the fundamental concept of an economic function and describes how to calculate equilibrium prices and quantities in supply and demand theory. Section 1.7 deals with national income determination in simple macroeconomic models.

The first six sections underpin the rest of the book and are essential reading. The final section is not quite as important and can be omitted at this stage.

SECTION 1.1
Introduction to algebra

Objectives

At the end of this section you should be able to:

- Add, subtract, multiply and divide negative numbers.
- Understand what is meant by an algebraic expression.
- Evaluate algebraic expressions numerically.
- Simplify algebraic expressions by collecting like terms.
- Multiply out brackets.
- Factorize algebraic expressions.

ALGEBRA IS BORING

There is no getting away from the fact that algebra *is* boring. Doubtless there are a few enthusiasts who get a kick out of algebraic manipulation, but economics and business students are rarely to be found in this category. Indeed, the mere mention of the word 'algebra' is enough to strike fear into the heart of many a first-year student. Unfortunately, you cannot get very far with mathematics unless you have completely mastered this topic. An apposite analogy is the game of chess. Before you can begin to play a game of chess it is necessary to go through the tedium of learning the moves of individual pieces. In the same way it is essential that you learn the rules of algebra before you can enjoy the 'game' of mathematics. Of course, just because you know the rules does not mean that you are going to excel at the game and no one is expecting you to become a grandmaster of mathematics. However, you should at least be able to follow the mathematics presented in economics books and journals, as well as being able to solve simple problems for yourself.

Advice

If you have studied mathematics recently then you will find the material in the first few sections of the book fairly straightforward. You may prefer just to try the questions in the starred exercise at the end of each section to get yourself back up to speed. However, if it has been some time since you have studied this subject our advice is very different. Please work through the material thoroughly even if it is vaguely familiar. Make sure that you do the problems as they arise, checking your answers with those on the website. The material has been broken down into three subsections:

- negative numbers
- expressions
- brackets.

You might like to work through these subsections on separate occasions to enable the ideas to sink in. To rush this topic now is likely to give you only a half-baked understanding which will result in hours of frustration when you study the later chapters of this book.

1.1.1 Negative numbers

In mathematics numbers are classified into one of three types: positive, negative or zero. At school you were probably introduced to the idea of a negative number via the temperature on a thermometer scale measured in degrees centigrade. A number such as −5 would then be interpreted as a temperature of 5 degrees below freezing. In personal finance a negative bank balance would indicate that an account is in 'in the red' or 'in debit'. Similarly, a firm's profit of −500 000 signifies a loss of half a million.

The rules for the multiplication of negative numbers are

$$\boxed{\text{negative}} \times \boxed{\text{negative}} = \boxed{\text{positive}}$$
$$\boxed{\text{negative}} \times \boxed{\text{positive}} = \boxed{\text{negative}}$$

It does not matter in which order two numbers are multiplied, so

$$\boxed{\text{positive}} \times \boxed{\text{negative}} = \boxed{\text{negative}}$$

These rules produce

$$(-2) \times (-3) = 6$$
$$(-4) \times 5 = -20$$
$$7 \times (-5) = -35$$

respectively. Also, because division is the same sort of operation as multiplication (it just undoes the result of multiplication and takes you back to where you started), exactly the same rules apply when one number is divided by another. For example,

$$(-15) \div (-3) = 5$$
$$(-16) \div 2 = -8$$
$$2 \div (-4) = -1/2$$

In general, to multiply or divide lots of numbers it is probably simplest to ignore the signs to begin with and just to work the answer out. The final result is negative if the total number of minus signs is odd and positive if the total number is even.

Example

Evaluate

(a) $(-2) \times (-4) \times (-1) \times 2 \times (-1) \times (-3)$

(b) $\dfrac{5 \times (-4) \times (-1) \times (-3)}{(-6) \times 2}$

Solution

(a) Ignoring the signs gives

$$2 \times 4 \times 1 \times 2 \times 1 \times 3 = 48$$

There are an odd number of minus signs (in fact, five) so the answer is −48.

(b) Ignoring the signs gives

$$\frac{5 \times 4 \times 1 \times 3}{6 \times 2} = \frac{60}{12} = 5$$

There are an even number of minus signs (in fact, four) so the answer is 5.

Advice

Attempt the following problem yourself both with and without a calculator. On most machines a negative number such as –6 is entered by pressing the button labelled $\boxed{(-)}$ followed by 6.

Practice Problem

1. (1) Without using a calculator evaluate

   (a) $5 \times (-6)$ (b) $(-1) \times (-2)$ (c) $(-50) \div 10$

   (d) $(-5) \div (-1)$ (e) $2 \times (-1) \times (-3) \times 6$ (f) $\dfrac{2 \times (-1) \times (-3) \times 6}{(-2) \times 3 \times 6}$

   (2) Confirm your answer to part (1) using a calculator.

To add or subtract negative numbers it helps to think in terms of a number line:

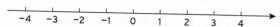

If b is a positive number then

$$a - b$$

can be thought of as an instruction to start at a and to move b units to the left. For example,

$$1 - 3 = -2$$

because if you start at 1 and move 3 units to the left, you end up at –2:

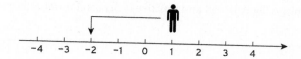

Similarly,

$$-2 - 1 = -3$$

because 1 unit to the left of –2 is –3.

On the other hand,

$$a - (-b)$$

is taken to be $a + b$. This follows from the rule for multiplying two negative numbers, since

$$-(-b) = (-1) \times (-b) = b$$

Consequently, to evaluate

$$a - (-b)$$

you start at a and move b units to the right (that is, in the positive direction). For example,

$$-2 - (-5) = -2 + 5 = 3$$

because if you start at -2 and move 5 units to the right you end up at 3.

Example

Evaluate

(a) $-32 - 4$

(b) $-68 - (-62)$

Solution

(a) $-32 - 4 = -36$ because 4 units to the left of -32 is -36.

(b) $-68 - (-62) = -68 + 62 = -6$ because 62 units to the right of -68 is -6.

Practice Problem

2. (1) Without using a calculator evaluate

    (a) $1 - 2$ **(b)** $-3 - 4$ **(c)** $1 - (-4)$

    (d) $-1 - (-1)$ **(e)** $-72 - 19$ **(f)** $-53 - (-48)$

(2) Confirm your answer to part (1) using a calculator.

1.1.2 Expressions

In algebra letters are used to represent numbers. In pure mathematics the most common letters used are x and y. However, in applications it is helpful to choose letters that are more meaningful, so we might use Q for quantity and I for investment. An algebraic expression is then simply a combination of these letters, brackets and other mathematical symbols such as $+$ or $-$. For example, the expression

$$P\left(1 + \frac{r}{100}\right)^n$$

can be used to work out how money in a savings account grows over a period of time. The letters P, r and n represent the original sum invested (called the principal – hence the use of the letter P), the rate of interest and the number of years, respectively. To work it all out, you not only need to replace these letters by actual numbers, but you also need to understand the various conventions that go with algebraic expressions such as this.

In algebra when we multiply two numbers represented by letters we usually suppress the multiplication sign between them. The product of a and b would simply be written as ab without bothering to put the multiplication sign between the symbols. Likewise when a number represented by the letter Y is doubled we write $2Y$. In this case we not only suppress the multiplication sign but adopt the convention of writing the number in front of the letter. Here are some further examples:

$P \times Q$ is written as PQ

$d \times 8$ is written as $8d$

$n \times 6 \times t$ is written as $6nt$

$z \times z$ is written as z^2 (using the index 2 to indicate squaring a number)

$1 \times t$ is written as t (since multiplying by 1 does not change a number)

In order to evaluate these expressions it is necessary to be given the numerical value of each letter. Once this has been done you can work out the final value by performing the operations in the following order:

Brackets first   (B)

Indices second   (I)

Division and Multiplication third   (DM)

Addition and Subtraction fourth   (AS)

This is sometimes remembered using the acronym BIDMAS and it is essential that this ordering is used for working out all mathematical calculations. For example, suppose you wish to evaluate each of the following expressions when $n = 3$:

$2n^2$ and $(2n)^2$

Substituting $n = 3$ into the first expression gives

$2n^2 = 2 \times 3^2$ (the multiplication sign is revealed when we switch from algebra to numbers)

$\quad\quad = 2 \times 9$ (according to BIDMAS indices are worked out before multiplication)

$\quad\quad = 18$

whereas in the second expression we get

$(2n)^2 = (2 \times 3)^2$ (again the multiplication sign is revealed)

$\quad\quad\; = 6^2$ (according to BIDMAS we evaluate the inside of the brackets first)

$\quad\quad\; = 36$

The two answers are not the same so the order indicated by BIDMAS really does matter. Looking at the previous list notice that there is a tie between multiplication and division for third place, and another tie between addition and subtraction for fourth place. These pairs of operations have equal priority and under these circumstances you work from left to right when evaluating expressions. For example, substituting $x = 5$ and $y = 4$ in the expression, $x - y + 2$, gives

$x - y + 2 = 5 - 4 + 2$

$\quad\quad\quad = 1 + 2$ (reading from left to right, subtraction comes first)

$\quad\quad\quad = 3$

Example

(a) Find the value of $2x - 3y$ when $x = 9$ and $y = 4$.

(b) Find the value of $2Q^2 - 4Q + 150$ when $Q = 10$.

(c) Find the value of $5a - 2b + c$ when $a = 4$, $b = 6$ and $c = 1$.

(d) Find the value of $(12 - t) - (t - 1)$ when $t = 4$.

Solution

(a) $2x - 3y = 2 \times 9 - 3 \times 4$ (substituting numbers)

$\qquad\quad = 18 - 12$ (multiplication has priority over subtraction)

$\qquad\quad = 6$

(b) $2Q^2 + 4Q + 150 = 2 \times 10^2 + 4 \times 10 + 150$ (substituting numbers)

$\qquad\qquad\qquad = 2 \times 100 + 4 \times 10 + 150$ (indices have priority over multiplication and addition)

$\qquad\qquad\qquad = 200 + 40 + 150$ (multiplication has priority over addition)

$\qquad\qquad\qquad = 390$

(c) $5a - 2b + c = 5 \times 4 - 2 \times 6 + 1$ (substituting numbers)

$\qquad\qquad = 20 - 12 + 1$ (multiplication has priority over addition and subtraction)

$\qquad\qquad = 8 + 1$ (addition and subtraction have equal priority so work from left to right)

$\qquad\qquad = 9$

(d) $(12 - t) - (t - 1) = (12 - 4) - (4 - 1)$ (substituting numbers)

$\qquad\qquad\qquad = 8 - 3$ (brackets first)

$\qquad\qquad\qquad = 5$

Practice Problem

3. Evaluate each of the following by replacing the letters by the given numbers:

    (a) $2Q + 5$ when $Q = 7$.

    (b) $5x^2y$ when $x = 10$ and $y = 3$.

    (c) $4d - 3f + 2g$ when $d = 7, f = 2$ and $g = 5$.

    (d) $a(b + 2c)$ when $a = 5, b = 1$ and $c = 3$.

Like terms are multiples of the same letter (or letters). For example, $2P$, $-34P$ and $0.3P$ are all multiples of P and so are like terms. In the same way, xy, $4xy$ and $69xy$ are all multiples of xy so are like terms. If an algebraic expression contains like terms which are added or subtracted together then it can be simplified to produce an equivalent shorter expression.

Example

Simplify each of the following expressions (where possible):

(a) $2a + 5a - 3a$

(b) $4P - 2Q$

(c) $3w + 9w^2 + 2w$

(d) $3xy + 2y^2 + 9x + 4xy - 8x$

Solution

(a) All three are like terms since they are all multiples of a so the expression can be simplified:

$$2a + 5a - 3a = 4a$$

(b) The terms $4P$ and $2Q$ are unlike because one is a multiple of P and the other is a multiple of Q so the expression cannot be simplified.

(c) The first and last are like terms since they are both multiples of w so we can collect these together and write

$$3w + 9w^2 + 2w = 5w + 9w^2$$

This cannot be simpified any further because $5w$ and $9w^2$ are unlike terms.

(d) The terms $3xy$ and $4xy$ are like terms, and $9x$ and $8x$ are also like terms. These pairs can therefore be collected together to give

$$3xy + 2y^2 + 9x + 4xy - 8x = 7xy + 2y^2 + x$$

Notice that we write just x instead of $1x$ and also that no further simplication is possible since the final answer involves three unlike terms.

Practice Problem

4. Simplify each of the following expressions, where possible:

    (a) $2x + 6y - x + 3y$ **(b)** $5x + 2y - 5x + 4z$ **(c)** $4Y^2 + 3Y - 43$

    (d) $8r^2 + 4s - 6rs - 3s - 3s^2 + 7rs$ **(e)** $2e^2 + 5f - 2e^2 - 9f$ **(f)** $3w + 6W$

    (g) $ab - ba$

1.1.3 Brackets

It is useful to be able to take an expression containing brackets and rewrite it as an equivalent expression without brackets and vice versa. The process of removing brackets is called 'expanding brackets' or 'multiplying out brackets'. This is based on the **distributive law**, which states that for any three numbers a, b and c

$$\boxed{a(b + c) = ab + ac}$$

It is easy to verify this law in simple cases. For example, if $a = 2$, $b = 3$ and $c = 4$ then the left-hand side is

$$2(3 + 4) = 2 \times 7 = 14$$

However,

$$ab = 2 \times 3 = 6 \text{ and } ac = 2 \times 4 = 8$$

and so the right-hand side is $6 + 8$, which is also 14.

This law can be used when there are any number of terms inside the brackets. We have

$$a(b + c + d) = ab + ac + ad$$
$$a(b + c + d + e) = ab + ac + ad + ae$$

and so on.

It does not matter in which order two numbers are multiplied, so we also have

$$(b + c)a = ba + ca$$
$$(b + c + d)a = ba + ca + da$$
$$(b + c + d + e)a = ba + ca + da + ea$$

Example

Multiply out the brackets in

(a) $x(x - 2)$

(b) $2(x + y - z) + 3(z + y)$

(c) $x + 3y - (2y + x)$

Solution

(a) The use of the distributive law to multiply out $x(x - 2)$ is straightforward. The x outside the bracket multiplies the x inside to give x^2. The x outside the bracket also multiplies the -2 inside to give $-2x$. Hence

$$x(x - 2) = x^2 - 2x$$

(b) To expand

$$2(x + y - z) + 3(z + y)$$

we need to apply the distributive law twice. We have

$$2(x + y - z) = 2x + 2y - 2z$$
$$3(z + y) = 3z + 3y$$

Adding together gives

$$2(x + y - z) + 3(z + y) = 2x + 2y - 2z + 3z + 3y$$
$$= 2x + 5y + z \quad \text{(collecting like terms)}$$

(c) It may not be immediately apparent how to expand

$$x + 3y - (2y + x)$$

However, note that

$$-(2y + x)$$

is the same as

$$(-1)(2y + x)$$

which expands to give

$$(-1)(2y) +(-1)x = -2y - x$$

Hence

$$x + 3y - (2y + x) = x + 3y - 2y - x = y$$

after collecting like terms.

Advice

In this example the solutions are written out in painstaking detail. This is done to show you precisely how the distributive law is applied. The solutions to all three parts could have been written down in only one or two steps of working. You are, of course, at liberty to compress the working in your own solutions, but please do not be tempted to overdo this. You might want to check your answers at a later date and may find it difficult if you have tried to be too clever.

Practice Problem

5. Multiply out the brackets, simplifying your answer as far as possible.

    (a) $(5 - 2z)z$ **(b)** $6(x - y) + 3(y - 2x)$ **(c)** $x - y + z - (x^2 + x - y)$

Before we leave this topic a word of warning is in order. Be careful when removing brackets from very simple expressions such as those considered in part (c) in the above worked example and practice problem. A common mistake is to write

$$(a + b) - (c + d) = a + b - c + d \quad \textbf{This is NOT true}$$

The distributive law tells us that the -1 multiplying the second bracket applies to the d as well as the c so the correct answer has to be

$$(a + b) - (c + d) = a + b - c - d$$

In algebra, it is sometimes useful to reverse the procedure and put the brackets back in. This is called **factorization**. Consider the expression $12a + 8b$. There are many numbers which divide into both 8 and 12. However, we always choose the biggest number, which is 4 in this case, so we attempt to take the factor of 4 outside the brackets:

$$12a + 8b = 4(? + ?)$$

where the ? indicate some mystery terms inside the brackets. We would like 4 multiplied by the first term in the brackets to be $12a$ so we are missing $3a$. Likewise if we are to generate an $8b$ the second term in the brackets will have to be $2b$.

Hence

$$12a + 8b = 4(3a + 2b)$$

As a check, notice that when you expand the brackets on the right-hand side you really do get the expression on the left-hand side.

Example

Factorize

(a) $6x - 3x^2$

(b) $5a - 10b + 20c$

Solution

(a) Both terms have a common factor of 3. Also, because $x^2 = x \times x$, both $6x$ and $-3x^2$ have a factor of x. Hence we can take out a common factor of $3x$ altogether.

$$6x - 3x^2 = 3x(2) - 3x(x) = 3x(2 - x)$$

(b) All three terms have a common factor of 5 so we write

$$5a - 10b + 20c = 5(a) - 5(2b) + 5(4c) = 5(a - 2b + 4c)$$

Practice Problem

6. Factorize

    (a) $7d + 21$ **(b)** $16w - 20q$ **(c)** $6x - 3y + 9z$ **(d)** $5Q - 10Q^2$

We conclude our discussion of brackets by describing how to multiply two brackets together. In the expression $(a + b)(c + d)$ the two terms a and b must each multiply the single bracket $(c + d)$ so

$$(a + b)(c + d) = a(c + d) + b(c + d)$$

The first term $a(c + d)$ can itself be expanded as $ac + ad$. Likewise, $b(c + d) = bc + bd$. Hence

$$(a + b)(c + d) = ac + ad + bc + bd$$

This procedure then extends to brackets with more than two terms:

$$(a + b)(c + d + e) = a(c + d + e) + b(c + d + e) = ac + ad + ae + bc + bd + be$$

Example

Multiply out the brackets

(a) $(x + 1)(x + 2)$ **(b)** $(x + 5)(x - 5)$ **(c)** $(2x - y)(x + y - 6)$

simplifying your answer as far as possible.

Solution

(a) $(x + 1)(x + 2) = x(x + 2) + (1)(x + 2)$
$$= x^2 + 2x + x + 2$$
$$= x^2 + 3x + 2$$

(b) $(x + 5)(x - 5) = x(x - 5) + 5(x - 5)$
$$= x^2 - 5x + 5x - 25$$
$$= x^2 - 25$$

the x's cancel

(c) $(2x - y)(x + y - 6) = 2x(x + y - 6) - y(x + y - 6)$
$$= 2x^2 + 2xy - 12x - yx - y^2 + 6y$$
$$= 2x^2 + xy - 12x - y^2 + 6y$$

Practice Problem

7. Multiply out the brackets.

    (a) $(x + 3)(x - 2)$
    (b) $(x + y)(x - y)$
    (c) $(x + y)(x + y)$
    (d) $(5x + 2y)(x - y + 1)$

Looking back at part (b) of the previous worked example, notice that

$$(x + 5)(x - 5) = x^2 - 25 = x^2 - 5^2$$

Quite generally

$$(a + b)(a - b) = a(a - b) + b(a - b)$$
$$= a^2 - ab + ba - b^2$$
$$= a^2 - b^2$$

The result

$$\boxed{a^2 - b^2 = (a + b)(a - b)}$$

is called the **difference of two squares** formula. It provides a quick way of factorizing certain expressions.

Example

Factorize the following expressions:

(a) $x^2 - 16$ **(b)** $9x^2 - 100$

Solution

(a) Noting that

$$x^2 - 16 = x^2 - 4^2$$

we can use the difference of two squares formula to deduce that

$$x^2 - 16 = (x + 4)(x - 4)$$

(b) Noting that

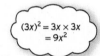

$(3x)^2 = 3x \times 3x$
$= 9x^2$

$$9x^2 - 100 = (3x)^2 - (10)^2$$

we can use the difference of two squares formula to deduce that

$$9x^2 - 100 = (3x + 10)(3x - 10)$$

Practice Problem

8. Factorise the following expressions:

    (a) $x^2 - 64$ **(b)** $4x^2 - 81$

Advice

This completes your first piece of mathematics. We hope that you have not found it quite as bad as you first thought. There now follow a few extra problems to give you more practice. Not only will they help to strengthen your mathematical skills, but also they should improve your overall confidence. There are two alternative exercises available. Exercise 1.1 is suitable for students whose mathematics may be rusty and who need to consolidate their understanding. Exercise 1.1* contains more challenging problems and so is more suitable for those students who have found this section very easy.

Key Terms

Distributive law   The law of arithmetic which states that $a(b + c) = ab + ac$ for any numbers, a, b, c.

Factorization   The process of writing an expression as a product of simpler expressions using brackets.

Like terms   Multiples of the same algebraic symbol.

Exercise 1.1

1. Without using a calculator evaluate

   (a) $10 \times (-2)$ (b) $(-1) \times (-3)$ (c) $(-8) \div 2$ (d) $(-5) \div (-5)$

   (e) $24 \div (-2)$ (f) $(-10) \times (-5)$ (g) $\dfrac{20}{-4}$ (h) $\dfrac{-27}{-9}$

   (i) $(-6) \times 5 \times (-1)$ (j) $\dfrac{2 \times (-6) \times 3}{(-9)}$

2. Without using a calculator evaluate

   (a) $5 - 6$ (b) $-1 - 2$ (c) $6 - 17$ (d) $-7 + 23$

   (e) $-7 - (-6)$ (f) $-4 - 9$ (g) $7 - (-4)$ (h) $-9 - (-9)$

   (i) $12 - 43$ (j) $2 + 6 - 10$

3. Without using a calculator evaluate

   (a) $5 \times 2 - 13$ (b) $\dfrac{-30 - 6}{-18}$ (c) $\dfrac{(-3) \times (-6) \times (-1)}{2 - 3}$ (d) $5 \times (1 - 4)$

   (e) $1 - 6 \times 7$ (f) $-5 + 6 \div 3$ (g) $2 \times (-3)^2$ (h) $-10 + 2^2$

   (i) $(2)^2 - 5 \times 6 + 1$ (j) $\dfrac{(-4)^2 \times (-3) \times (-1)}{(-2)^3}$

4. Simplify each of the following algebraic expressions:

   (a) $2 \times P \times Q$ (b) $I \times 8$ (c) $3 \times x \times y$

   (d) $4 \times q \times w \times z$ (e) $b \times b$ (f) $k \times 3 \times k$

5. Simplify the following algebraic expressions by collecting like terms:

   (a) $6w - 3w + 12w + 4w$ (b) $6x + 5y - 2x - 12y$

   (c) $3a - 2b + 6a - c + 4b - c$ (d) $2x^2 + 4x - x^2 - 2x$

   (e) $2cd + 4c - 5dc$ (f) $5st + s^2 - 3ts + t^2 + 9$

6. Without using a calculator find the value of the following:

   (a) $2x - y$ when $x = 7$ and $y = 4$.

   (b) $x^2 - 5x + 12$ when $x = 6$.

   (c) $2m^3$ when $m = 10$.

   (d) $5fg^2 + 2g$ when $f = 2$ and $g = 3$.

   (e) $2v + 4w - (4v - 7w)$ when $v = 20$ and $w = 10$.

7. If $x = 2$ and $y = -3$ evaluate

   (a) $2x + y$ (b) $x - y$ (c) $3x + 4y$

   (d) xy (e) $5xy$ (f) $4x - 6xy$

8. (a) Without using a calculator, work out the value of $(-4)^2$.

   (b) Press the following key sequence on your calculator:

   $\boxed{(-)}$ $\boxed{4}$ $\boxed{x^2}$

   Explain carefully why this does not give the same result as part (a) and give an alternative key sequence that *does* give the correct answer.

9. Without using a calculator work out

   (a) $(5 - 2)^2$ **(b)** $5^2 - 2^2$

   Is it true in general that $(a - b)^2 = a^2 - b^2$?

10. Use your calculator to work out the following. Round your answer, if necessary, to 2 decimal places.

   (a) $5.31 \times 8.47 - 1.01^2$ **(b)** $(8.34 + 2.27)/9.41$

   (c) $9.53 - 3.21 + 4.02$ **(d)** $2.41 \times 0.09 - 1.67 \times 0.03$

   (e) $45.76 - (2.55 + 15.83)$ **(f)** $(3.45 - 5.38)^2$

   (g) $4.56(9.02 + 4.73)$ **(h)** $6.85/(2.59 + 0.28)$

11. Multiply out the brackets:

   (a) $7(x - y)$ **(b)** $3(5x - 2y)$ **(c)** $4(x + 3)$ **(d)** $7(3x - 1)$

   (e) $3(x + y + z)$ **(f)** $x(3x - 4)$ **(g)** $y + 2z - 2(x + 3y - z)$

12. Factorize

   (a) $25c + 30$ **(b)** $9x - 18$ **(c)** $x^2 + 2x$

   (d) $16x - 12y$ **(e)** $4x^2 - 6xy$ **(f)** $10d - 15e + 50$

13. Multiply out the brackets:

   (a) $(x + 2)(x + 5)$ **(b)** $(a + 4)(a - 1)$ **(c)** $(d + 3)(d - 8)$ **(d)** $(2s + 3)(3s + 7)$

   (e) $(2y + 3)(y + 1)$ **(f)** $(5t + 2)(2t - 7)$ **(g)** $(3n + 2)(3n - 2)$ **(h)** $(a - b)(a - b)$

14. Simplify the following expressions by collecting together like terms:

   (a) $2x + 3y + 4x - y$ **(b)** $2x^2 - 5x + 9x^2 + 2x - 3$

   (c) $5xy + 2x + 9yx$ **(d)** $7xyz + 3yx - 2zyx + yzx - xy$

   (e) $2(5a + b) - 4b$ **(f)** $5(x - 4y) + 6(2x + 7y)$

   (g) $5 - 3(p - 2)$ **(h)** $x(x - y + 7) + xy + 3x$

15. Use the formula for the difference of two squares to factorize

   (a) $x^2 - 4$ **(b)** $Q^2 - 49$ **(c)** $x^2 - y^2$ **(d)** $9x^2 - 100y^2$

16. Simplify the following algebraic expressions:

   (a) $3x - 4x^2 - 2 + 5x + 8x^2$ **(b)** $x(3x + 2) - 3x(x + 5)$

Exercise 1.1*

1. Without using a calculator evaluate

   (a) $(12 - 8) - (6 - 5)$ **(b)** $12 - (8 - 6) - 5$ **(c)** $12 - 8 - 6 - 5$

2. Put a pair of brackets in the left-hand side of each of the following to give correct statements:

   (a) $2 - 7 - 9 + 3 = -17$

   (b) $8 - 2 + 3 - 4 = -1$

   (c) $7 - 2 - 6 + 10 = 1$

3. Without using a calculator work out the value of each of the following expressions in the case when $a = 3$, $b = -4$ and $c = -2$:

   (a) $a(b - c)$ **(b)** $3c(a + b)$ **(c)** $a^2 + 2b + 3c$ **(d)** $2abc^2$

   (e) $\dfrac{c + b}{2a}$ **(f)** $\sqrt{2(b^2 - c)}$ **(g)** $\dfrac{b}{2c} - \dfrac{a}{3b}$ **(h)** $5a - b^3 - 4c^2$

4. Without using a calculator evaluate each of the following expressions in the case when $x = -1$, $y = -2$ and $z = 3$:

   (a) $x^3 + y^2 + z$ **(b)** $\sqrt{\left(\dfrac{x^2 + y^2 + z}{x^2 + 2xy - z} \right)}$ **(c)** $\dfrac{xyz(x + z)(z - y)}{(x + y)(x - z)}$

5. Multiply out the brackets and simplify

   $(x - y)(x + y) - (x + 2)(x - y + 3)$

6. Simplify

   (a) $x - y - (y - x)$ **(b)** $(x - ((y - x) - y))$ **(c)** $x + y - (x - y) - (x - (y - x))$

7. Multiply out the brackets:

   (a) $(x + 4)(x - 6)$ **(b)** $(2x - 5)(3x - 7)$ **(c)** $2x(3x + y - 2)$

   (d) $(3 + g)(4 - 2g + h)$ **(e)** $(2x + y)(1 - x - y)$ **(f)** $(a + b + c)(a - b - c)$

8. Factorize ❓

   (a) $9x - 12y$ **(b)** $x^2 - 6x$ **(c)** $10xy + 15x^2$

   (d) $3xy^2 - 6x^2y + 12xy$ **(e)** $x^3 - 2x^2$ **(f)** $60x^4y^6 - 15x^2y^4 + 20xy^3$

9. Use the formula for the difference of two squares to factorize

   (a) $p^2 - 25$ **(b)** $9c^2 - 64$ **(c)** $32v^2 - 50d^2$ **(d)** $16x^4 - y^4$

10. Evaluate the following without using a calculator:

   (a) $50\ 563^2 - 49\ 437^2$ **(b)** $90^2 - 89.99^2$

   (c) $759^2 - 541^2$ **(d)** $123\ 456\ 789^2 - 123\ 456\ 788^2$

SECTION 1.2
Further algebra

Objectives

At the end of this section you should be able to:

- Simplify fractions by cancelling common factors.
- Add, subtract, multiply and divide fractions.
- Solve equations by doing the same thing to both sides.
- Recognize the symbols $<$, $>$, $\leq$ and $\geq$.
- Solve linear inequalities.

This section is broken down into three manageable subsections:

- fractions
- equations
- inequalities.

The advice offered in Section 1.1 applies equally well here. Please try to study these topics on separate occasions and be prepared to put the book down and work through the practice problems as they arise in the text.

1.2.1 Fractions

For a numerical fraction such as

$$\frac{7}{8}$$

the number 7, on the top, is called the **numerator** and the number 8, on the bottom, is called the **denominator**. In this book we are also interested in the case when the numerator and denominator involve letters as well as numbers. These are referred to as **algebraic fractions**. For example,

$$\frac{1}{x^2 - 2} \quad \text{and} \quad \frac{2x^2 - 1}{y + z}$$

are both algebraic fractions. The letters x, y and z are used to represent numbers, so the rules for the manipulation of algebraic fractions are the same as those for ordinary numerical fractions. It is therefore essential that you are happy manipulating numerical fractions without a calculator so that you can extend this skill to fractions with letters.

Two fractions are said to be **equivalent** if they represent the same numerical value. We know that $\frac{3}{4}$ is equivalent to $\frac{6}{8}$ since they are both equal to the decimal number 0.75. It is also intuitively obvious. Imagine breaking a bar of chocolate into four equal pieces and eating three of them. You eat the same amount of chocolate as someone who breaks the bar into eight equal pieces and eats six of them. Each piece is only half the size so you need to compensate by eating twice as many. Formally we say that when the numerator and denominator are both multiplied by the same number the value of the fraction remains unchanged. In this example we have

$$\frac{3}{4} = \frac{3 \times 2}{4 \times 2} = \frac{6}{8}$$

This process can be reversed so equivalent fractions are produced when the numerator and denominator are both divided by the same number. For example,

$$\frac{16}{24} = \frac{16/8}{24/8} = \frac{2}{3}$$

so the fractions $\frac{16}{24}$ and $\frac{2}{3}$ are equivalent. A fraction is said to be in its simplest form or reduced to its lowest terms when there are no factors common to both the numerator and denominator. To express any given fraction in its simplest form you need to find the highest common factor of the numerator and denominator and then divide top and bottom of the fraction by this.

Example

Reduce each of the following fractions to its lowest terms:

(a) $\frac{14}{21}$ (b) $\frac{48}{60}$ (c) $\frac{2x}{3xy}$ (d) $\frac{3a}{6a + 3b}$ (e) $\frac{x - 2}{(x - 2)(x + 1)}$

Solution

(a) The largest number which divides into both 14 and 21 is 7 so we choose to divide top and bottom by 7:

$$\frac{14}{21} = \frac{14/7}{21/7} = \frac{2}{3}$$

An alternative way of writing this (which will be helpful when we tackle algebraic fractions) is:

$$\frac{14}{21} = \frac{2 \times \cancel{7}}{3 \times \cancel{7}} = \frac{2}{3}$$

(b) The highest common factor of 48 and 60 is 12 so we write:

$$\frac{48}{60} = \frac{4 \times \cancel{12}}{5 \times \cancel{12}} = \frac{4}{5}$$

(c) The factor x is common to both $2x$ and $3xy$ so we need to divide top and bottom by x, that is, we cancel the x's:

$$\frac{2x}{3xy} = \frac{2 \times \cancel{x}}{3 \times \cancel{x} \times y} = \frac{2}{3y}$$

(d) Factorizing the denominator gives

$$6a + 3b = 3(2a + b)$$

which shows that there is a common factor of 3 in the top and bottom which can be cancelled:

$$\frac{3a}{6a+3b}=\frac{\cancel{3}a}{\cancel{3}(2a+b)}=\frac{a}{2a+b}$$

(e) We see immediately that there is a common factor of $(x-2)$ in the top and bottom so this can be cancelled:

$$\frac{\cancel{x-2}}{\cancel{(x-2)}(x+1)}=\frac{1}{x+1}$$

Before we leave this topic a word of warning is in order. Notice that you can only cancel by dividing by a **factor** of the numerator or denominator. In part (d) of the above example you must not get carried away and attempt to cancel the a's, and write something daft like:

$$\frac{a}{2a+b}=\frac{1}{2+b} \qquad \textbf{This is NOT true}$$

To see that this is totally wrong let us try substituting numbers, $a=3$, $b=4$, say, into both sides. The left-hand side gives $\dfrac{a}{2a+b}=\dfrac{3}{2\times3+4}=\dfrac{3}{10}$ whereas the right-hand side gives $\dfrac{1}{2+b}=\dfrac{1}{2+4}=\dfrac{1}{6}$, which is not the same value.

Practice Problem

1. Reduce each of the following fractions to its lowest terms:

(a) $\dfrac{9}{15}$ (b) $\dfrac{24}{30}$ (c) $\dfrac{x}{2xy}$ (d) $\dfrac{3x}{6x+9x^2}$ (e) $\dfrac{x(x+1)}{x(x-4)(x+1)}$

The rules for multiplication and division are as follows:

> **to multiply fractions you multiply their corresponding numerators and denominators**

In symbols,

$$\frac{a}{b}\times\frac{c}{d}=\frac{a\times c}{b\times d}=\frac{ac}{bd}$$

> **to divide by a fraction you turn it upside down and multiply**

In symbols,

$$\frac{a}{b}\div\frac{c}{d}=\frac{a}{b}\times\frac{d}{c}$$

turn the divisor upside down

$$=\frac{ad}{bc}$$

rule for multiplying fractions

Example

Calculate

(a) $\dfrac{2}{3} \times \dfrac{5}{4}$ **(b)** $2 \times \dfrac{6}{13}$ **(c)** $\dfrac{6}{7} \div \dfrac{4}{21}$ **(d)** $\dfrac{1}{2} \div 3$

Solution

(a) The multiplication rule gives

$$\frac{2}{3} \times \frac{5}{4} = \frac{2 \times 5}{3 \times 4} = \frac{10}{12}$$

We could leave the answer like this, although it can be simplified by dividing top and bottom by 2 to get $^5/_6$. It is also valid to 'cancel' by 2 at the very beginning: that is,

$$\frac{{}^{1}\cancel{2}}{3} \times \frac{5}{\cancel{4}_2} = \frac{1 \times 5}{3 \times 2} = \frac{5}{6}$$

(b) The whole number 2 is equivalent to the fraction $^2/_1$, so

$$2 \times \frac{6}{13} = \frac{2}{1} \times \frac{6}{13} = \frac{2 \times 6}{1 \times 13} = \frac{12}{13}$$

(c) To calculate

$$\frac{6}{7} \div \frac{4}{21}$$

the divisor is turned upside down to get $^{21}/_4$ and then multiplied to get

$$\frac{6}{7} \div \frac{4}{21} = \frac{{}^{3}\cancel{6}}{\cancel{7}_1} \times \frac{\cancel{21}^{3}}{\cancel{4}_2} = \frac{3 \times 3}{1 \times 2} = \frac{9}{2}$$

(d) We write 3 as $^3/_1$, so

$$\frac{1}{2} \div 3 = \frac{1}{2} \div \frac{3}{1} = \frac{1}{2} \times \frac{1}{3} = \frac{1}{6}$$

Practice Problem

2. (1) Without using a calculator evaluate

   (a) $\dfrac{1}{2} \times \dfrac{3}{4}$ **(b)** $7 \times \dfrac{1}{14}$ **(c)** $\dfrac{2}{3} \div \dfrac{8}{9}$ **(d)** $\dfrac{8}{9} \div 16$

(2) Confirm your answer to part (1) using a calculator.

The rules for addition and subtraction are as follows:

> **to add (or subtract) two fractions you write them as equivalent fractions
> with a common denominator and add (or subtract) their numerators**

Example

Calculate

(a) $\dfrac{1}{5} + \dfrac{2}{5}$ (b) $\dfrac{1}{4} + \dfrac{2}{3}$ (c) $\dfrac{7}{12} - \dfrac{5}{8}$

Solution

(a) The fractions $^1/_5$ and $^2/_5$ already have the same denominator, so to add them we just add their numerators to get

$$\frac{1}{5} + \frac{2}{5} = \frac{1+2}{5} = \frac{3}{5}$$

(b) The fractions $^1/_4$ and $^2/_5$ have denominators 4 and 3. One number that is divisible by both 3 and 4 is 12, so we choose this as the common denominator. Now 4 goes into 12 exactly 3 times, so

$$\frac{1}{4} = \frac{1 \times 3}{4 \times 3} = \frac{3}{12}$$

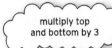

multiply top and bottom by 3

and 3 goes into 12 exactly 4 times, so

$$\frac{2}{3} = \frac{2 \times 4}{3 \times 4} = \frac{8}{12}$$

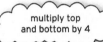

multiply top and bottom by 4

Hence

$$\frac{1}{4} + \frac{2}{3} = \frac{3}{12} + \frac{8}{12} = \frac{3+8}{12} = \frac{11}{12}$$

(c) The fractions $^7/_{12}$ and $^5/_8$ have denominators 12 and 8. One number that is divisible by both 12 and 8 is 24, so we choose this as the common denominator. Now 12 goes into 24 exactly twice, so

$$\frac{7}{12} = \frac{7 \times 2}{24} = \frac{14}{24}$$

and 8 goes into 24 exactly 3 times, so

$$\frac{5}{8} = \frac{5 \times 3}{24} = \frac{15}{24}$$

Hence

$$\frac{7}{12} - \frac{5}{8} = \frac{14}{24} - \frac{15}{24} = -\frac{1}{24}$$

It is not essential that the lowest common denominator is used. Any number will do provided that it is divisible by the two original denominators. If you are stuck then you could always multiply the original two denominators together. In part (c) the denominators multiply to give 96, so this can be used instead. Now

$$\frac{7}{12} = \frac{7 \times 8}{96} = \frac{56}{96}$$

and

$$\frac{5}{8} = \frac{5 \times 12}{96} = \frac{60}{96}$$

so

$$\frac{7}{12} - \frac{5}{8} = \frac{56}{96} - \frac{60}{96} = \frac{56 - 60}{96} = \frac{-1}{24} = -\frac{1}{24}$$

as before.

Notice how the final answer to part (c) of this example has been written. We have simply used the fact that when a negative number is divided by a positive number the answer is negative. It is standard practice to write negative fractions like this so we would write $-\frac{3}{4}$ in preference to either $\frac{3}{-4}$ or $\frac{-3}{4}$ and, of course, $\frac{-3}{-4}$ is written as $\frac{3}{4}$.

Before we leave this topic a word of warning is in order. Notice that you can only add or subtract fractions after you have gone to the trouble of finding a common denominator. In particular, the following short-cut does not give the correct answer:

$$\frac{a}{b} + \frac{c}{d} = \frac{a + c}{b + d} \qquad \textbf{This is NOT true}$$

As usual you can check for yourself that it is complete rubbish by using actual numbers of your own choosing.

Practice Problem

3. (1) Without using a calculator evaluate

(a) $\dfrac{3}{7} - \dfrac{1}{7}$ (b) $\dfrac{1}{3} + \dfrac{2}{5}$ (c) $\dfrac{7}{18} - \dfrac{1}{4}$

(2) Confirm your answer to part (1) using a calculator.

Provided that you can manipulate ordinary fractions, there is no reason why you should not be able to manipulate algebraic fractions just as easily, since the rules are the same.

Example

Find expressions for each of the following:

(a) $\dfrac{x}{x-1} \times \dfrac{2}{x(x+4)}$ (b) $\dfrac{2}{x-1} \div \dfrac{x}{x-1}$ (c) $\dfrac{x+1}{x^2+2} + \dfrac{x-6}{x^2+2}$ (d) $\dfrac{x}{x+2} - \dfrac{1}{x+1}$

Solution

(a) To multiply two fractions we multiply their corresponding numerators and denominators, so

$$\frac{x}{x-1} \times \frac{2}{x(x+4)} = \frac{2x}{(x-1)x(x+4)} = \frac{2}{(x-1)(x+4)}$$

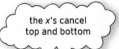 the *x*'s cancel top and bottom

(b) To divide by

$$\frac{x}{x-1}$$

we turn it upside down and multiply, so

$$\frac{2}{x-1} \div \frac{x}{x-1} = \frac{2}{x-1} \times \frac{x-1}{x} = \frac{2}{x}$$

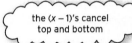 the (*x* – 1)'s cancel top and bottom

(c) The fractions

$$\frac{x+1}{x^2+2} \text{ and } \frac{x-6}{x^2+2}$$

already have the same denominator, so to add them we just add their numerators to get

$$\frac{x+1}{x^2+2} + \frac{x-6}{x^2+2} = \frac{x+1+x-6}{x^2+2} = \frac{2x-5}{x^2+2}$$

(d) The fractions

$$\frac{x}{x+2} \text{ and } \frac{1}{x+1}$$

have denominators $x+2$ and $x+1$. An obvious common denominator is given by their product, $(x+2)(x+1)$. Now $x+2$ goes into $(x+2)(x+1)$ exactly $x+1$ times, so

$$\frac{x}{x+2} = \frac{x(x+1)}{(x+2)(x+1)}$$

 multiply top and bottom by (*x* + 1)

Also $x+1$ goes into $(x+2)(x+1)$ exactly $x+2$ times, so

$$\frac{1}{x+1} = \frac{(x+2)}{(x+2)(x+1)}$$

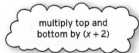 multiply top and bottom by (*x* + 2)

Hence

$$\frac{x}{x+2} - \frac{1}{x+1} = \frac{(x+1)}{(x+2)(x+1)} - \frac{(x+2)}{(x+2)(x+1)} = \frac{x(x+1) - (x+2)}{(x+2)(x+1)}$$

It is worth multiplying out the brackets on the top to simplify: that is,

$$\frac{x^2+x-x-2}{(x+2)(x+1)} = \frac{x^2-2}{(x+2)(x+1)}$$

Practice Problem

4. Find expressions for the following algebraic fractions, simplifying your answers as far as possible.

(a) $\dfrac{5}{x-1} \times \dfrac{x-1}{x+2}$ (b) $\dfrac{x^2}{x+10} \div \dfrac{x}{x+1}$ (c) $\dfrac{4}{x+1} + \dfrac{1}{x+1}$ (d) $\dfrac{2}{x+1} - \dfrac{1}{x+2}$

1.2.2 Equations

In Section 1.1.2 and again in Section 1.2.1 we have seen how to re-write an algebraic expression in a simpler but equivalent form. For example, when we write things like

$$x^2 + 3x + 3x^2 - 10x = 4x^2 - 7x \qquad \text{(collecting like terms)}$$

or

$$\frac{x}{x+2} - \frac{1}{x+1} = \frac{x^2 - 2}{(x+2)(x+1)} \qquad \text{(part (d) of the previous worked example)}$$

we have at the back of our minds the knowledge that the left- and right-hand sides are identical so that each statement is true for all possible values of x. For this reason the above relations are called **identities**. Compare these with statements such as:

$$7x - 1 = 13$$

or

$$x^2 - 5x = 1$$

These relations are called **equations** and are only true for particular values of x which need to be found. It turns out that the first equation above has just one solution whereas the second has two solutions. The latter is called a quadratic equation and will be considered in the next chapter.

One naïve approach to the solution of equations such as $7x - 1 = 13$ might be to use trial and error: that is, we could just keep guessing values of x until we find the one that works. Can you see what x is in this case? However, a more reliable and systematic approach is to actually solve this equation using the rules of mathematics. In fact, the only rule that we need is:

> you can apply whatever mathematical operation you like to an equation, provided that you do the same thing to both sides

There is only one exception to this rule: you must never divide both sides by zero. This should be obvious because a number such as 11/0 does not exist. (If you do not believe this, try dividing 11 by 0 on your calculator.)

The first obstacle that prevents us from writing down the value of x immediately from the equation $7x - 1 = 13$ is the presence of the -1 on the left-hand side. This can be removed by adding 1. For this to be legal we must also add 1 to the right-hand side to get

$$7x - 1 + 1 = 13 + 1$$
$$7x = 14$$

The second obstacle is the number 7 which is multiplying the *x*. This can be removed by dividing the left-hand side by 7. Of course, we must also do the same thing to the right-hand side to get

$$\frac{7x}{7} = \frac{14}{7}$$

$$x = 2$$

This is no doubt the solution that you spotted earlier by simple trial and error and you may be wondering why you need to bother with the formal method. The reason is simple: guesswork will not help to solve more complicated equations in which the solution is non-obvious or even simple equations in which the solution is a fraction. In these circumstances we need to follow the approach of 'balancing the equation' described above.

Example

Solve

(a) $6x + 1 = 10x - 9$ **(b)** $3(x - 1) + 2(2x + 1) = 4$

(c) $\dfrac{20}{3x - 1} = 7$ **(d)** $\dfrac{9}{x + 2} = \dfrac{7}{2x + 1}$ **(e)** $\sqrt{\dfrac{2x}{x - 6}} = 2$

Solution

(a) To solve

$$6x + 1 = 10x - 9$$

the strategy is to collect terms involving *x* on one side of the equation, and to collect all of the number terms on to the other side. It does not matter which way round this is done. In this particular case, there are more *x*'s on the right-hand side than there are on the left-hand side. Consequently, to avoid negative numbers, you may prefer to stack the *x* terms on the right-hand side. The details are as follows:

$$1 = 4x - 9 \quad \text{(subtract } 6x \text{ from both sides)}$$

$$10 = 4x \quad \text{(add 9 to both sides)}$$

$$\frac{10}{4} = x \quad \text{(divide both sides by 4)}$$

Hence $x = \frac{5}{2} = 2\frac{1}{2}$.

(b) The novel feature of the equation

$$3(x - 1) + 2(2x + 1) = 4$$

is the presence of brackets. To solve it, we first remove the brackets by multiplying out, and then collect like terms:

$$3x - 3 + 4x + 2 = 4 \quad \text{(multiply out the brackets)}$$

$$7x - 1 = 4 \quad \text{(collect like terms)}$$

Note that this equation is now of the form that we know how to solve:

$$7x = 5 \quad \text{(add 1 to both sides)}$$

$$x = \frac{5}{7} \quad \text{(divide both sides by 7)}$$

(c) The novel feature of the equation

$$\frac{20}{3x - 1} = 7$$

is the fact that it involves an algebraic fraction. This can easily be removed by multiplying both sides by the bottom of the fraction:

$$\frac{20}{3x - 1} \times (3x - 1) = 7(3x - 1)$$

which cancels down to give

$$20 = 7(3x - 1)$$

The remaining steps are similar to those in part (b):

$20 = 21x - 7$ (multiply out the brackets)

$27 = 21x$ (add 7 to both sides)

$$\frac{27}{21} = x$$ (divide both sides by 21)

Hence $x = \frac{9}{7} = 1\frac{2}{7}$.

(d) The next equation,

$$\frac{9}{x + 2} = \frac{7}{2x + 1}$$

looks particularly daunting since there are fractions on both sides. However, these are easily removed by multiplying both sides by the denominators, in turn:

$$9 = \frac{7(x + 2)}{2x + 1}$$ (multiply both sides by $x + 2$)

$$9(2x + 1) = 7(x + 2)$$ (multiply both sides by $2x + 1$)

With practice you can do these two steps simultaneously and write this as the first line of working. The procedure of going straight from

$$\frac{9}{x + 2} = \frac{7}{2x + 1}$$

to

$$9(2x + 1) = 7(x + 2)$$

is called 'cross-multiplication'. In general, if

$$\frac{a}{b} = \frac{c}{d}$$

then

$$ad = bc$$

The remaining steps are similar to those used in the earlier parts of this example:

$$18x + 9 = 7x + 14 \quad \text{(multiply out the brackets)}$$
$$11x + 9 = 14 \quad \text{(subtract } 7x \text{ from both sides)}$$
$$11x = 5 \quad \text{(subtract 9 from both sides)}$$
$$x = \frac{5}{11} \quad \text{(divide both sides by 11)}$$

(e) The left-hand side of the final equation

$$\sqrt{\frac{2x}{x-6}} = 2$$

is surrounded by a square root, which can easily be removed by squaring both sides to get

$$\frac{2x}{x-6} = 4$$

The remaining steps are 'standard':

$$2x = 4(x-6) \quad \text{(multiply both sides by } x-6)$$
$$2x = 4x - 24 \quad \text{(multiply out the brackets)}$$
$$-2x = -24 \quad \text{(subtract } 4x \text{ from both sides)}$$
$$x = 12 \quad \text{(divide both sides by } -2)$$

Looking back over each part of the previous example, notice that there is a common strategy. In each case, the aim is to convert the given equation into one of the form

$$ax + b = c$$

which is the sort of equation that we can easily solve. If the original equation contains brackets then remove them by multiplying out. If the equation involves fractions then remove them by cross-multiplying.

Advice

If you have the time, it is always worth checking your answer by substituting your solution back into the original equation. For the last part of the above example, putting $x = 12$ into $\sqrt{\dfrac{2x}{x-6}}$ gives

$$\sqrt{\frac{2 \times 12}{12-6}} = \sqrt{\frac{24}{6}} = \sqrt{4} = 2 \quad ✓$$

Practice Problem

5. Solve each of the following equations. Leave your answer as a fraction, if necessary.

    (a) $4x + 1 = 25$ **(b)** $4x + 5 = 5x - 7$ **(c)** $3(3 - 2x) + 2(x - 1) = 10$

    (d) $\dfrac{4}{x-1} = 5$ **(e)** $\dfrac{3}{4} = \dfrac{5}{x-1}$

1.2.3 Inequalities

In Section 1.1.1 we made use of a **number line**:

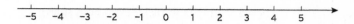

Now, although only whole numbers are marked on this diagram, it is implicitly assumed that it can also be used to indicate fractions and decimal numbers as well. To each point on the line there corresponds a particular number. Conversely, every number can be represented by a particular point on the line. For example, $-2\frac{1}{2}$ lies exactly halfway between -3 and -2. Similarly, $4\frac{7}{8}$ lies $\frac{7}{8}$ths of the way between 4 and 5. In theory, we can even find a point on the line corresponding to a number such as $\sqrt{2}$, although it may be difficult to sketch such a point accurately in practice. My calculator gives the value of $\sqrt{2}$ to be 1.414 213 56 to eight decimal places. This number therefore lies just less than halfway between 1 and 2.

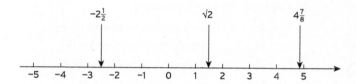

A number line can be used to decide whether or not one number is greater or less than another number. We say that a number a is greater than a number b if a lies to the right of b on the line and write this as

$a > b$

Likewise, we say that a is less than b if a lies to the left of b and write this as

$a < b$

From the diagram we see that

$-2 > -4$

because -2 lies to the right of 4. This is equivalent to the statement

$-4 < -2$

Similarly,

$0 > -1$ (or equivalently $-1 < 0$)
$2 > -2\frac{1}{2}$ (or equivalently $-2\frac{1}{2} < 2$)
$4\frac{7}{8} > \sqrt{2}$ (or equivalently $\sqrt{2} < 4\frac{7}{8}$)

There are occasions when we would like the letters a and b to stand for mathematical expressions rather than actual numbers. In this situation we sometimes use the symbols $\geq$ and $\leq$ to mean 'greater than or equal to' and 'less than or equal to' respectively.

We have already seen that we can manipulate equations in any way we like, provided that we do the same thing to both sides. An obvious question to ask is whether this rule extends to inequalities. To investigate this, consider the following example.

Example

Starting with the true statement

$$1 < 3$$

decide which of the following are valid operations when performed on both sides:

(a) add 4   **(b)** add −5   **(c)** multiply by 2   **(d)** multiply by −6

Solution

(a) If we add 4 to both sides of the inequality

$$1 < 3 \tag{1}$$

then we obtain

$$5 < 7$$

which is a true statement.

(b) If we add −5 to both sides of inequality (1) then we obtain

$$-4 < -2$$

which is also true.

(c) If we multiply both sides of inequality (1) by 2 then we obtain

$$2 < 6$$

which is again true.

(d) So far so good, but if we now multiply both sides of inequality (1) by −6 then we obtain

$$-6 < -18$$

which is false. In fact, quite the reverse is true, since −6 lies to the right of −18 on the number line and so −6 is actually greater than −18. This indicates that the rule needs modifying before we can extend it to inequalities and that we need to be careful when manipulating such things.

Practice Problem

6. Starting with the true statement

$$6 > 3$$

decide which of the following are valid operations when performed on both sides:

(a) add 6   **(b)** multiply by 2   **(c)** subtract 3

(d) add −3   **(e)** divide by 3   **(f)** multiply by −4

(g) multiply by −1 **(h)** divide by −3   **(i)** add −10

These examples show that the usual rule does apply to inequalities with the important proviso that

> **if both sides are multiplied or divided by a negative number then the sense of the inequality is reversed**

By this we mean that '>' changes to '<', '≤' changes to '≥' and so on.

Example

Simplify the inequality

$$2x + 3 < 4x + 7$$

Solution

The first problem is to decide what is meant by the word 'simplify'. At the moment there are x's on both sides of the inequality sign and it would obviously look neater if these were collected together. We do this by subtracting $4x$ from both sides to get

$$-2x + 3 < 7$$

We can also put all of the constant terms on to the right-hand side by subtracting 3 from both sides to get

$$-2x < 4$$

This is certainly an improvement, but we can go further to make the inequality even more meaningful. We may divide both sides by -2 to get

$$x > -2$$

Notice that the sense has been reversed at this stage because we have divided by a negative number. We have therefore shown that any number x satisfies the original inequality provided that it lies to the right of the number -2 on the number line.

Advice

You should check your answer using a couple of test values. Substituting $x = 1$ (which lies to the right of -2, so should work) into both sides of the original inequality $2x + 3 < 4x + 7$ gives $5 < 11$, which is true. On the other hand, substituting $x = -3$ (which lies to the left of -2, so should fail) gives $-3 < -5$, which is false.

Of course, just checking a couple of numbers like this does not prove that the final inequality is correct, but it should protect you against gross blunders.

Practice Problem

7. Simplify the inequalities

   (a) $2x < 3x + 7$ **(b)** $21x - 19 \geq 4x + 15$

Key Terms

Algebraic fraction   Ratio of two expressions; $p(x)/q(x)$ where $p(x)$ and $q(x)$ are algebraic expressions such as $ax^2 + bx + c$ or $dx + e$.

Denominator   The number (or expression) on the bottom of a fraction.

Equation   Equality of two algebraic expressions which is only true for certain values of the variable.

Equivalent fractions   Fractions which may appear different but which have the same numerical value.

Identity   Equality of two algebraic expressions which is true for all values of the variable.

Number line   An infinite line on which the points represent real numbers by their (signed) distance from the origin.

Numerator   The number (or expression) on the top of a fraction.

Exercise 1.2

1. Reduce each of the following numerical fractions to their lowest terms:

   (a) $\dfrac{13}{26}$ (b) $\dfrac{9}{12}$ (c) $\dfrac{18}{30}$ (d) $\dfrac{24}{72}$ (e) $\dfrac{36}{27}$

2. Reduce each of the following algebraic fractions to their lowest terms:

   (a) $\dfrac{6x}{9}$ (b) $\dfrac{x}{2x^2}$ (c) $\dfrac{b}{abc}$ (d) $\dfrac{4x}{6x^2y}$ (e) $\dfrac{15a^2b}{20ab^2}$

3. By factorizing the numerators and/or denominators of each of the following fractions reduce each to its lowest terms:

   (a) $\dfrac{2p}{4q + 6r}$ (b) $\dfrac{x}{x^2 - 4x}$ (c) $\dfrac{3ab}{6a^2 + 3a}$ (d) $\dfrac{14d}{21d - 7de}$ (e) $\dfrac{x + 2}{x^2 - 4}$

4. Which one of the following algebraic fractions can be simplified? Explain why the other two fractions cannot be simplified.

   $$\dfrac{x - 1}{2x - 2}, \dfrac{x - 2}{x + 2}, \dfrac{5t}{10t - s}$$

5. **(1)** Without using a calculator work out the following giving your answer in its lowest terms:

   (a) $\dfrac{1}{7} + \dfrac{2}{7}$ (b) $\dfrac{2}{9} - \dfrac{5}{9}$ (c) $\dfrac{1}{2} + \dfrac{1}{3}$ (d) $\dfrac{3}{4} - \dfrac{2}{5}$ (e) $\dfrac{1}{6} + \dfrac{2}{9}$ (f) $\dfrac{1}{6} + \dfrac{2}{3}$

   (g) $\dfrac{5}{6} \times \dfrac{3}{4}$ (h) $\dfrac{4}{15} \div \dfrac{2}{3}$ (i) $\dfrac{7}{8} \times \dfrac{2}{3}$ (j) $\dfrac{2}{75} \div \dfrac{4}{5}$ (k) $\dfrac{2}{9} \div 3$ (l) $3 \div \dfrac{2}{7}$

   (2) Use your calculator to check your answers to part (1).

6. Work out each of the following, simplifying your answer as far as possible:

   (a) $\dfrac{2}{3x} + \dfrac{1}{3x}$ (b) $\dfrac{2}{x} \times \dfrac{x}{5}$ (c) $\dfrac{3}{x} - \dfrac{2}{x^2}$ (d) $\dfrac{7}{x} + \dfrac{2}{y}$ (e) $\dfrac{a}{2} \div \dfrac{a}{6}$

   (f) $\dfrac{5c}{12} + \dfrac{5d}{18}$ (g) $\dfrac{x+2}{y-5} \times \dfrac{y-5}{x+3}$ (h) $\dfrac{4gh}{7} \div \dfrac{2g}{9h}$ (i) $\dfrac{t}{4} \div 5$ (j) $\dfrac{P}{Q} \times \dfrac{Q}{P}$

7. Solve each of the following equations. If necessary give your answer as a mixed fraction reduced to its lowest terms.

   (a) $x + 2 = 7$ (b) $3x = 18$ (c) $\dfrac{x}{9} = 2$ (d) $x - 4 = -2$

   (e) $2x - 3 = 17$ (f) $3x + 4 = 1$ (g) $\dfrac{x}{6} - 7 = 3$ (h) $3(x - 1) = 2$

   (i) $4 - x = 9$ (j) $6x + 2 = 5x - 1$ (k) $5(3x + 8) = 10$ (l) $2(x - 3) = 5(x + 1)$

   (m) $\dfrac{4x - 7}{3} = 2$ (n) $\dfrac{4}{x + 1} = 1$ (o) $5 - \dfrac{1}{x} = 1$

8. Which of the following inequalities are true?

   (a) $-2 < 1$ (b) $-6 > -4$ (c) $3 < 3$

   (d) $3 \le 3$ (e) $-21 \ge -22$ (f) $4 < \sqrt{25}$

9. Simplify the following inequalities:

   (a) $2x > x + 1$ (b) $7x + 3 \le 9 + 5x$ (c) $x - 5 > 4x + 4$ (d) $x - 1 < 2x - 3$

10. Simplify the following algebraic expression:

   $$\dfrac{4}{x^2 y} \div \dfrac{2x}{y}$$

11. (a) Solve the equation

   $$6(2 + x) = 5(1 - 4x)$$

   (b) Solve the inequality

   $$3x + 6 \ge 5x - 14$$

Exercise 1.2*

1. Simplify each of the following algebraic fractions:

   (a) $\dfrac{2x - 6}{4}$ (b) $\dfrac{9x}{6x^2 - 3x}$ (c) $\dfrac{4x + 16}{x + 4}$ (d) $\dfrac{x - 1}{1 - x}$

   (e) $\dfrac{x + 6}{x^2 - 36}$ (f) $\dfrac{(x + 3)(2x - 5)}{(2x - 5)(x + 4)}$ (g) $\dfrac{3x}{6x^3 - 15x^2 + 9x}$ (h) $\dfrac{4x^2 - 25y^2}{6x - 15y}$

2. **(1)** Without using your calculator evaluate

(a) $\dfrac{4}{5} \times \dfrac{25}{28}$ (b) $\dfrac{2}{7} \times \dfrac{14}{25} \times \dfrac{5}{8}$ (c) $\dfrac{9}{16} \div \dfrac{3}{8}$ (d) $\dfrac{2}{5} \times \dfrac{1}{12} \div \dfrac{8}{25}$

(e) $\dfrac{10}{13} - \dfrac{12}{13}$ (f) $\dfrac{5}{9} + \dfrac{2}{3}$ (g) $2\dfrac{3}{5} + 1\dfrac{3}{7}$ (h) $5\dfrac{9}{10} - \dfrac{1}{2} + 1\dfrac{2}{5}$

(i) $3\dfrac{3}{4} \times 1\dfrac{3}{5}$ (j) $\dfrac{3}{5} \times \left(2\dfrac{1}{3} + \dfrac{1}{2}\right)$ (k) $\dfrac{5}{6} \times \left(2\dfrac{1}{3} - 1\dfrac{2}{5}\right)$ (l) $\left(3\dfrac{1}{3} \div 2\dfrac{1}{6}\right) \div \dfrac{5}{13}$

(2) Confirm your answer to part (1) using a calculator.

3. Find expressions for the following fractions:

(a) $\dfrac{x^2 + 6x}{x - 2} \times \dfrac{x - 2}{x}$ (b) $\dfrac{1}{x} \div \dfrac{1}{x + 1}$ (c) $\dfrac{2}{xy} + \dfrac{3}{xy}$ (d) $\dfrac{x}{2} + \dfrac{x + 1}{3}$

(e) $\dfrac{3}{x} + \dfrac{4}{x + 1}$ (f) $\dfrac{3}{x} + \dfrac{5}{x^2}$ (g) $x - \dfrac{2}{x + 1}$ (h) $\dfrac{5}{x(x + 1)} - \dfrac{2}{x} + \dfrac{3}{x + 1}$

4. Solve the following equations:

(a) $5(2x + 1) = 3(x - 2)$

(b) $5(x + 2) + 4(2x - 3) = 11$

(c) $5(1 - x) = 4(10 + x)$

(d) $3(3 - 2x) - 7(1 - x) = 10$

(e) $9 - 5(2x - 1) = 6$

(f) $\dfrac{3}{2x + 1} = 2$

(g) $\dfrac{2}{x - 1} = \dfrac{3}{5x + 4}$

(h) $\dfrac{x}{2} + 3 = 7$

(i) $5 - \dfrac{x}{3} = 2$

(j) $\dfrac{5(x - 3)}{2} = \dfrac{2(x - 1)}{5}$

(k) $\sqrt{(2x - 5)} = 3$

(l) $(x + 3)(x - 1) = (x + 4)(x - 3)$

(m) $(x + 2)^2 + (2x - 1)^2 = 5x(x + 1)$

(n) $\dfrac{2x + 7}{3} = \dfrac{x - 4}{6} + \dfrac{1}{2}$

(o) $\sqrt{\dfrac{45}{2x - 1}} = 3$

(p) $\dfrac{4}{x} - \dfrac{3}{4} = \dfrac{1}{4x}$

5. Two-thirds of Ariadne's money together with five-sevenths of Brian's money is equal to three-fifths of Catriona's money. If Ariadne has $2.40 and Catriona has $11.25, write down an equation that you could use to work out how much Brian has. Solve this equation.

6. An amount $P is placed in a savings account. The interest rate is $r\%$ compounded annually so that after n years the savings, S, will be

$$S = P\left(1 + \dfrac{r}{100}\right)^n$$

(a) Find S when $P = 2000$, $n = 5$ and $r = 10$.

(b) Find P when $S = 65\ 563.62$, $n = 3$ and $r = 3$.

(c) Find r when $S = 7320.50$, $P = 5000$, and $n = 4$.

7. Solve the following inequalities:

(a) $2x - 19 > 7x + 24$ (b) $2(x - 1) < 5(3x + 2)$ (c) $\dfrac{2x - 1}{5} \geq \dfrac{x - 3}{2}$

(d) $3 + \dfrac{x}{3} < 2(x + 4)$ (e) $x < 2x + 1 \leq 7$

8. List all the whole numbers that satisfy both of the following inequalities simultaneously:

$$-7 \leq 2x < 6 \text{ and } 4x + 1 \leq x + 2$$

9. (a) Simplify

$$\frac{31x - 8}{(2x - 1)(x + 2)} - \frac{14}{x + 2}$$

(b) Solve the equation

$$\frac{x + 1}{8} = \frac{x + 3}{4} - \frac{1}{2}$$

(c) Simplify the inequality

$$(2x + 1)(x - 5) \leq 2(x + 2)(x - 4)$$

10. Simplify

$$\frac{x^2}{x + 1} \div \frac{2x}{x^2 - 1}$$

SECTION 1.3
Graphs of linear equations

Objectives

At the end of this section you should be able to:

- Plot points on graph paper given their coordinates.
- Sketch a line by finding the coordinates of two points on the line.
- Solve simultaneous linear equations graphically.
- Sketch a line by using its slope and intercept.

Consider the two straight lines shown in Figure 1.1. The horizontal line is referred to as the **x axis** and the vertical line is referred to as the **y axis**. The point where these lines intersect is known as the **origin** and is denoted by the letter O. These lines enable us to identify uniquely any point, P, in terms of its **coordinates** (x, y). The first number, x, denotes the horizontal distance along the x axis and the second number, y, denotes the vertical distance along the y axis. The arrows on the axes indicate the positive direction in each case.

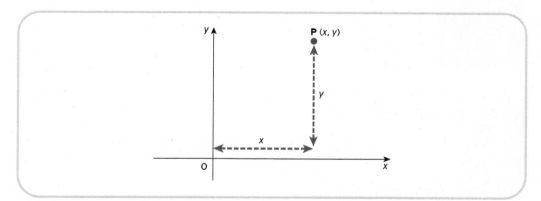

Figure 1.1

Example

Plot the points A(2, 3), B(−1, 4), C(−3, −1), D(3, −2) and E(5, 0).

Solution
The point A with coordinates (2, 3) is obtained by starting at the origin, moving 2 units to the right and then moving 3 units vertically upwards. Similarly, the point B with coordinates (−1, 4) is located 1 unit to the left of O (because the x coordinate is negative) and 4 units up. These points, together with C(−3, −1), D(3, −2) and E(5, 0) are plotted in Figure 1.2.

Note that the point C lies in the bottom left-hand quadrant since its x and y coordinates are both negative. It is also worth noticing that E actually lies on the x axis since its y coordinate is zero. Likewise, a point with coordinates of the form $(0, y)$ for some number y would lie somewhere on the y axis. Of course, the point with coordinates $(0, 0)$ is the origin, O.

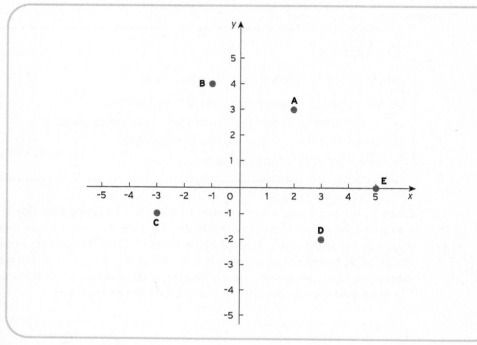

Figure 1.2

Practice Problem

1. Plot the following points on graph paper. What do you observe?

    $(2, 5)$, $(1, 3)$, $(0, 1)$, $(-2, -3)$, $(-3, -5)$

In economics we need to do rather more than just plot individual points on graph paper. We would like to be able to sketch curves represented by equations and to deduce information from such a picture. We restrict our attention in this section to those equations whose graphs are straight lines, deferring consideration of more general curve sketching until Chapter 2.

In Practice Problem 1 you will have noticed that the five points $(2, 5)$, $(1, 3)$, $(0, 1)$, $(-2, -3)$ and $(-3, -5)$ all lie on a straight line. In fact, the equation of this line is

$$-2x + y = 1$$

Any point lies on this line if its x and y coordinates satisfy this equation. For example, $(2, 5)$ lies on the line because when the values $x = 2$ and $y = 5$ are substituted into the left-hand side of the equation we obtain

$$-2(2) + 5 = -4 + 5 = 1$$

which is the right-hand side of the equation. The other points can be checked similarly (Table 1.1).

Table 1.1

Point	Check	
(1, 3)	$-2(1) + 3 = -2 + 3 = 1$	✓
(0, 1)	$-2(0) + 1 = 0 + 1 = 1$	✓
(−2, −3)	$-2(-2) - 3 = 4 - 3 = 1$	✓
(−3, −5)	$-2(-3) - 5 = 6 - 5 = 1$	✓

The general equation of a straight line takes the form

$$\boxed{\text{a multiple of } x} + \boxed{\text{a multiple of } y} = \boxed{\text{a number}}$$

that is,

$$dx + ey = f$$

for some given numbers d, e and f. Consequently, such an equation is called a **linear equation**. The numbers d and e are referred to as the **coefficients**. The coefficients of the linear equation,

$$-2x + y = 1$$

are −2 and 1 (the coefficient of y is 1 because y can be thought of as $1 \times y$).

Example

Decide which of the following points lie on the line $5x - 2y = 6$:

A(0, −3), B(2, 2), C(−10, −28) and D(4, 8)

Solution

$$5(0) - 2(-3) = 0 - (-6) = 0 + 6 = 6$$
$$5(2) - 2(2) = 10 - 4 = 6$$
$$5(-10) - 2(-28) = -50 - (-56) = -50 + 56 = 6$$
$$5(4) - 2(8) = 20 - 16 = 4 \neq 6$$

Hence points A, B and C lie on the line, but D does not.

Practice Problem

2. Check that the points

(−1, 2), (−4, 4), (5, −2), (2, 0)

all lie on the line

$$2x + 3y = 4$$

and hence sketch this line on graph paper. Does the point (3, −1) lie on this line?

In general, to sketch a line from its mathematical equation, it is sufficient to calculate the coordinates of any two distinct points lying on it. These two points can be plotted on graph paper and a ruler used to draw the line passing through them. One way of finding the coordinates of a point on a line is simply to choose a numerical value for x and to substitute it into the equation.

The equation can then be used to deduce the corresponding value of y. The whole process can be repeated to find the coordinates of the second point by choosing another value for x.

Example

Sketch the line

$$4x + 3y = 11$$

Solution

For the first point, let us choose $x = 5$. Substitution of this number into the equation gives

$$4(5) + 3y = 11$$
$$20 + 3y = 11$$

The problem now is to solve this equation for y:

$3y = -9$ (subtract 20 from both sides)

$y = -3$ (divide both sides by 3)

Consequently, the coordinates of one point on the line are $(5, -3)$.

For the second point, let us choose $x = -1$. Substitution of this number into the equation gives

$$4(-1) + 3y = 11$$
$$-4 + 3y = 11$$

This can be solved for y as follows:

$3y = 15$ (add 4 to both sides)

$y = 5$ (divide both sides by 3)

Hence $(-1, 5)$ lies on the line, which can now be sketched on graph paper as shown in Figure 1.3.

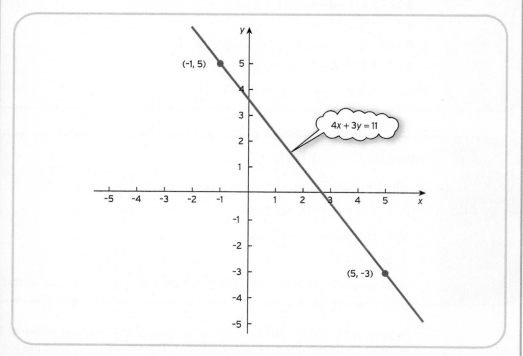

Figure 1.3

Practice Problem

3. Find the coordinates of two points on the line

$$3x - 2y = 4$$

by taking $x = 2$ for the first point and $x = -2$ for the second point. Hence sketch its graph.

In this example we arbitrarily picked two values of x and used the linear equation to work out the corresponding values of y. There is nothing particularly special about the variable x. We could equally well have chosen values for y and solved the resulting equations for x. In fact, the easiest thing to do (in terms of the amount of arithmetic involved) is to put $x = 0$ and find y and then to put $y = 0$ and find x.

Example

Sketch the line

$$2x + y = 5$$

Solution

Setting $x = 0$ gives

$$2(0) + y = 5$$
$$0 + y = 5$$
$$y = 5$$

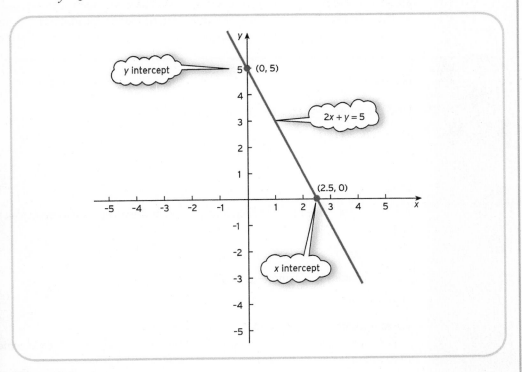

Figure 1.4

Hence (0, 5) lies on the line.
Setting $y = 0$ gives

$$2x + 0 = 5$$
$$2x = 5$$
$$x = 5/2 \quad \text{(divide both sides by 2)}$$

Hence (5/2, 0) lies on the line.

The line $2x + y = 5$ is sketched in Figure 1.4. Notice how easy the algebra is using this approach. The two points themselves are also slightly more meaningful. They are the points where the line intersects the coordinate axes.

Practice Problem

4. Find the coordinates of the points where the line

$$x - 2y = 2$$

intersects the axes. Hence sketch its graph.

In economics it is sometimes necessary to handle more than one equation at the same time. For example, in supply and demand analysis we are interested in two equations, the supply equation and the demand equation. Both involve the same variables Q and P, so it makes sense to sketch them on the same diagram. This enables the market equilibrium quantity and price to be determined by finding the point of intersection of the two lines. We shall return to the analysis of supply and demand in Section 1.5. There are many other occasions in economics and business studies when it is necessary to determine the coordinates of points of intersection. The following is a straightforward example which illustrates the general principle.

Example

Find the point of intersection of the two lines

$$4x + 3y = 11$$
$$2x + y = 5$$

Solution

We have already seen how to sketch these lines in the previous two examples. We discovered that

$$4x + 3y = 11$$

passes through (5, −3) and (−1, 5), and that

$$2x + y = 5$$

passes through (0, 5) and (5/2, 0).

These two lines are sketched on the same diagram in Figure 1.5, from which the point of intersection is seen to be (2, 1).

It is easy to verify that we have not made any mistakes by checking that (2, 1) lies on both lines. It lies on

$$4x + 3y = 11 \text{ because } 4(2) + 3(1) = 8 + 3 = 11 \qquad ✓$$

and lies on $2x + y = 5$ because $2(2) + 1 = 4 + 1 = 5$ ✓

For this reason, we say that $x = 2$, $y = 1$, is the solution of the **simultaneous linear equations**

$$4x + 3y = 11$$
$$2x + y = 5$$

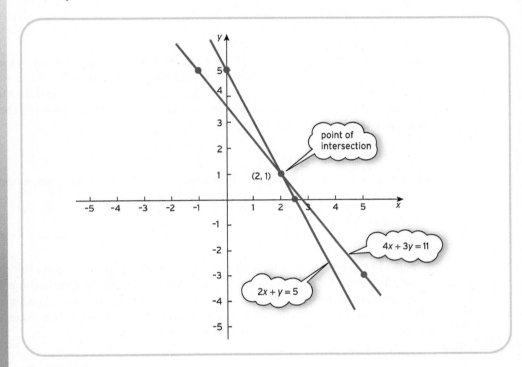

Figure 1.5

Practice Problem

5. Find the point of intersection of

$$3x - 2y = 4$$
$$x - 2y = 2$$

[Hint: you might find your answers to Problems 3 and 4 useful.]

Quite often it is not necessary to produce an accurate plot of an equation. All that may be required is an indication of the general shape together with a few key points or features. It can be shown that, provided e is non-zero, any equation given by

$$dx + ey = f$$

can be rearranged into the special form

$$y = ax + b$$

An example showing you how to perform such a rearrangement will be considered in a moment. The coefficients a and b have particular significance, which we now examine. To be specific, consider

$$y = 2x - 3$$

in which $a = 2$ and $b = -3$.

When x is taken to be zero, the value of y is

$$y = 2(0) - 3 = -3$$

The line passes through $(0, -3)$, so the y intercept is -3. This is just the value of b. In other words, the constant term, b, represents the **intercept** on the y axis.

In the same way it is easy to see that a, the coefficient of x, determines the **slope** of the line. The slope of a straight line is simply the change in the value of y brought about by a 1 unit increase in the value of x. For the equation

$$y = 2x - 3$$

let us choose $x = 5$ and increase this by a single unit to get $x = 6$. The corresponding values of y are then

$$y = 2(5) - 3 = 10 - 3 = 7$$
$$y = 2(6) - 3 = 12 - 3 = 9$$

respectively. The value of y increases by 2 units when x rises by 1 unit. The slope of the line is therefore 2, which is the value of a. The slope of a line is fixed throughout its length, so it is immaterial which two points are taken. The particular choice of $x = 5$ and $x = 6$ was entirely arbitrary. You might like to convince yourself of this by choosing two other points, such as $x = 20$ and $x = 21$, and repeating the previous calculations.

A graph of the line

$$y = 2x - 3$$

is sketched in Figure 1.6. This is sketched using the information that the intercept is -3 and that for every 1 unit along we go 2 units up. In this example the coefficient of x is positive. This does not have to be the case. If a is negative then for every increase in x there is a corresponding decrease in y, indicating that the line is downhill. If a is zero then the equation is just

$$y = b$$

indicating that y is fixed at b and the line is horizontal. The three cases are illustrated in Figure 1.7.

It is important to appreciate that in order to use the slope–intercept approach it is necessary for the equation to be written as

$$y = ax + b$$

If a linear equation does not have this form, it is usually possible to perform a preliminary rearrangement to isolate the variable y on the left-hand side, as the following example demonstrates.

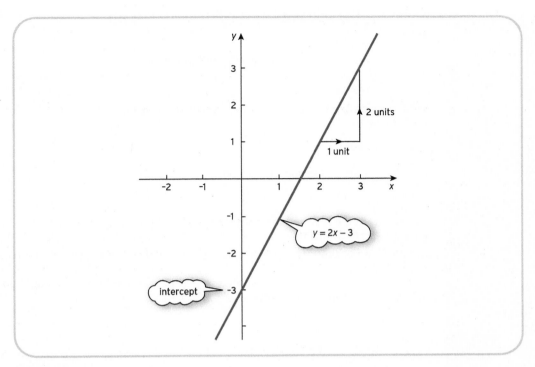

Figure 1.6

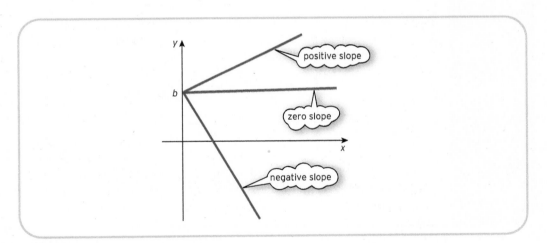

Figure 1.7

Example

Use the slope–intercept approach to sketch the line

$$2x + 3y = 12$$

Solution

We can remove the x term on the left-hand side of

$$2x + 3y = 12$$

by subtracting $2x$. As usual, to balance the equation we must also subtract $2x$ from the right-hand side to get

$$3y = 12 - 2x$$

We now just divide through by 3 to get

$$y = 4 - \tfrac{2}{3}x$$

This is now in the required form with $a = -2/3$ and $b = 4$. The line is sketched in Figure 1.8. A slope of $-2/3$ means that, for every 1 unit along, we go 2/3 units down (or, equivalently, for every 3 units along, we go 2 units down). An intercept of 4 means that it passes through $(0, 4)$.

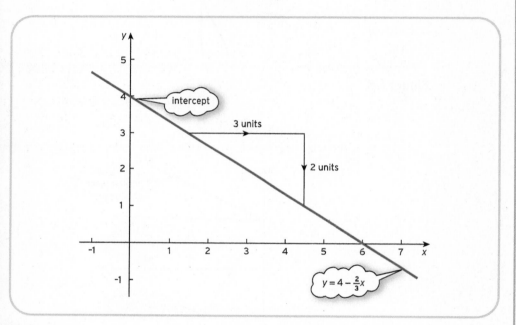

Figure 1.8

Practice Problem

6. Use the slope–intercept approach to sketch the lines

    (a) $y = x + 2$

    (b) $4x + 2y = 1$

Example   EXCEL

(a) Use Excel to draw the graphs of

$$y = 3x + 2$$
$$y = -2x + 2$$
$$y = \tfrac{1}{2}x + 2$$

on the same set of axes, taking values of x between -3 and 3.

(b) On another set of axes, use Excel to draw the graphs of

$$y = 2x$$
$$y = 2x - 3$$
$$y = 2x + 1$$

for $-3 \leq x \leq 3$.

(c) What do you notice about the two sets of graphs?

Solution

(a) To draw graphs with Excel, we first have to set up a table of values. By giving a title to each column, we will be able to label the graphs at a later stage, so we type the headings x, $y = 3x + 2$, $y = -2x + 2$ and $y = x/2 + 2$ in cells A1, B1, C1 and D1 respectively.

The x values are now typed into the first column, as shown in the diagram below. In the next three columns, we generate the corresponding values for y by entering formulae for each of the three lines.

The formula for the first graph goes in cell B2. As the x value is in cell A2, we type

```
=3*A2+2
```

	A	B	C	D
1	x	y = 3x + 2	y = -2x + 2	y = x/2 + 2
2	-3	=3*A2+2		
3	-2			
4	-1			
5	0			
6	1			
7	2			
8	3			
9				
10				

By clicking and dragging this formula down the second column (up to, and including, cell B8), the values of y are calculated.

Similarly, the formula for calculating the y coordinates for the second line is entered into cell C2 as

```
=-2*A2+2
```

and the formula for the third line is entered into cell D2 as

```
=A2/2+2
```

To plot these points on a graph, we highlight all the cells in the table, including the column titles, and click on the Chart Wizard button on the toolbar. The Chart Wizard box will appear:

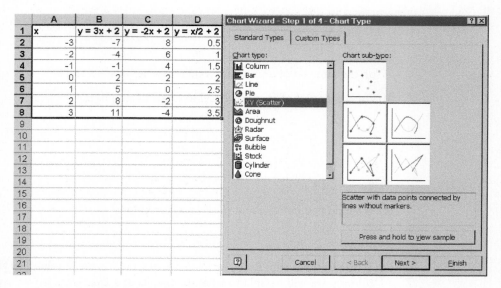

From the list of chart types, we choose **XY (Scatter)**, and then choose an appropriate sub-type. As we are plotting straight lines, we have selected **Scatter with data points connected by lines without markers**.

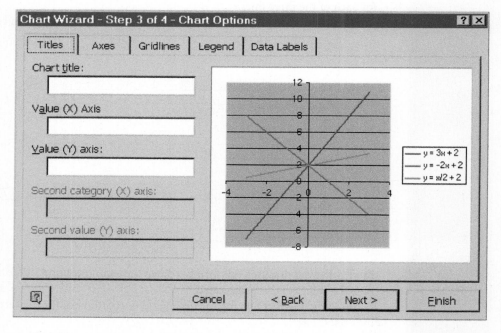

Click Next to see a preview of the graph, with the option to change the range of the cells that have been plotted. If the graph looks wrong, it is usually because the wrong cells have been highlighted before going into Chart Wizard, so go back and check this, rather than altering the range.

The third screen allows you to label your graph, and alter its gridlines. You should always label your axes, but you could, for example, delete the Legend if you feel it is inappropriate. Adding gridlines can make it easier to read values off the graph.

Finally, we click Next and Finish, to transfer the graph on to the spreadsheet, as shown in Figure 1.9. Notice that Excel provides a key showing which line is which.

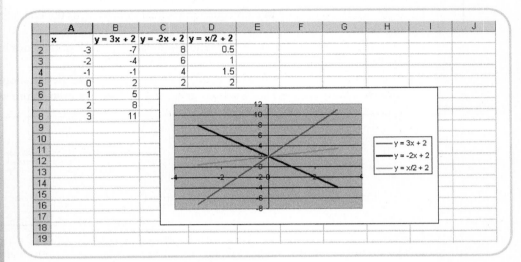

Figure 1.9

(b) Following the same procedure for the three lines

$$y = 2x$$

$$y = 2x - 3$$

$$y = 2x + 1$$

produces a graph as shown in Figure 1.10.

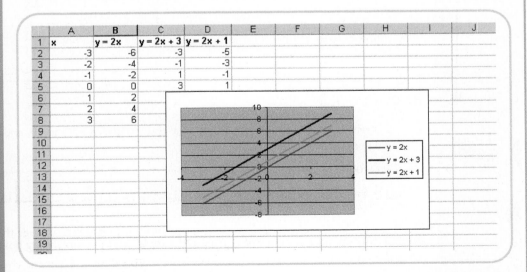

Figure 1.10

(c) Notice that in part (a), all of the graphs cut the y axis at the point (0, 2). In part (b), the graphs are parallel, which means that they have the same gradient.

This illustrates the fact that every straight line has an equation of the form

$$y = ax + b$$

where a is the gradient, and b is the intercept on the y axis.

In (a), the value of b in each equation is equal to 2, so all of the lines cut the y axis at this point.

In (b), the value of a in each equation is equal to 2, so all of the lines have the same gradient and are parallel.

It is very useful to be able to recognize these properties from the equations, as it means we have a fairly good idea of what our graph should look like even before we draw it.

Key Terms

Coefficient   A numerical multiplier of the variables in an algebraic term, such as the numbers 4 and 7 in the expression $4x + 7yz^2$.

Coordinates   A set of numbers that determine the position of a point relative to a set of axes.

Intercept   The point(s) where a graph crosses one of the coordinate axes.

Linear equation   An equation of the form $y = ax + b$.

Origin   The point where the coordinate axes intersect.

Simultaneous linear equations   A set of linear equations in which there are (usually) the same number of equations and unknowns. The solution consists of values of the unknowns which satisfy all of the equations at the same time.

Slope of a line   Also known as the gradient, it is the change in the value of y when x increases by 1 unit.

x axis   The horizontal coordinate axis pointing from left to right.

y axis   The vertical coordinate axis pointing upwards.

Exercise 1.3

1. On graph paper draw axes with values of x and y between −3 and 10, and plot the following points:

P (4, 0), Q (−2, 9), R (5, 8), S (−1, −2)

Hence find the coordinates of the point of intersection of the line passing through P and Q, and the line passing through R and S.

2. By substituting values into the equation, decide which of the following points lie on the line, $x + 4y = 12$:

A(12, 0), B(2, 2), C(4, 2), D(−8, 5), E(0, 3)

3. For the line $3x - 5y = 8$,

   (a) Find the value of x when $y = 2$.

   (b) Find the value of y when $x = 1$.

   Hence write down the coordinates of two points which lie on this line.

4. If $4x + 3y = 24$, complete the following table and hence sketch this line.

x	y
0	
	0
3	

5. Solve the following pairs of simultaneous linear equations graphically:

   (a) $-2x + y = 2$ **(b)** $3x + 4y = 12$ **(c)** $2x + y = 4$ **(d)** $x + y = 1$

   $\quad\ \ 2x + y = -6$ $\quad\ \ \ x + 4y = 8$ $\quad\ 4x - 3y = 3$ $\quad\ 6x + 5y = 15$

6. State the value of the slope and y-intercept for each of the following lines:

   (a) $y = 5x + 9$ **(b)** $y = 3x - 1$ **(c)** $y = 13 - x$

   (d) $-x + y = 4$ **(e)** $4x + 2y = 5$ **(f)** $5x - y = 6$

7. Use the slope–intercept approach to produce a rough sketch of the following lines:

   (a) $y = -x$ **(b)** $x - 2y = 6$

Exercise 1.3*

1. Which of the following points lie on the line $3x - 5y = 25$?

   $(5, -2), (10, 1), (-5, 0), (5, 10), (-5, 10), (0, -5)$

2. Solve the following pairs of simultaneous equations graphically:

   (a) $y = 3x - 1$ **(b)** $2x + y = 6$ **(c)** $2x + 3y = 5$ **(d)** $3x + 4y = -12$

   $\quad\ y = 2x + 1$ $\quad\ \ x - y = -3$ $\quad\ 5x - 2y = -16$ $\quad\ -2x + 3y = 25$

3. State the value of the slope and y intercept for each of the following lines:

   (a) $y = 7x - 34$ **(b)** $y = 1 - x$ **(c)** $3x - 2y = 6$ **(d)** $-4x + 2y = 5$

   (e) $x - 5y = 0$ **(f)** $y = 2$ **(g)** $x = 4$

4. Identify the two lines in the following list which are parallel:

(a) $3x + 5y = 2$ (b) $5x - 3y = 1$ (c) $5x + 3y = 13$

(d) $10x - 6y = 9$ (e) $y = 0.6x + 2$

5. (a) The Wonderful Mobile Phone Company charges \$70 per month, and calls cost \$0.50 per minute. If I use my phone for x minutes in a month, write down an expression for the total cost in terms of x.

(b) Repeat part (a) for the Fantastic Mobile Phone Company, which charges \$20 per month and \$1 per minute.

(c) Plot both graphs on the same axes and hence find the call time per month which gives the same total cost for these two companies.

6. (1) Show that the lines $ax + by = c$ and $dx + ey = f$ are parallel whenever $ae - bd = 0$.

(2) Use the result of part (1) to comment on the solution of the following simultaneous equations:

$$2x - 4y = 1$$
$$-3x + 6y = 7$$

7. Write down the coordinates of the points where the line $ax + by = c$ intercepts the axes.

SECTION 1.4
Algebraic solution of simultaneous linear equations

Objectives

At the end of this section you should be able to:

- Solve a system of two simultaneous linear equations in two unknowns using elimination.
- Detect when a system of equations does not have a solution.
- Detect when a system of equations has infinitely many solutions.
- Solve a system of three simultaneous linear equations in three unknowns using elimination.

In Section 1.3 a graphical method was described for the solution of simultaneous linear equations. Both lines are sketched on the same piece of graph paper and the coordinates of the point of intersection are then simply read off from the diagram. Unfortunately this approach has several drawbacks. It is not always easy to decide on a suitable scale for the axes. Even if the scale allows all four points (two from each line) to fit on the diagram, there is no guarantee that the point of intersection itself also lies on it. When this happens you have no alternative but to throw away your graph paper and to start again, choosing a smaller scale in the hope that the solution will now fit. The second drawback concerns the accuracy of the graphical solution. All of the problems in Section 1.3 were deliberately chosen so that the answers had nice numbers in them; whole numbers such as -1, 2 and 5 or at worst simple fractions such as $1/2$, $2^1/2$ and $-1/4$. In practice, the coefficients of the equations may well involve decimals and we might expect a decimal solution. Indeed, even if the coefficients are whole numbers the solution itself could involve nasty fractions such as 7/8 or perhaps something like 231/571. A moment's thought should convince you that in these circumstances it is virtually impossible to obtain the solution graphically, even if we use a really large scale and our sharpest HB pencil in the process. The final drawback concerns the nature of the problem itself. Quite frequently in economics we need to solve three equations in three unknowns or maybe four equations in four unknowns. Unfortunately, the graphical method of solution does not extend to these cases.

In this section an alternative method of solution is described which relies on algebra. It is called the **elimination method**, since each stage of the process eliminates one (or more) of the unknowns. This method always produces the exact solution and can be applied to systems of equations larger than just two equations in two unknowns. In order to illustrate the method, we return to the simple example considered in the previous section:

$$4x + 3y = 11 \tag{1}$$

$$2x + y = 5 \tag{2}$$

The coefficient of x in equation (1) is 4 and the coefficient of x in equation (2) is 2. If these numbers had turned out to be exactly the same then we could have eliminated the variable x by subtracting one equation from the other. However, we can arrange for this to be the case by multiplying the left-hand side of the second equation by 2. Of course, we must also remember to multiply the right-hand side of the second equation by 2 in order for this operation to be valid. The second equation then becomes

$$4x + 2y = 10 \tag{3}$$

We may now subtract equation (3) from (1) to get

$$y = 1$$

You may like to think of this in terms of the usual layout for the subtraction of two ordinary numbers: that is,

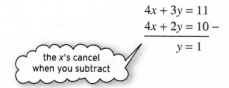

$$
\begin{array}{r}
4x + 3y = 11 \\
4x + 2y = 10\ - \\
\hline
y = 1
\end{array}
$$

the x's cancel when you subtract

This number can now be substituted into one of the original equations to deduce x. From equation (1)

$$
\begin{aligned}
4x + 3(1) &= 11 \quad \text{(substitute } y = 1\text{)} \\
4x + 3 &= 1 \\
4x &= 8 \quad \text{(subtract 3 from both sides)} \\
x &= 2 \quad \text{(divide both sides by 4)}
\end{aligned}
$$

Hence the solution is $x = 2$, $y = 1$. As a check, substitution of these values into the other original equation (2) gives

$$2(2) + 1 = 5 \quad ✓$$

The method of elimination can be summarized as follows.

Step 1

Add/subtract a multiple of one equation to/from a multiple of the other to eliminate x.

Step 2

Solve the resulting equation for y.

Step 3

Substitute the value of y into one of the original equations to deduce x.

Step 4

Check that no mistakes have been made by substituting both x and y into the other original equation.

Example

Solve the system of equations

$$3x + 2y = 1 \tag{1}$$
$$-2x + y = 2 \tag{2}$$

Solution

Step 1

The coefficients of x in equations (1) and (2) are 3 and -2 respectively. We can arrange for these to be the same size (but of opposite sign) by multiplying equation (1) by 2 and multiplying (2) by 3. The new equations will then have x coefficients of 6 and -6, so we can eliminate x this time by adding the equations together. The details are as follows.

Doubling the first equation produces

$$6x + 4y = 2 \tag{3}$$

Tripling the second equation produces

$$-6x + 3y = 6 \tag{4}$$

If equation (4) is added to equation (3) then

$$
\begin{aligned}
6x + 4y &= 2 \\
-6x + 3y &= 6\ + \\
\hline
7y &= 8
\end{aligned}
\tag{5}
$$

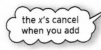
the x's cancel when you add

Step 2

Equation (5) can be solved by dividing both sides by 7 to get

$$y = 8/7$$

Step 3

If 8/7 is substituted for y in equation (1) then

$$3x + 2\left(\frac{8}{7}\right) = 1$$

$$3x + \frac{16}{7} = 1$$

$$3x = 1 - \frac{16}{7} \qquad \text{(subtract 16/7 from both sides)}$$

$$3x = \frac{7 - 16}{7} \qquad \text{(put over a common denominator)}$$

$$3x = -\frac{9}{7}$$

$$x = \frac{1}{3} \times \left(-\frac{9}{7}\right) \qquad \text{(divide both sides by 3)}$$

$$x = -\frac{3}{7}$$

The solution is therefore $x = -3/7$, $y = 8/7$.

Step 4

As a check, equation (2) gives

$$-2\left(-\frac{3}{7}\right) + \frac{8}{7} = \frac{6}{7} + \frac{8}{7} = \frac{6+8}{7} = \frac{14}{7} = 2 \quad \checkmark$$

Advice

In the general description of the method, we suggested that the variable x is eliminated in step 1. There is nothing special about x. We could equally well eliminate y at this stage and then solve the resulting equation in step 2 for x.

You might like to solve the above example using this alternative strategy. You need to double equation (2) and then subtract from (1).

Practice Problem

1. **(a)** Solve the equations

    $$3x - 2y = 4$$
    $$x - 2y = 2$$

    by eliminating one of the variables.

    (b) Solve the equations

    $$3x + 5y = 19$$
    $$-5x + 2y = -11$$

    by eliminating one of the variables.

The following examples provide further practice in using the method and illustrate some special cases which may occur.

Example

Solve the system of equations

$$x - 2y = 1$$
$$2x - 4y = -3$$

Solution

Step 1

The variable x can be eliminated by doubling the first equation and subtracting the second:

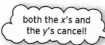

both the x's and the y's cancel!

$$
\begin{array}{r}
2x - 4y = 2 \\
2x - 4y = -3 \; - \\
\hline
0 = 5
\end{array}
$$

The statement '0 = 5' is clearly nonsense and something has gone seriously wrong. To understand what is going on here, let us try and solve this problem graphically.

The line $x - 2y = 1$ passes through the points $(0, -1/2)$ and $(1, 0)$ (check this). The line $2x - 4y = -3$ passes through the points $(0, 3/4)$ and $(-3/2, 0)$ (check this). Figure 1.11 shows that these lines are parallel and so they do not intersect. It is therefore not surprising that we were unable to find a solution using algebra, because this system of equations does not have one. We could have deduced this before when subtracting the equations. The equation that only involves y in step 2 can be written as

$$0y = 5$$

and the problem is to find a value of y for which this equation is true. No such value exists, since

$$\boxed{\text{zero}} \times \boxed{\text{any number}} = \boxed{\text{zero}}$$

and so the original system of equations does not have a solution.

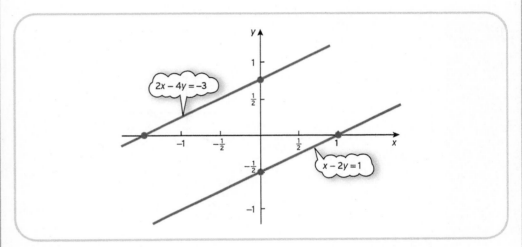

Figure 1.11

Example

Solve the equations

$$2x - \;\;4y = 1$$
$$5x - 10y = 5/2$$

Solution

Step 1
The variable x can be eliminated by multiplying the first equation by 5, multiplying the second equation by 2 and subtracting

$$10x - 20y = 5$$
$$\underline{10x - 20y = 5} -$$
$$0 = 0$$

everything cancels including the right-hand side!

Again, it is easy to explain this using graphs. The line $2x - 4y = 1$ passes through $(0, -1/4)$ and $(1/2, 0)$. The line $5x - 10y = 5/2$ passes through $(0, -1/4)$ and $(1/2, 0)$. Consequently, both equations represent the same line. From Figure 1.12 the lines intersect along the whole of their length and any point on this line is a solution. This particular system of equations has infinitely many solutions. This can also be deduced algebraically. The equation involving y in step 2 is

$$0y = 0$$

which is true for any value of y.

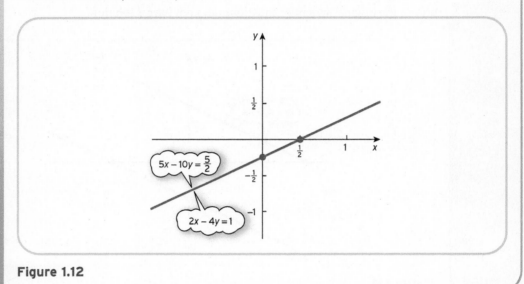

Figure 1.12

These examples show that a system of equations can possess a unique solution, no solution or infinitely many solutions. Algebraically, this can be detected in step 2. If the equation resulting from the elimination of x looks like

$$\boxed{\text{any non-zero number}} \times \boxed{y} = \boxed{\text{any number}}$$

then the equations have a unique solution, or if it looks like

$$\boxed{\text{zero}} \times \boxed{y} = \boxed{\text{any non-zero number}}$$

then the equations have no solution, or if it looks like

$$\boxed{\text{zero}} \times \boxed{y} = \boxed{\text{zero}}$$

then the equations have infinitely many solutions.

It is interesting to notice how the graphical approach 'saved the day' in the previous two examples. They show how useful pictures are as an aid to understanding in mathematics.

Practice Problem

2. Attempt to solve the following systems of equations:

(a) $3x - 6y = -2$ **(b)** $-5x + y = 4$

$-4x + 8y = -1$ $10x - 2y = -8$

Comment on the nature of the solution in each case.

We now show how the algebraic method can be used to solve three equations in three unknowns. As you might expect, the details are more complicated than for just two equations, but the principle is the same. We begin with a simple example to illustrate the general method. Consider the system

$$x + 3y - z = 4 \tag{1}$$
$$2x + y + 2z = 10 \tag{2}$$
$$3x - y + z = 4 \tag{3}$$

The objective is to find three numbers x, y and z which satisfy these equations simultaneously. Our previous work suggests that we should begin by eliminating x from all but one of the equations.

The variable x can be eliminated from the second equation by multiplying equation (1) by 2 and subtracting equation (2):

$$\begin{aligned} 2x + 6y - 2z &= 8 \\ 2x + y + 2z &= 10 - \\ \hline 5y - 4z &= -2 \end{aligned} \tag{4}$$

Similarly, we can eliminate x from the third equation by multiplying equation (1) by 3 and subtracting equation (3):

$$\begin{aligned} 3x + 9y - 3z &= 12 \\ 3x - y + z &= 4 - \\ \hline 10y - 4z &= 8 \end{aligned} \tag{5}$$

At this stage the first equation is unaltered but the second and third equations of the system have changed to equations (4) and (5) respectively, so the current equations are

$$x + 3y - z = 4 \tag{1}$$
$$5y - 4z = -2 \tag{4}$$
$$10y - 4z = 8 \tag{5}$$

Notice that the last two equations constitute a system of just two equations in two unknowns, y and z. This, of course, is precisely the type of problem that we already know how to solve. Once y and z have been calculated, the values can be substituted into equation (1) to deduce x.

We can eliminate y in the last equation by multiplying equation (4) by 2 and subtracting equation (5):

$$\begin{aligned} 10y - 8z &= -4 \\ 10y - 4z &= 8 - \\ \hline -4z &= -12 \end{aligned} \tag{6}$$

Collecting together the current equations gives

$$x + 3y - z = 4 \tag{1}$$
$$5y - 4z = -2 \tag{4}$$
$$-4z = -12 \tag{6}$$

From the last equation,

$$z = \frac{-12}{-4} = 3 \quad \text{(divide both sides by } -4)$$

If this is substituted into equation (4) then

$$5y - 4(3) = -2$$
$$5y - 12 = -2$$
$$5y = 10 \quad \text{(add 12 to both sides)}$$
$$y = 2 \quad \text{(divide both sides by 5)}$$

Finally, substituting $y = 2$ and $z = 3$ into equation (1) produces

$$x + 3(2) - 3 = 4$$
$$x + 3 = 4$$
$$x = 1 \quad \text{(subtract 3 from sides)}$$

Hence the solution is $x = 1$, $y = 2$, $z = 3$.

As usual, it is possible to check the answer by putting these numbers back into the original equations (1), (2) and (3):

$$1 + 3(2) - 3 = 4 \quad \checkmark$$
$$2(1) + 2 + 2(3) = 10 \quad \checkmark$$
$$3(1) - 2 + 3 = 4 \quad \checkmark$$

The general strategy may be summarized as follows. Consider the system

$$?x + ?y + ?z = ?$$
$$?x + ?y + ?z = ?$$
$$?x + ?y + ?z = ?$$

where ? denotes some numerical coefficient.

Step 1

Add/subtract multiples of the first equation to/from multiples of the second and third equations to eliminate x. This produces a new system of the form

$$?x + ?y + ?z = ?$$
$$?y + ?z = ?$$
$$?y + ?z = ?$$

Step 2

Add/subtract a multiple of the second equation to/from a multiple of the third to eliminate y. This produces a new system of the form

$$?x + ?y + ?z = ?$$
$$?y + ?z = ?$$
$$?z = ?$$

Step 3

Solve the last equation for z. Substitute the value of z into the second equation to deduce y. Finally, substitute the values of both y and z into the first equation to deduce x.

Step 4

Check that no mistakes have been made by substituting the values of x, y and z into the original equations.

It is possible to adopt different strategies from that suggested above. For example, it may be more convenient to eliminate z from the last equation in step 2 rather than y. However, it is important to notice that we use the second equation to do this, not the first. Any attempt to use the first equation in step 2 would reintroduce the variable x into the equations, which is the last thing we want to do at this stage.

Example

Solve the equations

$$4x + y + 3z = 8 \tag{1}$$
$$-2x + 5y + z = 4 \tag{2}$$
$$3x + 2y + 4z = 9 \tag{3}$$

Solution

Step 1

To eliminate x from the second equation we multiply it by 2 and add to equation (1):

$$
\begin{aligned}
4x + y + 3z &= 8 \\
-4x + 10y + 2z &= 8 \ +
\end{aligned}
$$
$$\overline{\qquad 11y + 5z = 16 } \tag{4}$$

To eliminate x from the third equation we multiply equation (1) by 3, multiply equation (3) by 4 and subtract:

$$
\begin{aligned}
12x + 3y + 9z &= 24 \\
12x + 8y + 16z &= 36 \ -
\end{aligned}
$$
$$\overline{\qquad -5y - 7z = -12 } \tag{5}$$

This produces a new system:

$$4x + y + 3z = 8 \tag{1}$$
$$11y + 5z = 16 \tag{4}$$
$$-5y - 7z = -12 \tag{5}$$

Step 2

To eliminate y from the new third equation (that is, equation (5)) we multiply equation (4) by 5, multiply equation (5) by 11 and add:

$$
\begin{aligned}
55y + 25z &= 80 \\
-55y - 77z &= -132 \ +
\end{aligned}
$$
$$\overline{\qquad -52z = -52 } \tag{6}$$

This produces a new system

$$4x + y + 3z = 8 \tag{1}$$
$$11y + 5z = 16 \tag{4}$$
$$-52z = -52 \tag{6}$$

Step 3
The last equation gives

$$z = \frac{-52}{-52} = 1 \quad \text{(divide both sides by } -52)$$

If this is substituted into equation (4) then

$$11y + 5(1) = 16$$
$$11y + 5 = 16$$
$$11y = 11 \quad \text{(subtract 5 from both sides)}$$
$$y = 1 \quad \text{(divide both sides by 11)}$$

Finally, substituting $y = 1$ and $z = 1$ into equation (1) produces

$$4x + 1 + 3(1) = 8$$
$$4x + 4 = 8$$
$$4x = 4 \quad \text{(subtract 5 from both sides)}$$
$$x = 1 \quad \text{(divide both sides by 4)}$$

Hence the solution is $x = 1$, $y = 1$, $z = 1$.

Step 4
As a check the original equations (1), (2) and (3) give

$$4(1) + 1 + 3(1) = 8 \quad \checkmark$$
$$-2(1) + 5(1) + 1 = 4 \quad \checkmark$$
$$3(1) + 2(1) + 4(1) = 9 \quad \checkmark$$

respectively.

Practice Problem

3. Solve the following system of equations:

$$2x + 2y - 5z = -5 \tag{1}$$
$$x - y + z = 3 \tag{2}$$
$$-3x + y + 2z = -2 \tag{3}$$

As you might expect, it is possible for three simultaneous linear equations to have either no solution or infinitely many solutions. An illustration of this is given in Question 4 of Exercise 1.4*. The method described in this section has an obvious extension to larger systems of equations. However, the calculations are extremely tedious to perform by hand. Fortunately there are many computer packages available which are capable of solving large systems accurately and efficiently (a matter of a few seconds to solve 10 000 equations in 10 000 unknowns).

Advice

We shall return to the solution of simultaneous linear equations in Chapter 7 when we describe how matrix theory can be used to solve them. This does not depend on any subsequent chapters in this book, so you might like to read through this material now. Two techniques are suggested. A method based on inverse matrices is covered in Section 7.2 and an alternative using Cramer's rule can be found in Section 7.3.

Key Terms

Elimination method   The method in which variables are removed from a system of simultaneous equations by adding (or subtracting) a multiple of one equation to (or from) a multiple of another.

Exercise 1.4

1. Use the elimination method to solve the following pairs of simultaneous linear equations:

   (a) $-2x + y = 2$ **(b)** $3x + 4y = 12$ **(c)** $2x + y = 4$ **(d)** $x + y = 1$
   $\quad\ \ 2x + y = -6$ $\quad\ \ x + 4y = 8$ $\quad\ 4x - 3y = 3$ $\quad\ 6x + 5y = 15$

2. Sketch the following lines on the same diagram:

   $$2x - 3y = 6, \quad 4x - 6y = 18, \quad x - \frac{3}{2}y = 3$$

   Hence comment on the nature of the solutions of the following systems of equations:

   (a) $2x - 3y = 6$ **(b)** $4x - 6y = 18$

   $\quad\ x - \dfrac{3}{2}y = 3$ $\quad\ x - \dfrac{3}{2}y = 3$

3. Use the elimination method to attempt to solve the following systems of equations. Comment on the nature of the solution in each case.

   (a) $-3x + 5y = 4$ **(b)** $6x - 2y = 3$
   $\quad\ \ 9x - 15y = -12$ $\quad\ 15x - 5y = 4$

4. If the following system of linear equations has infinitely many solutions, find the value of k.

   $$6x - 4y = 2$$
   $$-3x + 2y = k$$

Exercise 1.4*

1. Solve the following pairs of simultaneous equations:

    (a) $y = 3x - 1$ **(b)** $2x + y = 6$ **(c)** $2x + 3y = 5$ **(d)** $3x + 4y = -12$

          $y = 2x + 1$ $x - y = -3$ $5x - 2y = -16$ $-2x + 3y = 25$

2. Write down a possible set of values of the numbers a and b for which the simultaneous equations:

    (a) $2x + 3y = 4$ have infinitely many solutions

          $ax + 6y = b$

    (b) $4x - 6y = 1$ have no solutions

          $2x + ay = b$

3. Solve the following systems of equations:

    (a) $x - 3y + 4z = 5$ (1)   **(b)** $3x + 2y - 2z = -5$ (1)

          $2x + y + z = 3$ (2) $4x + 3y + 3z = 17$ (2)

          $4x + 3y + 5z = 1$ (3) $2x - y + z = -1$ (3)

4. Attempt to solve the following systems of equations. Comment on the nature of the solution in each case.

    (a) $x - 2y + z = -2$ (1)   **(b)** $2x + 3y - z = 13$ (1)

          $x + y - 2z = 4$ (2) $x - 2y + 2z = -3$ (2)

          $-2x + y + z = 12$ (3) $3x + y + z = 10$ (3)

5. If the following system of equations has infinitely many solutions, find the value of the constant, k.

          $x + 2y - 5z = 1$

          $2x - y + 3z = 4$

          $4x + 3y - 7z = k$

    What can you say about the nature of the solution for other values of k?

CHAPTER 2
Non-linear Equations

SECTION 2.3
Indices and logarithms

Objectives

At the end of this section you should be able to:

- Evaluate b^n in the case when n is positive, negative, a whole number or a fraction.
- Simplify algebraic expressions using the rules of indices.
- Investigate the returns to scale of a production function.
- Evaluate logarithms in simple cases.
- Use the rules of logarithms to solve equations in which the unknown occurs as a power.

Advice

This section is quite long with some important ideas. If you are comfortable using the rules of indices and already know what a logarithm is, you should be able to read through the material in one sitting, concentrating on the applications. However, if your current understanding is hazy (or non-existent), you should consider studying this topic on separate occasions. To help with this, the material in this section has been split into the following convenient sub-sections:

- index notation
- rules of indices
- logarithms
- summary.

2.3.1 Index notation

We have already used b^2 as an abbreviation for $b \times b$. In this section we extend the notation to b^n for any value of n, positive, negative, whole number or fraction. In general, if

$$M = b^n$$

we say that b^n is the **exponential form of M to base b**. The number n is then referred to as the **index**, **power** or **exponent**. An obvious way of extending

$$b^2 = b \times b$$

to other positive whole-number powers, n, is to define

$$b^3 = b \times b \times b$$
$$b^4 = b \times b \times b \times b$$

and, in general,

$$b^n = b \times b \times b \times b \times \ldots b$$

a total of n b's multiplied together

To include the case of negative powers, consider the following table of values of 2^n:

2^{-3}	2^{-2}	2^{-1}	2^0	2^1	2^2	2^3	2^4
?	?	?	?	2	4	8	16

To work from left to right along the completed part of the table, all you have to do is to multiply each number by 2. Equivalently, if you work from right to left, you simply divide by 2. It makes sense to continue this pattern beyond $2^1 = 2$. Dividing this by 2 gives

$$2^0 = 2 \div 2 = 1$$

and dividing again by 2 gives

$$2^{-1} = 1 \div 2 = \tfrac{1}{2}$$

and so on. The completed table is then

2^{-3}	2^{-2}	2^{-1}	2^0	2^1	2^2	2^3	2^4
$\frac{1}{8}$	$\frac{1}{4}$	$\frac{1}{2}$	1	2	4	8	16

Notice that

$$2^{-1} = \frac{1}{2} = \frac{1}{2^1}$$

$$2^{-2} = \frac{1}{4} = \frac{1}{2^2}$$

$$2^{-3} = \frac{1}{8} = \frac{1}{2^3}$$

In other words, negative powers are evaluated by taking the reciprocal of the corresponding positive power. Motivated by this particular example, we define

$$\boxed{b^0 = 1}$$

and

$$\boxed{b^{-n} = \frac{1}{b^n}}$$

where n is any positive whole number.

Example

Evaluate

(a) 3^2 **(b)** 4^3 **(c)** 7^0 **(d)** 5^1 **(e)** 5^{-1}

(f) $(-2)^6$ **(g)** 3^{-4} **(h)** $(-2)^3$ **(i)** $(1.723)^0$

Solution

Using the definitions

$$b^n = b \times b \times b \times \ldots \times b$$

$$b^0 = 1$$

$$b^{-n} = \frac{1}{b^n}$$

we obtain

(a) $3^2 = 3 \times 3 = 9$

(b) $4^3 = 4 \times 4 \times 4 = 64$

(c) $7^0 = 1$

because any number raised to the power of zero equals 1.

(d) $5^1 = 5$

(e) $5^{-1} = \dfrac{1}{5^{-1}} = \dfrac{1}{5}$

(f) $(-2)^6 = (-2) \times (-2) \times (-2) \times (-2) \times (-2) \times (-2) = 64$

where the answer is positive because there are an even number of minus signs.

(g) $3^{-4} = \dfrac{1}{3^4} = \dfrac{1}{3 \times 3 \times 3 \times 3} = \dfrac{1}{81}$

(h) $(-2)^{-3} = \dfrac{1}{(-2)^3} = \dfrac{1}{(-2) \times (-2) \times (-2)} = -\dfrac{1}{8}$

where the answer is negative because there are an odd number of minus signs.

(i) $(1.723)^0 = 1$

Practice Problem

1. **(1)** Without using a calculator evaluate

    (a) 10^2 **(b)** 10^1 **(c)** 10^0 **(d)** 10^{-1} **(e)** 10^{-2} **(f)** $(-1)^{100}$

    (g) $(-1)^{99}$ **(h)** 7^{-3} **(i)** $(-9)^2$ **(j)** $(72\ 101)^1$ **(k)** $(2.718)^0$

    (2) Confirm your answer to part (1) using a calculator.

We handle fractional powers in two stages. We begin by defining b^m where m is a reciprocal such as $^1/_2$ or $^1/_8$ and then consider more general fractions such as $^3/_4$ or $^3/_8$ later. Assuming that n is a positive whole number, we define

$$\boxed{b^{1/n} = n\text{th root of } b}$$

By this we mean that $b^{1/n}$ is a number which, when raised to the power n, produces b. In symbols, if $c = b^{1/n}$ then $c^n = b$. Using this definition,

$$9^{1/2} = \text{square root of 9} \quad = 3 \quad (\text{because } 3^2 = 9)$$
$$8^{1/3} = \text{cube root of 8} \quad\quad = 2 \quad (\text{because } 2^3 = 8)$$
$$625^{1/4} = \text{fourth root of 625} \quad = 5 \quad (\text{because } 5^4 = 625)$$

Of course, the nth root of a number may not exist. There is no number c satisfying $c^2 = -4$, for example, and so $(-4)^{1/2}$ is not defined. It is also possible for some numbers to have more than one nth root. For example, there are two values of c which satisfy $c^4 = 16$, namely $c = 2$ and $c = -2$. In these circumstances it is standard practice to take the positive root, so $16^{1/4} = 2$.

We now turn our attention to the case of b^m, where m is a general fraction of the form p/q for some whole numbers p and q. What interpretation are we going to put on a number such as $16^{3/4}$? To be consistent with our previous definitions, the numerator, 3, can be thought of as an instruction for us to raise 16 to the power of 3, and the denominator tells us to take the fourth root. In fact, it is immaterial in which order these two operations are carried out. If we begin by cubing 16 we get

$$16^3 = 16 \times 16 \times 16 = 4096$$

and taking the fourth root of this gives

$$16^{3/4} = (4096)^{1/4} = 8 \quad \text{(because } 8^4 = 4096\text{)}$$

On the other hand, taking the fourth root first gives

$$16^{1/4} = 2 \quad \text{(because } 2^4 = 16\text{)}$$

and cubing this gives

$$16^{3/4} = 2^3 = 8$$

which is the same answer as before. We therefore see that

$$(16^3)^{1/4} = (16^{1/4})^3$$

This result holds for any base b and fraction p/q (provided that q is positive), so we define

$$\boxed{b^{p/q} = (b^p)^{1/q} = (b^{1/q})^p}$$

Example

Evaluate

(a) $8^{4/3}$ **(b)** $25^{-3/2}$

Solution

(a) To evaluate $8^{4/3}$ we need both to raise the number to the power of 4 and to find a cube root. Choosing to find the cube root first,

$$8^{4/3} = (8^{1/3})^4 = 2^4 = 16$$

(b) Again it is easy to find the square root of 25 first before raising the number to the power of -3, so

$$25^{-3/2} = (25^{1/2})^{-3} = 5^{-3} = \frac{1}{5^3} = \frac{1}{125}$$

For this particular exponential form we have actually carried out three distinct operations. The minus sign tells us to reciprocate, the fraction $1/2$ tells us to take the square root and the 3 tells us to cube. You might like to check for yourself that you get the same answer irrespective of the order in which these three operations are performed.

Advice

Given that we are allowed to perform these operations in any order, it is usually easier to find the qth root first to avoid having to spot roots of large numbers.

Practice Problem

2. **(1)** Without using your calculator, evaluate

(a) $16^{1/2}$ **(b)** $27^{1/3}$ **(c)** $4^{5/2}$ **(d)** $8^{-2/3}$ **(e)** $1^{-17/25}$

(2) Confirm your answer to part (1) using a calculator.

2.3.2 Rules of indices

There are two reasons why the exponential form is useful. Firstly, it is a convenient shorthand for what otherwise might be a very lengthy number. The exponential form

$$9^8$$

is much easier to write down than either of the equivalent forms

$$9 \times 9 \times 9 \times 9 \times 9 \times 9 \times 9 \times 9$$

or

$$43\ 046\ 721$$

Secondly, there are four basic rules of indices which facilitate the manipulation of such numbers. The four rules may be stated as follows:

> *Rule 1* $b^m \times b^n = b^{m+n}$
>
> *Rule 2* $b^m \div b^n = b^{m-n}$
>
> *Rule 3* $(b^m)^n = b^{mn}$
>
> *Rule 4* $(ab)^n = a^n b^n$

It is certainly not our intention to provide mathematical proofs in this book. However, it might help you to remember these rules if we give you a justification based on some simple examples. We consider each rule in turn.

Rule 1

Suppose we want to multiply together 2^2 and 2^5. Now $2^2 = 2 \times 2$ and $2^5 = 2 \times 2 \times 2 \times 2 \times 2$, so

$$2^2 \times 2^5 = (2 \times 2) \times (2 \times 2 \times 2 \times 2 \times 2)$$

Notice that we are multiplying together a total of seven 2s and so by definition this is just 2^7: that is,

$$2^2 \times 2^5 = 2^7 = 2^{2+5}$$

This confirms rule 1, which tells you that if you multiply two numbers, all you have to do is to add the indices.

Rule 2

Suppose we want to divide 2^2 by 2^5. This gives

$$\frac{\cancel{2} \times \cancel{2}}{2 \times 2 \times 2 \times \cancel{2} \times \cancel{2}} = \frac{1}{2 \times 2 \times 2} = \frac{1}{2^3}$$

Now, by definition, reciprocals are denoted by negative indices, so this is just 2^{-3}: that is,

$$2^2 \div 2^5 = 2^{-3} = 2^{2-5}$$

This confirms rule 2, which tells you that if you divide two numbers, all you have to do is to subtract the indices.

Rule 3

Suppose we want to raise 10^2 to the power 3. By definition, for any number b,

$$b^3 = b \times b \times b$$

so replacing b by 10^2 we have

$$(10^2)^3 = 10^2 \times 10^2 \times 10^2 = (10 \times 10) \times (10 \times 10) \times (10 \times 10) = 10^6$$

because there are six 10s multiplied together: that is,

$$(10^2)^3 = 10^6 = 10^{2 \times 3}$$

This confirms rule 3, which tells you that if you take a 'power of a power', all you have to do is to multiply the indices.

Rule 4

Suppose we want to raise 2×3 to the power 4. By definition,

$$b^4 = b \times b \times b \times b$$

so replacing b by 2×3 gives

$$(2 \times 3)^4 = (2 \times 3) \times (2 \times 3) \times (2 \times 3) \times (2 \times 3)$$

and, because it does not matter in which order numbers are multiplied, this can be written as

$$(2 \times 2 \times 2 \times 2) \times (3 \times 3 \times 3 \times 3)$$

that is,

$$(2 \times 3)^4 = 2^4 \times 3^4$$

This confirms rule 4, which tells you that if you take the power of a product of two numbers, all you have to do is to take the power of each number separately and multiply.

A word of warning is in order regarding these laws. Notice that in rules 1 and 2 the bases of the numbers involved are the same. These rules do not apply if the bases are different. For example, rule 1 gives no information about

$$2^4 \times 3^5$$

Similarly, please notice that in rule 4 the numbers a and b are multiplied together. For some strange reason, some business and economics students seem to think that rule 4 also applies to addition, so that

$$(a + b)^n = a^n + b^n \qquad \text{This statement is \textbf{NOT TRUE}}$$

It would make algebraic manipulation a whole lot easier if it were true, but I am afraid to say that it is definitely false! If you need convincing of this, note, for example, that

$$(1 + 2)^3 = 3^3 = 27$$

which is not the same as

$$1^3 + 2^3 = 1 + 8 = 9$$

One variation of rule 4 which is true is

$$\left(\frac{a}{b}\right)^n = \frac{a^n}{b^n} \quad (b \neq 0)$$

This is all right because division (unlike addition or subtraction) is the same sort of operation as multiplication. In fact,

$$\left(\frac{a}{b}\right)^n$$

can be thought of as

$$\left(a \times \frac{1}{b}\right)^n$$

so applying rule 4 to this product gives

$$a^n\left(\frac{1}{b}\right)^n = \frac{a^n}{b^n}$$

as required.

Advice

There might be occasions (such as in examinations!) when you only half remember a rule or perhaps think that you have discovered a brand new rule for yourself. If you are ever worried about whether some rule is legal or not, you should always check it out by trying numbers, just as we did for $(a + b)^n$. Obviously, one numerical example which actually works does not prove that the rule will always work. However, one example which fails is good enough to tell you that your supposed rule is rubbish.

The following example demonstrates how rules 1–4 are used to simplify algebraic expressions.

Example

Simplify

(a) $x^{1/4} \times x^{3/4}$ **(b)** $\dfrac{x^2 y^3}{x^4 y}$ **(c)** $(x^2 y^{-1/3})^3$

Solution

(a) The expression

$$x^{1/4} \times x^{3/4}$$

represents the product of two numbers in exponential form with the same base. From rule 1 we may add the indices to get

$$x^{1/4} \times x^{3/4} = x^{1/4+3/4} = x^1$$

which is just x.

(b) The expression

$$\frac{x^2 y^3}{x^4 y}$$

is more complicated than that in part (a) since it involves numbers in exponential form with two different bases, x and y. From rule 2,

$$\frac{x^2}{x^4}$$

may be simplified by subtracting indices to get

$$x^2 \div x^4 = x^{2-4} = x^{-2}$$

Similarly,

$$\frac{y^3}{y} = y^3 \div y^1 = y^{3-1} = y^2$$

Hence

$$\frac{x^2 y^3}{x^4 y} = x^{-2} y^2$$

It is not possible to simplify this any further, because x^{-2} and y^2 have different bases. However, if you prefer, this can be written as

$$\frac{y^2}{x^2}$$

because negative powers denote reciprocals.

(c) An obvious first step in the simplification of

$$(x^2 y^{-1/3})^3$$

is to apply rule 4, treating x^2 as the value of a and $y^{-1/3}$ as b to get

$$(x^2 y^{-1/3})^3 = (x^2)^3 (y^{-1/3})^3$$

Rule 3 then allows us to write

$$(x^2)^3 = x^{2\times 3} = x^6$$
$$(y^{-1/3})^3 = y^{(-1/3)\times 3} = y^{-1}$$

Hence

$$(x^2 y^{-1/3})^3 = x^6 y^{-1}$$

As in part (b), if you think it looks neater, you can write this as

$$\frac{x^6}{y}$$

because negative powers denote reciprocals.

Practice Problem

3. Simplify

(a) $(x^{3/4})^8$ **(b)** $\dfrac{x^2}{x^{3/2}}$ **(c)** $(x^2 y^4)^3$ **(d)** $\sqrt{x}(x^{5/2} + y^3)$

[Hint: in part (d) note that $\sqrt{x} = x^{1/2}$ and multiply out the brackets.]

There are occasions throughout this book when we use the rules of indices and definitions of b^n. For the moment, we concentrate on one specific application where we see these ideas in action. The output, Q, of any production process depends on a variety of inputs, known as **factors of production**. These comprise land, capital, labour and enterprise. For simplicity we restrict our attention to capital and labour. **Capital**, K, denotes all man-made aids to production such as buildings, tools and plant machinery. **Labour**, L, denotes all paid work in the production process. The dependence of Q on K and L may be written

$$Q = f(K, L)$$

which is called a **production function**. Once this relationship is made explicit, in the form of a formula, it is straightforward to calculate the level of production from any given combination of inputs. For example, if

$$Q = 100K^{1/3}L^{1/2}$$

then the inputs $K = 27$ and $L = 100$ lead to an output

$$Q = 100(27)^{1/3}(100)^{1/2}$$
$$= 100(3)(10)$$
$$= 3000$$

Of particular interest is the effect on output when inputs are scaled in some way. If capital and labour both double, does the production level also double, does it go up by more than double or does it go up by less than double? For the particular production function,

$$Q = 100K^{1/3}L^{1/2}$$

we see that, when K and L are replaced by $2K$ and $2L$, respectively,

$$Q = 100(2K)^{1/3}(2L)^{1/2}$$

Now, by rule 4,

$$(2K)^{1/3} = 2^{1/3}K^{1/3} \text{ and } (2L)^{1/2} = 2^{1/2}L^{1/2}$$

so

$$Q = 100(2^{1/3}K^{1/3})(2^{1/2}L^{1/2})$$
$$= (2^{1/3}2^{1/2})(100K^{1/3}L^{1/2})$$

The second term, $100K^{1/3}L^{1/2}$, is just the original value of Q, so we see that the output is multiplied by

$$2^{1/3}2^{1/2}$$

Using rule 1, this number may be simplified by adding the indices to get

$$2^{1/3}2^{1/2} = 2^{5/6}$$

Moreover, because 5/6 is less than 1, the scale factor is smaller than 2. In fact, my calculator gives

$$2^{5/6} = 1.78 \text{ (to 2 decimal places)}$$

so output goes up by just less than double.

It is important to notice that the above argument does not depend on the particular value, 2, that is taken as the scale factor. Exactly the same procedure can be applied if the inputs, K and L, are scaled by a general number λ (where λ is a Greek letter pronounced 'lambda'). Replacing K and L by λK and λL respectively in the formula

$$Q = 100K^{1/3}L^{1/2}$$

gives

$$Q = 100(\lambda K)^{1/3}(\lambda L)^{1/2}$$
$$= 100\lambda^{1/3}K^{1/3}\lambda^{1/2}L^{1/2} \qquad \text{(rule 4)}$$
$$= (\lambda^{1/3}\lambda^{1/2})(100K^{1/3}L^{1/2})$$
$$= \lambda^{5/6}(100K^{1/3}L^{1/2}) \qquad \text{(rule 1)}$$

We see that the output gets scaled by $\lambda^{5/6}$, which is smaller than λ since the power, 5/6, is less than 1. We describe this by saying that the production function exhibits decreasing returns to scale.

In general, a function

$$Q = f(K, L)$$

is said to be **homogeneous** if

$$f(\lambda K, \lambda L) = \lambda^n f(K, L)$$

for some number, n. This means that when both variables K and L are multiplied by λ we can pull out all of the λs as a common factor, λ^n. The power, n, is called the **degree of homogeneity**. In the previous example we showed that

$$f(\lambda K, \lambda L) = \lambda^{5/6} f(K, L)$$

and so it is homogeneous of degree 5/6. In general, if the degree of homogeneity, n, satisfies:

- $n < 1$, the function is said to display **decreasing returns to scale**
- $n = 1$, the function is said to display **constant returns to scale**
- $n > 1$, the function is said to display **increasing returns to scale**.

Example

Show that the following production function is homogeneous and find its degree of homogeneity:

$$Q = 2K^{1/2}L^{3/2}$$

Does this function exhibit decreasing returns to scale, constant returns to scale or increasing returns to scale?

Solution

We are given that

$$f(K, L) = 2K^{1/2}L^{3/2}$$

so replacing K by λK and L by λL gives

$$f(\lambda K, \lambda L) = 2(\lambda K)^{1/2}(\lambda L)^{3/2}$$

We can pull out all of the λs by using rule 4 to get

$$2\lambda^{1/2}K^{1/2}\lambda^{3/2}L^{3/2}$$

and then using rule 1 to get

$$\lambda^2(2K^{1/2}L^{3/2})$$

$$\lambda^{1/2}\lambda^{3/2} = \lambda^{1/2 + 3/2}$$
$$= \lambda^2$$

We have therefore shown that

$$f(\lambda K, \lambda L) = \lambda^2 f(K, L)$$

and so the function is homogeneous of degree 2. Moreover, since $2 > 1$ we deduce that it has increasing returns to scale.

Practice Problem ❓

4. Show that the following production functions are homogeneous and comment on their returns to scale:

(a) $Q = 7KL^2$ **(b)** $Q = 50K^{1/4}L^{3/4}$

You may well have noticed that all of the production functions considered so far are of the form

$$Q = AK^\alpha L^\beta$$

for some positive constants, A, α and β. (The Greek letters α and β are pronounced 'alpha' and 'beta' respectively.) Such functions are called **Cobb–Douglas** production functions. It is easy to see that they are homogeneous of degree $\alpha + \beta$ because if

$$f(K, L) = AK^\alpha L^\beta$$

then

$$\begin{aligned} f(\lambda K, \lambda L) &= A(\lambda K)^\alpha(\lambda L)^\beta \\ &= A\lambda^\alpha K^\alpha \lambda^\beta L^\beta \quad \text{(rule 4)} \\ &= \lambda^{\alpha+\beta}(AK^\alpha L^\beta) \quad \text{(rule 1)} \\ &= \lambda^{\alpha+\beta} f(K, L) \end{aligned}$$

Consequently, Cobb–Douglas production functions exhibit

- decreasing returns to scale, if $\alpha + \beta < 1$
- constant returns to scale, if $\alpha + \beta = 1$
- increasing returns to scale, if $\alpha + \beta > 1$.

By the way, not all production functions are of this type. Indeed, it is not even necessary for a production function to be homogeneous. Some examples illustrating these cases are given in Question 5 in Exercise 2.3 and Question 5 in Exercise 2.3* at the end of this section. We shall return to the topic of production functions in Chapter 5.

2.3.3 Logarithms

At the beginning of this section we stated that if a number, M, is expressed as

$$M = b^n$$

then b^n is called the exponential form of M to base b. The approach taken so far has simply been to evaluate M from any given values of b and n. In practice, it may be necessary to reverse this process and to find n from known values of M and b. To solve the equation

$$32 = 2^n$$

we need to express 32 as a power of 2. In this case it is easy to work out n by inspection. Simple trial and error easily gives $n = 5$ because

$$2^5 = 32$$

We describe this expression by saying that the logarithm of 32 to base 2 is 5. In symbols we write

$$\log_2 32 = 5$$

Quite generally,

> if $M = b^n$ then $\log_b M = n$

where n is called the logarithm of M to base b.

Advice

Students have been known to regard logarithms as something rather abstract and difficult to understand. There is, however, no need to worry about logarithms, since they simply provide an alternative way of thinking about numbers such as b^n. Read through the following example and then try Practice Problem 5 for yourself. You might discover that they are easier than you expect.

Example

Evaluate

(a) $\log_3 9$ **(b)** $\log_4 2$ **(c)** $\log_7 {}^1\!/_7$

Solution

(a) To find the value of $\log_3 9$ we convert the problem into one involving powers. From the definition of a logarithm to base 3 we see that the statement

$$\log_3 9 = n$$

is equivalent to

$$9 = 3^n$$

The problem of finding the logarithm of 9 to base 3 is exactly the same as that of writing 9 as a power of 3. The solution of this equation is clearly $n = 2$ since

$$9 = 3^2$$

Hence $\log_3 9 = 2$.

(b) Again to evaluate $\log_4 2$ we merely rewrite

$$\log_4 2 = n$$

in exponential form as

$$2 = 4^n$$

The problem of finding the logarithm of 2 to base 4 is exactly the same as that of writing 2 as a power of 4. The value of 2 is obtained from 4 by taking the square root, which involves raising 4 to the power of $1/2$, so

$$2 = 4^{1/2}$$

Hence $\log_2 4 = 1/2$.

(c) If

$$\log_7 1/7 = n$$

then

$$1/7 = 7^n$$

The value of $1/7$ is found by taking the reciprocal of 7, which involves raising 7 to the power of -1: that is,

$$1/7 = 7^{-1}$$

Hence $\log_7 1/7 = -1$.

Practice Problem

5. **(1)** Write down the values of n which satisfy

 (a) $1000 = 10^n$ **(b)** $100 = 10^n$ **(c)** $10 = 10^n$

 (d) $1 = 10^n$ **(e)** $\dfrac{1}{10} = 10^n$ **(f)** $\dfrac{1}{100} = 10^n$

(2) Use your answer to part (1) to write down the values of

 (a) $\log_{10} 1000$ **(b)** $\log_{10} 100$ **(c)** $\log_{10} 10$

 (d) $\log_{10} 1$ **(e)** $\log_{10} 1/10$ **(f)** $\log_{10} 1/100$

(3) Confirm your answer to part (2) using a calculator.

Given the intimate relationship between exponentials and logarithms, you should not be too surprised to learn that logarithms satisfy three rules that are comparable with those for indices. The rules of logarithms are as follows:

Rule 1 $\log_b(x \times y) = \log_b x + \log_b y$

Rule 2 $\log_b(x \div y) = \log_b x - \log_b y$

Rule 3 $\log_b x^m = m\log_b x$

A long time ago, before the pocket calculator was invented, people used tables of logarithms to perform complicated arithmetic calculations. It was generally assumed that everyone could add or subtract numbers using pen and paper, but that people found it hard to multiply and divide. The first two rules gave a means of converting calculations involving multiplication and division into easier calculations involving addition and subtraction. For example, to work out

$$1.765\,12 \times 25.329\,71$$

we would first look up the logarithms of 1.765 12 and 25.329 71 using tables and then add these logarithms together on paper. According to rule 1, the value obtained is just the logarithm of the answer. Finally, using tables of antilogarithms (which in effect raised the base to an appropriate power), the result of the calculation was obtained. Fortunately for us, this is all history and we can now perform arithmetic calculations in a fraction of the time it took our predecessors to multiply or divide two numbers. This might suggest that logarithms are redundant. However, the idea of a logarithm remains an important one. The logarithm function itself – that is,

$$f(x) = \log_b(x)$$

is of value and we shall investigate its properties later in the book. For the time being we first show how to use the laws of logarithms in algebra and then demonstrate how logarithms can be used to solve algebraic equations in which the unknown appears as a power. This technique will be of particular use in the next chapter when we solve compound interest problems.

Example

Use the rules of logarithms to express each of the following as a single logarithm:

(a) $\log_b x + \log_b y - \log_b z$ **(b)** $2\log_b x - 3\log_b y$

Solution

(a) The first rule of logs shows that the *sum* of two logs can be written as the log of a *product*, so

$$\log_b x + \log_b y - \log_b z = \log_b(xy) - \log_b z$$

Also, according to rule 2, the *difference* of two logs is the log of a *quotient*, so we can simplify further to get

$$\log_b\left(\frac{xy}{z}\right)$$

(b) Given any combination of logs such as

$$2\log_b x - 3\log_b y$$

the trick is to use the third rule to 'get rid' of the coefficients. Since

$$2\log_b x = \log_b x^2 \quad \text{and} \quad 3\log_b y = \log_b y^3$$

we see that

$$2\log_b x - 3\log_b y = \log_b x^2 - \log_b y^3$$

Only now can we use the second rule of logs, which allows us to write the expression as the single logarithm

$$\log_b\left(\frac{x^2}{y^3}\right)$$

Practice Problem

6. Use the rules of logs to express each of the following as a single logarithm:

(a) $\log_b x - \log_b y + \log_b z$ (b) $4\log_b x + 2\log_b y$

Before we leave this topic a word of warning is in order. Be careful to learn the rules of logs correctly. A common mistake is to misread rule 1 as

$\log_b(x + y) = \log_b x + \log_b y$ **This is NOT true**

Remember that logs are just a posh way of thinking about indices and it is when you *multiply* numbers together you end up adding the indices, so the correct version has to be

$\log_b(xy) = \log_b x + \log_b y$

Example

Find the value of x which satisfies

(a) $200(1.1)^x = 20\,000$ (b) $5^x = 2(3)^x$

Solution

(a) An obvious first step in the solution of

$200(1.1)^x = 20\,000$

is to divide both sides by 200 to get

$(1.1)^x = 100$

In Chapter 1 it was pointed out that we can do whatever we like to an equation, provided that we do the same thing to both sides. In particular, we may take logarithms of both sides to get

$\log(1.1)^x = \log(100)$

Now by rule 3 we have

$\log(1.1)^x = x\log(1.1)$

so the equation becomes

$x\log(1.1) = \log(100)$

Notice the effect that rule 3 has on the equation. It brings the unknown down to the same level as the rest of the expression. This is the whole point of taking logarithms, since it converts an equation in which the unknown appears as a power into one which can be solved using familiar algebraic methods. Dividing both sides of the equation

$x\log(1.1) = \log(100)$

by $\log(1.1)$ gives

$$x = \frac{\log(100)}{\log(1.1)}$$

So far no mention has been made of the base of the logarithm. The above equation for x is true no matter what base is used. It makes sense to use logarithms to base 10 because all scientific calculators have this facility as one of their function keys. Using base 10, my calculator gives

$$x = \frac{\log(100)}{\log(1.1)} = \frac{2}{0.041\ 392\ 685} = 48.32$$

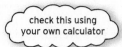

check this using
your own calculator

to 2 decimal places.

As a check, if this number is substituted back into the original equation, then

$$200(1.1)^x = 200(1.1)^{48.32} = 20\ 004 \quad \checkmark$$

We cannot expect to obtain the exact answer, because we rounded x to only two decimal places.

(b) To solve

$$5^x = 2(3)^x$$

we take logarithms of both sides to get

$$\log(5^x) = \log(2 \times 3^x)$$

The right-hand side is the logarithm of a product and, according to rule 1, can be written as the sum of the logarithms, so the equation becomes

$$\log(5^x) = \log(2) + \log(3^x)$$

As in part (a) the key step is to use rule 3 to 'bring down the powers'. If rule 3 is applied to both $\log(5^x)$ and $\log(3^x)$ then the equation becomes

$$x\log(5) = \log(2) + x\log(3)$$

This is now the type of equation that we know how to solve. We collect x's on the left-hand side to get

$$x\log(5) - x\log(3) = \log(2)$$

and then pull out a common factor of x to get

$$x[\log(5) - \log(3)] = \log(2)$$

Now, by rule 2, the difference of two logarithms is the same as the logarithm of their quotient, so

$$\log(5) - \log(3) = \log(5 \div 3)$$

Hence the equation becomes

$$x\log\left(\frac{5}{3}\right) = \log(2)$$

so

$$x = \frac{\log(2)}{\log(5/3)}$$

Finally, taking logarithms to base 10 using a calculator gives

$$x = \frac{0.301\ 029\ 996}{0.221\ 848\ 750} = 1.36$$

to 2 decimal places.

As a check, the original equation

$$5^x = 2(3)^x$$

becomes

$$5^{1.36} = 2(3)^{1.36}$$

that is,

$$8.92 = 8.91 \quad \checkmark$$

Again the slight discrepancy is due to rounding errors in the value of x.

Practice Problem

7. Solve the following equations for x:

(a) $3^x = 7$ (b) $5(2)^x = 10^x$

Advice

In this section we have met a large number of definitions and rules concerning indices and logarithms. For convenience, we have collected these together in the form of a summary. The facts relating to indices are particularly important and you should make every effort to memorize these before proceeding with the rest of this book.

2.3.4 Summary

Indices

If n is a positive whole number then

$$b^n = b \times b \times \ldots \times b$$

$$b^0 = 1$$

$$b^{-n} = 1/b^n$$

$$b^{1/n} = n\text{th root of } b$$

Also, if p and q are whole numbers with $q > 0$ then

$$b^{p/q} = (b^p)^{1/q} = (b^{1/q})^p$$

The four rules of indices are:

Rule 1 $b^m \times b^n = b^{m+n}$

Rule 2 $b^m \div b^n = b^{m-n}$

Rule 3 $(b^m)^n = b^{mn}$

Rule 4 $(ab)^n = a^n b^n$

Logarithms

If $M = b^n$ then $n = \log_b M$. The three rules of logarithms are:

Rule 1 $\log_b(x \times y) = \log_b x + \log_b y$

Rule 2 $\log_b(x \div y) = \log_b x - \log_b y$

Rule 3 $\log_b x^m = m\log_b x$

Key Terms

Capital   Man-made assets used in the production of goods and services.

Cobb–Douglas production function   A production function of the form: $Q = AK^\alpha L^\beta$.

Constant returns to scale   Exhibited by a production function when a given percentage increase in input leads to the same percentage increase in output: $f(\lambda K, \lambda L) = \lambda f(K, L)$.

Decreasing returns to scale   Exhibited by a production function when a given percentage increase in input leads to a smaller percentage increase in output: $f(\lambda K, \lambda L) = \lambda^n f(K, L)$ where $0 < n < 1$.

Degree of homogeneity   The number n in the relation $f(\lambda K, \lambda L) = \lambda^n f(K, L)$.

Exponent   A superscript attached to a variable; the number 5 is the exponent in the expression, $2x^5$.

Exponential form   A representation of a number which is written using powers. For example, 2^5 is the exponential form of the number 32.

Factors of production   The inputs into the production of goods and services: labour, land, capital and raw materials.

Homogeneous function   A function with the property that when all of the inputs are multiplied by a constant, λ, the output is multiplied by λ^n where n is the degree of homogeneity.

Increasing returns to scale   Exhibited by a production function when a given percentage increase in input leads to a larger percentage increase in output: $f(\lambda K, \lambda L) = \lambda^n f(K, L)$ where $n > 1$.

Index   Another word for exponent.

Labour   All forms of human input to the production process.

Logarithm   The power to which a base must be raised to yield a particular number.

Power   Another word for exponent. If this is a positive integer then it gives the number of times a number is multiplied by itself.

Production function   The relationship between the output of a good and the inputs used to produce it.

Exercise 2.3

1. **(1)** Without using your calculator evaluate

   (a) 8^2 **(b)** 2^1 **(c)** 3^{-1} **(d)** 17^0 **(e)** $1^{1/5}$ **(f)** $36^{1/2}$ **(g)** $8^{2/3}$ **(h)** $49^{-3/2}$

   (2) Confirm your answer to part (1) using a calculator.

2. Use the rules of indices to simplify

   (a) $a^3 \times a^8$ **(b)** $\dfrac{b^7}{b^2}$ **(c)** $(c^2)^3$ **(d)** $\dfrac{x^4 y^5}{x^2 y^3}$ **(e)** $(xy^2)^3$

   (f) $y^3 \div y^7$ **(g)** $(x^{1/2})^8$ **(h)** $f^2 \times f^4 \times f$ **(i)** $\sqrt{(y^6)}$ **(j)** $\dfrac{x^3}{x^{-2}}$

3. Write the following expressions using index notation ❓

   (a) $\sqrt{x}$ **(b)** $\dfrac{1}{x^2}$ **(c)** $\sqrt[3]{x}$ **(d)** $\dfrac{1}{x}$ **(e)** $\dfrac{1}{\sqrt{x}}$ **(f)** $x\sqrt{x}$

4. For the production function, $Q = 200K^{1/4}L^{2/3}$ find the output when

   (a) $K = 16, L = 27$ **(b)** $K = 10\,000, L = 1000$

5. Which of the following production functions are homogeneous? For those functions which are homogeneous write down their degrees of homogeneity and comment on their returns to scale.

   (a) $Q = 500K^{1/3}L^{1/4}$

   (b) $Q = 3LK + L^2$

   (c) $Q = L + 5L^2K^3$

6. Write down the values of x which satisfy each of the following equations:

   (a) $5^x = 25$ **(b)** $3^x = \dfrac{1}{3}$ **(c)** $2^x = \dfrac{1}{8}$

   (d) $2^x = 64$ **(e)** $100^x = 10$ **(f)** $8^x = 1$

7. Write down the value of

   (a) $\log_b b^2$ **(b)** $\log_b b$ **(c)** $\log_b 1$ **(d)** $\log_b \sqrt{b}$ **(e)** $\log_b(1/b)$

8. Use the rules of logs to express each of the following as a single log:

   (a) $\log_b x + \log_b z$

   (b) $3\log_b x - 2\log_b y$

   (c) $\log_b y - 3\log_b z$

9. Express the following in terms of $\log_b x$ and $\log_b y$:

   (a) $\log_b x^2 y$

   (b) $\log_b\left(\dfrac{x}{y^2}\right)$

   (c) $\log_b x^2 y^7$

10. Solve the following equations for x. Give your answers to 2 decimal places.

(a) $5^x = 8$ (b) $10^x = 50$ (c) $1.2^x = 3$ (d) $1000 \times 1.05^x = 1500$

11. **(1)** State the values of

(a) $\log_2 32$ (b) $\log_9\left(\dfrac{1}{3}\right)$

(2) Use the rules of logs to express

$$2\log_b x - 4\log_b y$$

as a single logarithm.

(3) Use logs to solve the equation

$$10(1.05)^x = 300$$

Give your answer correct to 1 decimal place.

12. **(1)** State the values of x that satisfy the following equations:

(a) $81 = 3^x$ (b) $\dfrac{1}{25} = 5^x$ (c) $16^{1/2} = 2^x$

(2) Use the rules of indices to simplify:

(a) $\dfrac{x^6 y^9}{x^3 y^8}$ (b) $(x^3 y)^5$ (c) $\sqrt{\dfrac{x^9 y^4}{x^5}}$

Exercise 2.3*

1. **(1)** Evaluate the following without using a calculator

(a) $32^{3/5}$ (b) $64^{-5/6}$ (c) $\left(\dfrac{1}{125}\right)^{-4/3}$ (d) $\left(3\dfrac{3}{8}\right)^{2/3}$ (e) $\left(2\dfrac{1}{4}\right)^{-1/2}$

(2) Confirm your answer to part (1) using a calculator.

2. Use the rules of indices to simplify

(a) $y^{3/2} \times y^{1/2}$ (b) $\dfrac{x^2 y}{xy^{-1}}$ (c) $(xy^{1/2})^4$

(d) $(p^2)^{1/3} \div (p^{1/3})^2$ (e) $(24q)^{1/3} \div (3q)^{1/3}$ (f) $(25p^2 q^4)^{1/2}$

3. Write the following expressions using index notation

(a) $\dfrac{1}{x^7}$ (b) $\sqrt[4]{x}$ (c) $\dfrac{1}{x\sqrt{x}}$ (d) $2x^5\sqrt{x}$ (e) $\dfrac{8}{x(\sqrt[3]{x})}$

4. If $a = \dfrac{2\sqrt{x}}{y^3}$ and $b = 3x^4 y$, simplify $\dfrac{4b}{a^2}$

5. Show that the production function

$$Q = A[bK^\alpha + (1 - b)L^\alpha]^{1/\alpha}$$

is homogeneous and displays constant returns to scale.

6. Solve the following equations:

(a) $2^{3x} = 4$ (b) $4 \times 2^x = 32$ (c) $8^x = 2 \times \left(\dfrac{1}{2}\right)^x$

7. Use the rules of logs to express each of the following as a single log:

(a) $\log_b(xy) - \log_b x - \log_b y$

(b) $3\log_b x - 2\log_b y$

(c) $\log_b y + 5\log_b x - 2\log_b z$

(d) $2 + 3\log_b x$

8. Express the following in terms of $\log_b x$, $\log_b y$ and $\log_b z$:

(a) $\log_b(x^2 y^3 z^4)$

(b) $\log_b\left(\dfrac{x^4}{y^2 z^5}\right)$

(c) $\log_b\left(\dfrac{x}{\sqrt{yz}}\right)$

9. If $\log_b 2 = p$, $\log_b 3 = q$ and $\log_b 10 = r$, express the following in terms of p, q and r:

(a) $\log_b\left(\dfrac{1}{3}\right)$ (b) $\log_b 12$ (c) $\log_b 0.000\,3$ (d) $\log_b 600$

10. Solve the following equations. Round your answers to 2 decimal places.

(a) $10(1.07)^x = 2000$ (b) $10^{x-1} = 3$ (c) $5^{x-2} = 5$ (d) $2(7)^{-x} = 3^x$

11. Solve the inequalities giving the bounds to 3 decimal places:

(a) $3^{2x+1} \leq 7$ (b) $0.8^x < 0.04$

12. Solve the equation
$$\log_{10}(x + 2) + \log_{10} x - 1 = \log_{10}\left(\dfrac{3}{2}\right)$$

13. (1) Define the term *homogeneous* when used to describe a production function $f(K, L)$.

(2) If the production function
$$f(K, L) = 4K^m L^{1/3} + 3K$$
is homogeneous, state the value of m.
Does the function display decreasing, constant or increasing returns to scale?

14. (1) State the values of x that satisfy the following equations:

(a) $4 = 8^x$ (b) $5 = \left(\dfrac{1}{25}\right)^x$

(2) Express y in terms of x:
$$2\log_a x = \log_a 7 + \log_a y$$

15. Show that $2\log_{10} x - \dfrac{1}{2}\log_{10} y - \dfrac{1}{3}\log_{10} 1000$ can be simplified to
$$\log_{10}\left(\sqrt{\dfrac{x^4}{y}}\right) - 1$$

SECTION 2.4

The exponential and natural logarithm functions

Objectives

At the end of this section you should be able to:

- Sketch graphs of general exponential functions.
- Understand how the number e is defined.
- Use the exponential function to model growth and decay.
- Use log graphs to find unknown parameters in simple models.
- Use the natural logarithm function to solve equations.

In the previous section we described how to define numbers of the form b^x, and discussed the idea of a logarithm, $\log_b x$. It turns out that there is one base (the number e = 2.718 281 . . .) that is particularly important in mathematics. The purpose of this present section is to introduce you to this strange number and to consider a few simple applications.

Example

Sketch the graphs of the functions

(a) $f(x) = 2^x$ **(b)** $g(x) = 2^{-x}$

Comment on the relationship between these graphs.

Solution

(a) As we pointed out in Section 2.3, a number such as 2^x is said to be in exponential form. The number 2 is called the base and x is called the exponent. Values of this function are easily found either by pressing the power key $\boxed{x^y}$ on a calculator or by using the definition of b^n given in Section 2.3. A selection of these is given in the following table:

x	−3	−2	−1	0	1	2	3	4	5
2^x	0.125	0.25	0.5	1	2	4	8	16	32

A graph of $f(x)$ based on this table is sketched in Figure 2.14. Notice that the graph approaches the x axis for large negative values of x and it rises rapidly as x increases.

(b) The negative exponential

$$g(x) = 2^{-x}$$

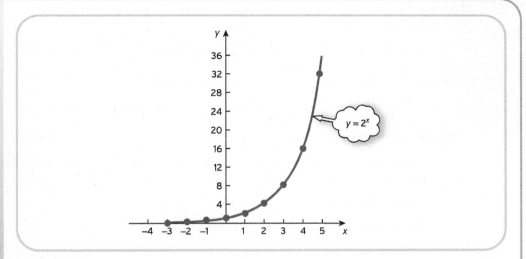

Figure 2.14

has values

x	−5	−4	−3	−2	−1	0	1	2	3
2^{-x}	32	16	8	4	2	1	0.5	0.25	0.125

This function is sketched in Figure 2.15. It is worth noticing that the numbers appearing in the table of 2^{-x} are the same as those of 2^x but arranged in reverse order. Hence the graph of 2^{-x} is obtained by reflecting the graph of 2^x in the y axis.

Figure 2.14 displays the graph of a particular exponential function, 2^x. Quite generally, the graph of any exponential function

$$f(x) = b^x$$

has the same basic shape provided $b > 1$. The only difference is that larger values of b produce steeper curves. A similar comment applies to the negative exponential, b^{-x}.

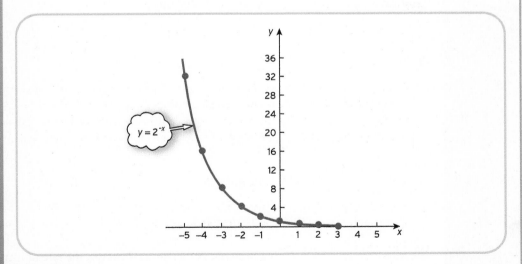

Figure 2.15

Practice Problem

1. Complete the following table of function values of 3^x and 3^{-x} and hence sketch their graphs.

x	−3	−2	−1	0	1	2	3
3^x							
3^{-x}							

Obviously there is a whole class of functions, each corresponding to a different base, b. Of particular interest is the case when b takes the value

2.718 281 828 459 . . .

This number is written as e and the function

$$f(x) = e^x$$

is referred to as *the* **exponential function**. In fact, it is not necessary for you to understand where this number comes from. All scientific calculators have an e^x button and you may simply wish to accept the results of using it. However, it might help your confidence if you have some appreciation of how it is defined. To this end consider the following example and subsequent problem.

Example

Evaluate the expression

$$\left(1 + \frac{1}{m}\right)^m$$

where $m = 1, 10, 100$ and 1000, and comment briefly on the behaviour of this sequence.

Solution

Substituting the values $m = 1, 10, 100$ and 1000 into

$$\left(1 + \frac{1}{m}\right)^m$$

gives

$$\left(1 + \frac{1}{1}\right)^1 = 2^1 = 2$$

$$\left(1 + \frac{1}{10}\right)^{10} = (1.1)^{10} = 2.593\ 742\ 460$$

$$\left(1 + \frac{1}{100}\right)^{100} = (1.01)^{100} = 2.704\ 813\ 829$$

$$\left(1 + \frac{1}{1000}\right)^{1000} = (1.001)^{1000} = 2.716\ 923\ 932$$

The numbers are clearly getting bigger as m increases. However, the rate of increase appears to be slowing down, suggesting that numbers are converging to some fixed value.

The following problem gives you an opportunity to continue the sequence and to discover for yourself the limiting value.

Practice Problem

2. (a) Use the power key x^y on your calculator to evaluate

$$\left(1 + \frac{1}{m}\right)^m$$

where $m = 10\,000$, $100\,000$ and $1\,000\,000$.

(b) Use your calculator to evaluate e^1 and compare with your answer to part (a).

Hopefully, the results of Practice Problem 2 should convince you that as m gets larger, the value of

$$\left(1 + \frac{1}{m}\right)^m$$

approaches a limiting value of $2.718\,281\,828\ldots$, which we choose to denote by the letter e. In symbols we write

$$e = \lim_{m \to \infty}\left(1 + \frac{1}{m}\right)^m$$

The significance of this number can only be fully appreciated in the context of calculus, which we study in Chapter 4. However, it is useful at this stage to consider some preliminary examples. These will give you practice in using the e^x button on your calculator and will give you some idea how this function can be used in modelling.

Advice

The number e has a similar status in mathematics as the number π and is just as useful. It arises in the mathematics of finance, which we discuss in the next chapter. You might like to glance through Section 3.2 now if you need convincing of the usefulness of e.

Example

The percentage, y, of households possessing refrigerators, t years after they have been intro-duced in a developed country, is modelled by

$$y = 100 - 95e^{-0.15t}$$

(1) Find the percentage of households that have refrigerators

    (a) at their launch

    (b) after 1 year

    (c) after 10 years

    (d) after 20 years.

(2) What is the market saturation level?

(3) Sketch a graph of y against t and hence give a qualitative description of the growth of refrigerator ownership over time.

Solution

(1) To calculate the percentage of households possessing refrigerators now and in 1, 10 and 20 years' time, we substitute $t = 0, 1, 10$ and 20 into the formula

$$y = 100 - 95e^{-0.15t}$$

to get

    (a) $y(0) = 100 - 95e^{0} = 5\%$

    (b) $y(1) = 100 - 95e^{-0.15} = 18\%$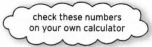

    (c) $y(10) = 100 - 95e^{-1.5} = 79\%$

    (d) $y(20) = 100 - 95e^{-3.0} = 95\%$

check these numbers on your own calculator

(2) To find the saturation level we need to investigate what happens to y as t gets ever larger. We know that the graph of a negative exponential function has the basic shape shown in Figure 2.15. Consequently, the value of $e^{-0.15t}$ will eventually approach zero as t increases. The market saturation level is therefore given by

$$y = 100 - 95(0) = 100\%$$

(3) A graph of y against t, based on the information obtained in parts (1) and (2), is sketched in Figure 2.16.

    This shows that y grows rapidly to begin with, but slows down as the market approaches saturation level. An economic variable which increases over time but approaches a fixed value like this is said to display **limited growth**. A saturation level of 100% indicates that eventually all households are expected to possess refrigerators, which is not surprising given the nature of the product.

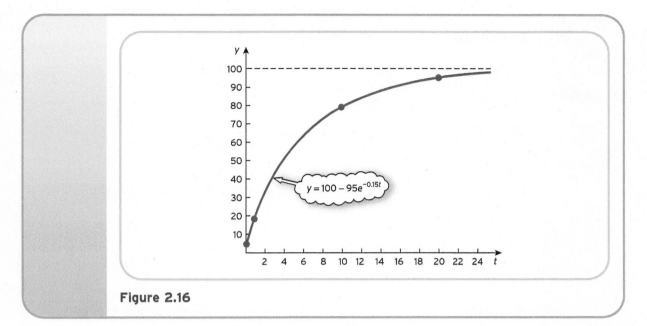

Figure 2.16

Practice Problem

3. The percentage, y, of households possessing camcorders t years after they have been launched is modelled by

$$y = \frac{55}{1 + 800e^{-0.3t}}$$

(1) Find the percentage of households that have camcorders

    (a) at their launch

    (b) after 10 years

    (c) after 20 years

    (d) after 30 years.

(2) What is the market saturation level?

(3) Sketch a graph of y against t and hence give a qualitative description of the growth of camcorder ownership over time.

In Section 2.3 we noted that if a number M can be expressed as b^n then n is called the logarithm of M to base b. In particular, for base e,

    if $M = e^n$ then $n = \log_e M$

We call logarithms to base e **natural logarithms**. These occur sufficiently frequently to warrant their own notation. Rather than writing $\log_e M$ we simply put $\ln M$ instead. The three rules of logs can then be stated as

> *Rule* 1 $\ln(x \times y) = \ln x + \ln y$
>
> *Rule* 2 $\ln(x + y) = \ln x - \ln y$
>
> *Rule* 3 $\ln x^m = m \ln x$

Example

Use the rules of logs to express

(a) $\ln\left(\dfrac{x}{\sqrt{y}}\right)$ in terms of $\ln x$ and $\ln y$

(b) $3 \ln p + \ln q - 2 \ln r$ as a single logarithm.

Solution

(a) In this part we need to 'expand', so we read the rules of logs from left to right:

$$\ln\left(\frac{x}{\sqrt{y}}\right) = \ln x - \ln\sqrt{y} \quad \text{(rule 2)}$$

$$= \ln x - \ln y^{1/2} \quad \text{(fractional powers denote roots)}$$

$$= \ln x - \frac{1}{2}\ln y \quad \text{(rule 3)}$$

(b) In this part we need to reverse this process and so read the rules from right to left:

$$3 \ln p + \ln q - 2 \ln r = \ln p^3 + \ln q - \ln r^2 \quad \text{(rule 3)}$$

$$= \ln(p^3 q) - \ln r^2 \quad\quad\quad \text{(rule 1)}$$

$$= \ln\left(\frac{p^3 q}{r^2}\right) \quad\quad\quad\quad \text{(rule 2)}$$

Practice Problem

4. Use the rules of logs to express

   (a) $\ln(a^2 b^3)$ in terms of $\ln a$ and $\ln b$

   (b) $\frac{1}{2} \ln x - 3 \ln y$ as a single logarithm.

As we pointed out in Section 2.3, logs are particularly useful for solving equations in which the unknown occurs as a power. If the base is the number e then the equation can be solved by using natural logarithms.

Example

An economy is forecast to grow continuously so that the gross national product (GNP), measured in billions of dollars, after t years is given by

$$GNP = 80e^{0.02t}$$

After how many years is GNP forecast to be $88 billion? What does the model predict about the value of GNP in the long run?

Solution

We need to solve

$$88 = 80e^{0.02t}$$

for t. Dividing through by 80 gives

$$1.1 = e^{0.02t}$$

Using the definition of natural logarithms we know that

if $M = e^n$ then $n = \ln M$

If we apply this definition to the equation

$$1.1 = e^{0.02t}$$

we deduce that

$$0.02t = \ln 1.1 = 0.095\ 31 \ldots \quad \text{(check this using your own calculator)}$$

so

$$t = \frac{0.095\ 31}{0.02} = 4.77$$

We therefore deduce that GNP reaches a level of $88 billion after 4.77 years.

A graph of GNP plotted against time would be similar in shape to the graph in Figure 2.14. This shows that GNP just keeps on rising over time (in fact at an increasing rate). Such a model is said to display **unlimited growth**.

Practice Problem ❷

5. During a recession a firm's revenue declines continuously so that the revenue, TR (measured in millions of dollars), in t years' time is modelled by

$$TR = 5e^{-0.15t}$$

(a) Calculate the current revenue and also the revenue in 2 years' time.

(b) After how many years will the revenue decline to $2.7 million?

One important (but rather difficult) problem in modelling is to extract a mathematical formula from a table of numbers. If this relationship is of the form of an exponential then it is possible to estimate values for some of the parameters involved.

Advice

The following example shows how to find such a formula from data points. This is an important skill. However, it is not crucial to your understanding of subsequent material in this book. You may wish to miss this out on first reading and move straight on to the Exercises at the end of this chapter.

Example

The values of GNP, g, measured in billions of dollars, over a period of t years was observed to be

t (years)	2	5	10	20
g (billions of dollars)	12	16	27	74

Model the growth of GNP using a formula of the form

$$g = Be^{At}$$

for appropriate values of A and B. Hence estimate the value of GNP after 15 years.

Solution

Figure 2.17 shows the four points plotted with g on the vertical axis and t on the horizontal axis. The basic shape of the curve joining these points certainly suggests that an exponential function is likely to provide a reasonable model, but it gives no information about what values to use for the parameters A and B. However, since one of the unknown parameters, A, occurs as a power in the relation

$$g = Be^{At}$$

it is a good idea to take natural logs of both sides to get

$$\ln g = \ln(Be^{At})$$

The rules of logs enable us to expand the right-hand side to get

$$\ln(Be^{At}) = \ln B + \ln(e^{At}) \quad \text{(rule 1)}$$
$$= \ln B + At \quad \text{(definition of a log to base e)}$$

Hence

$$\ln g = At + \ln B$$

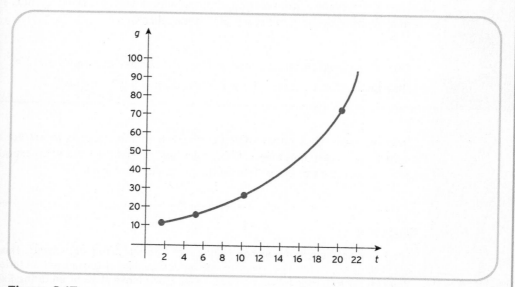

Figure 2.17

Although this does not look like it at first sight, this relation is actually the equation of a straight line! To see this recall that the usual equation of a line is $y = ax + b$. The log equation is indeed of this form if we put

$$y = \ln g \quad \text{and} \quad x = t$$

The equation then becomes

$$y = Ax + \ln B$$

so a graph of $\ln g$ plotted on the vertical axis with t plotted on the horizontal axis should produce a straight line with slope A and with an intercept on the vertical axis of $\ln B$.

Figure 2.18 shows this graph based on the table of values

$x = t$	2	5	10	20
$y = \ln g$	2.48	2.77	3.30	4.30

As one might expect, the points do not exactly lie on a straight line, since the formula is only a model. However, the line sketched in Figure 2.18 is a remarkably good fit. The slope can be calculated as

$$A = \frac{4 - 3}{18.6 - 7.6} = 0.09$$

and the vertical intercept can be read off the graph as 2.25. This is $\ln B$ and so

$$B = e^{2.25} = 9.49$$

Hence the formula for the approximate relation between g and t is

$$g = 9.49e^{0.09t}$$

An estimate of the GNP after 15 years can be obtained by substituting $t = 15$ into this formula to get

$$g = 36.6 \quad \text{(billion dollars)}$$

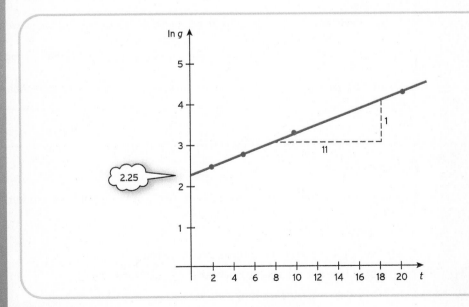

Figure 2.18

Practice Problem

6. Immediately after the launch of a new product, the monthly sales figures (in thousands) are as follows:

t (months)	1	3	6	12
s (sales)	1.8	2.7	5.0	16.5

(1) Complete the following table of values of ln s:

t	1	3	6	12
ln s	0.59		1.61	

(2) Plot these points on graph paper with the values of ln s on the vertical axis and t on the horizontal axis. Draw a straight line passing close to these points. Write down the value of the vertical intercept and calculate the slope.

(3) Use your answers to part (2) to estimate the values of A and B in the relation $s = Be^{At}$.

(4) Use the exponential model derived in part (3) to estimate the sales when

    (a) $t = 9$ (b) $t = 60$

Which of these estimates would you expect to be the more reliable? Give a reason for your answer.

Key Terms

Exponential function The function, $f(x) = e^x$; an exponential function in which the base is the number $e = 2.718\,281\ldots$.

Limited growth Used to describe an economic variable which increases over time but which tends to a fixed quantity.

Natural logarithm A logarithm to base, e; if $M = e^n$ then n is the natural logarithm of M and we write, $n = \ln M$.

Unlimited growth Used to describe an economic variable which increases without bound.

Exercise 2.4

1. The number of items, N, produced each day by an assembly-line worker, t days after an initial training period, is modelled by

$$N = 100 - 100e^{-0.4t}$$

(1) Calculate the number of items produced daily

    (a) 1 day after the training period

    (b) 2 days after the training period

    (c) 10 days after the training period.

(2) What is the worker's daily production in the long run?

(3) Sketch a graph of N against t and explain why the general shape might have been expected.

2. Use the rules of logs to expand each of the following:

(a) $\ln xy$ **(b)** $\ln xy^4$ **(c)** $\ln(xy)^2$

(d) $\ln \dfrac{x^5}{y^7}$ **(e)** $\ln \sqrt{\dfrac{x}{y}}$ **(f)** $\ln \sqrt{\dfrac{xy^3}{z}}$

3. Use the rules of logs to express each of the following as a single logarithm:

(a) $\ln x + 2 \ln x$ **(b)** $4 \ln x - 3 \ln y + 5 \ln z$

4. Solve each of the following equations. (Round your answer to 2 decimal places.)

(a) $e^x = 5.9$ **(b)** $e^x = 0.45$ **(c)** $e^x = -2$

(d) $e^{3x} = 13.68$ **(e)** $e^{-5x} = 0.34$ **(f)** $4e^{2x} = 7.98$

5. The value of a second-hand car reduces exponentially with age, so that its value \$$y$ after t years can be modelled by the formula

$$y = Ae^{-ax}$$

If the car was \$50 000 when new and was worth \$38 000 after 2 years, find the values of A and a, correct to 3 decimal places.

Use this model to predict the value of the car

(a) when the car is 5 years old

(b) in the long run.

6. **(Excel)** Tabulate values of the following functions for $x = 0, 0.2, 0.4, \ldots, 2$. Hence sketch graphs of these functions, on the same diagram, over the range $0 \le x \le 2$. Discuss, in qualitative terms, any differences or similarities between these functions:

(a) $y = x$ **(b)** $y = x^2$ **(c)** $y = x^3$ **(d)** $y = \sqrt{x}$ **(e)** $y = e^x$

[In Excel, e^x is typed EXP(x).]

Exercise 2.4*

1. The value (in cents) of shares, t years after their flotation on the stock market, is modelled by

$$V = 6e^{0.8t}$$

Find the increase in the value of these shares, 4 years and 2 months later. Give your answer to the nearest cent.

2. Solve each of the following equations, correct to 2 decimal places:

(a) $6e^{-2x} = 0.62$ **(b)** $5 \ln(4x) = 9.84$ **(c)** $3 \ln(5x) - 2 \ln(x) = 7$

3. A team of financial advisers guiding the launch of a national newspaper has modelled the future circulation of the newspaper by the equation

$$N = c(1 - e^{-kt})$$

where N is the daily circulation after t days of publication, and c and k are positive constants. Transpose this formula to show that

$$t = \frac{1}{k} \ln\left(\frac{c}{c - N}\right)$$

When the paper is launched, audits show that

$$c = 700\,000 \quad \text{and} \quad k = \frac{1}{30} \ln 2$$

(a) Calculate the daily circulation after 30 days of publication.

(b) After how many days will the daily circulation first reach 525 000?

(c) What advice can you give the newspaper proprietor if it is known that the paper will break even only if the daily circulation exceeds 750 000?

4. A Cobb–Douglas production function is given by

$$Q = 3L^{1/2}K^{1/3}$$

Find an expression for $\ln Q$ in terms of $\ln L$ and $\ln K$.

   If a graph were to be sketched of $\ln Q$ against $\ln K$ (for varying values of Q and K but with L fixed), explain briefly why the graph will be a straight line and state its slope and vertical intercept.

5. The following table gives data relating a firm's output, Q and labour, L:

L	1	2	3	4	5
Q	0.50	0.63	0.72	0.80	0.85

The firm's short-run production function is believed to be of the form

$$Q = AL^n$$

(a) Show that

$$\ln Q = n \ln L + \ln A$$

(b) Using the data supplied, copy and complete the following table:

$\ln L$		0.69		1.39	
$\ln Q$	−0.69		−0.33		−0.16

Plot these points with $\ln L$ on the horizontal axis and $\ln Q$ on the vertical axis. Draw a straight line passing as close as possible to all five points.

(c) By finding the slope and vertical intercept of the line sketched in part (b), estimate the values of the parameters n and A.

6. (a) Multiply out the brackets

$$(3y - 2)(y + 5)$$

(b) Solve the equation

$$3e^{2x} + 13e^{x} = 10$$

Give your answer correct to 3 decimal places.

7. (a) Make y the subject of the equation

$$x = ae^{by}$$

(b) Make x the subject of the equation

$$y = \ln(3 + e^{2x})$$

8. (**Excel**) Tabulate values of the functions $\ln x$, $\log_{10} x$ and $\log_{6} x$ for $x = 0.2, 0.4, 0.6, 0.8, 1.0,$ $2, 3, 4, \ldots, 8$. Hence sketch graphs of these functions on the same diagram, over the range $0.2 \le x \le 8$.

Briefly comment on any similarities and differences between them.

[In Excel, natural logs and logs to base 10 are typed as $LN(x)$ and $LOG(x)$ respectively. In general, to find the logarithm of a number x to base n, type $LOG(x, n)$.]

9. (**Excel**) The demand function of a good can be modelled approximately by

$$P = 100 - \frac{2}{3}Q^{n}$$

(a) Show that if this relation is exact then a graph of $\ln(150 - 1.5P)$ against $\ln Q$ will be a straight line passing through the origin with slope n.

(b) For the data given below, tabulate the values of $\ln(150 - 1.5P)$ and $\ln Q$. Find the line of best fit and hence estimate the value of n correct to 1 decimal place.

Q	10	50	60	100	200	400
P	95	85	80	70	50	20

CHAPTER 3
Mathematics of Finance

This chapter provides an understanding of the way in which financial calculations are worked out. There are four sections, which should be read in the order that they appear.

Section 3.1 revises work on percentages. In particular, a quick method of dealing with percentage increase and decrease calculations is described. This enables an overall percentage change to be deduced easily from a sequence of individual changes. Percentages are used to calculate and interpret index numbers, and to adjust value data for inflation.

Section 3.2 shows how to calculate the future value of a lump sum which is invested to earn interest. This interest can be added to the investment annually, semi-annually, quarterly or even more frequently. The exponential function is used to solve problems in which interest is compounded continuously.

A wide variety of applications are considered in Sections 3.3 and 3.4. In Section 3.3 a mathematical device known as a geometric progression, which is used to calculate the future value of a savings plan and the monthly repayments of a loan, is introduced. Section 3.4 describes the opposite problem of calculating the present value given a future value. The process of working backwards is called discounting. It can be used to decide how much money to invest today in order to achieve a specific target sum in a few years' time. Discounting can be used to appraise different investment projects. On the macroeconomic level, the relationship between interest rates and speculative demand for money is investigated.

The material in this chapter will be of greatest benefit to students on business studies and accountancy courses. This chapter could be omitted without affecting your understanding of the rest of this book.

SECTION 3.1
Percentages

Objectives

At the end of this section you should be able to:

- Understand what a percentage is.
- Solve problems involving a percentage increase or decrease.
- Write down scale factors associated with percentage changes.
- Work out overall percentage changes.
- Calculate and interpret index numbers.
- Adjust value data for inflation.

Advice

The first part of this section provides a leisurely revision of the idea of a percentage as well as reminding you about how to use scale factors to cope with percentage changes. These ideas are crucial to any understanding of financial mathematics. However, if you are already confident in using percentages, you may wish to miss this out and move straight on to the applications covered in subsections 3.1.1 and 3.1.2.

In order to be able to handle financial calculations, it is necessary to use percentages proficiently. The word 'percentage' literally means 'per cent', i.e. per hundredth, so that whenever we speak of $r\%$ of something, we simply mean the fraction $(r/100)$ ths of it.

For example,

$$25\% \text{ is the same as} \quad \frac{25}{100} = \frac{1}{4}$$

$$30\% \text{ is the same as} \quad \frac{30}{100} = \frac{3}{10}$$

$$50\% \text{ is the same as} \quad \frac{50}{100} = \frac{1}{2}$$

Example

Calculate

(a) 15% of 12

(b) 98% of 17

(c) 150% of 290

Solution

(a) 15% of 12 is the same as

$$\frac{15}{100} \times 12 = 0.15 \times 12 = 1.8$$

(b) 98% of 17 is the same as

$$\frac{98}{100} \times 17 = 0.98 \times 17 = 16.66$$

(c) 150% of 290 is the same as

$$\frac{150}{100} \times 290 = 1.5 \times 290 = 435$$

Practice Problem

1. Calculate

    (a) 10% of $2.90   **(b)** 75% of $1250   **(c)** 24% of $580

Whenever any numerical quantity increases or decreases, it is customary to refer to this change in percentage terms. The following example serves to remind you how to perform calculations involving percentage changes.

Example

(a) An investment rises from $2500 to $3375. Express the increase as a percentage of the original.

(b) At the beginning of a year, the population of a small village is 8400. If the annual rise in population is 12%, find the population at the end of the year.

(c) In a sale, all prices are reduced by 20%. Find the sale price of a good originally costing $580.

Solution

(a) The rise in the value of the investment is

$$3375 - 2500 = 875$$

As a fraction of the original this is

$$\frac{875}{2500} = 0.35$$

This is the same as 35 hundredths, so the percentage rise is 35%.

(b) As a fraction

$$12\% \text{ is the same as } \frac{12}{100} = 0.12$$

so the rise in population is

$$0.12 \times 8400 = 1008$$

Hence the final population is

$$8400 + 1008 = 9408$$

(c) As a fraction

$$20\% \text{ is the same as } \frac{20}{100} = 0.2$$

so the fall in price is

$$0.2 \times 580 = 116$$

Hence the final price is

$$580 - 116 = \$464$$

Practice Problem

2. (a) A firm's annual sales rise from 50 000 to 55 000 from one year to the next. Express the rise as a percentage of the original.

(b) The government imposes a 15% tax on the price of a good. How much does the consumer pay for a good priced by a firm at $1360?

(c) Investments fall during the course of a year by 7%. Find the value of an investment at the end of the year if it was worth $9500 at the beginning of the year.

In the previous example and in Practice Problem 2, the calculations were performed in two separate stages. The actual rise or fall was first worked out, and these changes were then applied to the original value to obtain the final answer. It is possible to obtain this answer in a single calculation, and we now describe how this can be done. Not only is this new approach quicker, but it also enables us to tackle more difficult problems. To be specific, let us suppose that the price of good is set to rise by 9%, and that its current price is $78. The new price consists of the original (which can be thought of as 100% of the $78) plus the increase (which is 9% of $78). The final price is therefore

$$100\% + 9\% = 109\% \text{ (of the } \$78)$$

which is the same as

$$\frac{109}{100} = 1.09$$

In other words, in order to calculate the final price all we have to do is to multiply by the **scale factor**, 1.09. Hence the new price is

$1.09 \times 78 = \$85.02$

One advantage of this approach is that it is then just as easy to go backwards and work out the original price from the new price. To go backwards in time we simply *divide* by the scale factor. For example, if the final price of a good is \$1068.20 then before a 9% increase the price would have been

$1068.20 \div 1.09 = \$980$

In general, if the percentage rise is r% then the final value consists of the original (100%) together with the increase (r%), giving a total of

$$\frac{100}{100} + \frac{r}{100} = 1 + \frac{r}{100}$$

To go forwards in time we multiply by this scale factor, whereas to go backwards we divide.

Example

(a) If the annual rate of inflation is 4%, find the price of a good at the end of a year if its price at the beginning of the year is \$25.

(b) The cost of a good is \$799 including 17.5% VAT (value added tax). What is the cost excluding VAT?

(c) Express the rise from 950 to 1007 as a percentage.

Solution

(a) The scale factor is

$$1 + \frac{4}{100} = 1.04$$

We are trying to find the price *after* the increase, so we *multiply* to get

$25 \times 1.04 = \$26$

(b) The scale factor is

$$1 + \frac{17.5}{100} = 1.175$$

This time we are trying to find the price *before* the increase, so we *divide* by the scale factor to get

$799 \div 1.175 = \$680$

(c) The scale factor is

$$\frac{\text{new value}}{\text{old value}} = \frac{1007}{950} = 1.06$$

which can be thought of as

$$1 + \frac{6}{100}$$

so the rise is 6%.

Practice Problem ❷

3. **(a)** The value of a good rises by 13% in a year. If it was worth $6.5 million at the beginning of the year, find its value at the end of the year.

(b) The GNP of a country has increased by 63% over the past 5 years and is now $124 billion. What was the GNP 5 years ago?

(c) Sales rise from 115 000 to 123 050 in a year. Find the annual percentage rise.

It is possible to use scale factors to solve problems involving percentage decreases. To be specific, suppose that an investment of $76 falls by 20%. The new value is the original (100%) less the decrease (20%), so is 80% of the original. The scale factor is therefore 0.8, giving a new value of

$$0.8 \times 76 = \$60.80$$

In general, the scale factor for an r% decrease is

$$\frac{100}{100} - \frac{r}{100} = 1 - \frac{r}{100}$$

Once again, you multiply by this scale factor when going forwards in time and divide when going backwards.

Example

(a) The value of a car depreciates by 25% in a year. What will a car, currently priced at $43 000, be worth in a year's time?

(b) After a 15% reduction in a sale, the price of a good is $39.95. What was the price before the sale began?

(c) The number of passengers using a rail link fell from 190 205 to 174 989. Find the percentage decrease.

Solution

(a) The scale factor is

$$1 - \frac{25}{100} = 0.75$$

so the new price is

$$43\ 000 \times 0.75 = \$32\ 250$$

forwards in time so multiply

(b) The scale factor is

$$1 - \frac{15}{100} = 0.85$$

so the original price was

$$39.95 \div 0.85 = \$47$$

backwards in time so divide

(c) The scale factor is

$$\frac{\text{new value}}{\text{old value}} = \frac{174\ 989}{190\ 205} = 0.92$$

which can be thought of as

$$1 - \frac{8}{100}$$

not 92%!

so the fall is 8%.

Practice Problem

4. **(a)** Current monthly output from a factory is 25 000. In a recession, this is expected to fall by 65%. Estimate the new level of output.

   (b) As a result of a modernization programme, a firm is able to reduce the size of its workforce by 24%. If it now employs 570 workers, how many people did it employ before restructuring?

   (c) Shares originally worth $10.50 fall in a stock market crash to $2.10. Find the percentage decrease.

The final application of scale factors that we consider is to the calculation of overall percentage changes. It is often the case that over various periods of time the price of a good is subject to several individual percentage changes. It is useful to be able to replace these by an equivalent single percentage change spanning the entire period. This can be done by simply multiplying together successive scale factors.

Example

(a) Share prices rise by 32% during the first half of the year and rise by a further 10% during the second half. What is the overall percentage change?

(b) Find the overall percentage change in the price of a good if it rises by 5% in a year but is then reduced by 30% in a sale.

Solution

(a) To find the value of shares at the end of the first 6 months we would multiply by

$$1 + \frac{32}{100} = 1.32$$

and at the end of the year we would multiply again by the scale factor

$$1 + \frac{10}{100} = 1.1$$

The net effect is to multiply by their product

$$1.32 \times 1.1 = 1.452$$

which can be thought of as

$$1 + \frac{45.2}{100}$$

so the overall change is 45.2%.

Notice that this is not the same as

$$32\% + 10\% = 42\%$$

This is because during the second half of the year we not only get a 10% rise in the original value, but we also get a 10% rise on the gain accrued during the first 6 months.

(b) The individual scale factors are 1.05 and 0.7, so the overall scale factor is

$$1.05 \times 0.7 = 0.735$$

The fact that this is less than 1 indicates that the overall change is a decrease. Writing

$$0.735 = 1 - 0.265 = 1 - \frac{26.5}{100}$$

we see that this scale factor represents a 26.5% decrease.

Practice Problem

5. Find the single percentage increase or decrease equivalent to

(a) an increase of 30% followed by an increase of 40%

(b) a decrease of 30% followed by a decrease of 40%

(c) an increase of 10% followed by a decrease of 50%.

We conclude this section by describing two applications of percentages in macroeconomics:

- index numbers
- inflation.

We consider each of these in turn.

3.1.1 Index numbers

Economic data often take the form of a **time series**; values of economic indicators are available on an annual, quarterly or monthly basis, and we are interested in analysing the rise and fall of these numbers over time. **Index numbers** enable us to identify trends and relationships in the data. The following example shows you how to calculate index numbers and how to interpret them.

Example

Table 3.1 shows the values of household spending (in billions of dollars) during a 5-year period. Calculate the index numbers when 2000 is taken as the base year and give a brief interpretation.

Table 3.1

| | | Year | | |
	1999	2000	2001	2002	2003
Household spending	686.9	697.2	723.7	716.6	734.5

Solution

When finding index numbers, a base year is chosen and the value of 100 is allocated to that year. In this example, we are told to take 2000 as the base year, so the index number of 2000 is 100. To find the index number of the year 2001 we work out the scale factor associated with the change in household spending from the base year, 2000 to 2001, and then multiply the answer by 100.

$$\boxed{\text{index number} = \text{scale factor from base year} \times 100}$$

In this case, we get

$$\frac{723.7}{697.2} \times 100 = 103.8$$

This shows that the value of household spending in 2001 was 103.8% of its value in 2000. In other words, household spending increased by 3.8% during 2001.

For the year 2002, the value of household spending was 716.6, giving an index number

$$\frac{716.6}{697.2} \times 100 = 102.8$$

This shows that the value of household spending in 2002 was 102.8% of its value in 2000. In other words, household spending increased by 2.8% between 2000 and 2002. Notice that this is less than that calculated for 2001, reflecting the fact that spending actually fell slightly during 2002. The remaining two index numbers are calculated in a similar way and are shown in Table 3.2.

Table 3.2

| | | Year | | |
	1999	2000	2001	2002	2003
Household spending	686.9	697.2	723.7	716.6	734.5
Index number	98.5	100	103.8	102.8	105.3

Practice Problem

6. Calculate the index numbers for the data shown in Table 3.1, this time taking 1999 as the base year.

Index numbers themselves have no units. They merely express the value of some quantity as a percentage of a base number. This is particularly useful, since it enables us to compare how values of quantities, of varying magnitudes, change in relation to each other. The following example shows the rise and fall of two share prices during an 8-month period. The prices (in dollars) listed for each share are taken on the last day of each month. Share A is exceptionally cheap. Investors often include this type of share in their portfolio, since they can occasionally make spectacular gains. This was the case with many dot.com shares at the end of the 1990s. The second share is more expensive and corresponds to a larger, more established firm.

Example

Find the index numbers of each share price shown in Table 3.3, taking April as the base month. Hence compare the performances of these two share prices during this period.

Table 3.3

Month	Jan	Feb	Mar	Apr	May	Jun	Jul	Aug
Share A	0.31	0.28	0.31	0.34	0.40	0.39	0.45	0.52
Share B	6.34	6.40	6.45	6.52	6.57	6.43	6.65	7.00

Solution

The index numbers have been listed in Table 3.4. Notice that both shares are given the same index number of 100 in April, which is the base month. This is despite the fact that the values of the two shares are very different. This creates 'a level playing-field', enabling us to monitor the relative performance of the two shares. The index numbers show quite clearly that share A has outperformed share B during this period. Indeed, if an investor had spent $1000 on shares of type A in January, they could have bought 3225 of them, which would be worth $1677 in August, making a profit of $677. The corresponding profit for share B is only $99.

Table 3.4

Month	Jan	Feb	Mar	Apr	May	Jun	Jul	Aug
Index of share price A (April = 100)	91.2	82.3	91.2	100	117.6	114.7	132.4	152.9
Index of share price B (April = 100)	97.2	98.2	98.9	100	100.8	98.6	102.0	107.4

Incidentally, if the only information you have about the time series is the set of index numbers, then it is possible to work out the percentage changes between any pair of values. Table 3.5 shows the index numbers of the output of a particular firm for the years 2004 and 2005.

The table shows that the base quarter is the first quarter of 2005 because the index number is 100 in 05Q1. It is, of course, easy to find the percentage change from this quarter to any subsequent quarter. For example, the index number associated with the third quarter of 2005 is

Table 3.5

				Output				
	04Q1	04Q2	04Q3	04Q4	05Q1	05Q2	05Q3	05Q4
Index	89.3	98.1	105.0	99.3	100	106.3	110.2	105.7

110.2, so we know immediately that the percentage change in output from 05Q1 to 05Q3 is 10.2%. However, it is not immediately obvious what the percentage change is from, say, 04Q2 to 05Q2. To work this out, notice that the index number has increased by

$$106.3 - 98.1 = 8.2$$

so the percentage increase is

$$\frac{8.2}{98.1} \times 100 = 8.4\%$$

Alternatively, note that the scale factor of this change is

$$\frac{106.3}{98.1} = 1.084$$

which corresponds to an 8.4% increase.

Similarly, the scale factor of the change from 04Q3 to 05Q1 is

$$\frac{100}{105} = 0.952$$

This is less than 1, reflecting the fact that output has fallen. To find the percentage change we write the scale factor as

$$1 - 0.048$$

which shows that the percentage decrease is 4.8%.

Practice Problem

7. Use the index numbers listed in Table 3.5 to find the percentage change in output from

(a) 05Q1 to 05Q4

(b) 04Q1 to 05Q4

(c) 04Q1 to 05Q1

Example

EXCEL

Table 3.6 shows the unit costs of labour, energy, communications and raw materials during a 3-year period. In year 0, a firm used 70 units of labour, 25 units of energy, 10 units of communication and 140 units of raw materials. Taking year 0 as the base year, calculate an appropriate index number for years 1 and 2.

Table 3.6

	Year 0	Year 1	Year 2
Labour	16	23	28
Energy	7	10	9
Communications	12	14	10
Raw materials	5	9	12

Solution

We are told to take year 0 as the base year, so the index number for year 0 is 100. One way of calculating the index number for subsequent years would be to work out the totals of each column in Table 3.6 and find the associated scale factors of these. On this basis, the index number for year 1 would be calculated as

$$\frac{23 + 10 + 14 + 9}{16 + 7 + 12 + 5} \times 100 = 140$$

However, this fails to take into account the fact, for example, that we use twice as many units of raw materals than labour. It is important that each item is weighted according to how many units of each type are used. To do this, all we have to do is to multiply each of the unit costs by the associated quantities. The appropriate index number is then worked out as

$$\frac{23 \times 70 + 10 \times 25 + 14 \times 10 + 9 \times 140}{16 \times 70 + 7 \times 25 + 12 \times 10 + 5 \times 140} \times 100 = 154.1$$

The fact that this number is greater than before is to be expected because the unit price of raw materials has nearly doubled, and the firm uses a greater proportion of these in its total costs. Index numbers that are weighted according to the quantity consumed in the base year are called **Laspeyre indices**. Spreadsheets provide an easy way of presenting the calculations. For each year, we simply include an extra column in the table, for the products $P_n Q_0$ where Q_0 denotes the quantities used in the base year, and P_n denotes the unit prices in year n. The Laspeyre index for year n is then worked out as

$$\frac{\text{total of column } P_n Q_0}{\text{total of column } P_0 Q_0} \times 100$$

Figure 3.1 shows the completed spreadsheet. The Laspeyre indices for years 1 and 2 are seen to be 154.1 and 187.5, respectively. Notice that this index has increased rapidly over this period, in spite of the fact that communication and energy costs have hardly changed. This is because expenditure is dominated by labour and raw material costs, which have both increased substantially during this time.

Calculation of the Laspeyre Index

Input	Year 0 Quantity	Year 0 Price	Year 1 Price	Year 2 Price	$P_0 Q_0$	$P_1 Q_0$	$P_2 Q_0$
Labour	70	16	23	28	1120	1610	1960
Energy	25	7	10	9	175	250	225
Communications	10	12	14	10	120	140	100
Raw materials	140	5	9	12	700	1260	1680
				Totals:	2115	3260	3965
				Laspeyre Index =		154.1	187.5

Figure 3.1

3.1.2 Inflation

Over a period of time, the prices of many goods and services usually increase. The annual rate of **inflation** is the average percentage change in a given selection of these goods and services, over the previous year. Seasonal variations are taken into account, and the particular basket of goods and services is changed periodically to reflect changing patterns of household expenditure. The presence of inflation is particularly irritating when trying to interpret a time series that involves a monetary value. It is inevitable that this will be influenced by inflation during any year, and what is of interest is the fluctuation of a time series 'over and above' inflation. Economists deal with this by distinguishing between nominal and real data. **Nominal data** are the original, raw data such as those listed in tables in the previous subsection. These are based on the prices that prevailed at the time. **Real data** are the values that have been adjusted to take inflation into account. The standard way of doing this is to pick a year and then convert the values for all other years to the level that they would have had in this base year. This may sound rather complicated, but the idea and calculations involved are really quite simple as the following example demonstrates.

Example

Table 3.7 shows the price (in thousands of dollars) of an average house in a certain town during a 5-year period. The price quoted is the value of the house at the end of each year. Use the annual rates of inflation given in Table 3.8 to adjust the prices to those prevailing at the end of 1991. Compare the rise in both the nominal and real values of house prices during this period.

Table 3.7

	Year				
	1990	1991	1992	1993	1994
Average house price	72	89	93	100	106

Table 3.8

	Year			
	1991	1992	1993	1994
Annual rate of inflation	10.7%	7.1%	3.5%	2.3%

Solution

The raw figures shown in Table 3.7 give the impression that houses increased steadily in value throughout this period, with a quite substantial gain during the first year. However, if inflation had been very high then the gain in real terms would have been quite small. Indeed, if the rate of inflation were to exceed the percentage rise of this nominal data, then the price of a house would actually fall in real terms. To analyse this situation we will use Table 3.8, which shows the rates of inflation during this period. Notice that since the house prices listed in Table 3.8 are quoted at the end of each year, we are not interested in the rate of inflation during 1990.

We are told in the question to choose 1991 as the base year and calculate the value of the house at '1991 prices'. The value of the house at the end of 1991 is obviously $89 000, since no adjustment need be made. At the end of 1992, the house is worth $93 000. However, during that year inflation was 7.1%. To adjust this price to '1991 prices' we simply divide by the scale factor 1.071, since we are going backwards in time. We get

$$\frac{93\,000}{1.071} = 86\,835$$

In real terms the house has fallen in value by over $2000.

To adjust the price of the house in 1993 we first need to divide by 1.035 to backtrack to the year 1992, and then divide again by 1.071 to reach 1991. We get

$$\frac{100\,000}{1.035 \times 1.071} = 90\,213$$

In real terms there has at least been some gain during 1993. However, this is less than impressive, and from a purely financial point of view, there would have been more lucrative ways of investing this capital.

For the 1994 price, the adjusted value is

$$\frac{106\,000}{1.023 \times 1.035 \times 1.071} = 93\,476$$

and, for 1990, the adjusted value is

$$72\,000 \times 1.107 = 79\,704$$

going forward in time so multiply

Table 3.9 lists both the nominal and the 'constant 1991' values of the house (rounded to the nearest thousand) for comparison. It shows quite clearly that, apart from the gain during 1991, the increase in value has, in fact, been quite modest.

Table 3.9

| | Year | | | | |
	1990	1991	1992	1993	1994
Nominal house price	72	89	94	100	106
1991 house price	80	89	87	90	93

Practice Problem

8. Table 3.10 shows the average annual salary (in thousands of dollars) of employees in a small firm, together with the annual rate of inflation for that year. Adjust these salaries to the prices prevailing at the end of 2001 and so give the real values of the employees' salaries at constant '2001 prices'. Comment on the rise in earnings during this period.

Table 3.10

	Year				
	2000	2001	2002	2003	2004
Salary	17.3	18.1	19.8	23.5	26.0
Inflation		4.9	4.3	4.0	3.5

Key Terms

Index number   The scale factor of a variable measured from the base year multiplied by 100.

Inflation   The percentage increase in the level of prices over a 12-month period.

Laspeyre index   An index number for groups of data which are weighted by the quantities used in the base year.

Nominal data   Monetary values prevailing at the time that they were measured.

Paasche index   An index number for groups of data which are weighted by the quantities used in the current year.

Real data   Monetary values adjusted to take inflation into account.

Scale factor   The multiplier that gives the final value in percentage problems.

Time series   A sequence of numbers indicating the variation of data over time.

Exercise 3.1

1. Express the following percentages as fractions in their simplest form:

(a) 35%   (b) 88%   (c) 250%   (d) $17\frac{1}{2}$%   (e) 0.2%

2. Calculate each of the following:

(a) 5% of 24   (b) 8% of 88   (c) 48% of 4563   (d) 112% of 56

3. Write down the scale factors corresponding to

(a) an increase of 19%

(b) an increase of 250%

(c) a decrease of 2%

(d) a decrease of 43%.

4. Write down the percentage changes corresponding to the following scale factors:

   (a) 1.04   (b) 1.42   (c) 0.86

   (d) 3.45   (e) 1.0025   (f) 0.04

5. Find the new quantities when

   (a) £16.25 is increased by 12%

   (b) the population of a town, currently at 113 566, rises by 5%

   (c) a good priced by a firm at £87.90 is subject to value added tax at 15%

   (d) a good priced at £2300 is reduced by 30% in a sale

   (e) a car, valued at £23 000, depreciates by 32%.

6. A shop sells books at '20% below the recommended retail price (r.r.p.)'. If it sells a book for £12.40 find

   (a) the r.r.p.

   (b) the cost of the book after a further reduction of 15% in a sale

   (c) the overall percentage discount obtained by buying the book from the shop in the sale compared with the manufacturer's r.r.p.

7. A TV costs £940 including 17.5% VAT. Find the new price if VAT is reduced to 8%.

8. An antiques dealer tries to sell a vase at 45% above the £18 000 which the dealer paid at auction.

   (a) What is the new sale price?

   (b) By what percentage can the dealer now reduce the price before making a loss?

9. Find the single percentage increase or decrease equivalent to

   (a) a 10% increase followed by a 25% increase

   (b) a 34% decrease followed by a 65% increase

   (c) a 25% increase followed by a 25% decrease.

   Explain in words why the overall change in part (c) is not 0%.

10. Table 3.11 gives the annual rate of inflation during a 5-year period.

   Table 3.11

	2000	2001	2002	2003	2004
Annual rate of inflation	1.8%	2.1%	2.9%	2.4%	2.7%

   If a nominal house price at the end of 2000 was $10.8 million, find the real house price adjusted to prices prevailing at the end of the year 2003. Round your answer to three significant figures.

11. Table 3.12 shows the index numbers associated with transport costs during a 20-year period. The public transport costs reflect changes to bus and train fares, whereas private transport costs include purchase, service, petrol, tax and insurance costs of cars.

Table 3.12

	1985	1990	Year 1995	2000	2005
Public transport	100	130	198	224	245
Private transport	100	125	180	199	221

(1) Which year is chosen as the base year?

(2) Find the percentage increases in the cost of public transport from

    (a) 1985 to 1990   **(b)** 1990 to 1995   **(c)** 1995 to 2000   **(d)** 2000 to 2005

(3) Repeat part (2) for private transport.

(4) Comment briefly on the relative rise in public and private transport costs during this 20-year period.

12. Table 3.13 shows the number of items (in thousands) produced from a factory production line during the course of a year. Taking the second quarter as the base quarter, calculate the associated index numbers. Suggest a possible reason for the fluctuations in output.

Table 3.13

	Quarter Q1	Q2	Q3	Q4
Output	13.5	1.4	2.5	10.5

13. Table 3.14 shows the prices of a good for each year between 1999 and 2004.

Table 3.14

Year	1999	2000	2001	2002	2003	2004
Price ($)	40	48	44	56	60	71

(a) Work out the index numbers, correct to 1 decimal place, taking 2000 as the base year.

(b) If the index number for 2005 is 135, calculate the corresponding price.

    You may assume that the base year is still 2000.

(c) If the index number in 2001 is approximately 73, find the year that is used as the base year.

Exercise 3.1*

1. The cost of a computer is £998.75 including 17.5% VAT. In a generous gesture, the government decides to reduce the rate of VAT to just 15%.

    Find the cost of the computer after VAT has changed.

2. A coat originally costing £150 is reduced by 25% in a sale and, since nobody bought the coat, a further reduction of 20% of the sale price is applied.

(a) Find the final cost of the coat after both reductions.

(b) Find the overall percentage reduction and explain why this is not the same as a single reduction of 45%.

3. A furniture store has a sale of 40% on selected items.
   A sales assistant, Carol, reduces the price of a sofa originally costing £1200.

   (a) What is the new price?
   The manager does not want this sofa to be in the sale and the following day tells another sales assistant, Michael, to restore the sofa back to the original price. He does not know what the original price was and decides to show off his mathematical knowledge by taking the answer to part (a) and multiplying it by 1.4.

   (b) Explain carefully why this does not give the correct answer of £1200.

   (c) Suggest an alternative calculation that would give the right answer.

4. During 2008 the price of a good increased by 8%. In the sales on 1 January 2009 all items are reduced by 25%.

   (a) If the sale price of the good is $688.50, find the original price at the beginning of 2008.

   (b) Find the overall percentage change.

   (c) What percentage increase would be needed to restore cost to the original price prevailing on 1 January 2008? Give your answer to 1 decimal place.

5. Table 3.15 shows government expenditure (in billions of dollars) on education for four consecutive years, together with the rate of inflation for each year.

   (a) Taking 2004 as the base year, work out the index numbers of the nominal data given in the second row of the table.

   (b) Find the values of expenditure at constant 2004 prices and hence recalculate the index numbers of real government expenditure.

   (c) Give an interpretation of the index numbers calculated in part (b).

Table 3.15

	Year			
	2004	2005	2006	2007
Spending	236	240	267	276
Inflation		4.7	4.2	3.4

6. Index numbers associated with the growth of unemployment during an 8-year period are shown in Table 3.16.

   (a) What are the base years for the two indices?

   (b) If the government had not switched to index 2, what would be the values of index 1 in years 7 and 8?

   (c) What values would index 2 have been in years 1, 2, 3, 4 and 5?

   (d) If unemployment was 1.2 million in year 4, how many people were unemployed in years 1 and 8?

Table 3.16

	Year							
	1	2	3	4	5	6	7	8
Index 1	100	95	105	110	119	127		
Index 2						100	112	118

7. The prices of a good at the end of each year between 2003 and 2008 are listed in the Table 3.17, which also shows the annual rate of inflation.

Table 3.17

Year	2003	2004	2005	2006	2007	2008
Price	230	242	251	257	270	284
Inflation		4%	3%	2.5%	2%	2%

(a) Find the values of the prices adjusted to the end of year 2004, correct to 2 decimal places.

Hence, calculate the index numbers of the real data with 2004 as the base year. Give your answers correct to 1 decimal place.

(b) If the index number of the real price for 2009 is 109 and the rate of inflation for that year is 2.5%, work out the nominal value of the price in 2009.

Give your answer rounded to the nearest whole number.

(c) If the index number of the real data in 2002 is 95.6 and the nominal price is $215, find the rate of inflation for 2002. Give your answer correct to 1 decimal place.

8. (Excel) Table 3.18 shows the annual salaries (in thousands of dollars) of four categories of employee during a 3-year period. In year 0 the firm employed 24, 250, 109 and 7 people of types A, B, C and D, respectively. Calculate the Laspeyre index of the total wage bill in years 1 and 2 taking year 0 as the base year. Comment briefly on these values.

Table 3.18

	Year 0	Year 1	Year 2
Type A	12	13	13
Type B	26	28	29
Type C	56	56	64
Type D	240	340	560

9. (Excel) In the Laspeyre index, the quantities used for the weights are those of the base year. If these are replaced by quantities for the current year, then the index is called the Paasche index. In Question 8, suppose that the numbers of employees of types A, B, C and D in year 1 are 30, 240, 115 and 8, respectively. For year 2 the corresponding figures are 28, 220, 125 and 20. By adding two extra columns for the products P_1Q_1 and P_2Q_2 to the spreadsheet of Question 8, calculate the Paasche index for years 1 and 2. Compare with the Laspeyre index calculated in Question 8. State one advantage and one disadvantage of using the Laspeyre and Paasche methods for the calculation of combined index numbers.

SECTION 3.2
Compound interest

Objectives

At the end of this section you should be able to:

- Understand the difference between simple and compound interest.
- Calculate the future value of a principal under annual compounding.
- Calculate the future value of a principal under continuous compounding.
- Determine the annual percentage rate of interest given a nominal rate of interest.

Today, businesses and individuals are faced with a bewildering array of loan facilities and investment opportunities. In this section we explain how these financial calculations are carried out to enable an informed choice to be made between the various possibilities available. We begin by considering what happens when a single lump sum is invested and show how to calculate the amount accumulated over a period of time.

Suppose that someone gives you the option of receiving $500 now or $500 in 3 years' time. Which of these alternatives would you accept? Most people would take the money now, partly because they may have an immediate need for it, but also because they recognize that $500 is worth more today than in 3 years' time. Even if we ignore the effects of inflation, it is still better to take the money now, since it can be invested and will increase in value over the 3-year period. In order to work out this value we need to know the rate of interest and the basis on which it is calculated. Let us begin by assuming that the $500 is invested for 3 years at 10% interest compounded annually. What exactly do we mean by '10% interest compounded annually'? Well, at the end of each year, the interest is calculated and is added on to the amount currently invested. If the original amount is $500 then after 1 year the interest is 10% of $500, which is

$$\frac{10}{100} \times \$500 = \frac{1}{10} \times \$500 = \$50$$

so the amount rises by $50 to $550.

What happens to this amount at the end of the second year? Is the interest also $50? This would actually be the case with **simple interest**, when the amount of interest received is the same for all years. However, with **compound interest**, we get 'interest on the interest'. Nearly all financial investments use compound rather than simple interest, because investors need to be rewarded for not taking the interest payment out of the fund each year. Under annual compounding the interest obtained at the end of the second year is 10% of the amount invested at the start of that year. This not only consists of the original $500, but also the $50 already received as interest on the first year's investment. Consequently, we get an additional

$$\frac{1}{10} \times \$550 = \$55$$

raising the sum to $605. Finally, at the end of the third year, the interest is

$$\frac{1}{10} \times \$605 = \$60.50$$

so the investment is $665.50. You are therefore $165.50 better off by taking the $500 now and investing it for 3 years. The calculations are summarized in Table 3.19.

Table 3.19

End of year	Interest ($)	Investment ($)
1	50	550
2	55	605
3	60.50	665.50

Example

Find the value, in 4 years' time, of $10 000 invested at 5% interest compounded annually.

Solution

- At the end of year 1 the interest is 0.05 × 10 000 = 500, so the investment is $10 500.
- At the end of year 2 the interest is 0.05 × 10 500 = 525, so the investment is $11 025.
- At the end of year 3 the interest is 0.05 × 11 025 = 551.25, so the investment is $11 576.25.
- At the end of year 4 the interest is 0.05 × 11 576.25 = 578.81 rounded to 2 decimal places, so the final investment is $12 155.06 to the nearest cent.

Practice Problem

1. Find the value, in 10 years' time, of $1000 invested at 8% interest compounded annually.

The previous calculations were performed by finding the interest earned each year and adding it on to the amount accumulated at the beginning of the year. As you may have discovered in Practice Problem 1, this can be rather laborious, particularly if the money is invested over a long period of time. What is really needed is a method of calculating the investment after, say, 10 years without having to determine the amount for the 9 intermediate years. This can be done using the scale factor approach discussed in the previous section. To illustrate this, let us return to the problem of investing $500 at 10% interest compounded annually. The original sum of money is called the **principal** and is denoted by P, and the final sum is called the **future value** and is denoted by S. The scale factor associated with an increase of 10% is

$$1 + \frac{10}{100} = 1.1$$

so at the end of 1 year the total amount invested is $P(1.1)$.

After 2 years we get

$$P(1.1) \times (1.1) = P(1.1)^2$$

and after 3 years the future value is

$$S = P(1.1)^2 \times (1.1) = P(1.1)^3$$

Setting $P = 500$, we see that

$$S = 500(1.1)^3 = \$665.50$$

which is, of course, the same as the amount calculated previously.

In general, if the interest rate is r% compounded annually then the scale factor is

$$1 + \frac{r}{100}$$

so, after n years,

$$\boxed{S = P\left(1 + \frac{r}{100}\right)^n}$$

Given the values of r, P and n it is simple to evaluate S using the power key $\boxed{x^y}$ on a calculator. To see this let us rework the previous example using this formula.

Example

Find the value, in 4 years' time, of \$10 000 invested at 5% interest compounded annually.

Solution

In this problem, $P = 10\ 000$, $r = 5$ and $n = 4$, so the formula $S = P\left(1 + \frac{r}{100}\right)^n$ gives

$$S = \left(+\frac{5}{100}\right)^4 = 10\ 000(1.05)^4 = 12\ 155.06$$

which is, of course, the same answer as before.

Practice Problem

2. Use the formula

$$S = P\left(1 + \frac{r}{100}\right)^n$$

to find the value, in 10 years' time, of \$1000 invested at 8% interest compounded annually. [You might like to compare your answer with that obtained in Practice Problem 1.]

The compound interest formula derived above involves four variables, r, n, P and S. Provided that we know any three of these, we can use the formula to determine the remaining variable. This is illustrated in the following example.

Example

A principal of \$25 000 is invested at 12% interest compounded annually. After how many years will the investment first exceed \$250 000?

Solution

We want to save a total of \$250 000 starting with an initial investment of \$25 000. The problem is to determine the number of years required for this on the assumption that the interest is fixed at 12% throughout this time. The formula for compound interest is

$$S = P\left(1 + \frac{r}{100}\right)^n$$

We are given that

$$P = 25\,000, \ S = 250\,000, \ r = 12$$

so we need to solve the equation

$$250\,000 = 25\,000\left(1 + \frac{12}{100}\right)^n$$

for n.

One way of doing this would just be to keep on guessing values of n until we find the one that works. However, a more mathematical approach is to use logarithms, because we are being asked to solve an equation in which the unknown occurs as a power. Following the method described in Section 2.3, we first divide both sides by 25 000 to get

$$10 = (1.12)^n$$

Taking logarithms of both sides gives

$$\log(10) = \log(1.12)^n$$

and if you apply rule 3 of logarithms you get

$$\log(10) = n \log(1.12)$$ $\log_b x^m = m \log_b x$

Hence

$$n = \frac{\log(10)}{\log(1.12)}$$

$$= \frac{1}{0.049\,218\,023} \quad \text{(taking logarithms to base 10)}$$

$$= 20.3 \quad \text{(to 1 decimal place)}$$

Now we know that n must be a whole number because interest is only added on at the end of each year. We assume that the first interest payment occurs exactly 12 months after the initial investment and every 12 months thereafter. The answer, 20.3, tells us that after only 20 years the amount is less than \$250 000, so we need to wait until 21 years have elapsed before it exceeds this amount. In fact, after 20 years

$$S = \$25\,000(1.12)^{20} = \$241\,157.33$$

and after 21 years

$$S = \$25\,000(1.12)^{21} = \$270\,096.21$$

In this example we calculated the time taken for $25 000 to increase by a factor of 10. It can be shown that this time depends only on the interest rate and not on the actual value of the principal. To see this, note that if a general principal, P, increases tenfold then its future value is $10P$. If the interest rate is 12%, then we need to solve

$$10P = P\left(1 + \frac{12}{100}\right)^n$$

for n. The Ps cancel (indicating that the answer is independent of P) to produce the equation

$$10 = (1.12)^n$$

This is identical to the equation obtained in the previous example and, as we have just seen, has the solution $n = 20.3$.

Practice Problem

3. A firm estimates that its sales will rise by 3% each year and that it needs to sell at least 10 000 goods each year in order to make a profit. Given that its current annual sales are only 9000, how many years will it take before the firm breaks even?

You may have noticed that in all of the previous problems it is assumed that the interest is compounded annually. It is possible for interest to be added to the investment more frequently than this. For example, suppose that a principal of $500 is invested for 3 years at 10% interest compounded quarterly. What do we mean by '10% interest compounded quarterly'? Well, it does *not* mean that we get 10% interest every 3 months. Instead, the 10% is split into four equal portions, one for each quarter. Every 3 months the interest accrued is

$$\frac{10\%}{4} = 2.5\%$$

so after the first quarter the investment gets multiplied by 1.025 to give

$$500(1.025)$$

and after the second quarter it gets multiplied by another 1.025 to give

$$500(1.025)^2$$

and so on. Moreover, since there are exactly twelve 3-month periods in 3 years we deduce that the future value is

$$500(1.025)^{12} = \$672.44$$

Notice that this is greater than the sum obtained at the start of this section under annual compounding. (Why is this?)

This example highlights the fact that the compound interest formula

$$S = P\left(1 + \frac{r}{100}\right)^n$$

derived earlier for annual compounding can also be used for other types of compounding. All that is needed is to reinterpret the symbols r and n. The variable r now represents the rate of interest per time period and n represents the total number of periods.

Example

A principal of $10 is invested at 12% interest for 1 year. Determine the future value if the interest is compounded

(a) annually   **(b)** semi-annually   **(c)** quarterly   **(d)** monthly   **(e)** weekly

Solution

The formula for compound interest gives

$$S = 10\left(1 + \frac{r}{100}\right)^n$$

(a) If the interest is compounded annually then $r = 12$, $n = 1$, so

$$S = \$10(1.12)^1 = \$11.20$$

(b) If the interest is compounded semi-annually then an interest of $12/2 = 6\%$ is added on every 6 months and, since there are two 6-month periods in a year,

$$S = \$10(1.06)^2 = \$11.24$$

(c) If the interest is compounded quarterly then an interest of $12/4 = 3\%$ is added on every 3 months and, since there are four 3-month periods in a year,

$$S = \$10(1.03)^4 = \$11.26$$

(d) If the interest is compounded monthly then an interest of $12/12 = 1\%$ is added on every month and, since there are 12 months in a year,

$$S = \$10(1.01)^{12} = \$11.27$$

(e) If the interest is compounded weekly then an interest of $12/52 = 0.23\%$ is added on every week and, since there are 52 weeks in a year,

$$S = \$10(1.0023)^{52} = \$11.27$$

In the above example we see that the future value rises as the frequency of compounding rises. This is to be expected because the basic feature of compound interest is that we get 'interest on the interest'. However, one important observation that you might not have expected is that, although the future values increase, they appear to be approaching a fixed value. It can be shown that this always occurs. The type of compounding in which the interest is added on with increasing frequency is called **continuous compounding**. In theory, we can find the future value of a principal under continuous compounding using the approach taken in the previous example. We work with smaller and smaller time periods until the numbers settle down to a fixed value. However, it turns out that there is a special formula that can be used to compute this directly. The future value, S, of a principal, P, compounded continuously for t years at an annual rate of $r\%$ is

$$S = Pe^{rt/100}$$

where e is the number

2.718 281 828 459 045 235 36 (to 20 decimal places)

If $r = 12$, $t = 1$ and $P = 10$ then this formula gives

$$S = \$10e^{12 \times 1/100} = \$10e^{0.12} = \$11.27$$

check this using
your own
calculator

which is in agreement with the limiting value obtained in the previous example.

Advice

The number e and the related natural logarithm function were first introduced in Section 2.4. If you missed this section out, you should go back and read through this work now before proceeding. The link between the number e and the above formula for continuous compounding is given in Question 6 in Exercise 3.2* at the end of this section. However, you may prefer to accept it without justification and concentrate on the applications.

Example

A principal of $2000 is invested at 10% interest compounded continuously. After how many days will the investment first exceed $2100?

Solution

We want to save a total of $2100 starting with an initial investment of $2000. The problem is to determine the number of days required for this on the assumption that the interest rate is 10% compounded continuously. The formula for continuous compounding is

$$S = Pe^{rt/100}$$

We are given that

$$S = 2100, P = 2000, r = 10$$

so we need to solve the equation

$$2100 = 2000e^{10t/100}$$

for t. Dividing through by 2000 gives

$$1.05 = e^{0.1t}$$

As explained in Section 2.4, equations such as this can be solved using natural logarithms. Recall that

$$\text{if } M = e^n \quad \text{then} \quad n = \ln M$$

If we apply this definition to the equation

$$1.05 = e^{0.1t}$$

with $M = 1.05$ and $n = 0.1t$ then

$$0.1t = \ln(1.05) = 0.048\ 790\ 2$$

and so $t = 0.488$ to three decimal places.

The variable t which appears in the formula for continuous compounding is measured in years, so to convert it to days we multiply by 365 (assuming that there are 365 days in a year). Hence

$$t = 365 \times 0.488 = 178.1 \text{ days}$$

We deduce that the amount invested first exceeds $2100 some time during the 179th day.

Practice Problems

4. **(1)** A principal, $30, is invested at 6% interest for 2 years. Determine the future value if the interest is compounded

    (a) annually   **(b)** semi-annually   **(c)** quarterly

    (d) monthly   **(e)** weekly   **(f)** daily

(2) Use the formula

$$S = Pe^{rt/100}$$

to determine the future value of $30 invested at 6% interest compounded continuously for 2 years. Confirm that it is in agreement with the results of part (1).

5. Determine the rate of interest required for a principal of $1000 to produce a future value of $4000 after 10 years compounded continuously.

Example

EXCEL

A principal of $10 000 is invested at one of the following banks:

(a) Bank A offers 4.75% interest, compounded annually.

(b) Bank B offers 4.70% interest, compounded semi-annually.

(c) Bank C offers 4.65% interest, compounded quarterly.

(d) Bank D offers 4.6% interest, compounded continuously.

For each bank, tabulate the value of the investment at the end of every year, for the next 10 years. Which of these banks would you recommend?

Solution

In Figure 3.2 the numbers 0 to 10 have been entered in the first column, together with appropriate headings. The initial investment is the same for each bank, so the value 10 000 is typed into cells B4 to E4.

For banks A, B and C, the future values can be worked out using the formula

$$10\,000\left(1 + \frac{r}{100}\right)^n$$

for appropriate values of r and n.

	A	B	C	D	E	F
	Book1					
1	Compound Interest					
2						
3	Year	Bank A	Bank B	Bank C	Bank D	
4	0	10000	10000	10000	10000	
5	1					
6	2					
7	3					
8	4					
9	5					
10	6					
11	7					
12	8					
13	9					
14	10					
15						
16						

Figure 3.2

(a) In Bank A, the interest rate is 4.75% compounded annually, so at the end of year 1, the investment is

$$10\,000(1 + 0.0475)^1$$

The reason for writing it to the power of 1 is so that when we enter it into Excel, and copy down the first column, the power will automatically increase in accordance with the changing years. We type

```
=10000*(1+0.0475)^A5
```

in cell B5, and then click and drag down to cell B14.

(b) Bank B offers a return of 4.7% compounded semi-annually, so that at the end of year 1, the investment is

$$10\,000(1 + 0.047/2)^{2\times1}$$

In general, after t years, the investment is

$$10\,000(1 + 0.0475/2)^{2\times t}$$

so in Excel, we type

```
=10000*(1+0.0475/2)^(2*A5)
```

in cell C5, and copy down this column in the usual way.

(c) Bank C offers a return of 4.65% compounded quarterly, so we type

```
=10000*(1+0.0465/4)^(4*A5)
```

in cell D5, and copy down the column.

(d) Bank D offers a return of 4.6% compounded continuously, so after t years the future value is given by

$$10\,000e^{4.6t/100} = 10\,000e^{0.046t}$$

The corresponding values are calculated in column E by typing

```
=10000*EXP(0.046*A5)
```

in cell E5 and copying down the column.

The completed spreadsheet is shown in Figure 3.3. The amounts have been rounded to 2 decimal places by highlighting cells B5 through to E14, and using the Decrease Decimal icon on the toolbar.

Figure 3.3 shows that there is very little to choose between these banks and that, in practice, other issues (such as any conditions or penalties attached to future withdrawals from the account) may well influence our recommendation. However, from a purely monetary point of view, we should advise the investor to put the money into Bank B, as this offers the greatest return. Notice that Bank B is not the one with the highest rate of interest. This example highlights the importance of taking into account the frequency of compounding, as well as the actual rate of interest.

	A	B	C	D	E	F
1	**Compound Interest**					
2						
3	**Year**	**Bank A**	**Bank B**	**Bank C**	**Bank D**	
4	**0**	10000	10000	10000	10000	
5	**1**	10475.00	10480.64	10473.17	10470.74	
6	**2**	10972.56	10984.38	10968.73	10963.65	
7	**3**	11493.76	11512.34	11487.74	11479.76	
8	**4**	12039.71	12065.67	12031.31	12020.16	
9	**5**	12611.60	12645.59	12600.60	12586.00	
10	**6**	13210.65	13253.39	13196.82	13178.48	
11	**7**	13838.16	13890.40	13821.26	13798.85	
12	**8**	14495.47	14558.03	14475.24	14448.42	
13	**9**	15184.00	15257.75	15160.16	15128.57	
14	**10**	15905.24	15991.10	15877.50	15840.74	
15						
16						

Figure 3.3

Given that there are so many ways of calculating compound interest, people often find it difficult to appraise different investment opportunities. What is needed is a standard 'benchmark' that enables an individual to compare different forms of savings or credit schemes on an equal basis. The one that is commonly used is annual compounding. All firms offering investment or loan facilities are required to provide the effective annual rate. This is often referred to as the **annual percentage rate**, which is abbreviated to APR. The APR is the rate of interest which, when compounded annually, produces the same yield as the nominal (that is, the stated) rate of interest. The phrase 'annual equivalent rate' (AER) is frequently used when applied to savings. However, in this book we shall use APR for both savings and loans.

Example

Determine the annual percentage rate of interest of a deposit account that has a nominal rate of 8% compounded monthly.

Solution

The APR is the overall rate of interest, which can be calculated using scale factors. If the account offers a return of 8% compounded monthly then each month the interest is

$$\frac{8}{12} = \frac{2}{3} = 0.67\%$$

of the amount invested at the beginning of that month. The monthly scale factor is

$$1 + \frac{0.67}{100} = 1.0067$$

so in a whole year the principal gets multiplied by

$$(1.0067)^{12} = 1.0834$$

which can be written as

$$1 + \frac{8.34}{100}$$

so the APR is 8.34%.

Practice Problem ❷

6. Determine the annual percentage rate of interest if the nominal rate is 12% compounded quarterly.

Although the aim of this chapter is to investigate the mathematics of finance, the mathematical techniques themselves are more widely applicable. We conclude this section with two examples to illustrate this.

Example

A country's annual GNP (gross national product), currently at $25 000 million, is predicted to grow by 3.5% each year. The population is expected to increase by 2% a year from its current level of 40 million. After how many years will GNP per capita (that is, GNP per head of population) reach $700?

Solution

The per capita value of GNP is worked out by dividing GNP by the size of the population. Initially, this is

$$\frac{25\ 000\ 000\ 000}{40\ 000\ 000} = \$625$$

During the next few years, GNP is forecast to grow at a faster rate than the population so this value will increase.

The scale factor associated with a 3.5% increase is 1.035, so after n years GNP (in millions of dollars) will be

$$\text{GNP} = 25\,000 \times (1.035)^n$$

Similarly, the population (also in millions) will be

$$\text{population} = 40 \times (1.02)^n$$

Hence GNP per capita is

$$\frac{25\,000 \times (1.035)^n}{40 \times (1.02)^n} = \frac{25\,000}{40} \times \frac{(1.035)^n}{(1.02)^n} = 625 \times \left(\frac{1.035}{1.02}\right)^n$$

We want to find the number of years required for this to reach 700, so we need to solve the equation

$$625 \times \left(\frac{1.035}{1.02}\right)^n = 700$$

for n. Dividing both sides by 625 gives

$$\left(\frac{1.035}{1.02}\right)^n = 1.12$$

and after taking logs of both sides we get

$$\log\left(\frac{1.035}{1.02}\right)^n = \log(1.12)$$

$$n \log\left(\frac{1.035}{1.02}\right) = \log(1.12) \quad \text{(rule 3 of logs)}$$

so that

$$n = \frac{\log(1.12)}{\log(1.035/1.02)} = 7.76$$

We deduce that the target figure of \$700 per capita will be achieved after 8 years.

Example

A firm decides to increase output at a constant rate from its current level of 50 000 to 60 000 during the next 5 years. Calculate the annual rate of increase required to achieve this growth.

Solution

If the rate of increase is $r\%$ then the scale factor is $1 + \dfrac{r}{100}$ so, after 5 years, output will be

$$50\,000\left(1 + \frac{r}{100}\right)^5$$

To achieve a final output of 60 000, the value of r is chosen to satisfy the equation

$$50\,000\left(1 + \frac{r}{100}\right)^5 = 60\,000$$

Dividing both sides by 50 000 gives

$$\left(1 + \frac{r}{100}\right)^5 = 1.2$$

The difficulty in solving this equation is that the unknown, r, is trapped inside the brackets, which are raised to the power of 5. This is analogous to the problem of solving an equation such as

$$x^2 = 5.23$$

which we would solve by taking square roots of both sides to find x. This suggests that we can find r by taking fifth roots of both sides of

$$\left(1 + \frac{r}{100}\right)^5 = 1.2$$

to get

$$1 + \frac{r}{100} = (1.2)^{1/5} = 1.037$$

Hence $r = 3.7\%$.

Practice Problem

7. The turnover of a leading supermarket chain, A, is currently $560 million and is expected to increase at a constant rate of 1.5% a year. Its nearest rival, supermarket B, has a current turnover of $480 million and plans to increase this at a constant rate of 3.4% a year. After how many years will supermarket B overtake supermarket A?

Key Terms

Annual percentage rate   The equivalent annual interest paid for a loan, taking into account the compounding over a variety of time periods.

Compound interest   The interest which is added on to the initial investment, so that this will itself gain interest in subsequent time periods.

Continuous compounding   The limiting value when interest is compounded with ever-increasing frequency.

Future value   The final value of an investment after one or more time periods.

Principal   The value of the original sum invested.

Simple interest   The interest which is paid direct to the investor instead of being added to the original amount.

Exercise 3.2

1. A bank offers a return of 7% interest compounded annually. Find the future value of a principal of $4500 after 6 years. What is the overall percentage rise over this period?

2. Find the future value of $20 000 in 2 years' time if compounded quarterly at 8% interest.

3. The value of an asset, currently priced at $100 000, is expected to increase by 20% a year.
   (a) Find its value in 10 years' time.
   (b) After how many years will it be worth $1 million?

4. How long will it take for a sum of money to double if it is invested at 5% interest compounded annually?

5. A piece of machinery depreciates in value by 5% a year. Determine its value in 3 years' time if its current value is $50 000.

6. A principal, $7000, is invested at 9% interest for 8 years. Determine its future value if the interest is compounded
   (a) annually   (b) semi-annually   (c) monthly   (d) continuously

7. Find the future value of $100 compounded continuously at an annual rate of 6% for 12 years.

8. How long will it take for a sum of money to triple in value if invested at an annual rate of 3% compounded continuously?

9. If a piece of machinery depreciates continuously at an annual rate of 4%, how many years will it take for the value of the machinery to halve?

10. A department store has its own credit card facilities, for which it charges interest at a rate of 2% each month. Explain briefly why this is not the same as an annual rate of 24%. What is the annual percentage rate?

11. Determine the APR if the nominal rate is 7% compounded continuously.

12. Current annual consumption of energy is 78 billion units and this is expected to rise at a fixed rate of 5.8% each year. The capacity of the industry to supply energy is currently 104 billion units.
    (a) Assuming that the supply remains steady, after how many years will demand exceed supply?
    (b) What constant rate of growth of energy production would be needed to satisfy demand for the next 50 years?

13. Find the value, in 2 years time, of $4000 invested at 5% compounded annually. In the following 2 years, the interest rate is expected to rise to 8%. Find the final value of the investment at the end of the 4-year period, and find the overall percentage increase. Give your answers correct to 2 decimal places.

14. Find the APR of a loan if the monthly interest rate is 1.65%. Give your answer correct to 2 decimal places.

15. The future value S of principal P invested for n years with an interest rate $r\%$ compounded annually may be calculated using the formula

$$S = P\left(1 + \frac{r}{100}\right)^n$$

Rearrange this formula to express P in terms of S, r and n.

16. (Excel) A department store charges interest on any outstanding debt at the end of each month. It decides to produce a simple table of APRs for its customers, based on a variety of monthly rates. Use a spreadsheet to produce such a table for monthly interest rates of 0.5%, 0.6%, 0.7%, . . . , 3%. Plot a graph of APR against monthly rate and comment briefly on its basic shape.

Exercise 3.2*

1. A principal of $7650 is invested at a rate of 3.7% compounded annually. After how many years will the investment first exceed $12 250?

2. A principal of $70 000 is invested at 6% interest for 4 years. Find the difference in the future value if the interest is compounded quarterly compared to continuous compounding. Round your answer to 2 decimal places.

3. Midwest Bank offers a return of 5% compounded annually for each and every year. The rival BFB offers a return of 3% for the first year and 7% in the second and subsequent years (both compounded annually). Which bank would you choose to invest in if you decided to invest a principal for **(a)** 2 years; **(b)** 3 years?

4. A car depreciates by 40% in the first year, 30% in the second year and 20% thereafter. I buy a car for $14 700 when it is 2 years old.

(a) How much did it cost when new?

(b) After how many years will it be worth less than 25% of the amount that I paid for it?

5. The population of a country is currently at 56 million and is forecast to rise by 3.7% each year. It is capable of producing 2500 million units of food each year, and it is estimated that each member of the population requires a minimum of 65 units of food each year. At the moment, the extra food needed to satisfy this requirement is imported, but the government decides to increase food production at a constant rate each year, with the aim of making the country self-sufficient after 10 years. Find the annual rate of growth required to achieve this.

6. If a principal, P, is invested at $r\%$ interest compounded annually then its future value, S, after n years is given by

$$S = P\left(1 + \frac{r}{100}\right)^n$$

(a) Use this formula to show that if an interest rate of $r\%$ is compounded k times a year then after t years

$$S = P\left(1 + \frac{r}{100k}\right)^{kt}$$

(b) Show that if $m = 100k/r$ then the formula in part (1) can be written as

$$S = P\left(\left(1 + \frac{1}{m}\right)^m\right)^{rt/100}$$

(c) Use the definition

$$e = \lim_{m \to \infty}\left(1 + \frac{1}{m}\right)^m$$

to deduce that if the interest is compounded with ever-increasing frequency (that is, continuously) then

$$S = Pe^{rt/100}$$

7. World oil reserves are currently estimated to be 600 billion units. If this quantity is reduced by 8% a year, after how many years will oil reserves drop below 100 billion units?

8. The nominal rate of interest of a store card is 18% compounded monthly.

(a) State the monthly interest rate.

(b) Find the equivalent annual rate of interest if the compounding is continuous. Round your answer to 2 decimal places.

9. **(Excel)** The sum of $100 is invested at 12% interest for 20 years. Tabulate the value of the investment at the end of each year, if the interest is compounded

(a) annually   **(b)** quarterly   **(c)** monthly   **(d)** continuously

Draw graphs of these values on the same diagram. Comment briefly on any similarities and differences between these graphs.

CHAPTER 4
Differentiation

This chapter provides a simple introduction to the general topic of calculus. In fact, 'calculus' is a Latin word and a literal translation of it is 'stone'. Unfortunately, all too many students interpret this as meaning a heavy millstone that they have to carry around with them! However, as we shall see, the techniques of calculus actually provide us with a quick way of performing calculations. (The process of counting was originally performed using stones a long time ago.)

There are eight sections, which should be read in the order that they appear. It should be possible to omit Sections 4.5 and 4.7 at a first reading and Section 4.6 can be read any time after Section 4.3.

Section 4.1 provides a leisurely introduction to the basic idea of differentiation. The material is explained using pictures, which will help you to understand the connection between the underlying mathematics and the economic applications in later sections.

There are six rules of differentiation, which are evenly split between Sections 4.2 and 4.4. Section 4.2 considers the easy rules that all students will need to know. However, if you are on a business studies or accountancy course, or are on a low-level economics route, then the more advanced rules in Section 4.4 may not be of relevance and could be ignored. As far as possible, examples given in later sections and chapters are based on the easy rules only so that such students are not disadvantaged. However, the more advanced rules are essential to any proper study of mathematical economics and their use in deriving general results is unavoidable.

Sections 4.3 and 4.5 describe standard economic applications. Marginal functions associated with revenue, cost, production, consumption and savings functions are all discussed in Section 4.3. The important topic of elasticity is described in Section 4.5. The distinction is made between price elasticity along an arc and price elasticity at a point. Familiar results involving general linear demand functions and the relationship between price elasticity of demand and revenue are derived.

Sections 4.6 and 4.7 are devoted to the topic of optimization, which is used to find the maximum and minimum values of economic functions. In the first half of Section 4.6 we concentrate on the mathematical technique. The second half contains four examination-type problems, all taken from economics, which are solved in detail. In Section 4.7, mathematics is used to derive general results relating to the optimization of profit and production functions.

The final section revises two important mathematical functions, namely the exponential and natural logarithm functions. We describe how to differentiate these functions and illustrate their use in economics.

Differentiation is probably the most important topic in the whole book, and one that we shall continue in Chapters 5 and 6, since it provides the necessary background theory for much of mathematical economics. You are therefore advised to make every effort to attempt the problems given in each section. The prerequisites include an understanding of the concept of a function together with the ability to manipulate algebraic expressions. These are covered in Chapters 1 and 2, and if you have worked successfully through this material, you should find that you are in good shape to begin calculus.

SECTION 4.1
The derivative of a function

Objectives

At the end of this section you should be able to:

- Find the slope of a straight line given any two points on the line.
- Detect whether a line is uphill, downhill or horizontal using the sign of the slope.
- Recognize the notation $f'(x)$ and dy/dx for the derivative of a function.
- Estimate the derivative of a function by measuring the slope of a tangent.
- Differentiate power functions.

This introductory section is designed to get you started with differential calculus in a fairly painless way. There are really only three things that we are going to do. We discuss the basic idea of something called a derived function, give you two equivalent pieces of notation to describe it and finally show you how to write down a formula for the derived function in simple cases.

In Chapter 1 the slope of a straight line was defined to be the change in the value of y brought about by a 1 unit increase in x. In fact, it is not necessary to restrict the change in x to a 1 unit increase. More generally, the **slope**, or **gradient**, of a line is taken to be the change in y divided by the corresponding change in x as you move between any two points on the line. It is customary to denote the change in y by Δy, where Δ is the Greek letter 'delta'.

Likewise, the change in x is written Δx. In this notation we have

$$\text{slope} = \frac{\Delta y}{\Delta x}$$

Example

Find the slope of the straight line passing through

(a) A $(1, 2)$ and B $(3, 4)$ **(b)** A $(1, 2)$ and C $(4, 1)$ **(c)** A $(1, 2)$ and D $(5, 2)$

Solution

(a) Points A and B are sketched in Figure 4.1. As we move from A to B, the y coordinate changes from 2 to 4, which is an increase of 2 units, and the x coordinate changes from 1 to 3, which is also an increase of 2 units. Hence

$$\text{slope} = \frac{\Delta y}{\Delta x} = \frac{4-2}{3-1} = \frac{2}{2} = 1$$

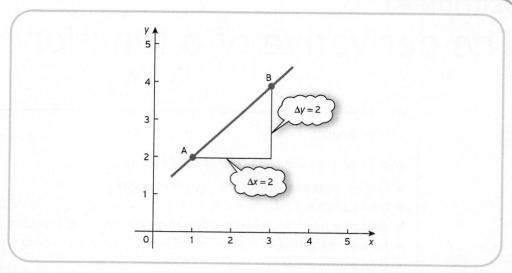

Figure 4.1

(b) Points A and C are sketched in Figure 4.2. As we move from A to C, the y coordinate changes from 2 to 1, which is a decrease of 1 unit, and the x coordinate changes from 1 to 4, which is an increase of 3 units. Hence

$$\text{slope} = \frac{\Delta y}{\Delta x} = \frac{1-2}{4-1} = \frac{-1}{3}$$

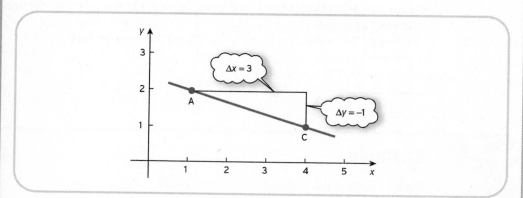

Figure 4.2

(c) Points A and D are sketched in Figure 4.3. As we move from A to D, the y coordinate remains fixed at 2, and the x coordinate changes from 1 to 5, which is an increase of 4 units. Hence

$$\text{slope} = \frac{\Delta y}{\Delta x} = \frac{2-2}{5-1} = \frac{0}{4} = 0$$

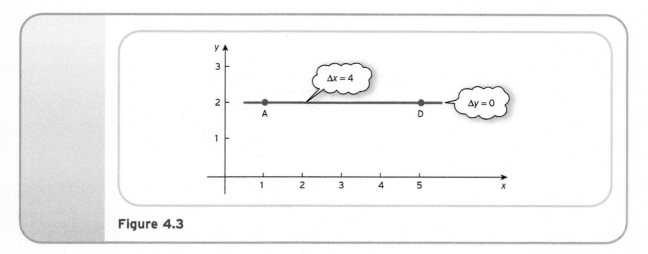

Figure 4.3

Practice Problem

1. Find the slope of the straight line passing through

(a) E (−1, 3) and F (3, 11)   (b) E (−1, 3) and G (4, −2)   (c) E (−1, 3) and H (49, 3)

From these examples we see that the gradient is positive if the line is uphill, negative if the line is downhill and zero if the line is horizontal.

Unfortunately, not all functions in economics are linear, so it is necessary to extend the definition of slope to include more general curves. To do this we need the idea of a tangent, which is illustrated in Figure 4.4.

A straight line which passes through a point on a curve and which just touches the curve at this point is called a **tangent**. The slope, or gradient, of a curve at $x = a$ is then defined to be that of the tangent at $x = a$. Since we have already seen how to find the slope of a straight line, this gives us a precise way of measuring the slope of a curve. A simple curve together with a selection of tangents at various points is shown in Figure 4.5 (overleaf). Notice how each tangent passes through exactly one point on the curve and strikes a glancing blow. In this case, the slopes of the tangents increase as we move from left to right along the curve. This reflects the fact that the curve is flat at $x = 0$ but becomes progressively steeper further away.

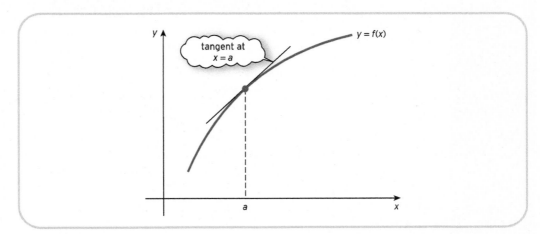

Figure 4.4

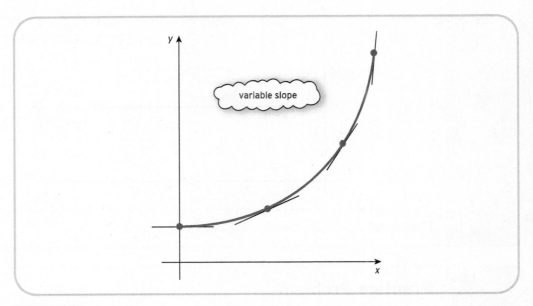

Figure 4.5

This highlights an important difference between the slope of a straight line and the slope of a curve. In the case of a straight line, the gradient is fixed throughout its length and it is immaterial which two points on a line are used to find it. For example, in Figure 4.6 all of the ratios $\Delta y/\Delta x$ have the value $1/2$. However, as we have just seen, the slope of a curve varies as we move along it. In mathematics we use the symbol

$$f'(a) \qquad \text{read 'f dashed of a'}$$

to represent the slope of the graph of a function f at $x = a$. This notation conveys the maximum amount of information with the minimum of fuss. As usual, we need the label f to denote which function we are considering. We certainly need the a to tell us at which point on the curve the gradient is being measured. Finally, the 'prime' symbol ' is used to distinguish the gradient from the function value. The notation $f(a)$ gives the height of the curve above the x axis at $x = a$, whereas $f'(a)$ gives the gradient of the curve at this point.

The slope of the graph of a function is called the **derivative** of the function. It is interesting to notice that corresponding to each value of x there is a uniquely defined derivative $f'(x)$. In other

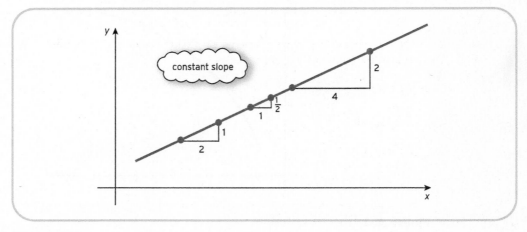

Figure 4.6

words, the rule 'find the slope of the graph of f at x' defines a function. This slope function is usually referred to as the **derived function**. An alternative notation for the derived function is

$$\frac{dy}{dx}$$ read 'dee y by dee x'

Historically, this symbol arose from the corresponding notation $\Delta y / \Delta x$ for the gradient of a straight line; the letter 'd' is the English equivalent of the Greek letter Δ. However, it is important to realize that

$$\frac{dy}{dx}$$

does not mean 'dy divided by dx'. It should be thought of as a single symbol representing the derivative of y with respect to x. It is immaterial which notation is used, although the context may well suggest which is more appropriate. For example, if we use

$$y = x^2$$

to identify the square function then it is natural to use

$$\frac{dy}{dx}$$

for the derived function. On the other hand, if we use

$$f(x) = x^2$$

then $f'(x)$ seems more appropriate.

Example

Complete the following table of function values and hence sketch an accurate graph of $f(x) = x^2$.

x	−2.0	−1.5	−1.0	−0.5	0.0	0.5	1.0	1.5	2.0
$f(x)$									

Draw the tangents to the graph at $x = -1.5, -0.5, 0, 0.5$ and 1.5. Hence estimate the values of $f'(-1.5), f'(-0.5), f'(0), f'(0.5)$ and $f'(1.5)$.

Solution

Using a calculator we obtain

x	−2.0	−1.5	−1.0	−0.5	0.0	0.5	1.0	1.5	2.0
$f(x)$	4	2.25	1	0.25	0	0.25	1	2.25	4

The corresponding graph of the square function is sketched in Figure 4.7. From the graph we see that the slopes of the tangents are

$$f'(-1.5) = \frac{-1.5}{0.5} = -3$$

$$f'(-0.5) = \frac{-1.5}{0.5} = -1$$

$$f'(0) = 0$$

$$f'(0.5) = \frac{0.5}{0.5} = 1$$

$$f'(1.5) = \frac{1.5}{0.5} = 3$$

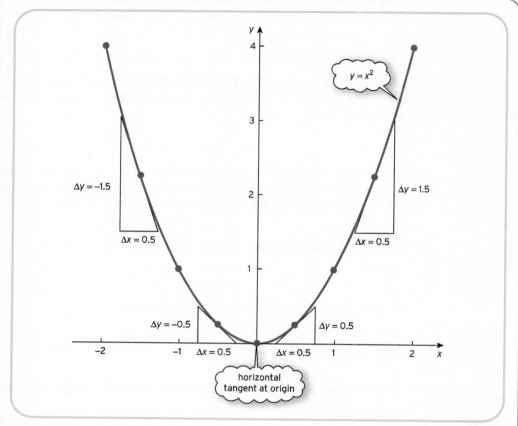

Figure 4.7

The value of $f'(0)$ is zero because the tangent is horizontal at $x = 0$. Notice that

$$f'(-1.5) = -f'(1.5) \quad \text{and} \quad f'(-0.5) = -f'(0.5)$$

This is to be expected because the graph is symmetric about the y axis. The slopes of the tangents to the left of the y axis have the same size as those of the corresponding tangents to the right. However, they have opposite signs since the curve slopes downhill on one side and uphill on the other.

Practice Problem

2. Complete the following table of function values and hence sketch an accurate graph of $f(x) = x^3$.

x	−1.50	−1.25	−1.00	−0.75	−0.50	−0.25	0.00
$f(x)$		−1.95			−0.13		

x	0.25	0.50	0.75	1.00	1.25	1.50
$f(x)$		0.13			1.95	

Draw the tangents to the graph at $x = -1$, 0 and 1. Hence estimate the values of $f'(-1)$, $f'(0)$ and $f'(1)$.

Practice Problem 2 should convince you how hard it is in practice to calculate $f'(a)$ exactly using graphs. It is impossible to sketch a perfectly smooth curve using graph paper and pencil, and it is equally difficult to judge, by eye, precisely where the tangent should be. There is also the problem of measuring the vertical and horizontal distances required for the slope of the tangent. These inherent errors may compound to produce quite inaccurate values for $f'(a)$. Fortunately, there is a really simple formula that can be used to find $f'(a)$ when f is a power function. It can be proved that

$$\boxed{\text{if } f(x) = x^n \text{ then } f'(x) = nx^{n-1}}$$

or, equivalently,

$$\boxed{\text{if } y = x^n \text{ then } \frac{dy}{dx} = nx^{n-1}}$$

The process of finding the derived function symbolically (rather than using graphs) is known as **differentiation**. In order to differentiate x^n all that needs to be done is to bring the power down to the front and then to subtract 1 from the power:

x^n differentiates to nx^{n-1}

subtract 1 from the power

bring down the power

To differentiate the square function we set $n = 2$ in this formula to deduce that

$f(x) = x^2$ differentiates to $f'(x) = 2x^{2-1}$

subtract 1

the 2 comes down

that is,

$$f'(x) = 2x^1 = 2x$$

Using this result we see that

$$f'(-1.5) = 2 \times (-1.5) = -3$$
$$f'(-0.5) = 2 \times (-0.5) = -1$$
$$f'(0) = 2 \times (0) = 0$$
$$f'(0.5) = 2 \times (0.5) = 1$$
$$f'(1.5) = 2 \times (1.5) = 3$$

which are in agreement with the results obtained graphically in the preceding example.

Practice Problem

3. If $f(x) = x^3$ write down a formula for $f'(x)$. Calculate $f'(-1)$, $f'(0)$ and $f'(1)$. Confirm that these are in agreement with your rough estimates obtained in Practice Problem 2.

Example

Differentiate

(a) $y = x^4$ **(b)** $y = x^{10}$ **(c)** $y = x$ **(d)** $y = 1$ **(e)** $y = 1/x^4$ **(f)** $y = \sqrt{x}$

Solution

(a) To differentiate $y = x^4$ we bring down the power (that is, 4) to the front and then subtract 1 from the power (that is, $4 - 1 = 3$) to deduce that

$$\frac{dy}{dx} = 4x^3$$

(b) Similarly,

$$\text{if } y = x^{10} \text{ then } \frac{dy}{dx} = 10x^9$$

(c) To use the general formula to differentiate x we first need to express $y = x$ in the form $y = x^n$ for some number n. In this case $n = 1$ because $x^1 = x$, so

$$\frac{dy}{dx} = 1x^0 = 1 \text{ since } x^0 = 1$$

This result is also obvious from the graph of $y = x$ sketched in Figure 4.8.

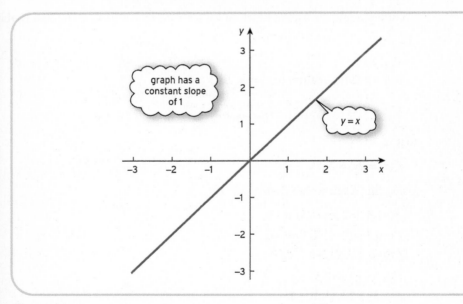

Figure 4.8

(d) Again, to differentiate 1 we need to express $y = 1$ in the form $y = x^n$. In this case $n = 0$ because $x^0 = 1$, so

$$\frac{dy}{dx} = 0x^{-1} = 0$$

This result is also obvious from the graph of $y = 1$ sketched in Figure 4.9.

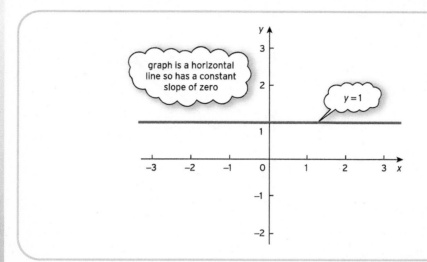

Figure 4.9

(e) Noting that $1/x^4 = x^{-4}$ it follows that

$$\text{if } y = \frac{1}{x^4} \text{ then } \frac{dy}{dx} = -4x^{-5} = -\frac{4}{x^5}$$

The power has decreased to −5 because −4 − 1 = −5.

(f) Noting that $\sqrt{x} = x^{1/2}$ it follows that if

$$y = \sqrt{x} \text{ then } \frac{dy}{dx} = \frac{1}{2}x^{-1/2}$$

$$= \frac{1}{2x^{1/2}}$$ negative powers denote reciprocals

$$= \frac{1}{2\sqrt{x}}$$ fractional powers denote roots

The power has decreased to −½ because ½ − 1 = −½.

Practice Problem

4. Differentiate

    (a) $y = x^5$ **(b)** $y = x^6$ **(c)** $y = x^{100}$ **(d)** $y = 1/x$ **(e)** $y = 1/x^2$

    [Hint: in parts (d) and (e) note that $1/x = x^{-1}$ and $1/x^2 = x^{-2}$]

In more advanced books on mathematics the derivative is defined via the concept of a limit and is usually written in symbols as

$$\frac{dy}{dx} = \lim_{\Delta x \to 0} \frac{\Delta y}{\Delta x}$$

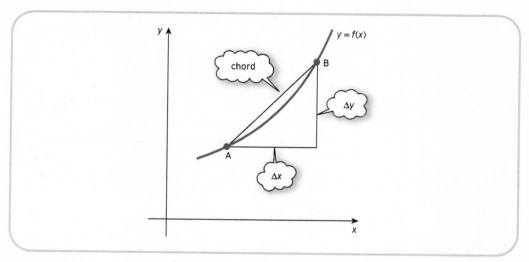

Figure 4.10

We have deliberately not introduced the derivative to you in this way because the notation can appear frightening to non-mathematics specialists. Look at Figure 4.10. Points A and B both lie on the curve $y = f(x)$ and their x and y coordinates differ by Δx and Δy respectively. A line AB which joins two points on the curve is known as a **chord** and it has slope $\Delta y/\Delta x$.

Now look at Figure 4.11, which shows a variety of chords, AB_1, AB_2, AB_3, ..., corresponding to smaller and smaller 'widths' Δx. As the right-hand end points, B_1, B_2, B_3, ..., get closer to A, the 'width', Δx, tends to zero. More significantly, the slope of the chord gets closer to that of the tangent at A. We describe this by saying that in the limit, as Δx tends to zero, the slope of the chord, $\Delta y/\Delta x$, is equal to that of the tangent. This limit is written

$$\lim_{\Delta x \to 0} \frac{\Delta y}{\Delta x}$$

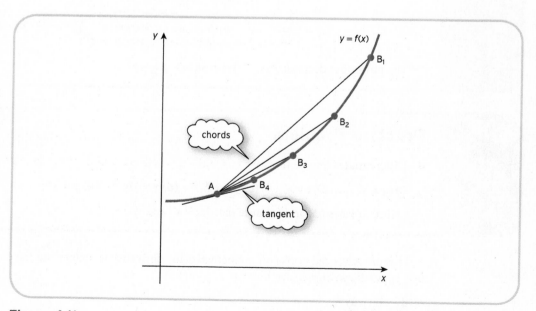

Figure 4.11

We deduce that the formal definition

$$\frac{dy}{dx} = \lim_{\Delta x \to 0} \frac{\Delta y}{\Delta x}$$

coincides with the idea that dy/dx represents the slope of the tangent, which is the approach adopted in this book.

Advice

If you have met differentiation before, you might be interested in using this definition to prove results. You are advised to consult Appendix 1 on the website.

Key Terms

Chord   A line joining two points on a curve.

Derivative   The gradient of the tangent to a curve at a point. The derivative at $x = a$ is written $f'(a)$.

Derived function   The rule, f', which gives the gradient of a function, f, at a general point.

Differentiation   The process or operation of determining the first derivative of a function.

Gradient   The gradient of a line measures steepness and is the vertical change divided by the horizontal change between any two points on the line. The gradient of a curve at a point is that of the tangent at that point.

Slope   An alternative word for gradient.

Tangent   A line that just touches a curve at a point.

Exercise 4.1

1. Find the slope of the straight line passing through
   (a) $(2, 5)$ and $(4, 9)$ **(b)** $(3, -1)$ and $(7, -5)$ **(c)** $(7, 19)$ and $(4, 19)$

2. Verify that the points $(0, 2)$ and $(3, 0)$ lie on the line
   $$2x + 3y = 6$$
   Hence find the slope of this line. Is the line uphill, downhill or horizontal?

3. Sketch the graph of the function
   $$f(x) = 5$$
   Explain why it follows from this that
   $$f'(x) = 0$$

4. Differentiate the function
   $$f(x) = x^7$$

Hence calculate the slope of the graph of

$$y = x^7$$

at the point $x = 2$.

5. Differentiate

(a) $y = x^8$ (b) $y = x^{50}$ (c) $y = x^{19}$ (d) $y = x^{999}$

6. Differentiate the following functions, giving your answer in a similar form, without negative or fractional indices:

(a) $f(x) = \dfrac{1}{x^3}$ (b) $f(x) = \sqrt{x}$ (c) $f(x) = \dfrac{1}{\sqrt{x}}$ (d) $y = x\sqrt{x}$

7. Complete the following table of function values for the function, $f(x) = x^2 - 2x$:

x	−1	−0.5	0	0.5	1	1.5	2	2.5
$x^2 - 2x$								

Sketch the graph of this function and, by measuring the slope of the tangents, estimate

(a) $f'(-0.5)$ (b) $f'(1)$ (c) $f'(1.5)$

Exercise 4.1*

1. Verify that the points $(0, b)$ and $(1, a + b)$ lie on the line

$$y = ax + b$$

Hence show that this line has slope a.

2. Differentiate each of the following functions expressing your answer in a similar form:

(a) $y = x^{15}$ (b) $x^4\sqrt{x}$ (c) $y = \sqrt[3]{x}$ (d) $\dfrac{1}{\sqrt[4]{x}}$ (e) $\dfrac{\sqrt{x}}{x^7}$

3. For each of the graphs

(a) $y = \sqrt{x}$ (b) $y = x\sqrt{x}$ (c) $y = \dfrac{1}{\sqrt{x}}$

A is the point where $x = 4$, and B is the point where $x = 4.1$. In each case find

(i)   the y coordinates of A and B

(ii) the gradient of the chord AB

(iii) the value of $\dfrac{dy}{dx}$ at A.

Compare your answers to parts (ii) and (iii).

4. Find the coordinates of the point(s) at which the curve has the specified gradient.

(a) $y = x^{2/3}$, gradient $= \dfrac{1}{3}$ (b) $y = x^5$, gradient $= 405$

(c) $y = \dfrac{1}{x^2}$, gradient $= 16$ (d) $y = \dfrac{1}{x\sqrt{x}}$, gradient $= -\dfrac{3}{64}$

SECTION 4.2
Rules of differentiation

Objectives

At the end of this section you should be able to:

- Use the constant rule to differentiate a function of the form $cf(x)$.
- Use the sum rule to differentiate a function of the form $f(x) + g(x)$.
- Use the difference rule to differentiate a function of the form $f(x) - g(x)$.
- Evaluate and interpret second-order derivatives.

Advice

In this section we consider three elementary rules of differentiation. Subsequent sections of this chapter describe various applications to economics. However, before you can tackle these successfully, you must have a thorough grasp of the basic techniques involved. The problems in this section are repetitive in nature. This is deliberate. Although the rules themselves are straightforward, it is necessary for you to practise them over and over again before you can become proficient in using them. In fact, you will not be able to get much further with the rest of this book until you have mastered the rules of this section.

Rule 1 The constant rule

If $h(x) = cf(x)$ then $h'(x) = cf'(x)$

for any constant c.

This rule tells you how to find the derivative of a constant multiple of a function:

> differentiate the function and multiply by the constant

Example

Differentiate

(a) $y = 2x^4$ **(b)** $y = 10x$

Solution

(a) To differentiate $2x^4$ we first differentiate x^4 to get $4x^3$ and then multiply by 2. Hence

If $y = 2x^4$ then $\dfrac{dy}{dx} = 2(4x^3) = 8x^3$

(b) To differentiate $10x$ we first differentiate x to get 1 and then multiply by 10. Hence

If $y = 10x$ then $\dfrac{dy}{dx} = 10(1) = 10$

Practice Problem

1. Differentiate

   (a) $y = 4x^3$ **(b)** $y = 2/x$

The constant rule can be used to show that

> constants differentiate to zero

To see this, note that the equation

$$y = c$$

is the same as

$$y = cx^0$$

because $x^0 = 1$. By the constant rule we first differentiate x^0 to get $0x^{-1}$ and then multiply by c. Hence

$$\text{if } y = c \quad \text{then} \quad \frac{dy}{dx} = c(0x^{-1}) = 0$$

This result is also apparent from the graph of $y = c$, sketched in Figure 4.12, which is a horizontal line c units away from the x axis. It is an important result and explains why lone constants lurking in mathematical expressions disappear when differentiated.

Rule 2 The sum rule

$$\text{If } h(x) = f(x) + g(x) \quad \text{then} \quad h'(x) = f'(x) + g'(x)$$

This rule tells you how to find the derivative of the sum of two functions:

> differentiate each function separately and add

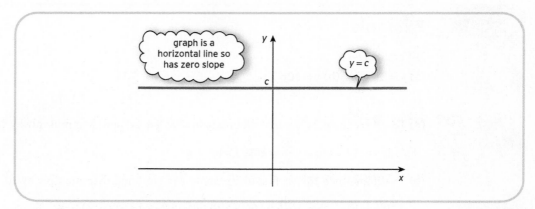

Figure 4.12

Example

Differentiate

(a) $y = x^2 + x^{50}$ **(b)** $y = x^3 + 3$

Solution

(a) To differentiate $x^2 + x^{50}$ we need to differentiate x^2 and x^{50} separately and add. Now

x^2 differentiates to $2x$

and

x^{50} differentiates to $50x^{49}$

so

if $y = x^2 + x^{50}$ then $\dfrac{dy}{dx} = 2x + 50x^{49}$

(b) To differentiate $x^3 + 3$ we need to differentiate x^3 and 3 separately and add. Now

x^3 differentiates to $3x^2$

and

3 differentiates to 0

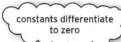

constants differentiate to zero

so

if $y = x^3 + 3$ then $\dfrac{dy}{dx} = 3x^2 + 0 = 3x^2$

Practice Problem

2. Differentiate
(a) $y = x^5 + x$ **(b)** $y = x^2 + 5$

Rule 3 The difference rule

If $h(x) = f(x) - g(x)$ then $h'(x) = f'(x) - g'(x)$

This rule tells you how to find the derivative of the difference of two functions:

differentiate each function separately and subtract

Example

Differentiate

(a) $y = x^5 - x^2$ **(b)** $y = x - \dfrac{1}{x^2}$

Solution

(a) To differentiate $x^5 - x^2$ we need to differentiate x^5 and x^2 separately and subtract. Now

x^5 differentiates to $5x^4$

and

x^2 differentiates to $2x$

so

if $y = x^5 - x^2$ then $\dfrac{dy}{dx} = 5x^4 - 2x$

(b) To differentiate $x - \dfrac{1}{x^2}$ we need to differentiate x and $\dfrac{1}{x^2}$ separately and subtract. Now

x differentiates to 1

and

$\dfrac{1}{x^2}$ differentiates to $-\dfrac{2}{x^3}$ 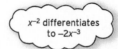

x^{-2} differentiates to $-2x^{-3}$

so

if $y = x - \dfrac{1}{x^2}$ then $\dfrac{dy}{dx} = 1 - \left(-\dfrac{2}{x^3}\right) = 1 + \dfrac{2}{x^3}$

Practice Problem

3. Differentiate

    (a) $y = x^2 - x^3$ **(b)** $y = 50 - \dfrac{1}{x^3}$

It is possible to combine these three rules and so to find the derivative of more involved functions, as the following example demonstrates.

Example

Differentiate

(a) $y = 3x^5 + 2x^3$ **(b)** $y = x^3 + 7x^2 - 2x + 10$ **(c)** $y = 2\sqrt{x} + \dfrac{3}{x}$

Solution

(a) The sum rule shows that to differentiate $3x^5 + 2x^3$ we need to differentiate $3x^5$ and $2x^3$ separately and add. By the constant rule

$$3x^5 \quad \text{differentiates to} \quad 3(5x^4) = 15x^4$$

and

$$2x^3 \quad \text{differentiates to} \quad 2(3x^2) = 6x^2$$

so

$$\text{if } y = 3x^5 + 2x^3 \quad \text{then} \quad \frac{dy}{dx} = 15x^4 + 6x^2$$

With practice you will soon find that you can just write the derivative down in a single line of working by differentiating term by term. For the function

$$y = 3x^5 + 2x^3$$

we could just write

$$\frac{dy}{dx} = 3(5x^4) + 2(3x^2) = 15x^4 + 6x^2$$

(b) So far we have only considered expressions comprising at most two terms. However, the sum and difference rules still apply to lengthier expressions, so we can differentiate term by term as before. For the function

$$y = x^3 + 7x^2 - 2x + 10$$

we get

$$\frac{dy}{dx} = 3x^2 + 7(2x) - 2(1) + 0 = 3x^2 + 14x - 2$$

(c) To differentiate

$$y = 2\sqrt{x} + \frac{3}{x}$$

we first rewrite it using the notation of indices as

$$y = 2x^{1/2} + 3x^{-1}$$

Differentiating term by term then gives

$$\frac{dy}{dx} = 2\left(\frac{1}{2}\right)x^{-1/2} + 3(-1)x^{-2} = x^{-1/2} - 3x^{-2}$$

which can be written in the more familiar form

$$= \frac{1}{\sqrt{x}} - \frac{3}{x^2}$$

Practice Problem

4. Differentiate

(a) $y = 9x^5 + 2x^2$

(b) $y = 5x^8 - \dfrac{3}{x}$

(c) $y = x^2 + 6x + 3$

(d) $y = 2x^4 + 12x^3 - 4x^2 + 7x - 400$

Whenever a function is differentiated, the thing that you end up with is itself a function. This suggests the possibility of differentiating a second time to get the 'slope of the slope function'. This is written as

$f''(x)$ 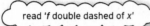 read 'f double dashed of x'

or

$\dfrac{d^2 y}{dx^2}$ read 'dee two y by dee x squared'

For example, if

$f(x) = 5x^2 - 7x + 12$

then differentiating once gives

$f'(x) = 10x - 7$

and if we now differentiate $f'(x)$ we get

$f''(x) = 10$

The function $f'(x)$ is called the **first-order derivative** and $f''(x)$ is called the **second-order derivative**.

Example

Evaluate $f''(1)$ where

$f(x) = x^7 + \dfrac{1}{x}$

Solution

To find $f''(1)$ we need to differentiate

$f(x) = x^7 + x^{-1}$

twice and put $x = 1$ into the end result. Differentiating once gives

$f'(x) = 7x^6 + (-1)x^{-2} = 7x^6 - x^{-2}$

and differentiating a second time gives

$f''(x) = 7(6x^5) - (-2)x^{-3} = 42x^5 + 2x^{-3}$

Finally, substituting $x = 1$ into

$f''(x) = 42x^5 + \dfrac{2}{x^3}$

gives

$f''(1) = 42 + 2 = 44$

Practice Problem

5. Evaluate $f''(6)$ where

$$f(x) = 4x^3 - 5x^2$$

It is possible to give a graphical interpretation of the sign of the second-order derivative. Remember that the first-order derivative, $f'(x)$, measures the gradient of a curve. If the derivative of $f'(x)$ is positive (that is, if $f''(x) > 0$) then $f'(x)$ is increasing. This means that the graph gets steeper as you move from left to right and so the curve bends upwards. On the other hand, if $f''(x) < 0$, the gradient, $f'(x)$ must be decreasing, so the curve bends downwards. These two cases are illustrated in Figure 4.13. For this function, $f''(x) < 0$ to the left of $x = a$, and $f''(x) > 0$ to the right of $x = a$. At $x = a$ itself, the curve changes from bending downwards to bending upwards and at this point, $f''(a) = 0$.

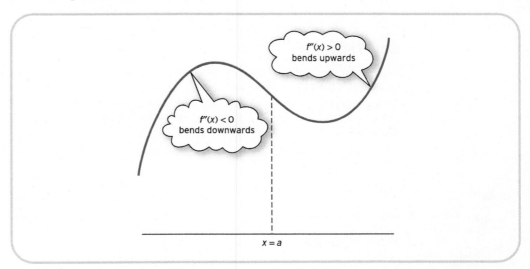

Figure 4.13

Example

Use the second-order derivative to show that the graph of the quadratic

$$y = ax^2 + bx + c$$

bends upwards when $a > 0$ and bends downwards when $a < 0$.

Solution

If $y = ax^2 + bx + c$ then $\dfrac{dy}{dx} = 2ax + b$ and $\dfrac{d^2y}{dx^2} = 2a$

If $a > 0$ then $\dfrac{d^2y}{dx^2} = 2a > 0$ so the parabola bends upwards

If $a < 0$ then $\dfrac{d^2y}{dx^2} = 2a < 0$ so the parabola bends downwards

Of course, if $a = 0$, the equation reduces to $y = bx + c$, which is the equation of a straight line, so the graph bends neither upwards nor downwards.

Throughout this section the functions have all been of the form $y = f(x)$, where the letters x and y denote the variables involved. In economic functions, different symbols are used. It should be obvious, however, that we can still differentiate such functions by applying the rules of this section. For example, if a supply function is given by

$$Q = P^2 + 3P + 1$$

and we need to find the derivative of Q with respect to P then we can apply the sum and difference rules to obtain

$$\frac{dQ}{dP} = 2P + 3$$

Key Terms

First-order derivative   The rate of change of a function with respect to its independent variable. It is the same as the 'derivative' of a function, $y = f(x)$, and is written as $f'(x)$ or dy/dx.

Second-order derivative   The derivative of the first-order derivative. The expression obtained when the original function, $y = f(x)$, is differentiated twice in succession and is written as $f''(x)$ or d^2y/dx^2.

Exercise 4.2

1. Differentiate ❓

    (a) $y = 5x^2$

    (b) $y = \dfrac{3}{x}$

    (c) $y = 2x + 3$

    (d) $y = x^2 + x + 1$

    (e) $y = x^2 - 3x + 2$

    (f) $y = 3x - \dfrac{7}{x}$

    (g) $y = 2x^3 - 6x^2 + 49x - 54$

    (h) $y = ax + b$

    (i) $y = ax^2 + bx + c$

    (j) $y = 4\sqrt{x} - \dfrac{3}{x} + \dfrac{7}{x^2}$

2. Evaluate $f'(x)$ for each of the following functions at the given point:

    (a) $f(x) = 3x^9$ at $x = 1$

    (b) $f(x) = x^2 - 2x$ at $x = 3$

    (c) $f(x) = x^3 - 4x^2 + 2x - 8$ at $x = 0$

    (d) $f(x) = 5x^4 - \dfrac{4}{x^4}$ at $x = -1$

    (e) $f(x) = \sqrt{x} - \dfrac{2}{x}$ at $x = 4$

3. By writing $x^2\left(x^2 + 2x - \dfrac{5}{x^2}\right) = x^4 + 2x^3 - 5$ differentiate $x^2\left(x^2 + 2x - \dfrac{5}{x^2}\right)$.

Use a similar approach to differentiate

(a) $x^2(3x - 4)$

(b) $x(3x^3 - 2x^2 + 6x - 7)$

(c) $(x + 1)(x - 6)$

(d) $\dfrac{x^2 - 3}{x}$

(e) $\dfrac{x - 4x^2}{x^3}$

(f) $\dfrac{x^2 - 3x + 5}{x^2}$

4. Find expressions for d^2y/dx^2 in the case when

(a) $y = 7x^2 - x$

(b) $y = \dfrac{1}{x^2}$

(c) $y = ax + b$

5. Evaluate $f''(2)$ for the function

$$f(x) = x^3 - 4x^2 + 10x - 7$$

6. If $f(x) = x^2 - 6x + 8$, evaluate $f'(3)$. What information does this provide about the graph of $y = f(x)$ at $x = 3$?

7. By writing $\sqrt{4x} = \sqrt{4} \times \sqrt{x} = 2\sqrt{x}$, differentiate $\sqrt{4x}$.
Use a similar approach to differentiate

(a) $\sqrt{25x}$ **(b)** $\sqrt[3]{27x}$ **(c)** $\sqrt[4]{16x^3}$ **(d)** $\sqrt{\dfrac{25}{x}}$

8. Find expressions for

(a) $\dfrac{dQ}{dP}$ for the supply function $Q = P^2 + P + 1$

(b) $\dfrac{d(TR)}{dQ}$ for the total revenue function $TR = 50Q - 3Q^2$

(c) $\dfrac{d(AC)}{dQ}$ for the average cost function $AC = \dfrac{30}{Q} + 10$

(d) $\dfrac{dC}{dY}$ for the consumption function $C = 3Y + 7$

(e) $\dfrac{dQ}{dL}$ for the production function $Q = 10\sqrt{L}$

(f) $\dfrac{d\pi}{dQ}$ for the profit function $\pi = -2Q^3 + 15Q^2 - 24Q - 3$

Exercise 4.2*

1. Find the value of the first-order derivative of the function

$$y = 3\sqrt{x} - \frac{81}{x} + 13$$

   when $x = 9$.

2. Find expressions for

   (a) $\dfrac{dQ}{dP}$ for the supply function $Q = 2P^2 + P + 1$

   (b) $\dfrac{d(TR)}{dQ}$ for the total revenue function $TR = 40Q - 3Q\sqrt{Q}$

   (c) $\dfrac{d(AC)}{dQ}$ for the average cost function $AC = \dfrac{20}{Q} + 7Q + 25$

   (d) $\dfrac{dC}{dY}$ for the consumption function $C = Y(2Y + 3) + 10$

   (e) $\dfrac{dQ}{dL}$ for the production function $Q = 200L + 4\sqrt[4]{L}$

   (f) $\dfrac{d\pi}{dQ}$ for the profit function $\pi = -Q^3 + 20Q^2 - 7Q - 1$

3. Find the value of the second-order derivative of the following function at the point $x = 4$:

   $$f(x) = -2x^3 + 4x^2 + x - 3$$

   What information does this provide about the shape of the graph of $f(x)$ at this point?

4. Consider the graph of the function

   $$f(x) = 2x^5 - 3x^4 + 2x^2 - 17x + 31$$

   at $x = -1$.
   Giving reasons for your answers,

   (a) state whether the tangent slopes uphill, downhill or is horizontal

   (b) state whether the graph bends downwards or upwards.

5. Use the second-order derivative to show that the graph of the cubic,

   $$f(x) = ax^3 + bx^2 + cx + d \ (a > 0)$$

   bends upwards when $x > -b/3a$ and bends downwards when $x = -b/3a$.

6. Find the equation of the tangent to the curve

   $$y = 4x^3 - 5x^2 + x - 3$$

   at the point where it crosses the y axis.

SECTION 4.3
Marginal functions

Objectives

At the end of this section you should be able to:

- Calculate marginal revenue and marginal cost.
- Derive the relationship between marginal and average revenue for both a monopoly and perfect competition.
- Calculate marginal product of labour.
- State the law of diminishing marginal productivity using the notation of calculus.
- Calculate marginal propensity to consume and marginal propensity to save.

At this stage you may be wondering what on earth differentiation has got to do with economics. In fact, we cannot get very far with economic theory without making use of calculus. In this section we concentrate on three main areas that illustrate its applicability:

- revenue and cost
- production
- consumption and savings.

We consider each of these in turn.

4.3.1 Revenue and cost

In Chapter 2 we investigated the basic properties of the revenue function, TR. It is defined to be PQ, where P denotes the price of a good and Q denotes the quantity demanded. In practice, we usually know the demand equation, which provides a relationship between P and Q. This enables a formula for TR to be written down solely in terms of Q. For example, if

$$P = 100 - 2Q$$

then

$$\text{TR} = PQ = (100 - 2Q)Q = 100Q - 2Q^2$$

The formula can be used to calculate the value of TR corresponding to any value of Q. Not content with this, we are also interested in the effect on TR of a change in the value of Q from some existing level. To do this we introduce the concept of marginal revenue. The **marginal revenue**, MR, of a good is defined by

$$\text{MR} = \frac{\text{d(TR)}}{\text{d}Q}$$

marginal revenue is the derivative of total revenue with respect to demand

For example, the marginal revenue function corresponding to

$$TR = 100Q - 2Q^2$$

is given by

$$\frac{d(TR)}{dQ} = 100 - 4Q$$

If the current demand is 15, say, then

$$MR = 100 - 4(15) = 40$$

You may be familiar with an alternative definition often quoted in elementary economics textbooks. Marginal revenue is sometimes taken to be the change in TR brought about by a 1 unit increase in Q. It is easy to check that this gives an acceptable approximation to MR, although it is not quite the same as the exact value obtained by differentiation. For example, substituting $Q = 15$ into the total revenue function considered previously gives

$$TR = 100(15) - 2(15)^2 = 1050$$

An increase of 1 unit in the value of Q produces a total revenue

$$TR = 100(16) - 2(16)^2 = 1088$$

This is an increase of 38, which, according to the non-calculus definition, is the value of MR when Q is 15. This compares with the exact value of 40 obtained by differentiation.

It is instructive to give a graphical interpretation of these two approaches. In Figure 4.14 the point A lies on the TR curve corresponding to a quantity Q_0. The exact value of MR at this point is equal to the derivative

$$\frac{d(TR)}{dQ}$$

and so is given by the slope of the tangent at A. The point B also lies on the curve but corresponds to a 1 unit increase in Q. The vertical distance from A to B therefore equals the change in TR when Q increases by 1 unit. The slope of the chord joining A and B is

$$\frac{\Delta(TR)}{\Delta Q} = \frac{\Delta(TR)}{1} = \Delta(TR)$$

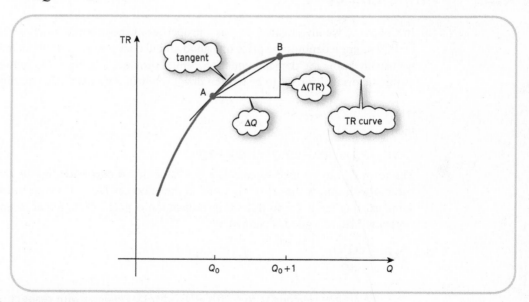

Figure 4.14

In other words, the slope of the chord is equal to the value of MR obtained from the non-calculus definition. Inspection of the diagram reveals that the slope of the tangent is approximately the same as that of the chord joining A and B. In this case the slope of the tangent is slightly the larger of the two, but there is not much in it. We therefore see that the 1 unit increase approach produces a reasonable approximation to the exact value of MR given by

$$\frac{d(TR)}{dQ}$$

Example

If the demand function is

$$P = 120 - 3Q$$

find an expression for TR in terms of Q.
   Find the value of MR at $Q = 10$ using

(a) differentiation

(b) the 1 unit increase approach

Solution

$$TR = PQ = (120 - 3Q)Q = 120Q - 3Q^2$$

(a) The general expression for MR is given by

$$\frac{d(TR)}{dQ} = 120 - 6Q$$

so at $Q = 10$,

$$MR = 120 - 6 \times 10 = 60$$

(b) From the non-calculus definition we need to find the change in TR as Q increases from 10 to 11.

   Putting $Q = 10$ gives $TR = 120 \times 10 - 3 \times 10^2 = 900$

   Putting $Q = 11$ gives $TR = 120 \times 11 - 3 \times 11^2 = 957$

   and so $MR \approx 57$

Practice Problem

1. If the demand function is

$$P = 60 - Q$$

find an expression for TR in terms of Q.

   (1) Differentiate TR with respect to Q to find a general expression for MR in terms of Q. Hence write down the exact value of MR at $Q = 50$.

   (2) Calculate the value of TR when

   (a) $Q = 50$ **(b)** $Q = 51$

   and hence confirm that the 1 unit increase approach gives a reasonable approximation to the exact value of MR obtained in part (1).

The approximation indicated by Figure 4.14 holds for any value of ΔQ. The slope of the tangent at A is the marginal revenue, MR. The slope of the chord joining A and B is $\Delta(TR)/\Delta Q$. It follows that

$$MR \simeq \frac{\Delta(TR)}{\Delta Q}$$

This equation can be transposed to give

$$\Delta(TR) \simeq MR \times \Delta Q \qquad \text{multiply both sides by } \Delta Q$$

that is,

$$\boxed{\text{change in total revenue}} \simeq \boxed{\text{marginal revenue}} \times \boxed{\text{change in demand}}$$

Moreover, Figure 4.14 shows that the smaller the value of ΔQ, the better the approximation becomes. This, of course, is similar to the argument used at the end of Section 4.1 when we discussed the formal definition of a derivative as a limit.

Example

If the total revenue function of a good is given by

$$100Q - Q^2$$

write down an expression for the marginal revenue function. If the current demand is 60, estimate the change in the value of TR due to a 2 unit increase in Q.

Solution

If

$$TR = 100Q - Q^2$$

then

$$MR = \frac{d(TR)}{dQ}$$
$$= 100 - 2Q$$

When $Q = 60$

$$MR = 100 - 2(60) = -20$$

If Q increases by 2 units, $\Delta Q = 2$ and the formula

$$\Delta(TR) \simeq MR \times \Delta Q$$

shows that the change in total revenue is approximately

$$(-20) \times 2 = -40$$

A 2 unit increase in Q therefore leads to a decrease in TR of about 40.

Practice Problem ❓

2. If the total revenue function of a good is given by

$$1000Q - 4Q^2$$

write down an expression for the marginal revenue function. If the current demand is 30, find the approximate change in the value of TR due to a

(a) 3 unit increase in Q

(b) 2 unit decrease in Q.

The simple model of demand, originally introduced in Section 1.5, assumed that price, P, and quantity, Q, are linearly related according to an equation

$$P = aQ + b$$

where the slope, a, is negative and the intercept, b, is positive. A downward-sloping demand curve such as this corresponds to the case of a **monopolist**. A single firm, or possibly a group of firms forming a cartel, is assumed to be the only supplier of a particular product and so has control over the market price. As the firm raises the price, so demand falls. The associated total revenue function is given by

$$\begin{aligned} TR &= PQ \\ &= (aQ + b)Q \\ &= aQ^2 + bQ \end{aligned}$$

An expression for marginal revenue is obtained by differentiating TR with respect to Q to get

$$MR = 2aQ + b$$

It is interesting to notice that, on the assumption of a linear demand equation, the marginal revenue is also linear with the same intercept, b, but with slope $2a$. The marginal revenue curve slopes downhill exactly twice as fast as the demand curve. This is illustrated in Figure 4.15(a).

The **average revenue**, AR, is defined by

$$AR = \frac{TR}{Q}$$

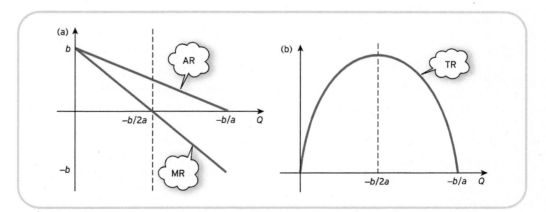

Figure 4.15

and, since TR = PQ, we have

$$AR = \frac{PQ}{Q} = P$$

For this reason the demand curve is labelled average revenue in Figure 4.15(a). The above derivation of the result AR = P is independent of the particular demand function. Consequently, the terms 'average revenue curve' and 'demand curve' are synonymous.

Figure 4.15(a) shows that the marginal revenue takes both positive and negative values. This is to be expected. The total revenue function is a quadratic and its graph has the familiar parabolic shape indicated in Figure 4.15(b). To the left of $-b/2a$ the graph is uphill, corresponding to a positive value of marginal revenue, whereas to the right of this point it is downhill, giving a negative value of marginal revenue. More significantly, at the maximum point of the TR curve, the tangent is horizontal with zero slope and so MR is zero.

At the other extreme from a monopolist is the case of **perfect competition**. For this model we assume that there are a large number of firms all selling an identical product and that there are no barriers to entry into the industry. Since any individual firm produces a tiny proportion of the total output, it has no control over price. The firm can sell only at the prevailing market price and, because the firm is relatively small, it can sell any number of goods at this price. If the fixed price is denoted by b then the demand function is

$$P = b$$

and the associated total revenue function is

$$TR = PQ = bQ$$

An expression for marginal revenue is obtained by differentiating TR with respect to Q and, since b is just a constant, we see that

$$MR = b$$

In the case of perfect competition, the average and marginal revenue curves are the same. They are horizontal straight lines, b units above the Q axis as shown in Figure 4.16.

So far we have concentrated on the total revenue function. Exactly the same principle can be used for other economic functions. For instance, we define the **marginal cost**, MC, by

$$MC = \frac{d(TC)}{dQ}$$

> **marginal cost is the derivative of total cost with respect to output**

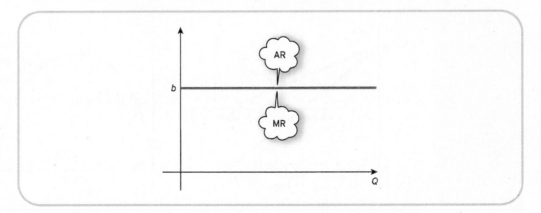

Figure 4.16

Again, using a simple geometrical argument, it is easy to see that if Q changes by a small amount ΔQ then the corresponding change in TC is given by

$$\Delta(\text{TC}) \simeq \text{MC} \times \Delta Q$$

$$\boxed{\text{change in total cost}} \simeq \boxed{\text{marginal cost}} \times \boxed{\text{change in output}}$$

In particular, putting $\Delta Q = 1$ gives

$$\Delta(\text{TC}) \simeq \text{MC}$$

so that MC gives the approximate change in TC when Q increases by 1 unit.

Example

If the average cost function of a good is

$$\text{AC} = 2Q + 6 + \frac{13}{Q}$$

find an expression for MC. If the current output is 15, estimate the effect on TC of a 3 unit decrease in Q.

Solution

We first need to find an expression for TC using the given formula for AC. Now we know that the average cost is just the total cost divided by Q: that is,

$$\text{AC} = \frac{\text{TC}}{Q}$$

Hence

$$\text{TC} = (\text{AC})Q$$
$$= \left(2Q + 6 + \frac{13}{Q}\right)Q$$

and, after multiplying out the brackets, we get

$$\text{TC} = 2Q^2 + 6Q + 13$$

In this formula the last term, 13, is independent of Q so must denote the fixed costs. The remaining part, $2Q^2 + 6Q$, depends on Q so represents the total variable costs. Differentiating gives

$$\text{MC} = \frac{d(\text{TC})}{dQ}$$
$$= 4Q + 6$$

Notice that because the fixed costs are constant they differentiate to zero and so have no effect on the marginal cost. When $Q = 15$,

$$\text{MC} = 4(15) + 6 = 66$$

Also, if Q decreases by 3 units then $\Delta Q = -3$. Hence the change in TC is given by

$$\Delta(\text{TC}) \simeq \text{MC} \times \Delta Q = 66 \times (-3) = -198$$

so TC decreases by 198 units approximately.

Practice Problem ❓

3. Find the marginal cost given the average cost function

$$AC = \frac{100}{Q} + 2$$

Deduce that a 1 unit increase in Q will always result in a 2 unit increase in TC, irrespective of the current level of output.

4.3.2 Production

Production functions were introduced in Section 2.3. In the simplest case output, Q, is assumed to be a function of labour, L, and capital, K. Moreover, in the short run the input K can be assumed to be fixed, so Q is then only a function of one input L. (This is not a valid assumption in the long run and in general Q must be regarded as a function of at least two inputs. Methods for handling this situation are considered in the next chapter.) The variable L is usually measured in terms of the number of workers or possibly in terms of the number of worker hours. Motivated by our previous work, we define the **marginal product of labour**, MP_L, by

$$MP_L = \frac{dQ}{dL}$$

> **marginal product of labour is the derivative of output with respect to labour**

As before, this gives the approximate change in Q that results from using 1 more unit of L.

Example

If the production function is

$$Q = 300\sqrt{L} - 4L$$

where Q denotes output and L denotes the size of the workforce, calculate the value of MP_L when

(a) $L = 1$
(b) $L = 9$
(c) $L = 100$
(d) $L = 2500$

and discuss the implications of these results.

Solution

If

$$Q = 300\sqrt{L} - 4L = 300L^{1/2} - 4L$$

then

$$MP_L = \frac{dQ}{dL}$$

$$= 300(\tfrac{1}{2}L^{-1/2}) - 4$$

$$= 150L^{-1/2} - 4$$

$$= \frac{150}{\sqrt{L}} - 4$$

(a) When $L = 1$

$$MP_L = \frac{150}{\sqrt{1}} - 4$$

(b) When $L = 9$

$$MP_L = \frac{150}{\sqrt{9}} - 4 = 46$$

(c) When $L = 100$

$$MP_L = \frac{150}{\sqrt{100}} - 4 = 11$$

(d) When $L = 2500$

$$MP_L = \frac{150}{\sqrt{2500}} - 4 = -1$$

Notice that the values of MP_L decline with increasing L. Part (a) shows that if the workforce consists of only one person then to employ two people would increase output by approximately 146. In part (b) we see that to increase the number of workers from 9 to 10 would result in about 46 additional units of output. In part (c) we see that a 1 unit increase in labour from a level of 100 increases output by only 11. In part (d) the situation is even worse. This indicates that to increase staff actually reduces output! The latter is a rather surprising result, but it is borne out by what occurs in real production processes. This may be due to problems of overcrowding on the shopfloor or to the need to create an elaborate administration to organize the larger workforce.

This example illustrates the **law of diminishing marginal productivity** (sometimes called the **law of diminishing returns**). It states that the increase in output due to a 1 unit increase in labour will eventually decline. In other words, once the size of the workforce has reached a certain threshold level, the marginal product of labour will get smaller. In the previous example, the value of MP_L continually goes down with rising L. This is not always so. It is possible for the marginal product of labour to remain constant or to go up to begin with for small values of L. However, if it is to satisfy the law of diminishing marginal productivity then there must be some value of L above which MP_L decreases.

A typical product curve is sketched in Figure 4.17, which has slope

$$\frac{dQ}{dL} = MP_L$$

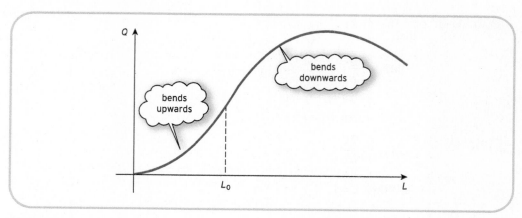

Figure 4.17

Between 0 and L_0 the curve bends upwards, becoming progressively steeper, and so the slope function, MP_L, increases. Mathematically, this means that the slope of MP_L is positive: that is,

$$\frac{d(MP_L)}{dQ} > 0$$

Now MP_L is itself the derivative of Q with respect to L, so we can use the notation for the second derivative and write this as

$$\frac{d^2Q}{dL^2} > 0$$

Similarly, if L exceeds the threshold value of L_0, then Figure 4.17 shows that the product curve bends downwards and the slope decreases. In this region, the slope of the slope function is negative, so that

$$\frac{d^2Q}{dL^2} < 0$$

The law of diminishing returns states that this must happen eventually: that is,

$$\frac{d^2Q}{dL^2} < 0$$

for sufficiently large L.

Practice Problem ❷

4. A Cobb–Douglas production function is given by

$$Q = 5L^{1/2}K^{1/2}$$

Assuming that capital, K, is fixed at 100, write down a formula for Q in terms of L only. Calculate the marginal product of labour when

(a) $L = 1$ **(b)** $L = 9$ **(c)** $L = 10\,000$

Verify that the law of diminishing marginal productivity holds in this case.

4.3.3 Consumption and savings

In Chapter 1 the relationship between consumption, C, savings, S, and national income, Y, was investigated. If we assume that national income is only used up in consumption and savings then

$Y = C + S$

Of particular interest is the effect on C and S due to variations in Y. Expressed simply, if national income rises by a certain amount, are people more likely to go out and spend their extra income on consumer goods or will they save it? To analyse this behaviour we use the concepts **marginal propensity to consume**, MPC, and **marginal propensity to save**, MPS, which are defined by

$$\text{MPC} = \frac{dC}{dY} \quad \text{and} \quad \text{MPS} = \frac{dS}{dY}$$

marginal propensity to consume is the derivative of consumption with respect to income

marginal propensity to save is the derivative of savings with respect to income

These definitions are consistent with those given in Section 1.7, where MPC and MPS were taken to be the slopes of the linear consumption and savings curves, respectively. At first sight it appears that, in general, we need to work out two derivatives in order to evaluate MPC and MPS. However, this is not strictly necessary. Recall that we can do whatever we like to an equation provided we do the same thing to both sides. Consequently, we can differentiate both sides of the equation

$Y = C + S$

with respect to Y to deduce that

$$\frac{dY}{dY} = \frac{dC}{dY} + \frac{dS}{dY} = \text{MPC} + \text{MPS}$$

Now we are already familiar with the result that when we differentiate x with respect to x the answer is 1. In this case Y plays the role of x, so

$$\frac{dY}{dY} = 1$$

Hence

$1 = \text{MPC} + \text{MPS}$

This formula is identical to the result given in Section 1.7 for simple linear functions. In practice, it means that we need only work out one of the derivatives. The remaining derivative can then be calculated directly from this equation.

Example

If the consumption function is

$C = 0.01Y^2 + 0.2Y + 50$

calculate MPC and MPS when $Y = 30$.

Solution

In this example the consumption function is given, so we begin by finding MPC. To do this we differentiate C with respect to Y. If

$$C = 0.01Y^2 + 0.2Y + 50$$

then

$$\frac{dC}{dY} = 0.02Y + 0.2$$

so, when $Y = 30$,

$$MPC = 0.02(30) + 0.2 = 0.8$$

To find the corresponding value of MPS we use the formula

$$MPC + MPS = 1$$

which gives

$$MPS = 1 - MPC = 1 - 0.8 = 0.2$$

This indicates that when national income increases by 1 unit (from its current level of 30) consumption rises by approximately 0.8 units, whereas savings rise by only about 0.2 units. At this level of income the nation has a greater propensity to consume than it has to save.

Practice Problem

5. If the savings function is given by

$$S = 0.02Y^2 - Y + 100$$

calculate the values of MPS and MPC when $Y = 40$. Give a brief interpretation of these results.

Key Terms

Average revenue   Total revenue per unit of output: $AR = TR/Q = P$.

Law of diminishing marginal productivity (law of diminishing returns)   Once the size of the workforce exceeds a particular value, the increase in output due to a 1 unit increase in labour will decline: $d^2Q/dL^2 < 0$ for sufficiently large L.

Marginal cost   The cost of producing 1 more unit of output: $MC = d(TC)/dQ$.

Marginal product of labour   The extra output produced by 1 more unit of labour: $MP_L = dQ/dL$.

Marginal propensity to consume   The fraction of a rise in national income which goes on consumption: $MPC = dC/dY$.

Marginal propensity to save   The fraction of a rise in national income which goes into savings: $MPS = dS/dY$.

Marginal revenue   The extra revenue gained by selling 1 more unit of a good: $MR = d(TR)/dQ$.

Monopolist   The only firm in the industry.

Perfect competition   A situation in which there are no barriers to entry in an industry where there are many firms selling an identical product at the market price.

Exercise 4.3

1. If the demand function is

    $$P = 100 - 4Q$$

    find expressions for TR and MR in terms of Q. Hence estimate the change in TR brought about by a 0.3 unit increase in output from a current level of 12 units.

2. If the demand function is

    $$P = 80 - 3Q$$

    show that

    $$MR = 2P - 80$$

3. A monopolist's demand function is given by

    $$P + Q = 100$$

    Write down expressions for TR and MR in terms of Q and sketch their graphs. Find the value of Q which gives a marginal revenue of zero and comment on the significance of this value.

4. If the average cost function of a good is

    $$AC = \frac{15}{Q} + 2Q + 9$$

    find an expression for TC. What are the fixed costs in this case? Write down an expression for the marginal cost function.

5. A firm's production function is

    $$Q = 50L - 0.01L^2$$

    where L denotes the size of the workforce. Find the value of MP_L in the case when

    (a) $L = 1$ **(b)** $L = 10$ **(c)** $L = 100$ **(d)** $L = 1000$

    Does the law of diminishing marginal productivity apply to this particular function?

6. If the consumption function is

    $$C = 50 + 2\sqrt{Y}$$

    calculate MPC and MPS when $Y = 36$ and give an interpretation of these results.

7. If the consumption function is

    $$C = 0.02Y^2 + 0.1Y + 25$$

    find the value of Y when MPS = 0.38.

Exercise 4.3*

1. A firm's demand function is given by

    $$P = 100 - 4\sqrt{Q} - 3Q$$

    (a) Write down an expression for total revenue, TR, in terms of Q.

    (b) Find an expression for the marginal revenue, MR, and find the value of MR when $Q = 9$.

    (c) Use the result of part (b) to *estimate* the change in TR when Q increases by 0.25 units from its current level of 9 units and compare this with the exact change in TR.

2. The consumption function is

    $$C = 0.01Y^2 + 0.8Y + 100$$

    (a) Calculate the values of MPC and MPS when $Y = 8$.

    (b) Use the fact that $C + S = Y$ to obtain a formula for S in terms of Y. By differentiating this expression find the value of MPS at $Y = 8$ and verify that this agrees with your answer to part (a).

3. The fixed costs of producing a good are 100 and the variable costs are $2 + Q/10$ per unit.

    (a) Find expressions for TC and MC.

    (b) Evaluate MC at $Q = 30$ and hence estimate the change in TC brought about by a 2 unit increase in output from a current level of 30 units.

    (c) At what level of output does MC = 22?

4. Show that the law of diminishing marginal productivity holds for the production function

    $$Q = 6L^2 - 0.2L^3$$

5. A firm's production function is given by

    $$Q = 5\sqrt{L} - 0.1L$$

    (a) Find an expression for the marginal product of labour, MP_L.

    (b) Solve the equation $MP_L = 0$ and briefly explain the significance of this value of L.

    (c) Show that the law of diminishing marginal productivity holds for this function.

6. A firm's average cost function takes the form

    $$AC = 4Q + a + \frac{6}{Q}$$

    and it is known that MC = 35 when $Q = 3$. Find the value of AC when $Q = 6$.

SECTION 4.4
Further rules of differentiation

Objectives

At the end of this section you should be able to:

- Use the chain rule to differentiate a function of a function.
- Use the product rule to differentiate the product of two functions.
- Use the quotient rule to differentiate the quotient of two functions.
- Differentiate complicated functions using a combination of rules.

Section 4.2 introduced you to the basic rules of differentiation. Unfortunately, not all functions can be differentiated using these rules alone. For example, we are unable to differentiate the functions

$$x\sqrt{(2x-3)} \quad \text{and} \quad \frac{x}{x^2+1}$$

using just the constant, sum or difference rules. The aim of the present section is to describe three further rules which allow you to find the derivative of more complicated expressions. Indeed, the totality of all six rules will enable you to differentiate any mathematical function. Although you may find that the rules described in this section take you slightly longer to grasp than before, they are vital to any understanding of economic theory.

The first rule that we investigate is called the chain rule and it can be used to differentiate functions such as

$$y = (2x+3)^{10} \quad \text{and} \quad y = \sqrt{(1+x^2)}$$

The distinguishing feature of these expressions is that they represent a 'function of a function'. To understand what we mean by this, consider how you might evaluate

$$y = (2x+3)^{10}$$

on a calculator. You would first work out an intermediate number u, say, given by

$$u = 2x+3$$

and then raise it to the power of 10 to get

$$y = u^{10}$$

This process is illustrated using the flow chart in Figure 4.18 (overleaf). Note how the incoming number x is first processed by the inner function, 'double and add 3'. The output u from this is then passed on to the outer function, 'raise to the power of 10', to produce the final outgoing number y.

The function

$$y = \sqrt{(1+x^2)}$$

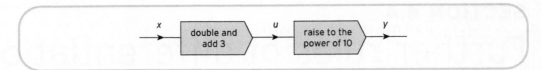

Figure 4.18

can be viewed in the same way. To calculate y you perform the inner function, 'square and add 1', followed by the outer function, 'take square roots'.

The chain rule for differentiating a function of a function may now be stated.

Rule 4 The chain rule

If y is a function of u, which is itself a function of x, then

$$\frac{dy}{dx} = \frac{dy}{du} \times \frac{du}{dx}$$

> differentiate the outer function and multiply
> by the derivative of the inner function

To illustrate this rule, let us return to the function

$$y = (2x + 3)^{10}$$

in which

$$y = u^{10} \quad \text{and} \quad u = 2x + 3$$

Now

$$\frac{dy}{du} = 10u^9 = 10(2x + 3)^9$$

$$\frac{du}{dx} = 2$$

The chain rule then gives

$$\frac{dy}{dx} = \frac{dy}{du} \times \frac{du}{dx} = 10(2x + 3)^9(2) = 20(2x + 3)^9$$

With practice it is possible to perform the differentiation without explicitly introducing the variable u. To differentiate

$$y = (2x + 3)^{10}$$

we first differentiate the outer power function to get

$$10(2x + 3)^9$$

and then multiply by the derivative of the inner function, $2x + 3$, which is 2, so

$$\frac{dy}{dx} = 20(2x + 3)^9$$

Example

Differentiate

(a) $y = (3x^2 - 5x + 2)^4$

(b) $y = \dfrac{1}{3x + 7}$

(c) $y = \sqrt{(1 + x^2)}$

Solution

(a) The chain rule shows that to differentiate $(3x^2 - 5x + 2)^4$ we first differentiate the outer power function to get

$$4(3x^2 - 5x + 2)^3$$

and then multiply by the derivative of the inner function, $3x^2 - 5x + 2$, which is $6x - 5$. Hence if

$$y = (3x^2 - 5x + 2)^4 \quad \text{then} \quad \frac{dy}{dx} = 4(3x^2 - 5x + 2)^3(6x - 5)$$

(b) To use the chain rule to differentiate

$$y = \frac{1}{3x + 7}$$

recall that reciprocals are denoted by negative powers, so that

$$y = (3x + 7)^{-1}$$

The outer power function differentiates to get

$$-(3x + 7)^{-2}$$

and the inner function, $3x + 7$, differentiates to get 3. By the chain rule we just multiply these together to deduce that

$$\text{if} \quad y = \frac{1}{3x + 7} \quad \text{then} \quad \frac{dy}{dx} = -(3x + 7)^{-2}(3) = \frac{-3}{(3x + 7)^2}$$

(c) To use the chain rule to differentiate

$$y = \sqrt{(1 + x^2)}$$

recall that roots are denoted by fractional powers, so that

$$y = (1 + x^2)^{1/2}$$

The outer power function differentiates to get

$$\frac{1}{2}(1 + x^2)^{-1/2}$$

and the inner function, $1 + x^2$, differentiates to get $2x$. By the chain rule we just multiply these together to deduce that

$$\text{if} \quad y = \sqrt{(1 + x^2)} \quad \text{then} \quad \frac{dy}{dx} = \frac{1}{2}(1 + x^2)^{-1/2}(2x) = \frac{x}{\sqrt{(1 + x^2)}}$$

Practice Problem

1. Differentiate

(a) $y = (3x - 4)^5$ **(b)** $y = (x^2 + 3x + 5)^3$ **(c)** $y = \dfrac{1}{2x - 3}$ **(d)** $y = \sqrt{(4x - 3)}$

The next rule is used to differentiate the product of two functions, $f(x)g(x)$. In order to give a clear statement of this rule, we write

$$u = f(x) \quad \text{and} \quad v = g(x)$$

Rule 5 The product rule

If $y = uv$ then $\dfrac{dy}{dx} = u\dfrac{dv}{dx} + v\dfrac{du}{dx}$

This rule tells you how to differentiate the product of two functions:

> multiply each function by the derivative of the other and add

Example

Differentiate

(a) $y = x^2(2x + 1)^3$ **(b)** $x\sqrt{(6x + 1)}$ **(c)** $y = \dfrac{x}{1 + x}$

Solution

(a) The function $x^2(2x + 1)^3$ involves the product of two simpler functions, namely x^2 and $(2x + 1)^3$, which we denote by u and v respectively. (It does not matter which function we label u and which we label v. The same answer is obtained if u is $(2x + 1)^3$ and v is x^2. You might like to check this for yourself later.) Now if

$$u = x^2 \quad \text{and} \quad v = (2x + 1)^3$$

then

$$\frac{du}{dx} = 2x \quad \text{and} \quad \frac{dv}{dx} = 6(2x + 1)^2$$

where we have used the chain rule to find dv/dx. By the product rule,

$$\frac{dy}{dx} = u\frac{dv}{dx} + v\frac{du}{dx}$$

$$= x^2[6(2x + 1)^2] + (2x + 1)^3(2x)$$

The first term is obtained by leaving u alone and multiplying it by the derivative of v. Similarly, the second term is obtained by leaving v alone and multiplying it by the derivative of u.

If desired, the final answer may be simplified by taking out a common factor of $2x(2x + 1)^2$. This factor goes into the first term $3x$ times and into the second $2x + 1$ times. Hence

$$\frac{dy}{dx} = 2x(2x + 1)^2[3x + (2x + 1)] = 2x(2x + 1)^2(5x + 1)$$

(b) The function $x\sqrt{(6x + 1)}$ involves the product of the simpler functions

$$u = x \quad \text{and} \quad v = \sqrt{(6x + 1)} = (6x + 1)^{1/2}$$

for which

$$\frac{du}{dx} = 1 \quad \text{and} \quad \frac{dv}{dx} = \frac{1}{2}(6x + 1)^{-1/2} \times 6 = 3(6x + 1)^{-1/2}$$

where we have used the chain rule to find dv/dx. By the product rule,

$$\frac{dy}{dx} = u\frac{dv}{dx} + v\frac{du}{dx}$$

$$= x[3(6x + 1)^{-1/2}] + (6x + 1)^{1/2}(1)$$

$$= \frac{3x}{\sqrt{(6x + 1)}} + \sqrt{(6x + 1)}$$

If desired, this can be simplified by putting the second term over a common denominator

$$\sqrt{(6x + 1)}$$

To do this we multiply the top and bottom of the second term by $\sqrt{(6x + 1)}$ to get

$$\frac{6x + 1}{\sqrt{(6x + 1)}} \qquad \overset{\textstyle \sqrt{(6x+1)} \times \sqrt{(6x+1)}}{\underset{\textstyle = 6x + 1}{}}$$

Hence

$$\frac{dy}{dx} = \frac{3x + (6x + 1)}{\sqrt{(6x + 1)}} = \frac{9x + 1}{\sqrt{(6x + 1)}}$$

(c) At first sight it is hard to see how we can use the product rule to differentiate

$$\frac{x}{1 + x}$$

since it appears to be the quotient and not the product of two functions. However, if we recall that reciprocals are equivalent to negative powers, we may rewrite it as

$$x(1 + x)^{-1}$$

It follows that we can put

$$u = x \quad \text{and} \quad v = (1 + x)^{-1}$$

which gives

$$\frac{du}{dx} = 1 \quad \text{and} \quad \frac{dv}{dx} = -(1 + x)^{-2}$$

where we have used the chain rule to find dv/dx. By the product rule

$$\frac{dy}{dx} = u\frac{dv}{dx} + v\frac{du}{dx}$$

$$\frac{dy}{dx} = x[-(1+x)^{-2}] + (1+x)^{-1}(1)$$

$$= \frac{-x}{(1+x)^2} + \frac{1}{1+x}$$

If desired, this can be simplified by putting the second term over a common denominator

$$(1+x)^2$$

To do this we multiply the top and bottom of the second term by $1+x$ to get

$$\frac{1+x}{(1+x)^2}$$

Hence

$$\frac{dy}{dx} = \frac{-x}{(1+x)^2} + \frac{1+x}{(1+x)^2} = \frac{-x+(1+x)}{(1+x)^2} = \frac{1}{(1+x)^2}$$

Practice Problem

2. Differentiate

(a) $y = x(3x-1)^6$ **(b)** $y = x^3\sqrt{(2x+3)}$ **(c)** $y = \dfrac{x}{x-2}$

Advice

You may have found the product rule the hardest of the rules so far. This may have been due to the algebraic manipulation that is required to simplify the final expression. If this is the case, do not worry about it at this stage. The important thing is that you can use the product rule to obtain some sort of an answer even if you cannot tidy it up at the end. This is not to say that the simplification of an expression is pointless. If the result of differentiation is to be used in a subsequent piece of theory, it may well save time in the long run if it is simplified first.

One of the most difficult parts of Practice Problem 2 is part (c), since this involves algebraic fractions. For this function, it is necessary to manipulate negative indices and to put two individual fractions over a common denominator. You may feel that you are unable to do either of these processes with confidence. For this reason we conclude this section with a rule that is specifically designed to differentiate this type of function. The rule itself is quite complicated. However, as will become apparent, it does the algebra for you, so you may prefer to use it rather than the product rule when differentiating algebraic fractions.

Rule 6 The quotient rule

$$\text{If} \quad y = \frac{u}{v} \quad \text{then} \quad \frac{dy}{dx} = \frac{v\,du/dx - u\,dv/dx}{v^2}$$

This rule tells you how to differentiate the quotient of two functions:

> **bottom times derivative of top, minus top times derivative of bottom, all over bottom squared**

Example

Differentiate

(a) $y = \dfrac{x}{1 + x}$ **(b)** $y = \dfrac{x^2}{2 - x^3}$

Solution

(a) In the quotient rule, u is used as the label for the numerator and v is used for the denominator, so to differentiate

$$\frac{x}{1 + x}$$

we must take

$$u = x \quad \text{and} \quad v = 1 + x$$

for which

$$\frac{du}{dx} = 1 \quad \text{and} \quad \frac{dv}{dx} = 1$$

By the quotient rule

$$\frac{dy}{dx} = \frac{v\,du/dx - u\,dv/dx}{v^2}$$

$$= \frac{(1 + x)(1) - x(1)}{(1 + x^2)}$$

$$= \frac{1 + x - x}{(1 + x)^2}$$

$$= \frac{1}{(1 + x)^2}$$

Notice how the quotient rule automatically puts the final expression over a common denominator. Compare this with the algebra required to obtain the same answer using the product rule in part (c) of the previous example.

(b) The numerator of the algebraic fraction

$$\frac{1 + x^2}{2 - x^3}$$

is $1 + x^2$ and the denominator is $2 - x^3$, so we take

$$u = 1 + x^2 \quad \text{and} \quad v = 2 - x^3$$

for which

$$\frac{du}{dx} = 2x \quad \text{and} \quad \frac{dv}{dx} = -3x^2$$

By the quotient rule

$$\frac{dy}{dx} = \frac{v\,du/dx - u\,dv/dx}{v^2}$$

$$= \frac{(2 - x^3)(2x) - (1 + x^2)(-3x^2)}{(2 - x^3)^2}$$

$$= \frac{4x - 2x^4 + 3x^2 + 3x^4}{(2 - x^3)^2}$$

$$= \frac{x^4 + 3x^2 + 4x}{(2 - x^3)^2}$$

Practice Problem

3. Differentiate

(a) $y = \dfrac{x}{x - 2}$ **(b)** $y = \dfrac{x - 1}{x + 1}$

[You might like to check that your answer to part (a) is the same as that obtained in Practice Problem 2(c).]

Advice

The product and quotient rules give alternative methods for the differentiation of algebraic fractions. It does not matter which rule you go for; use whichever rule is easiest for you.

Exercise 4.4

1. Use the chain rule to differentiate

(a) $y = (5x + 1)^3$ **(b)** $y = (2x - 7)^8$ **(c)** $y = (x + 9)^5$

(d) $y = (4x^2 - 7)^3$ **(e)** $y = (x^2 + 4x - 3)^4$ **(f)** $y = \sqrt{(2x + 1)}$

(g) $y = \dfrac{1}{3x + 1}$ **(h)** $y = \dfrac{1}{(4x - 3)^2}$ **(i)** $y = \dfrac{1}{\sqrt{(2x + 5)}}$

2. Use the product rule to differentiate

(a) $x(3x + 4)^2$ **(b)** $x^2(x - 2)^3$ **(c)** $x\sqrt{(x + 2)}$

(d) $(x - 1)(x + 6)^3$ **(e)** $(2x + 1)(x + 5)^3$ **(f)** $x^3(2x - 5)^4$

3. Use the quotient rule to differentiate

(a) $y = \dfrac{x}{x - 5}$ **(b)** $y = \dfrac{x}{(x + 7)}$ **(c)** $y = \dfrac{x + 3}{x - 2}$

(d) $y = \dfrac{2x + 9}{3x + 1}$ **(e)** $\dfrac{x}{(5x + 6)}$ **(f)** $y = \dfrac{x + 4}{3x - 7}$

4. Differentiate

$$y = (5x + 7)^2$$

(a) by using the chain rule

(b) by first multiplying out the brackets and then differentiating term by term.

5. Differentiate

$$y = x^5(x + 2)^2$$

(a) by using the product rule

(b) by first multiplying out the brackets and then differentiating term by term.

6. Find expressions for marginal revenue in the case when the demand equation is given by

(a) $P = (100 - Q)^3$ **(b)** $\dfrac{1000}{Q + 4}$

7. If the consumption function is

$$C = \frac{300 + 2Y^2}{1 + Y}$$

calculate MPC and MPS when $Y = 36$ and give an interpretation of these results.

Exercise 4.4*

1. Use the chain rule to differentiate

   (a) $y = (2x + 1)^{10}$ **(b)** $y = (x^2 + 3x - 5)^3$ **(c)** $y = \dfrac{1}{7x - 3}$

   (d) $y = \dfrac{1}{x^2 + 1}$ **(e)** $y = \sqrt{(8x - 1)}$ **(f)** $y = \dfrac{1}{\sqrt[3]{(6x - 5)}}$

2. Use the product rule to differentiate

   (a) $y = x^2(x + 5)^3$ **(b)** $y = x^5(4x + 5)^2$ **(c)** $y = x^4\sqrt{(x + 1)}$

3. Use the quotient rule to differentiate

   (a) $y = \dfrac{x^2}{x + 4}$ **(b)** $y = \dfrac{2x - 1}{x + 1}$ **(c)** $y = \dfrac{x^3}{\sqrt{(x - 1)}}$

4. Differentiate

   (a) $y = x(x - 3)^4$ **(b)** $y = x\sqrt{(2x - 3)}$ **(c)** $y = \dfrac{x^3}{(3x + 5)^2}$ **(d)** $y = \dfrac{x}{x^2 + 1}$

   (e) $y = \dfrac{ax + b}{cx + d}$ **(f)** $y = (ax + b)^m(cx + d)^n$ **(g)** $y = x(x + 2)^2(x + 3)^3$

5. Find an expression, simplified as far as possible, for the second-order derivative of the function, $y = \dfrac{x}{2x + 1}$.

6. Find expressions for marginal revenue in the case when the demand equation is given by

   (a) $P = \sqrt{(100 - 2Q)}$ **(b)** $P = \dfrac{1000}{\sqrt{2 + Q}}$

7. Determine the marginal propensity to consume for the consumption function

   $$C = \frac{650 + 2Y^2}{9 + Y}$$

   when $Y = 21$, correct to 3 decimal places.

   Deduce the corresponding value of the marginal propensity to save and comment on the implications of these results.

SECTION 4.5
Elasticity

> ## Objectives
>
> At the end of this section you should be able to:
>
> - Calculate price elasticity averaged along an arc.
> - Calculate price elasticity evaluated at a point.
> - Decide whether supply and demand are inelastic, unit elastic or elastic.
> - Understand the relationship between price elasticity of demand and revenue.
> - Determine the price elasticity for general linear demand functions.

One important problem in business is to determine the effect on revenue of a change in the price of a good. Let us suppose that a firm's demand curve is downward-sloping. If the firm lowers the price then it will receive less for each item, but the number of items sold increases. The formula for total revenue, TR, is

$$TR = PQ$$

and it is not immediately obvious what the net effect on TR will be as P decreases and Q increases. The crucial factor here is not the absolute changes in P and Q but rather the proportional or percentage changes. Intuitively, we expect that if the percentage rise in Q is greater than the percentage fall in P then the firm experiences an increase in revenue. Under these circumstances we say that demand is **elastic**, since the demand is relatively sensitive to changes in price. Similarly, demand is said to be **inelastic** if demand is relatively insensitive to price changes. In this case, the percentage change in quantity is less than the percentage change in price. A firm can then increase revenue by raising the price of the good. Although demand falls as a result, the increase in price more than compensates for the reduced volume of sales and revenue rises. Of course, it could happen that the percentage changes in price and quantity are equal, leaving revenue unchanged. We use the term **unit elastic** to describe this situation.

We quantify the responsiveness of demand to price change by defining the **price elasticity of demand** to be

$$E = \frac{\text{percentage change in demand}}{\text{percentage change in price}}$$

Notice that because the demand curve slopes downwards, a positive change in price leads to a negative change in quantity and vice versa. Consequently, the value of E is always negative. It is conventional to avoid this by deliberately changing the sign and taking

$$E = -\frac{\text{percentage change in demand}}{\text{percentage change in price}}$$

which makes E positive. The previous classification of demand functions can now be restated more succinctly in terms of E:

Demand is said to be

- inelastic if $E < 1$
- unit elastic if $E = 1$
- elastic if $E > 1$.

Advice

You should note that not all economists adopt the convention of ignoring the sign to make E positive. If the negative sign is left in, the demand will be inelastic if $E = -1$, unit elastic if $E > -1$ and elastic if $E < -1$. You should check with your lecturer the particular convention that you need to adopt.

As usual, we denote the changes in P and Q by ΔP and ΔQ respectively, and seek a formula for E in terms of these symbols. To motivate this, suppose that the price of a good is \$12 and that it rises to \$18. A moment's thought should convince you that the percentage change in price is then 50%. You can probably work this out in your head without thinking too hard. However, it is worthwhile identifying the mathematical process involved. To obtain this figure we first express the change

$$18 - 12 = 6$$

as a fraction of the original to get

$$\frac{6}{12} = 0.5$$

and then multiply by 100 to express it as a percentage. This simple example gives us a clue as to how we might find a formula for E. In general, the percentage change in price is

change in price expressed as a fraction of the original price ⟩ $\dfrac{\Delta P}{P} \times 100$ ⟨ multiply by 100 to convert fractions into percentages

Similarly, the percentage change in quantity is

$$\frac{\Delta Q}{Q} \times 100$$

Hence

$$E = -\left(\frac{\Delta Q}{Q} \times 100 \right) \div \left(\frac{\Delta P}{P} \times 100 \right)$$

Now, when we divide two fractions we turn the denominator upside down and multiply, so

$$E = -\left(\frac{\Delta Q}{Q} \times \cancel{100} \right) \times \left(\frac{P}{\cancel{100} \times \Delta P} \right)$$

$$= -\frac{P}{Q} \times \frac{\Delta Q}{\Delta P}$$

A typical demand curve is illustrated in Figure 4.19, in which a price fall from P_1 to P_2 causes an increase in demand from Q_1 to Q_2.

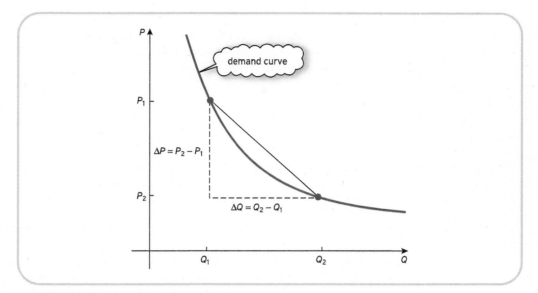

Figure 4.19

Example

Determine the elasticity of demand when the price falls from 136 to 119, given the demand function

$$P = 200 - Q^2$$

Solution

In the notation of Figure 4.19 we are given that

$$P_1 = 136 \text{ and } P_2 = 119$$

The corresponding values of Q_1 and Q_2 are obtained from the demand equation

$$P = 200 - Q^2$$

by substituting $P = 136$ and 119 respectively and solving for Q. For example, if $P = 136$ then

$$136 = 200 - Q^2$$

which rearranges to give

$$Q^2 = 200 - 136 = 64$$

This has solution $Q = \pm 8$ and, since we can obviously ignore the negative quantity, we have $Q_1 = 8$. Similarly, setting $P = 119$ gives $Q_2 = 9$. The elasticity formula is

$$E = -\frac{P}{Q} \times \frac{\Delta Q}{\Delta P}$$

and the values of ΔP and ΔQ are easily worked out to be

$$\Delta P = 119 - 136 = -17$$
$$\Delta Q = 9 - 8 = 1$$

However, it is not at all clear what to take for P and Q. Do we take P to be 136 or 119? Clearly we are going to get two different answers depending on our choice. A sensible compromise is to use their average and take

$P = \frac{1}{2}(136 + 119) = 127.5$

Similarly, averaging the Q values gives

$Q = \frac{1}{2}(8 + 9) = 8.5$

Hence

$E = -\dfrac{127.5}{8.5} \times \left(\dfrac{1}{-17}\right) = 0.88$

The particular application of the general formula considered in the previous example provides an estimate of elasticity averaged over a section of the demand curve between (Q_1, P_1) and (Q_2, P_2). For this reason it is called **arc elasticity** and is obtained by replacing P by $\frac{1}{2}(P_1 + P_2)$ and Q by $\frac{1}{2}(Q_1 + Q_2)$ in the general formula.

Practice Problem

1. Given the demand function

    $P = 1000 - 2Q$

    calculate the arc elasticity as P falls from 210 to 200.

A disappointing feature of the previous example is the need to compromise and calculate the elasticity averaged along an arc rather than calculate the exact value at a point. A formula for the latter can easily be deduced from

$E = -\dfrac{P}{Q} \times \dfrac{\Delta Q}{\Delta P}$

by considering the limit as ΔQ and ΔP tend to zero in Figure 4.19. All that happens is that the arc shrinks to a point and the ratio $\Delta Q/\Delta P$ tends to dQ/dP. The price elasticity at a point (**point elasticity**) may therefore be found from

$E = -\dfrac{P}{Q} \times \dfrac{dQ}{dP}$

Example

Given the demand function

$P = 50 - 2Q$

find the elasticity when the price is 30. Is demand inelastic, unit elastic or elastic at this price?

Solution

To find dQ/dP we need to differentiate Q with respect to P. However, we are actually given a formula for P in terms of Q, so we need to transpose

$$P = 50 - 2Q$$

for Q. Adding $2Q$ to both sides gives

$$P + 2Q = 50$$

and if we subtract P then

$$2Q = 50 - P$$

Finally, dividing through by 2 gives

$$Q = 25 - \tfrac{1}{2}P$$

Hence

$$\frac{dQ}{dP} = -\tfrac{1}{2}$$

We are given that $P = 30$ so, at this price, demand is

$$Q = 25 - \tfrac{1}{2}(30) = 10$$

These values can now be substituted into

$$E = -\frac{P}{Q} \times \frac{dQ}{dP}$$

to get

$$E = -\frac{30}{10} \times \left(-\frac{1}{2}\right) = 1.5$$

Moreover, since 1.5 > 1, demand is elastic at this price.

Practice Problem

2. Given the demand function

$$P = 100 - Q$$

calculate the price elasticity of demand when the price is

(a) 10   **(b)** 50   **(c)** 90

Is the demand inelastic, unit elastic or elastic at these prices?

It is quite common in economics to be given the demand function in the form

$$P = f(Q)$$

where P is a function of Q. In order to evaluate elasticity it is necessary to find

$$\frac{dQ}{dP}$$

which assumes that Q is actually given as a function of P. Consequently, we may have to transpose the demand equation and find an expression for Q in terms of P before we perform the differentiation. This was the approach taken in the previous example. Unfortunately, if $f(Q)$ is a complicated expression, it may be difficult, if not impossible, to carry out the initial rearrangement to extract Q. An alternative approach is based on the fact that

$$\frac{dQ}{dP} = \frac{1}{dP/dQ}$$

A proof of this can be obtained via the chain rule, although we omit the details. This result shows that we can find dQ/dP by just differentiating the original demand function to get dP/dQ and reciprocating.

Example

Given the demand function

$$P = -Q^2 - 4Q + 96$$

find the price elasticity of demand when $P = 51$. If this price rises by 2%, calculate the corresponding percentage change in demand.

Solution

We are given that $P = 51$, so to find the corresponding demand we need to solve the quadratic equation

$$-Q^2 - 4Q + 96 = 51$$

that is,

$$-Q^2 - 4Q + 45 = 0$$

To do this we use the standard formula

$$\frac{-b \pm \sqrt{(b^2 - 4ac)}}{2a}$$

discussed in Section 2.1, which gives

$$Q = \frac{-(-4) \pm \sqrt{((-4)^2 - 4(-1)(45))}}{2(-1)}$$

$$= \frac{4 \pm \sqrt{196}}{-2}$$

$$= \frac{4 \pm 14}{-2}$$

The two solutions are −9 and 5. As usual, the negative value can be ignored, since it does not make sense to have a negative quantity, so $Q = 5$.

To find the value of E we also need to calculate

$$\frac{dQ}{dP}$$

from the demand equation, $P = -Q^2 - 4Q + 96$. It is not at all easy to transpose this for Q. Indeed, we would have to use the formula for solving a quadratic, as before, replacing the number 51 with the letter P. Unfortunately this expression involves square roots and the subsequent differentiation is quite messy. (You might like to have a go at this yourself!) However, it is easy to differentiate the given expression with respect to Q to get

$$\frac{dP}{dQ} = -2Q - 4$$

and so

$$\frac{dQ}{dP} = \frac{1}{dP/dQ} = \frac{1}{-2Q - 4}$$

Finally, putting $Q = 5$ gives

$$\frac{dQ}{dP} = -\frac{1}{14}$$

The price elasticity of demand is given by

$$E = -\frac{P}{Q} \times \frac{dQ}{dP}$$

and if we substitute $P = 51$, $Q = 5$ and $dQ/dP = -1/14$ we get

$$E - \frac{51}{5} \times \left(-\frac{1}{14}\right) = 0.73$$

To discover the effect on Q due to a 2% rise in P we return to the original definition

$$E = -\frac{\text{percentage change in demand}}{\text{percentage change in price}}$$

We know that $E = 0.73$ and that the percentage change in price is 2, so

$$0.73 = -\frac{\text{percentage change in price}}{2}$$

which shows that demand changes by

$$-0.73 \times 2 = -1.46\%$$

A 2% rise in price therefore leads to a fall in demand of 1.46%.

Practice Problem

3. Given the demand equation

$$P = -Q^2 - 10Q + 150$$

find the price elasticity of demand when $Q = 4$. Estimate the percentage change in price needed to increase demand by 10%.

The **price elasticity of supply** is defined in an analogous way to that of demand. We define

$$E = \frac{\text{percentage change in supply}}{\text{percentage change in price}}$$

This time, however, there is no need to fiddle the sign. An increase in price leads to an increase in supply, so E is automatically positive. In symbols,

$$E = \frac{P}{Q} \times \frac{\Delta Q}{\Delta P}$$

If (Q_1, P_1) and (Q_2, P_2) denote two points on the supply curve then arc elasticity is obtained, as before, by setting

$$\Delta P = P_2 - P_1$$
$$\Delta Q = Q_2 - Q_1$$
$$P = 1/2(P_1 + P_2)$$
$$Q = 1/2(Q_1 + Q_2)$$

The corresponding formula for point elasticity is

$$E = \frac{P}{Q} \times \frac{dQ}{dP}$$

Example

Given the supply function

$$P = 10 + \sqrt{Q}$$

find the price elasticity of supply

(a) averaged along an arc between $Q = 100$ and $Q = 105$

(b) at the point $Q = 100$.

Solution

(a) We are given that

$$Q_1 = 100, \, Q_2 = 105$$

so that

$$P_1 = 10 + \sqrt{100} = 20 \text{ and } P_2 = 10 + \sqrt{105} = 20.247$$

Hence

$$\Delta P = 20.247 - 20 = 0.247, \qquad \Delta Q = 105 - 100 = 5$$

$$P = \frac{1}{2}(20 + 20.247) = 20.123, \qquad Q = \frac{1}{2}(100 + 105) = 102.5$$

The formula for arc elasticity gives

$$E = \frac{P}{Q} \times \frac{\Delta Q}{\Delta P} = \frac{20.123}{102.5} \times \frac{5}{0.247} = 3.97$$

(b) To evaluate the elasticity at the point $Q = 100$, we need to find the derivative, $\dfrac{dQ}{dP}$. The supply equation

$$P = 10 + Q^{1/2}$$

differentiates to give

$$\frac{dP}{dQ} = \frac{1}{2}Q^{-1/2} = \frac{1}{2\sqrt{Q}}$$

so that

$$\frac{dQ}{dP} = 2\sqrt{Q}$$

At the point $Q = 100$, we get

$$\frac{dQ}{dP} = 2\sqrt{100} = 20$$

The formula for point elasticity gives

$$E = \frac{P}{Q} \times \frac{dQ}{dP} = \frac{20}{100} \times 20 = 4$$

Notice that, as expected, the answers to parts (a) and (b) are nearly the same.

Practice Problem

4. If the supply equation is

$$Q = 150 + 5P + 0.1P^2$$

calculate the price elasticity of supply

(a) averaged along an arc between $P = 9$ and $P = 11$

(b) at the point $P = 10$.

Advice

The concept of elasticity can be applied to more general functions and we consider some of these in the next chapter. For the moment we investigate the theoretical properties of demand elasticity. The following material is more difficult to understand than the foregoing, so you may prefer just to concentrate on the conclusions and skip the intermediate derivations.

We begin by analysing the relationship between elasticity and marginal revenue. Marginal revenue, MR, is given by

$$MR = \frac{d(TR)}{dQ}$$

Now TR is equal to the product PQ, so we can apply the product rule to differentiate it. If

$$u = P \text{ and } v = Q$$

then

$$\frac{du}{dQ} = \frac{dP}{dQ} \text{ and } \frac{dv}{dQ} = \frac{dQ}{dQ} = 1$$

By the product rule

$$\text{MR} = u\frac{dv}{dQ} + v\frac{du}{dQ}$$

$$= P + Q \times \frac{dP}{dQ}$$

$$= P\left(1 + \frac{Q}{P} \times \frac{dP}{dQ}\right)$$

check this by multiplying out the brackets

Now

$$-\frac{P}{Q} \times \frac{dQ}{dP} = E$$

so

$$\frac{Q}{P} \times \frac{dP}{dQ} = -\frac{1}{E}$$

turn both sides upside down and multiply by −1

This can be substituted into the expression for MR to get

$$\text{MR} = P\left(1 - \frac{1}{E}\right)$$

The connection between marginal revenue and demand elasticity is now complete, and this formula can be used to justify the intuitive argument that we gave at the beginning of this section concerning revenue and elasticity. Observe that if $E < 1$ then $1/E > 1$, so MR is negative for any value of P. It follows that the revenue function is decreasing in regions where demand is inelastic, because MR determines the slope of the revenue curve. Similarly, if $E > 1$ then $1/E < 1$, so MR is positive for any price, P, and the revenue curve is upwards. In other words, the revenue function is increasing in regions where demand is elastic. Finally, if $E = 1$ then MR is 0, and so the slope of the revenue curve is horizontal at points where demand is unit elastic.

Throughout this section we have taken specific functions and evaluated the elasticity at particular points. It is more instructive to consider general functions and to deduce general expressions for elasticity. Consider the standard linear downward-sloping demand function

$$P = aQ + b$$

when $a < 0$ and $b > 0$. As noted in Section 4.3, this typifies the demand function faced by a monopolist. To transpose this equation for Q, we subtract b from both sides to get

$$aQ = P - b$$

and then divide through by a to get

$$Q = \frac{1}{a}(P - b)$$

Hence

$$\frac{dQ}{dP} = \frac{1}{a}$$

The formula for elasticity of demand is

$$E = -\frac{P}{Q} \times \frac{dQ}{dP}$$

so replacing Q by $(1/a)(P - b)$ and dQ/dP by $1/a$ gives

$$E = \frac{-P}{(1/a)(P - b)} \times \frac{1}{a}$$

$$= \frac{-P}{P - b}$$

$$= \frac{P}{b - P}$$

multiply top and bottom by −1

Notice that this formula involves P and b but not a. Elasticity is therefore independent of the slope of linear demand curves. In particular, this shows that, corresponding to any price P, the elasticities of the two demand functions sketched in Figure 4.20 are identical. This is perhaps a rather surprising result. We might have expected demand to be more elastic at point A than at point B, since A is on the steeper curve. However, the mathematics shows that this is not the case. (Can you explain, in economic terms, why this is so?)

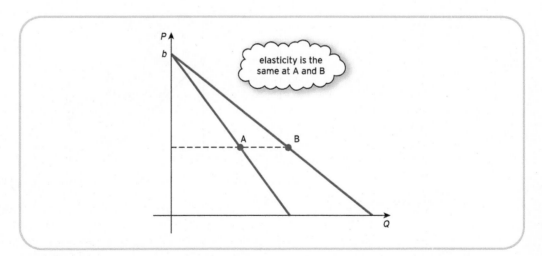

elasticity is the same at A and B

Figure 4.20

Another interesting feature of the result

$$E = \frac{P}{b - P}$$

is the fact that b occurs in the denominator of this fraction, so that corresponding to any price, P, the larger the value of the intercept, b, the smaller the elasticity. In Figure 4.21 (overleaf), elasticity at C is smaller than that at D because C lies on the curve with the larger intercept.

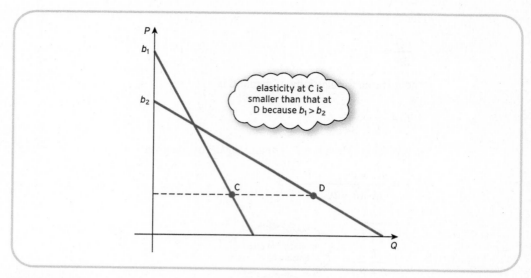

Figure 4.21

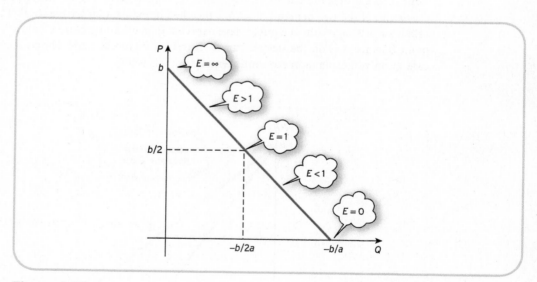

Figure 4.22

The dependence of E on P is also worthy of note. It shows that elasticity varies along a linear demand curve. This is illustrated in Figure 4.22. At the left-hand end, $P = b$, so

$$E = \frac{b}{b-b} = \frac{b}{0} = \infty$$ read 'infinity'

At the right-hand end, $P = 0$, so

$$E = \frac{0}{b-0} = \frac{0}{b} = 0$$

As you move down the demand curve, the elasticity decreases from ∞ to 0, taking all possible values. Demand is unit elastic when $E = 1$ and the price at which this occurs can be found by solving

$$\frac{P}{b - P} = 1 \text{ for } P$$

$\quad P = b - P \qquad$ (multiply both sides by $b - P$)

$\quad 2P = b \qquad\quad$ (add P to both sides)

$\quad P = \dfrac{b}{2} \qquad\quad$ (divide both sides by 2)

The corresponding quantity can be found by substituting $P = b/2$ into the transposed demand equation to get

$$Q = \frac{1}{a}\left(\frac{b}{2} - b\right) = -\frac{b}{2a}$$

Demand is unit elastic exactly halfway along the demand curve. To the left of this point $E > 1$ and demand is elastic, whereas to the right $E < 1$ and demand is inelastic.

In our discussion of general demand functions, we have concentrated on those which are represented by straight lines since they are commonly used in simple economic models. There are other possibilities and Question 4 in Exercise 4.5* investigates a class of functions that have constant elasticity.

Key Terms

Arc elasticity   Elasticity measured between two points on a curve.

Elastic demand   Where the percentage change in demand is more than the corresponding percentage change in price: $E > 1$.

Inelastic demand   Where the percentage change in demand is less than the corresponding percentage change in price: $E < 1$.

Point elasticity   Elasticity measured at a particular point on a curve, e.g. for a supply curve, $E = \dfrac{P}{Q} \times \dfrac{dQ}{dP}$.

Price elasticity of demand   A measure of the responsiveness of the change in demand due to a change in price: $-$(percentage change in demand) $\div$ (percentage change in price).

Price elasticity of supply   A measure of the responsiveness of the change in supply due to a change in price: (percentage change in supply) $\div$ (percentage change in price).

Unit elasticity demand   Where the percentage change in demand is the same as the percentage change in price: $E = 1$.

Exercise 4.5

1. Given the demand function

   $$P = 500 - 4Q^2$$

   calculate the price elasticity of demand averaged along an arc joining $Q = 8$ and $Q = 10$.

2. Find the price elasticity of demand at the point $Q = 9$ for the demand function

   $$P = 500 - 4Q^2$$

   and compare your answer with that of Question 1.

3. Find the price elasticity of demand at $P = 6$ for each of the following demand functions:

   (a) $P = 30 - 2Q$

   (b) $P = 30 - 12Q$

   (c) $P = \sqrt{(100 - 2Q)}$

4. Consider the supply equation

   $$Q = 4 + 0.1P^2$$

   (a) Write down an expression for dQ/dP.

   (b) Show that the supply equation can be rearranged as

   $$P = \sqrt{(10Q - 40)}$$

   Differentiate this to find an expression for dP/dQ.

   (c) Use your answers to parts (a) and (b) to verify that

   $$\frac{dQ}{dP} = \frac{1}{dP/dQ}$$

   (d) Calculate the elasticity of supply at the point $Q = 14$.

5. If the supply equation is

   $$Q = 7 + 0.1P + 0.004P^2$$

   find the price elasticity of supply if the current price is 80.

   (a) Is supply elastic, inelastic or unit elastic at this price?

   (b) Estimate the percentage change in supply if the price rises by 5%.

Exercise 4.5*

1. Find the elasticity for the demand function

   $$Q = 80 - 2P - 0.5P^2$$

   averaged along an arc joining $Q = 32$ to $Q = 50$. Give your answer to two decimal places.

2. Consider the supply equation

   $$P = 7 + 2Q^2$$

   By evaluating the price elasticity of supply at the point $P = 105$, estimate the percentage increase in supply when the price rises by 7%.

3. If the demand equation is

$$Q + 4P = 60$$

find a general expression for the price elasticity of demand in terms of P. For what value of P is demand unit elastic?

4. Show that the price elasticity of demand is constant for the demand functions

$$P = \frac{A}{Q^n}$$

where A and n are positive constants.

5. Find a general expression for the point elasticity of supply for the function,

$$Q = aP + b \quad (a > 0)$$

Deduce that the supply function is

(a) unit elastic when $b = 0$

(b) inelastic when $b > 0$.

Give a brief geometrical interpretation of these results.

6. A supply function is given by

$$Q = 40 + 0.1P^2$$

(1) Find the price elasticity of supply averaged along an arc between $P = 11$ and $P = 13$. Give your answer correct to 3 decimal places.

(2) Find an expression for price elasticity of supply at a general point, P.

Hence:

(a) Estimate the percentage change in supply when the price increases by 5% from its current level of 17. Give your answer correct to 1 decimal place.

(b) Find the price at which supply is unit elastic.

7. (a) Show that the elasticity of the supply function

$$P = aQ + b$$

is given by

$$E = \frac{P}{P - b}$$

(b) Consider the two supply functions

$$P = 2Q + 5 \text{ and } P = aQ + b$$

The quantity supplied is the same for both functions when $P = 10$, and at this point, the price elasticity of supply for the second function is five times larger than that for the first function. Find the values of a and b.

SECTION 4.6
Optimization of economic functions

Objectives

At the end of this section you should be able to:

- Use the first-order derivative to find the stationary points of a function.
- Use the second-order derivative to classify the stationary points of a function.
- Find the maximum and minimum points of an economic function.
- Use stationary points to sketch graphs of economic functions.

In Section 2.1 a simple three-step strategy was described for sketching graphs of quadratic functions of the form

$$f(x) = ax^2 + bx + c$$

The basic idea is to solve the corresponding equation

$$ax^2 + bx + c = 0$$

to find where the graph crosses the x axis. Provided that the quadratic equation has at least one solution, it is then possible to deduce the coordinates of the maximum or minimum point of the parabola. For example, if there are two solutions, then by symmetry the graph turns round at the point exactly halfway between these solutions. Unfortunately, if the quadratic equation has no solution then only a limited sketch can be obtained using this approach.

In this section we show how the techniques of calculus can be used to find the coordinates of the turning point of a parabola. The beauty of this approach is that it can be used to locate the maximum and minimum points of any economic function, not just those represented by quadratics. Look at the graph in Figure 4.23. Points B, C, D, E, F and G are referred to as the **stationary points** (sometimes called **critical points**, **turning points** or **extrema**) of the function. At a stationary point the tangent to the graph is horizontal and so has zero slope.

Consequently, at a stationary point of a function $f(x)$,

$$f'(x) = 0$$

The reason for using the word 'stationary' is historical. Calculus was originally used by astronomers to predict planetary motion. If a graph of the distance travelled by an object is sketched against time then the speed of the object is given by the slope, since this represents the rate of change of distance with respect to time. It follows that if the graph is horizontal at some point then the speed is zero and the object is instantaneously at rest: that is, stationary.

Stationary points are classified into one of three types: local maxima, local minima and stationary points of inflection.

At a **local maximum** (sometimes called a relative maximum) the graph falls away on both sides. Points B and E are the local maxima for the function sketched in Figure 4.23. The word

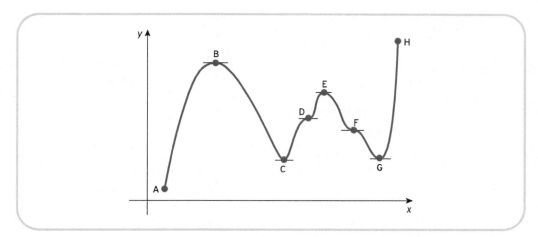

Figure 4.23

'local' is used to highlight the fact that, although these are the maximum points relative to their locality or neighbourhood, they may not be the overall or global maximum. In Figure 4.23 the highest point on the graph actually occurs at the right-hand end, H, which is not a stationary point, since the slope is not zero at H.

At a **local minimum** (sometimes called a relative minimum) the graph rises on both sides. Points C and G are the local minima in Figure 4.23. Again, it is not necessary for the global minimum to be one of the local minima. In Figure 4.23 the lowest point on the graph occurs at the left-hand end, A, which is not a stationary point.

At a **stationary point of inflection** the graph rises on one side and falls on the other. The stationary points of inflection in Figure 4.23 are labelled D and F. These points are of little value in economics, although they do sometimes assist in sketching graphs of economic functions. Maxima and minima, on the other hand, are important. The calculation of the maximum points of the revenue and profit functions is clearly worthwhile. Likewise, it is useful to be able to find the minimum points of average cost functions.

For most examples in economics, the local maximum and minimum points coincide with the global maximum and minimum. For this reason we shall drop the word 'local' when describing stationary points. However, it should always be borne in mind that the global maximum and minimum could actually be attained at an end point and this possibility may need to be checked. This can be done by comparing the function values at the end points with those of the stationary points and then deciding which of them gives rise to the largest or smallest values.

Two obvious questions remain. How do we find the stationary points of any given function and how do we classify them? The first question is easily answered. As we mentioned earlier, stationary points satisfy the equation

$$f'(x) = 0$$

so all we need do is to differentiate the function, to equate to zero and to solve the resulting algebraic equation. The classification is equally straightforward. It can be shown that if a function has a stationary point at $x = a$ then

- if $f''(a) > 0$ then $f(x)$ has a minimum at $x = a$
- if $f''(a) < 0$ then $f(x)$ has a maximum at $x = a$.

Therefore, all we need do is to differentiate the function a second time and to evaluate this second-order derivative at each point. A point is a minimum if this value is positive and a maximum if this value is negative. These facts are consistent with our interpretation of the second-order derivative in Section 4.2. If $f''(a) > 0$ the graph bends upwards at $x = a$ (points C and G in Figure 4.23). If $f''(a) < 0$ the graph bends downwards at $x = a$ (points B and E in Figure 4.23). There is, of course, a third possibility, namely $f''(a) = 0$. Sadly, when this happens it provides no information whatsoever about the stationary point. The point $x = a$ could be a maximum, minimum or inflection. This situation is illustrated in Question 2 in Exercise 4.6* at the end of this section.

Advice

If you are unlucky enough to encounter this case, you can always classify the point by tabulating the function values in the vicinity and use these to produce a local sketch.

To summarize, the method for finding and classifying stationary points of a function, $f(x)$, is as follows:

Step 1

Solve the equation $f'(x) = 0$ to find the stationary points, $x = a$.

Step 2

If

- $f''(a) > 0$ then the function has a minimum at $x = a$
- $f''(a) < 0$ then the function has a maximum at $x = a$
- $f''(a) = 0$ then the point cannot be classified using the available information.

Example

Find and classify the stationary points of the following functions. Hence sketch their graphs.

(a) $f(x) = x^2 - 4x + 5$ **(b)** $f(x) = 2x^3 + 3x^2 - 12x + 4$

Solution

(a) In order to use steps 1 and 2 we need to find the first- and second-order derivatives of the function

$$f'(x) = x^2 - 4x + 5$$

Differentiating once gives

$$f'(x) = 2x - 4$$

and differentiating a second time gives

$$f''(x) = 2$$

Step 1

The stationary points are the solutions of the equation

$$f'(x) = 0$$

so we need to solve

$$2x - 4 = 0$$

This is a linear equation so has just one solution. Adding 4 to both sides gives

$$2x = 4$$

and dividing through by 2 shows that the stationary point occurs at

$$x = 2$$

Step 2
To classify this point we need to evaluate

$$f''(2)$$

In this case

$$f''(x) = 2$$

for all values of x, so in particular

$$f''(2) = 2$$

This number is positive, so the function has a minimum at $x = 2$.

We have shown that the minimum point occurs at $x = 2$. The corresponding value of y is easily found by substituting this number into the function to get

$$y = (2)^2 - 4(2) + 5 = 1$$

so the minimum point has coordinates $(2, 1)$. A graph of $f(x)$ is shown in Figure 4.24.

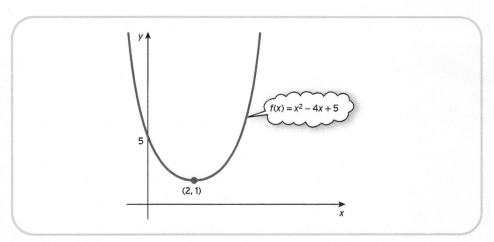

Figure 4.24

(b) In order to use steps 1 and 2 we need to find the first- and second-order derivatives of the function

$$f(x) = 2x^3 + 3x^2 - 12x + 4$$

Differentiating once gives

$$f'(x) = 6x^2 + 6x - 12$$

and differentiating a second time gives

$$f''(x) = 12x + 6$$

Step 1

The stationary points are the solutions of the equation

$$f'(x) = 0$$

so we need to solve

$$6x^2 + 6x - 12 = 0$$

This is a quadratic equation and so can be solved using 'the formula'. However, before doing so, it is a good idea to divide both sides by 6 to avoid large numbers. The resulting equation

$$x^2 + x - 2 = 0$$

has solution

$$x = \frac{-1 \pm \sqrt{(1^2 - 4(1)(-2))}}{2(1)} = \frac{-1 \pm \sqrt{9}}{2} = \frac{-1 \pm 3}{2} = -2, 1$$

In general, whenever $f(x)$ is a cubic function the stationary points are the solutions of a quadratic equation, $f'(x) = 0$. Moreover, we know from Section 2.1 that such an equation can have two, one or no solutions. It follows that a cubic equation can have two, one or no stationary points. In this particular example we have seen that there are two stationary points, at $x = -2$ and $x = 1$.

Step 2

To classify these points we need to evaluate $f''(-2)$ and $f''(1)$. Now

$$f''(-2) = 12(-2) + 6 = -18$$

This is negative, so there is a maximum at $x = -2$. When $x = -2$,

$$y = 2(-2)^3 + 3(-2)^2 - 12(-2) + 4 = 24$$

so the maximum point has coordinates $(-2, 24)$. Now

$$f''(1) = 12(1) + 6 = 18$$

This is positive, so there is a minimum at $x = 1$. When $x = 1$,

$$y = 2(1)^3 + 3(1)^2 - 12(1) + 4 = -3$$

so the minimum point has coordinates $(1, -3)$.

This information enables a partial sketch to be drawn as shown in Figure 4.25. Before we can be confident about the complete picture it is useful to plot a few more points such as those below:

x	−10	0	10
y	−1816	4	2184

This table indicates that when x is positive the graph falls steeply downwards from a great height. Similarly, when x is negative the graph quickly disappears off the bottom of the page. The curve cannot wiggle and turn round except at the two stationary points already plotted (otherwise it would have more stationary points, which we know is not the case). We now have enough information to join up the pieces and so sketch a complete picture as shown in Figure 4.26.

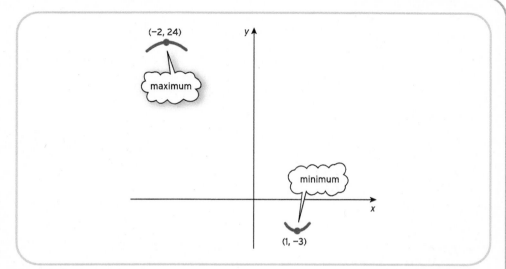

Figure 4.25

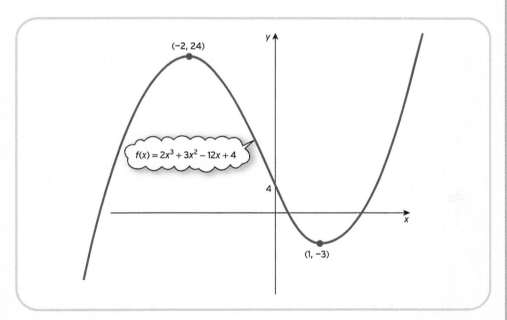

Figure 4.26

In an ideal world it would be nice to calculate the three points at which the graph crosses the x axis. These are the solutions of

$$2x^3 + 3x^2 - 12x + 4 = 0$$

There is a formula for solving cubic equations, just as there is for quadratic equations, but it is extremely complicated and is beyond the scope of this book.

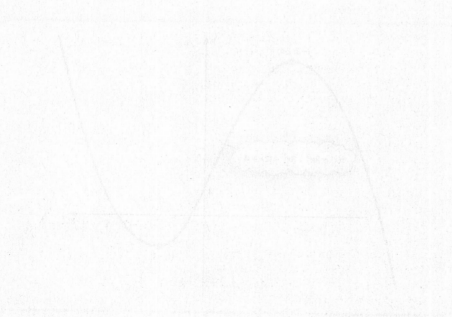

1

Descriptive statistics

Contents

→

By the end of this chapter you should be able to:

- recognise different types of data and use appropriate methods to summarise and analyse them;
- use graphical techniques to provide a visual summary of one or more data series;
- use numerical techniques (such as an average) to summarise data series;
- recognise the strengths and limitations of such methods;
- recognise the usefulness of data transformations to gain additional insight into a set of data.

Complete your diagnostic test for Chapter 1 now to create your personal study plan. Exercises with an icon ? *are also available for practice in MathXL with additional supporting resources.*

Introduction

The aim of descriptive statistical methods is simple: to present information in a clear, concise and accurate manner. The difficulty in analysing many phenomena, be they economic, social or otherwise, is that there is simply too much information for the mind to assimilate. The task of descriptive methods is therefore to summarise all this information and draw out the main features, without distorting the picture.

Consider, for example, the problem of presenting information about the wealth of British citizens (which follows later in this chapter). There are about 17 million adults for whom data are available: to present the data in raw form (i.e. the wealth holdings of each and every person) would be neither useful nor informative (it would take about 30 000 pages of a book, for example). It would be more useful to have much less information, but information that was still representative of the original data. In doing this, much of the original information would be deliberately lost; in fact, descriptive statistics might be described as the art of constructively throwing away much of the data!

There are many ways of summarising data and there are few hard and fast rules about how you should proceed. Newspapers and magazines often provide innovative (although not always successful) ways of presenting data. There are, however, a number of techniques that are tried and tested, and these are the subject of this chapter. These are successful because: (a) they tell us something useful about the underlying data; and (b) they are reasonably familiar to many people, so we can all talk in a common language. For example, the average tells us about the location of the data and is a familiar concept to most people. For example, my son talks of his day at school being 'average'.

The appropriate method of analysing the data will depend on a number of factors: the type of data under consideration; the sophistication of the audience;

and the 'message' that it is intended to convey. One would use different methods to persuade academics of the validity of one's theory about inflation than one would use to persuade consumers that Brand X powder washes whiter than Brand Y. To illustrate the use of the various methods, three different topics are covered in this chapter. First we look at the relationship between educational attainment and employment prospects. Do higher qualifications improve your employment chances? The data come from people surveyed in 2004/5, so we have a sample of cross-section data giving a picture of the situation at one point in time. We look at the distribution of educational attainments amongst those surveyed, as well as the relationship to employment outcomes. In this example we simply count the numbers of people in different categories (e.g. the number of people with a degree qualification who are employed).

Second, we examine the distribution of wealth in the UK in 2003. The data are again cross-section, but this time we can use more sophisticated methods since wealth is measured on a ratio scale. Someone with £200 000 of wealth is twice as wealthy as someone with £100 000 for example, and there is a meaning to this ratio. In the case of education, one cannot say with any precision that one person is twice as educated as another (hence the perennial debate about educational standards). The educational categories may be ordered (so one person can be more educated than another, although even that may be ambiguous) but we cannot measure the 'distance' between them. We refer to this as education being measured on an ordinal scale. In contrast, there is not an obvious natural ordering to the three employment categories (employed, unemployed, inactive), so this is measured on a nominal scale.

Third, we look at national spending on investment over the period 1973 to 2005. This is time series data, as we have a number of observations on the variable measured at different points in time. Here it is important to take account of the time dimension of the data: things would look different if the observations were in the order 1973, 1983, 1977, . . . rather than in correct time order. We also look at the relationship between two variables – investment and output – over that period of time and find appropriate methods of presenting it.

In all three cases we make use of both graphical and numerical methods of summarising the data. Although there are some differences between the methods used in the three cases these are not watertight compartments: the methods used in one case might also be suitable in another, perhaps with slight modification. Part of the skill of the statistician is to know which methods of analysis and presentation are best suited to each particular problem.

Summarising data using graphical techniques

Education and employment, or, after all this, will you get a job?

We begin by looking at a question which should be of interest to you: how does education affect your chances of getting a job? It is now clear that education improves one's life chances in various ways, one of the possible benefits being

Table 1.1 Economic status and educational qualifications, 2006   *(numbers in 000s)*

	Higher education	A levels	Other qualification	No qualification	Total
In work	8541	5501	10 702	2260	27 004
Unemployed	232	247	758	309	1546
Inactive	1024	1418	3150	2284	7876
Total	9797	7166	14 610	4853	36 426

that it reduces the chances of being out of work. But by how much does it reduce those chances? We shall use a variety of graphical techniques to explore the question.

The raw data for this investigation come from the *Education and Training Statistics for the U.K. 2006.*[1] Some of these data are presented in Table 1.1 and show the numbers of people by employment status (either in work, unemployed, or inactive, i.e. not seeking work) and by educational qualification (higher education, A-levels, other qualification or no qualification). The table gives a cross-tabulation of employment status by educational qualification and is simply a count (the frequency) of the number of people falling into each of the 12 cells of the table. For example, there were 8 541 000 people in work who had experience of higher education. This is part of a total of just over 36 million people of working age. Note that the numbers in the table are in thousands, for the sake of clarity.

The bar chart

The first graphical technique we shall use is the bar chart and this is shown in Figure 1.1. This summarises the educational qualifications of those in work, i.e. the data in the first row of the table. The four educational categories are arranged along the horizontal (x) axis, while the frequencies are measured on the vertical (y) axis. The height of each bar represents the numbers in work for that category.

The biggest group is seen to be those with 'other qualifications', although this is now not much bigger than the 'higher education' category (the numbers entering higher education have been increasing substantially in the UK over time, although this is not evident in this chart, which uses cross-section data). The 'no qualifications' category is the smallest, although it does make up a substantial fraction of those in work.

It would be interesting to compare this distribution with those for the unemployed and inactive. This is done in Figure 1.2, which adds bars for these other two categories. This multiple bar chart shows that, as for the 'in work' category, among the inactive and unemployed, the largest group consists

---

[1] This is now an internet-only publication, available at http://www.dcsf.gov.uk/rsgateway/DB/VOL/v000696/Vweb03-2006V1.pdf.

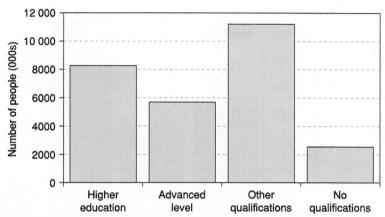

Figure 1.1
Educational
qualifications of people
in work in the UK, 2006

Note: The height of each bar is determined by the associated frequency. The first bar is 8541 units high, the second is 5501 units high and so on. The ordering of the bars could be reversed ('no qualifications' becoming the first category) without altering the message.

of those with 'other' qualifications (which are typically vocational qualifications). These findings simply reflect the fact that 'other qualifications' is the largest category. We can also begin to see whether more education increases your chance of having a job. For example, compare the height of the 'in work' bar to the 'inactive' bar. It is relatively much higher for those with higher education than for those with no qualifications. In other words, the likelihood of being inactive rather than employed is lower for graduates. However, we are having to make judgements about the relative heights of dif-

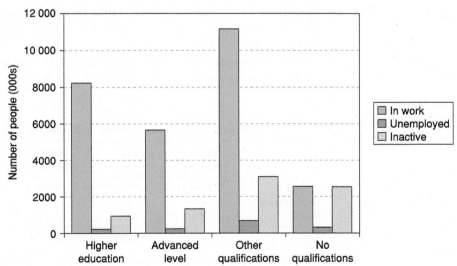

Figure 1.2
Educational
qualifications by
employment category

Note: The bars for the unemployed and inactive categories are constructed in the same way as for those in work: the height of the bar is determined by the frequency.

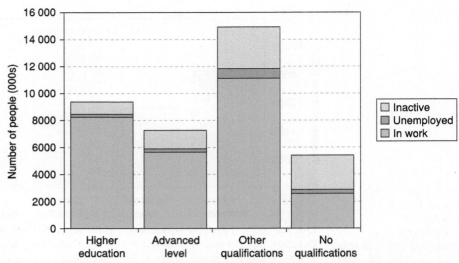

Figure 1.3
Stacked bar chart of educational qualifications and employment status

Note: The overall height of each bar is determined by the sum of the frequencies of the category, given in the final row of Table 1.1.

ferent bars simply by eye, and it is easy to make a mistake. It would be better if we could draw charts that would better highlight the differences. Figure 1.3 shows an alternative method of presentation: the stacked bar chart. In this case the bars are stacked one on top of another instead of being placed side by side. This is perhaps slightly better and the different overall sizes of the categories is clearly brought out. However, we are still having to make tricky visual judgements about proportions.

A clearer picture emerges if the data are transformed to (column) percentages, i.e. the columns are expressed as percentages of the column totals (e.g. the *proportion* of graduates are in work, rather than the number). This makes it easier directly to compare the different educational categories. These figures are shown in Table 1.2.

Having done this, it is easier to make a direct comparison of the different education categories (columns). This is shown in Figure 1.4, where all the bars

Table 1.2 Economic status and educational qualifications: column percentages

	Higher education	A levels	Other qualification	No qualification	All
In work	87%	77%	73%	47%	74%
Unemployed	2%	3%	5%	6%	4%
Inactive	10%	20%	22%	47%	22%
Totals	99%	100%	100%	100%	100%

Note: The column percentages are obtained by dividing each frequency by the column total. For example, 87% is 8541 divided by 9797; 77% is 5501 divided by 7166, and so on. Columns may not sum to 100% due to rounding.

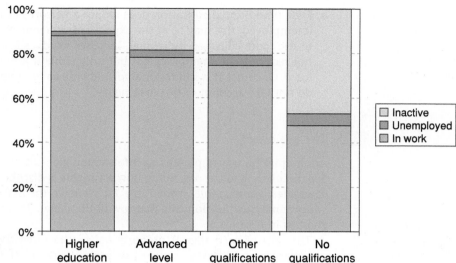

Figure 1.4
Percentages in each
employment category, by
educational qualification

are of the same height (representing 100%) and the components of each bar
now show the *proportions* of people in each educational category either in work,
unemployed or inactive.

It is now clear how economic status differs according to education and the
result is quite dramatic. In particular:

● The probability of unemployment increases rapidly with lower educational
  attainment (this interprets proportions as probabilities, i.e. if 10% are out of
  work then the probability that a person picked at random is unemployed
  is 10%).
● The biggest difference is between the no qualifications category and the other
  three, which have relatively smaller differences between them. In particular,
  A-levels and other qualifications show a similar pattern.

Notice that we have looked at the data in different ways, drawing different
charts for the purpose. You need to consider which type of chart of most
suitable for the data you have and the questions you want to ask. There is no
one graph that is ideal for all circumstances.

Can we safely conclude therefore that the probability of your being unemployed is significantly reduced by education? Could we go further and argue
that the route to lower unemployment generally is through investment in
education? The answer *may* be 'yes' to both questions, but we have not proved
it. Two important considerations are as follows:

● Innate ability has been ignored. Those with higher ability are more likely to
  be employed *and* are more likely to receive more education. Ideally we would
  like to compare individuals of similar ability but with different amounts of
  education.

● Even if additional education does reduce a person's probability of becoming unemployed, this may be at the expense of someone else, who loses their job to the more educated individual. In other words, additional education does not reduce total unemployment but only shifts it around among the labour force. Of course it is still rational for individuals to invest in education if they do not take account of this externality.

The pie chart

Another useful way of presenting information graphically is the **pie chart**, which is particularly good at describing how a variable is distributed between different categories. For example, from Table 1.1 we have the distribution of people by educational qualification (the first row of the table). This can be shown in a pie chart as in Figure 1.5.

The area of each slice is proportional to the respective frequency and the pie chart is an alternative means of presentation to the bar chart shown in Figure 1.1. The percentages falling into each education category have been added around the chart, but this is not essential. For presentational purposes it is best not to have too many slices in the chart: beyond about six the chart tends to look crowded. It might be worth amalgamating less important categories to make a chart look clearer.

The chart reveals that 40% of those employed fall into the 'other qualification' category, and that just 8% have no qualifications. This may be contrasted with Figure 1.6, which shows a similar chart for the unemployed (the second row of Table 1.1).

The 'other qualification' category is a little larger in this case, but the 'no qualification' group now accounts for 20% of the unemployed, a big increase. Further, the proportion with a degree approximately halves from 32% to 15%.

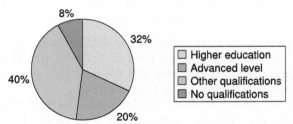

Note: If you have to draw a pie chart by hand, the angle of each slice can be calculated as follows:

$$angle = \frac{frequency}{total\ frequency} \times 360.$$

The angle of the first slice, for example, is

$$\frac{8541}{27\ 004} \times 360 = 113.9°.$$

Figure 1.5
Educational qualifications of those in work

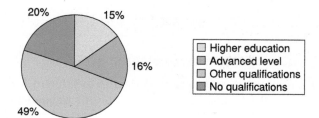

Figure 1.6
Educational
qualifications of the
unemployed

Producing charts using Microsoft Excel

Most of the charts in this book were produced using Excel's charting facility. Without wishing to dictate a precise style, you should aim for a similar, uncluttered look. Some tips you might find useful are:

- Make the grid lines dashed in a light grey colour (they are not actually part of the chart, hence should be discreet) or eliminate altogether.
- Get rid of the background fill (grey by default, alter to 'No fill'). It does not look great when printed.
- On the x-axis, make the labels horizontal or vertical, not slanted – it is then difficult to see which point they refer to. If they are slanted, double click on the x-axis then click the alignment tab.
- Colour charts look great on-screen but unclear if printed in black and white. Change the style type of the lines or markers (e.g. make some dashed) to distinguish them on paper.
- Both axes start at zero by default. If all your observations are large numbers this may result in the data points being crowded into one corner of the graph. Alter the scale on the axes to fix this: set the minimum value on the axis to be slightly less than the minimum observation.

Otherwise, Excel's default options will usually give a good result.

Exercise 1.1

The following table shows the total numbers (in millions) of tourists visiting each country and the numbers of English tourists visiting each country:

	France	Germany	Italy	Spain
All tourists	12.4	3.2	7.5	9.8
English tourists	2.7	0.2	1.0	3.6

(a) Draw a bar chart showing the total numbers visiting each country.

(b) Draw a stacked bar chart, which shows English and non-English tourists making up the total visitors to each country.

(c) Draw a pie chart showing the distribution of all tourists between the four destination countries.

(d) Do the same for English tourists and compare results.

Looking at cross-section data: wealth in the UK in 2003

 Frequency tables and histograms

We now move on to examine data in a different form. The data on employment and education consisted simply of frequencies, where a characteristic (such as higher education) was either present or absent for a particular individual. We now look at the distribution of wealth – a variable that can be measured on a ratio scale so that a different value is associated with each individual. For example, one person might have £1000 of wealth, another might have £1 million. Different presentational techniques will be used to analyse this type of data. We use these techniques to investigate questions such as how much wealth does the average person have and whether wealth is evenly distributed or not.

The data are given in Table 1.3, which shows the distribution of wealth in the UK for the year 2003 (the latest available at the time of writing), available at http://www.hmrc.gov.uk/stats/personal_wealth/menu.htm. This is an example of a frequency table. Wealth is difficult to define and to measure; the data shown here refer to *marketable* wealth (i.e. items such as the right to a pension, which cannot be sold, are excluded) and are estimates for the population (of adults) as a whole based on taxation data.

Wealth is divided into 14 class intervals: £0 up to (but not including) £10 000; £10 000 up to £24 999, etc., and the number (or frequency) of individuals within each class interval is shown. Note that the widths of the intervals (the class widths) vary up the wealth scale: the first is £10 000, the

Table 1.3 **The distribution of wealth, UK, 2003**

Class interval (£)	Numbers (thousands)
0–9999	2448
10 000–24 999	1823
25 000–39 999	1375
40 000–49 999	480
50 000–59 999	665
60 000–79 999	1315
80 000–99 999	1640
100 000–149 999	2151
150 000–199 000	2215
200 000–299 000	1856
300 000–499 999	1057
500 000–999 999	439
1 000 000–1 999 999	122
2 000 000 or more	50
Total	17 636

Note: It would be impossible to show the wealth of all 18 million individuals, so it has been summarised in this frequency table.

second £15 000 (= 25 000 − 10 000); the third £15 000 also and so on. This will prove an important factor when it comes to graphical presentation of the data.

This table has been constructed from the original 17 636 000 observations on individuals' wealth, so it is already a summary of the original data (note that all the frequencies have been expressed in thousands in the table) and much of the original information is lost. The first decision to make if one had to draw up such a frequency table from the raw data is how many class intervals to have, and how wide they should be. It simplifies matters if they are all of the same width but in this case it is not feasible: if 10 000 were chosen as the standard width there would be many intervals between 500 000 and 1 000 000 (50 of them in fact), most of which would have a zero or very low frequency. If 100 000 were the standard width, there would be only a few intervals and the first (0–100 000) would contain 9746 observations (55% of all observations), so almost all the interesting detail would be lost. A compromise between these extremes has to be found.

A useful rule of thumb is that the number of class intervals should equal the square root of the total frequency, subject to a maximum of about 12 intervals. Thus, for example, a total of 25 observations should be allocated to five intervals; 100 observations should be grouped into 10 intervals; and 17 636 should be grouped into about 12 (14 are used here). The class widths should be equal in so far as this is feasible, but should increase when the frequencies become very small.

To present these data graphically one could draw a bar chart as in the case of education above, and this is presented in Figure 1.7. Before reading on, spend some time looking at it and ask yourself what is wrong with it.

The answer is that the figure gives a completely misleading picture of the data! (Incidentally, this is the picture that you will get using a spreadsheet computer program, as I have done here. All the standard packages appear to do this, so beware. One wonders how many decisions have been influenced by data presented in this incorrect manner.)

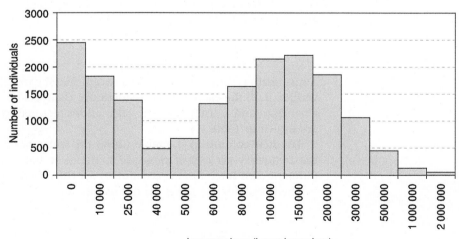

Figure 1.7
Bar chart of the distribution of wealth in the UK, 2003

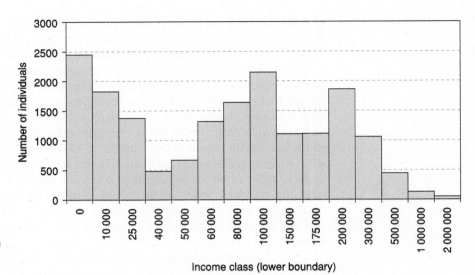

Figure 1.8
The wealth distribution with alternative class intervals

Why is the figure wrong? Consider the following argument. The diagram appears to show that there are few individuals around £40 000 to £60 000 (the frequency is at a low of 480 (thousand)) but many around £150 000. But this is just the result of the difference in the class width at these points (10 000 at £40 000 and 50 000 at £150 000). Suppose that we divide up the £150 000–£200 000 class into two: £150 000 to £175 000 and £175 000 to £200 000. We divide the frequency of 2215 equally between the two (this is an arbitrary decision but illustrates the point). The graph now looks like Figure 1.8.

Comparing Figures 1.7 and 1.8 reveals a difference: the hump around £150 000 has now disappeared, replaced by a small crater. But this is disturbing – it means that the shape of the distribution can be altered simply by altering the class widths. If so, how can we rely upon visual inspection of the distribution? What does the 'real' distribution look like? A better method would make the shape of the distribution independent of how the class intervals are arranged. This can be done by drawing a **histogram**.

The histogram

A histogram is similar to a bar chart except that it corrects for differences in class widths. If all the class widths are identical, then there is no difference between a bar chart and a histogram. The calculations required to produce the histogram are shown in Table 1.4.

The new column in the table shows the **frequency density**, which measures the frequency *per unit of class width*. Hence it allows a direct comparison of different class intervals, i.e. accounting for the difference in class widths.

The frequency density is defined as follows

$$frequency\ density = \frac{frequency}{class\ width} \tag{1.1}$$

Using this formula corrects the figures for differing class widths. Thus 0.2448 = 2448/10 000 is the first frequency density, 0.1215 = 1823/15 000 is the second,

Table 1.4 Calculation of frequency densities

Range	Number or frequency	Class width	Frequency density
0–	2448	10 000	0.2448
10 000–	1823	15 000	0.1215
25 000–	1375	15 000	0.0917
40 000–	480	10 000	0.0480
50 000–	665	10 000	0.0665
60 000–	1315	20 000	0.0658
80 000–	1640	20 000	0.0820
100 000–	2151	50 000	0.0430
150 000–	2215	50 000	0.0443
200 000–	3524	3 800 000	0.0009

Note: As an alternative to the frequency density, one could calculate the frequency per 'standard' class width, with the standard width chosen to be 10 000 (the narrowest class). The values in column 4 would then be 2448; 1215.3 (= 1823 ÷ 1.5); 916.7; etc. This would lead to the same shape of histogram as using the frequency density.

etc. Above £200 000 the class widths are very large and the frequencies small (too small to be visible on the histogram), so these classes have been combined.

The width of the final interval is unknown, so has to be estimated in order to calculate the frequency density. It is likely to be extremely wide since the wealthiest person may well have assets valued at several £m (or even £bn); the value we assume will affect the calculation of the frequency density and therefore of the shape of the histogram. Fortunately it is in the tail of the distribution and only affects a small number of observations. Here we assume (arbitrarily) a width of £3.8m to be a 'reasonable' figure, giving an upper class boundary of £4m.

The frequency density is then plotted on the vertical axis against wealth on the horizontal axis to give the histogram. One further point needs to be made: the scale on the wealth axis should be linear as far as possible, e.g. £50 000 should be twice as far from the origin as £25 000. However, it is difficult to fit all the values onto the horizontal axis without squeezing the graph excessively at lower levels of wealth, where most observations are located. Therefore the classes above £100 000 have been squeezed and the reader's attention is drawn to this. The result is shown in Figure 1.9.

The effect of taking frequency densities is to make the *area* of each block in the histogram represent the frequency, rather than the height, which now shows the density. This has the effect of giving an accurate picture of the shape of the distribution.

Having done all this, what does the histogram show?

- The histogram is heavily skewed to the right (i.e. the long tail is to the right).
- The modal class interval is £0–£10 000 (i.e. has the greatest density: no other £10 000 interval has more individuals in it).
- A little under half of all people (45.9% in fact) have less than £80 000 of marketable wealth.
- About 20% of people have more than £200 000 of wealth.[2]

---

[2] Due to the compressing of some class widths, it is difficult to see this accurately on the histogram. There are limitations to graphical presentation.

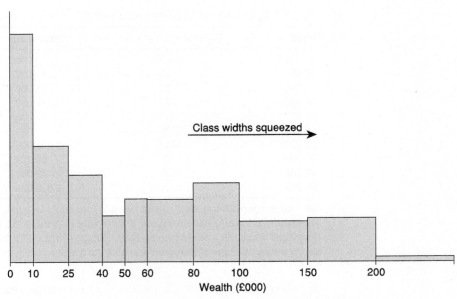

Figure 1.9
Histogram of the
distribution of wealth
in the UK, 2003

Note: A frequency polygon would be the result if, instead of drawing blocks for the histogram, lines were drawn connecting the centres of the top of each block. The diagram is better drawn with blocks, in general.

The figure shows quite a high degree of inequality in the wealth distribution. Whether this is acceptable or even desirable is a value judgement. It should be noted that part of the inequality is due to differences in age: younger people have not yet had enough time to acquire much wealth and therefore appear worse off, although in life-time terms this may not be the case. To obtain a better picture of the distribution of wealth would require some analysis of the acquisition of wealth over the life-cycle (or comparing individuals of a similar age). In fact, correcting for age differences does not make a big difference to the pattern of wealth distribution (on this point and on inequality in wealth in general, see Atkinson (1983), Chapters 7 and 8).

Relative frequency and cumulative frequency distributions

An alternative way of illustrating the wealth distribution uses the relative and cumulative frequencies of the data. The relative frequencies show the *proportion* of observations that fall into each class interval, so, for example, 2.72% of individuals have wealth holdings between £40 000 and £50 000 (480 000 out of 17 636 000 individuals). Relative frequencies are shown in the third column of Table 1.5, using the following formula[3]

$$Relative\ frequency = \frac{frequency}{sum\ of\ frequencies} = \frac{f}{\Sigma f} \tag{1.2}$$

---

[3] If you are unfamiliar with the Σ notation then read Appendix 1A to this chapter before continuing.

Table 1.5 Calculation of relative and cumulative frequencies

Range	Frequency	Relative frequency (%)	Cumulative frequency
0–	2448	13.9	2448
10 000–	1823	10.3	4271
25 000–	1375	7.8	5646
40 000–	480	2.7	6126
50 000–	665	3.8	6791
60 000–	1315	7.5	8106
80 000–	1640	9.3	9746
100 000–	2151	12.2	11 897
150 000–	2215	12.6	14 112
200 000–	1856	10.5	15 968
300 000–	1057	6.0	17 025
500 000–	439	2.5	17 464
1 000 000–	122	0.7	17 586
2 000 000–	50	0.3	17 636
Total	17 636	100.00	

Note: Relative frequencies are calculated in the same way as the column percentages in Table 1.2. Thus for example, 13.9% is 2448 divided by 17 636. Cumulative frequencies are obtained by cumulating, or successively adding, the frequencies. For example, 4271 is 2448 + 1823, 5646 is 4271 + 1375, etc.

The AIDS epidemic

To show how descriptive statistics can be helpful in presenting information we show below the 'population pyramid' for Botswana (one of the countries most seriously affected by AIDS), projected for the year 2020. This is essentially two bar charts (one for men, one for women) laid on their sides, showing the frequencies in each age category (rather than wealth categories). The inner pyramid (in the darker colour) shows the projected population given the existence of AIDS; the outer pyramid assumes no deaths from AIDS.

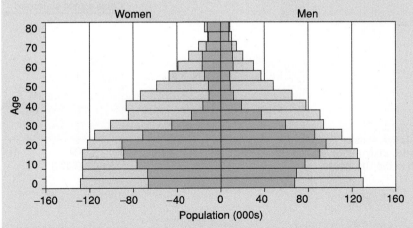

Original source of data: US Census Bureau, *World Population Profile 2000*. Graph adapted from the UNAIDS web site at http://www.unaids.org/epidemic_update/report/Epi_report.htm#thepopulation.

One can immediately see the huge effect of AIDS, especially on the 40–60 age group (currently aged 20–40), for both men and women. These people would normally be in the most productive phase of their lives but, with AIDS, the country will suffer enormously with many old and young people dependent on a small working population. The severity of the future problems is brought out vividly in this simple graphic, based on the bar chart.

The sum of the relative frequencies has to be 100% and this acts as a check on the calculations.

The cumulative frequencies, shown in the fourth column, are obtained by cumulating (successively adding) the frequencies. The cumulative frequencies show the total number of individuals with wealth *up to* a given amount; for example, about 10 million people have less than £100 000 of wealth.

Both relative and cumulative frequency distributions can be drawn, in a similar way to the histogram. In fact, the relative frequency distribution has exactly the same shape as the frequency distribution. This is shown in Figure 1.10. This time we have written the relative frequencies above the appropriate column, although this is not essential.

The cumulative frequency distribution is shown in Figure 1.11, where the blocks increase in height as wealth increases. The simplest way to draw this is to cumulate the frequency densities (shown in the final column of Table 1.4) and to use these values as the *y*-axis coordinates.

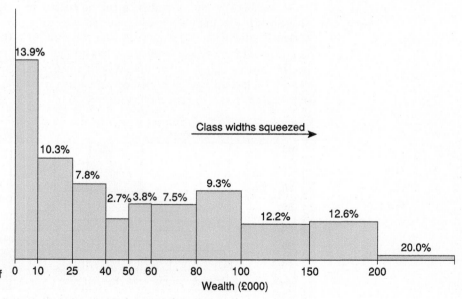

Figure 1.10
The relative density frequency distribution of wealth in the UK, 2003

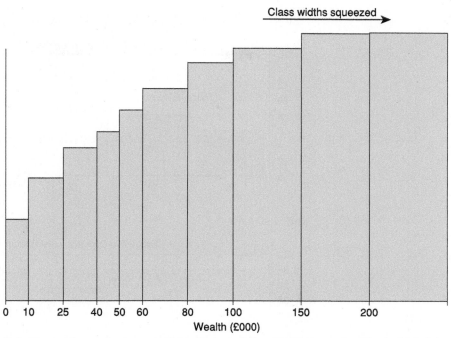

Class widths squeezed ➔

Wealth (£000)

Figure 1.11
The cumulative
frequency distribution of
wealth in the UK, 2003

Note: The *y*-axis coordinates are obtained by cumulating the frequency densities in Table 1.4 above. For example, the first two *y* coordinates are 0.2448, 0.3663.

Worked example 1.1

There is a mass of detail in the sections above, so this worked example is intended to focus on the essential calculations required to produce the summary graphs. Simple artificial data are deliberately used to avoid the distraction of a lengthy interpretation of the results and their meaning. The data on the variable X and its frequencies f are shown in the following table, with the calculations required:

X	Frequency, f	Relative frequency	Cumulative frequency, F
10	6	0.17	6
11	8	0.23	14
12	15	0.43	29
13	5	0.14	34
14	1	0.03	35
Total	35	1.00	

Notes:
The X values are unique but could be considered the mid-point of a range, as earlier.
The relative frequencies are calculated as 0.17 = 6/35, 0.23 = 8/35, etc.
The cumulative frequencies are calculated as 14 = 6 + 8, 29 = 6 + 8 + 15, etc.
The symbol F usually denotes the cumulative frequency in statistical work.

➔

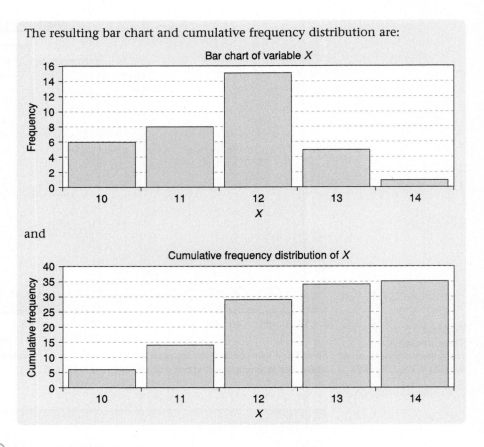

The resulting bar chart and cumulative frequency distribution are:

Bar chart of variable X

Cumulative frequency distribution of X

and

Exercise 1.2

Given the following data:

Range	Frequency
0–10	20
11–30	40
31–60	30
60–100	20

(a) Draw both a bar chart and a histogram of the data and compare them.

(b) Calculate cumulative frequencies and draw a cumulative frequency diagram.

Summarising data using numerical techniques

Graphical methods are an excellent means of obtaining a quick overview of the data, but they are not particularly precise, nor do they lend themselves to further analysis. For this we must turn to numerical measures such as the average. There are a number of different ways in which we may describe a distribution such as that for wealth. If we think of trying to describe the histogram, it is useful to have:

- A measure of location giving an idea of whether people own a lot of wealth or a little. An example is the average, which gives some idea of where the distribution is located along the *x*-axis. In fact, we will encounter three different measures of the 'average':
  - the mean;
  - the median;
  - the mode.
- A measure of dispersion showing how wealth is dispersed around (usually) the average, whether it is concentrated close to the average or is generally far away from it. An example here is the standard deviation.
- A measure of skewness showing how symmetric or not the distribution is, i.e. whether the left half of the distribution is a mirror image of the right half or not. This is obviously not the case for the wealth distribution.

We consider each type of measure in turn.

Measures of location: the mean

The arithmetic mean, commonly called the average, is the most familiar measure of location, and is obtained simply by adding all the observations and dividing by the number of observations. If we denote the wealth of the *i*th household by x_i (so that the index *i* runs from 1 to N, where N is the number of observations; as an example, x_3 would be the wealth of the third household) then the mean is given by the following formula

$$\mu = \frac{\sum_{i=1}^{i=N} x_i}{N} \tag{1.3}$$

where μ (the Greek letter mu, pronounced 'myu'[4]) denotes the mean and $\sum_{i=1}^{i=N} x_i$

(read 'sigma *x i*, from *i* = 1 to N', Σ being the Greek capital letter sigma) means the sum of the *x* values. We may simplify this to

$$\mu = \frac{\sum x}{N} \tag{1.4}$$

when it is obvious which *x* values are being summed (usually all the available observations). This latter form is more easily readable and we will generally use this.

Worked example 1.2

We will find the mean of the values 17, 25, 28, 20, 35. The total of these five numbers is 125, so we have $N = 5$ and $\sum x = 125$. Therefore the mean is

$$\mu = \frac{\sum x}{N} = \frac{125}{5} = 25$$

Formula (1.3) can only be used when all the individual *x* values are known. The frequency table for wealth does not show all 17 million observations, however,

---

[4] Well, mathematicians pronounce it like this, but modern Greeks do not. For them it is 'mi'.

but only the range of values for each class interval and the associated frequency. In this case of grouped data the following equivalent formula may be used

$$\mu = \frac{\sum\limits_{i=1}^{i=C} f_i x_i}{\sum\limits_{i=1}^{i=C} f_i} \qquad (1.5)$$

or, more simply

$$\mu = \frac{\sum fx}{\sum f} \qquad (1.6)$$

In this formula

- x denotes the **mid-point** of each class interval, since the individual x values are unknown. The mid-point is used as the representative x value for each class. In the first class interval, for example, we do not know precisely where each of the 2448 observations lies. Hence we *assume* they all lie at the mid-point, £5000. This will cause a slight inaccuracy – because the distribution is so skewed, there are more households below the mid-point than above it in every class interval except, perhaps, the first. We ignore this problem here, and it is less of a problem for most distributions which are less skewed than this one.
- The summation runs from 1 to C, the number of class intervals, or distinct x values. f times x gives the total wealth in each class interval. If we sum over the 14 class intervals we obtain the total wealth of all individuals.
- $\sum f_i = N$ gives the total number of observations, the sum of the individual frequencies. The calculation of the mean, μ, for the wealth data is shown in Table 1.6.

Table 1.6 The calculation of average wealth

Range	x	f	fx
0–	5.0	2448	12 240
10 000–	17.5	1823	31 902
25 000–	32.5	1375	44 687
40 000–	45.0	480	21 600
50 000–	55.0	665	36 575
60 000–	70.0	1315	92 050
80 000–	90.0	1640	147 600
100 000–	125.0	2151	268 875
150 000–	175.0	2215	387 625
200 000–	250.0	1856	464 000
300 000–	400.0	1057	422 800
500 000–	750.0	439	329 250
1 000 000–	1500.0	122	183 000
2 000 000–	3000.0	50	150 000
Total		17 636	2 592 205

Note: The *fx* column gives the product of the values in the *f* and *x* columns (so, for example, 5.0 × 2448 = 12 240, which is the total wealth held by those in the first class interval). The sum of the *fx* values gives total wealth.

From this we obtain

$$\mu = \frac{2\,592\,205}{17\,636} = 146.984$$

Note that the x values are expressed in £000, so we must remember that the mean will also be in £000; the average wealth holding is therefore £146 984. Note that the frequencies have also been divided by 1000, but this has no effect upon the calculation of the mean since f appears in both numerator and denominator of the formula for the mean.

The mean tells us that if the total wealth were divided up equally between all individuals, each would have £146 984. This value may seem surprising, since the histogram clearly shows most people have wealth below this point (approximately 65% of individuals are below the mean, in fact). The mean does not seem to be typical of the wealth that most people have. The reason the mean has such a high value is that there are some individuals whose wealth is way above the figure of £146 984 – up into the £millions, in fact. The mean is the 'balancing point' of the distribution – if the histogram were a physical model, it would balance on a fulcrum placed at 146 984. The few very high wealth levels exert a lot of leverage and counter-balance the more numerous individuals below the mean.

Worked example 1.3

Suppose we have 10 families with a single television in their homes, 12 families with two televisions each and 3 families with three. You can probably work out in your head that there are 43 televisions in total (10 + 24 + 9) owned by the 25 families (10 + 12 + 3). The average number of televisions per family is therefore 43/25 = 1.72.

Setting this out formally, we have (as for the wealth distribution, but simpler):

x	f	fx
1	10	10
2	12	24
3	3	9
Totals	25	43

This gives our resulting mean as 1.72. Note that our data are discrete values in this case and we have the actual values, not a broad class interval.

The mean as the expected value

We also refer to the mean as the **expected value** of x and write

$$E(x) = \mu = 146\,984 \tag{1.7}$$

$E(x)$ is read 'E of x' or 'the expected value of x'. The mean is the expected value in the sense that, if we selected a household at random from the population we would 'expect', its wealth to be £146 984. It is important to note that this is a *statistical* expectation, rather than the everyday use of the term. Most of the random individuals we encounter have wealth substantially below this value. Most people might therefore 'expect' a lower value because that is their everyday experience; but statisticians are different, they always expect the mean value.

The expected value notation is particularly useful in keeping track of the effects upon the mean of certain data transformations (e.g. dividing wealth by 1000 also divides the mean by 1000); Appendix 1B provides a detailed explanation. Use is also made of the E operator in inferential statistics, to describe the properties of estimators (see Chapter 4).

The sample mean and the population mean

Very often we have only a sample of data (as in the worked example above), and it is important to distinguish this case from the one where we have all the possible observations. For this reason, the sample mean is given by

$$\bar{x} = \frac{\sum x}{n} \text{ or } \bar{x} = \frac{\sum fx}{\sum f} \text{ for grouped data} \tag{1.8}$$

Note the distinctions between μ (the population mean) and $\bar{x}$ (the sample mean), and between N (the size of the population) and n (the sample size). Otherwise, the calculations are identical. It is a convention to use Greek letters, such as μ, to refer to the population and Roman letters, such as $\bar{x}$, to refer to a sample.

The weighted average

Sometimes observations have to be given different weightings in calculating the average, as the following example. Consider the problem of calculating the average spending per pupil by an education authority. Some figures for spending on primary (ages 5 to 11), secondary (11 to 16) and post-16 pupils are given in Table 1.7.

Clearly, significantly more is spent on secondary and post-16 pupils (a general pattern throughout England and most other countries) and the overall average should lie somewhere between 1750 and 3820. However, taking a simple average of these values would give the wrong answer, because there are different numbers of children in the three age ranges. The numbers and proportions of children in each age group are given in Table 1.8.

Table 1.7 Cost per pupil in different types of school (£ p.a.)

	Primary	Secondary	Post-16
Unit cost	1750	3100	3820

Table 1.8 Numbers and proportions of pupils in each age range

	Primary	Secondary	Post-16	Total
Numbers	8000	7000	3000	18 000
Proportion	44%	39%	17%	

As there are relatively more primary school children than secondary, and relatively fewer post-16 pupils, the primary unit cost should be given greatest weight in the averaging process and the post-16 unit cost the least. The **weighted average** is obtained by multiplying each unit cost figure by the proportion of children in each category and summing. The weighted average is therefore

$$0.44 \times 1750 + 0.39 \times 3100 + 0.17 \times 3820 = 2628 \qquad (1.9)$$

The weighted average gives an answer closer to the primary unit cost than does the simple average of the three figures (2890 in this case), which would be misleading. The formula for the weighted average is

$$\bar{x}_w = \Sigma_i w_i x_i \qquad (1.10)$$

where w represents the weights, *which must sum to one*, i.e.

$$\Sigma_i w_i = 1 \qquad (1.11)$$

and x represents the unit cost figures.

Notice that what we have done is equivalent to multiplying each unit cost by its frequency (8000, etc.) and then dividing the sum by the grand total of 18 000. This is the same as the procedure we used for the wealth calculation. The difference with weights is that we first divide 8000 by 18 000 (and 7000 by 18 000, etc.) to obtain the weights, which must then sum to one, and use these weights in formula (1.10).

Calculating your degree result

If you are a university student your final degree result will probably be calculated as a weighted average of your marks on the individual courses. The weights may be based on the credits associated with each course or on some other factors. For example, in my university the average mark for a year is a weighted average of the marks on each course, the weights being the credit values of each course.

The grand mean G, on which classification is based, is then a weighted average of the averages for the different years, as follows

$$G = \frac{0 \times Year\ 1 + 40 \times Year\ 2 + 60 \times Year\ 3}{100}$$

i.e. the year 3 mark has a weight of 60%, year 2 is weighted 40% and the first year is not counted at all.

For students taking a year abroad the formula is slightly different

$$G = \frac{0 \times Year\ 1 + 40 \times Year\ 2 + 25 \times Yabroad + 60 \times Year\ 3}{125}$$

Note that, to accommodate the year abroad mark, the weights on years 2 and 3 are reduced (to 40/125 = 32% and 60/125 = 48% respectively).

The median

Returning to the study of wealth, the unrepresentative result for the mean suggests that we may prefer a measure of location which is not so strongly affected by outliers (extreme observations) and skewness.

The median is a measure of location which is more robust to such extreme values; it may be defined by the following procedure. Imagine everyone in a line from poorest to wealthiest. Go to the individual located halfway along the line. Ask what their wealth is. Their answer is the median. The median is clearly unaffected by extreme values, unlike the mean: if the wealth of the richest person were doubled (with no reduction in anyone else's wealth) there would be no effect upon the median. The calculation of the median is not so straightforward as for the mean, especially for grouped data. The following worked example shows how to calculate the median for ungrouped data.

Worked example 1.4 The median

Calculate the median of the following values: 45, 12, 33, 80, 77.

First we put them into ascending order: 12, 33, 45, 77, 80.

It is then easy to see that the middle value is 45. This is the median. Note that if the value of the largest observation changes to, say, 150, the value of the median is unchanged. This is not the case for the mean, which would change from 49.4 to 63.4.

If there is an even number of observations, then there is no middle observation. The solution is to take the average of the two middle observations. For example:

Find the median of 12, 33, 45, 63, 77, 80.

Note the new observation, 63, making six observations. The median value is halfway between the third and fourth observations, i.e. (45 + 63)/2 = 54.

For grouped data there are two stages to the calculation: first we must first identify the class interval which contains the median person, then we must calculate where in the interval that person lies.

(1) To find the appropriate class interval: since there are 17 636 000 observations, we need the wealth of the person who is 8 818 000 in rank order. The table of cumulative frequencies (see Table 1.5 above) is the most suitable for this. There are 8 106 000 individuals with wealth of less than £80 000 and 9 746 000 with wealth of less than £100 000. The middle person therefore falls into the £80 000–100 000 class. Furthermore, given that 8 818 000 falls roughly half way between 8 106 000 and 9 746 000 it follows that the median is close to the middle of the class interval. We now go on to make this statement more precise.

(2) To find the position in the class interval, we can now use formula (1.12)

$$median = x_L + (x_U - x_L)\left\{\frac{\frac{N+1}{2} - F}{f}\right\}$$ (1.12)

where

x_L = the lower limit of the class interval containing the median

x_U = the upper limit of this class interval

N = the number of observations (using $N + 1$ rather than N in the formula is only important when N is relatively small)

F = the cumulative frequency of the class intervals up to (but not including) the one containing the median

f = the frequency for the class interval containing the median.

For the wealth distribution we have

$$median = 80\,000 + (100\,000 - 80\,000)\left\{\frac{\dfrac{17\,636\,000}{2} - 8\,106\,000}{1\,640\,000}\right\} = £90\,829$$

This alternative measure of location gives a very different impression: it is less than two-thirds of the mean. Nevertheless, it is equally valid despite having a different meaning. It demonstrates that the person 'in the middle' has wealth of £90 829 and in this sense is typical of the UK population. Before going on to compare these measures further we examine a third: the mode.

Generalising the median – quantiles

The idea of the median as the middle of the distribution can be extended: quartiles divide the distribution into four equal parts, quintiles into five, deciles into 10, and finally percentiles divide the distribution into 100 equal parts. Generically they are known as quantiles. We shall illustrate the idea by examining deciles (quartiles are covered below).

The first decile occurs one-tenth of the way along the line of people ranked from poorest to wealthiest. This means we require the wealth of the person ranked 1 763 600 (= $N/10$) in the distribution. From the table of cumulative frequencies, this person lies in the first class interval. Adapting formula (1.12), we obtain

$$first\ decile = 0 + (10\,000 - 0) \times \left\{\frac{1\,763\,600 - 0}{2\,448\,000}\right\} = £7203$$

Thus we estimate that any household with less than £7203 of wealth falls into the bottom 10% of the wealth distribution. In a similar fashion, the ninth decile can be found by calculating the wealth of the household ranked 15 872 400 (= $N \times 9/10$) in the distribution.

The mode

The **mode** is defined as that level of wealth which occurs with the greatest frequency, in other words the value that occurs most often. It is most useful and easiest to calculate when one has all the data and there are relatively few distinct observations. This is the case in the simple example below.

Suppose we have the following data on sales of dresses by a shop, according to size

Size	Sales
8	7
10	25
12	36
14	11
16	3
18	1

The modal size is 12. There are more women buying dresses of this size than any other. This may be the most useful form of average as far as the shop is concerned. Although it needs to stock a range of sizes, it knows it needs to order more dresses in size 12 than in any other size. The mean would not be so helpful in this case (it is $\bar{x} = 11.7$) as it is not an actual dress size.

In the case of grouped data matters are more complicated. It is the modal class interval which is required, once the intervals have been corrected for width (otherwise a wider class interval is unfairly compared with a narrower one). For this, we can again make use of the frequency densities. From Table 1.4 it can be seen that it is the first interval, from £0 to £10 000, which has the highest frequency density. It is 'typical' of the distribution because it is the one which occurs most often (using the frequency densities, *not* frequencies). The wealth distribution is most concentrated at this level and more people are like this in terms of wealth than anything else. Once again it is notable how different it is from both the median and the mean.

The three measures of location give different messages because of the skewness of the distribution: if it were symmetric they would all give approximately the same answer. Here we have a rather extreme case of skewness, but it does serve to illustrate how the different measures of location compare. When the distribution is skewed to the right, as here, they will be in the order mode, median, mean; if skewed to the left the ordering is reversed. If the distribution has more than one peak then this rule for orderings may not apply.

Which of the measures is 'correct' or most useful? In this particular case the mean is not very useful: it is heavily influenced by extreme values. The median is therefore often used when discussing wealth (and income) distributions. Where inequality is even more pronounced, as in some less developed countries, then the mean is even less informative. The mode is also quite useful in telling us about a large section of the population, although it can be sensitive to how the class intervals are arranged. If the data were arranged such that there was a class interval of £5000 to £15 000, then this might well be the modal class, conveying a slightly different impression.

The three different measures of location are marked on the histogram in Figure 1.12. This brings out the substantial difference between the measures for a skewed distribution such as for wealth.

Exercise 1.3

(a) For the data in Exercise 2, calculate the mean, median and mode of the data.

(b) Mark these values on the histogram you drew for Exercise 2.

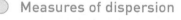

Measures of dispersion

Two different distributions (e.g. wealth in two different countries) might have the same mean yet look very different, as shown in Figure 1.13 (the distributions have been drawn using smooth curves rather than bars to improve clarity). In one country everyone might have a similar level of wealth (curve B). In another, although the average is the same there might be extremes of great wealth and poverty (curve A). A measure of dispersion is a number which allows us to distinguish between these two situations.

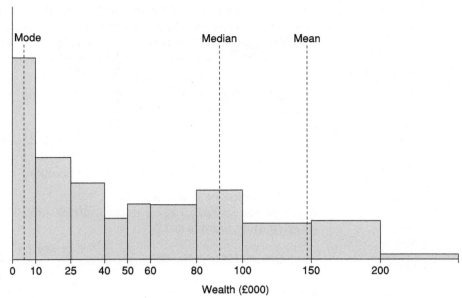

Figure 1.12
The histogram with
mean, median and mode
marked

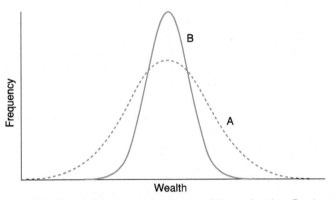

Figure 1.13
Two distributions with
different degrees of
dispersion

Note: Distribution A has a greater degree of dispersion than B, where everyone has a similar level of wealth.

The simplest measure of dispersion is the range, which is the difference between the smallest and largest observations. It is impossible to calculate accurately from the table of wealth holdings since the largest observation is not available. In any case, it is not a very useful figure since it relies on two extreme values and ignores the rest of the distribution. In simpler cases it might be more informative. For example, in an exam the marks may range from a low of 28% to a high of 74%. In this case the range is 74 − 28 = 46 and this tells us something useful.

An improvement is the inter-quartile range (IQR), which is the difference between the first and third quartiles. It therefore defines the limits of wealth of the middle half of the distribution and ignores the very extremes of the distribution. To calculate the first quartile (which we label Q_1) we have to go one-quarter of the way along the line of wealth holders (ranked from poorest to wealthiest) and ask the person in that position what their wealth is. Their answer is the first quartile. The calculation is as follows:

- one-quarter of 17 636 is 4409;
- the person ranked 4409 is in the £25 000–40 000 class;
- adapting formula (1.12)

$$Q_1 = 25\,000 + (40\,000 - 25\,000)\left\{\frac{4409 - 4271}{1375}\right\} = 26\,505.5 \qquad (1.13)$$

The third quartile is calculated in similar fashion:

- three-quarters of 17 636 is 13 227;
- the person ranked 13 227 is in the £150 000–200 000 class;
- again using formula (1.12)

$$Q_3 = 150\,000 + (200\,000 - 150\,000)\left\{\frac{13\,227 - 11\,897}{2215}\right\} = 180\,022.6$$

and therefore the inter-quartile range is $Q_3 - Q_1 = 180\,022 - 26\,505 = 153\,517$. This might be reasonably rounded to £150 000 given the approximations in our calculation, and is a much more memorable figure.

This gives one summary measure of the dispersion of the distribution: the higher the value the more spread-out is the distribution. Two different wealth distributions might be compared according to their inter-quartile ranges therefore, with the country having the larger figure exhibiting greater inequality. Note that the figures would have to be expressed in a common unit of currency for this comparison to be valid.

Worked example 1.5 The range and inter-quartile range

Suppose 110 children take a test, with the following results:

Mark, X	Frequency, f	Cumulative frequency, F
13	5	5
14	13	18
15	29	47
16	33	80
17	17	97
18	8	105
19	4	109
20	1	110
Total	110	

The range is simply $20 - 13 = 7$. The inter-quartile range requires calculation of the quartiles. Q_1 is given by the value of the 27.5th observation ($= 110/4$), which is 15. Q_3 is the value of the 82.5th observation ($= 110 \times 0.75$) which is 17. The IQR is therefore $17 - 15 = 2$ marks. Half the students achieve marks within this range.

Notice that a slight change in the data (three more students getting 16 rather than 17 marks) would alter the IQR to 1 mark (16–15). The result should be treated with some caution therefore. This is a common problem when there are few distinct values of the variable (eight in this example). It is often worth considering whether a few small changes to the data could alter the calculation considerably. In such a case, the original result might not be very robust.

The variance

A more useful measure of dispersion is the variance, which makes use of all of the information available, rather than trimming the extremes of the distribution. The variance is denoted by the symbol σ^2. σ is the Greek lower-case letter sigma, so σ^2 is read 'sigma squared'. It has a completely different meaning from Σ (capital sigma) used before. Its formula is

$$\sigma^2 = \frac{\Sigma(x - \mu)^2}{N} \qquad (1.14)$$

In this formula, $x - \mu$ measures the distance from each observation to the mean. Squaring these makes all the deviations positive, whether above or below the mean. We then take the average of all the squared deviations from the mean. A more dispersed distribution (such as A in Figure 1.13) will tend to have larger deviations from the mean, and hence a larger variance. In comparing two distributions with similar means, therefore, we could examine their variances to see which of the two has the greater degree of dispersion. With grouped data the formula becomes

$$\sigma^2 = \frac{\Sigma f(x - \mu)^2}{\Sigma f} \qquad (1.15)$$

The calculation of the variance is shown in Table 1.9 and from this we obtain

$$\sigma^2 = \frac{1\,001\,772\,261.83}{17\,636} = 56\,802.69$$

This calculated value is before translating back into the original units of measurement, as was done for the mean by multiplying by 1000. In the case of the variance, however, we must multiply by 1 000 000 which is the *square* of 1000. The variance is therefore 56 802 690 000. Multiplying by the square of 1000 is a consequence of using squared deviations in the variance formula (see Appendix 1B on E and V operators for more details of this).

One needs to be a little careful about the units of measurement therefore. If the mean is reported at 146.984 then it is appropriate to report the variance as 56 802.69. If the mean is reported as 146 984 then the variance should be reported as 56 802 690 000. Note that it is only the presentation that changes: the underlying facts are the same.

The standard deviation

In what units is the variance measured? As we have used a squaring procedure in the calculation, we end up with something like 'squared' £s, which is not very

Table 1.9 The calculation of the variance of wealth

Range	Mid-point x (£000)	Frequency, f	Deviation $(x - \mu)$	$(x - \mu)^2$	$f(x - \mu)^2$
0	5.0	2448	−142.0	20 159.38	49 350 158.77
10 000–	17.5	1823	−129.5	16 766.04	30 564 482.57
25 000–	32.5	1375	−114.5	13 106.52	18 021 469.99
40 000–	45.0	480	−102.0	10 400.68	4 992 326.62
50 000–	55.0	665	−92.0	8461.01	5 626 568.95
60 000–	70.0	1315	−77.0	5926.49	7 793 339.80
80 000–	90.0	1640	−57.0	3247.15	5 325 317.93
100 000–	125.0	2151	−22.0	483.28	1 039 544.38
150 000–	175.0	2215	28.0	784.91	1 738 579.16
200 000–	250.0	1856	103.0	10 612.35	19 696 526.45
300 000–	400.0	1057	253.0	64 017.23	67 666 217.05
500 000–	750.0	439	603.0	363 628.63	159 632 966.88
1 000 000–	1500.0	122	1353.0	1 830 653.04	223 339 670.45
2 000 000–	3000.0	50	2853.0	8 139 701.86	406 985 092.85
Total		17 636			1 001 772 261.83

convenient. Because of this, we define the square root of the variance to be the standard deviation, which is therefore back in £s. The standard deviation is therefore given by

$$\sigma = \sqrt{\frac{\Sigma(x - \mu)^2}{N}} \qquad (1.16)$$

or, for grouped data

$$\sigma = \sqrt{\frac{\Sigma f(x - \mu)^2}{N}} \qquad (1.17)$$

These are simply the square roots of equations (1.14) and (1.15). The standard deviation of wealth is therefore $\sqrt{56\,802.69} = 238.333$. This is in £000, so the standard deviation is actually £238 333 (note that this is the square root of 56 802 690 000, as it should be). On its own the standard deviation (and the variance) is not easy to interpret since it is not something we have an intuitive feel for, unlike the mean. It is more useful when used in a comparative setting. This will be illustrated later on.

The variance and standard deviation of a sample

As with the mean, a different symbol is used to distinguish a variance calculated from the population and one calculated from a sample. In addition, the sample variance is calculated using a slightly different formula from the one for the population variance. The sample variance is denoted by s^2 and its formula is given by equations (1.18) and (1.19) below

$$s^2 = \frac{\Sigma(x - \bar{x})^2}{n - 1} \qquad (1.18)$$

and, for grouped data

$$s^2 = \frac{\sum f(x - \bar{x})^2}{n - 1}$$ (1.19)

where n is the sample size. The reason $n - 1$ is used in the denominator rather than n (as one might expect) is the following. Our real interest is in the population variance, and the sample variance is an estimate of it. The former is measured by the dispersion around μ, and the sample variance should ideally be measured around μ also. However, μ is unknown, so $\bar{x}$ is used instead. But the variation of the sample observations around $\bar{x}$ tends to be smaller than that around μ. Using $n - 1$ rather than n in the formula compensates for this and the result is an unbiased[5] (i.e. correct on average) estimate of the population variance.

Using the correct formula is more important the smaller is the sample size, as the proportionate difference between $n - 1$ and n increases. For example, if $n = 10$, the adjustment amounts to 10% of the variance; when $n = 100$ the adjustment is only 1%.

The sample standard deviation is given by the square root of equation (1.18) or (1.19).

Worked example 1.6 The variance and standard deviation

We continue with the previous worked example, relating to students' marks. The variance and standard deviation can be calculated as:

X	f	fx	x − μ	(x − μ)²	f(x − μ)²
13	5	65	−2.81	7.89	39.45
14	13	182	−1.81	3.27	42.55
15	29	435	−0.81	0.65	18.98
16	33	528	0.19	0.04	1.20
17	17	289	1.19	1.42	24.11
18	8	144	2.19	4.80	38.40
19	4	76	3.19	10.18	40.73
20	1	20	4.19	17.56	17.56
Totals	110	1739			222.99

The mean is calculated as $1739/110 = 15.81$ and from this the deviations column $(x - \mu)$ is calculated (so $-2.81 = 13 - 15.81$, etc.).

The variance is calculated as $\sum f(x - \mu)^2/(n - 1) = 222.99/109 = 2.05$. The standard deviation is therefore 1.43, the square root of 2.05. (Calculations are shown to two decimal places but have been calculated using exact values.)

For distributions which are approximately symmetric and bell-shaped (i.e. the observations are clustered around the mean) there is an approximate relationship between the standard deviation and the inter-quartile range. This rule of thumb is that the IQR is 1.3 times the standard deviation. In this case, $1.3 \times 1.43 = 1.86$, close to the value calculated earlier, 2.

---

[5] The concept of *bias* is treated in more detail in Chapter 4.

Alternative formulae for calculating the variance and standard deviation

The following formulae give the same answers as equations (1.14) to (1.17) but are simpler to calculate, either by hand or using a spreadsheet. For the population variance one can use

$$\sigma^2 = \frac{\sum x^2}{N} - \mu^2 \tag{1.20}$$

or, for grouped data

$$\sigma^2 = \frac{\sum fx^2}{\sum f} - \mu^2 \tag{1.21}$$

The calculation of the variance using equation (1.21) is shown in Figure 1.14.

Figure 1.14
Descriptive statistics calculated using *Excel*

The sample variance can be calculated using

$$s^2 = \frac{\sum x^2 - n\bar{x}^2}{n - 1} \tag{1.22}$$

or, for grouped data

$$s^2 = \frac{\sum fx^2 - n\bar{x}^2}{n - 1} \tag{1.23}$$

The standard deviation may of course be obtained as the square root of these formulae.

Using a calculator or computer for calculation

Electronic calculators and (particularly) computers have simplified the calculation of the mean, etc. Figure 1.14 shows how to set out the above calculations in a spreadsheet (*Microsoft Excel* in this case) including some of the appropriate cell formulae.

The variance in this case is calculated using the formula $\sigma^2 = \dfrac{\sum fx^2}{\sum f} - \mu^2$, which is the formula given in equation (1.21) above. Note that it gives the same result as that calculated in the text.

The following formulae are contained in the cells:

D5:	= C5*B5	to calculate f times x
E5:	= D5*B5	to calculate f times x^2
C20:	= SUM(C5:C18)	to sum the frequencies
H6:	= D20/C20	calculates $\sum fx / \sum f$
H7:	= E20/C20 − H6^2	calculates $\sum fx^2 / \sum f - \mu^2$
H8:	= SQRT(H7)	calculates σ
H9:	= H8/H6	calculates σ / μ

The coefficient of variation

The measures of dispersion examined so far are all measures of **absolute dispersion** and, in particular, their values depend upon the units in which the variable is measured. It is therefore difficult to compare the degrees of dispersion of two variables which are measured in different units. For example, one could not compare wealth in the UK with that in Germany if the former uses £s and the latter euros for measurement. Nor could one compare the wealth distribution in one country between two points in time because inflation alters the value of the currency over time. The solution is to use a measure of **relative dispersion**, which is independent of the units of measurement. One such measure is the **coefficient of variation**, defined as

$$Coefficient\ of\ variation = \frac{\sigma}{\mu} \tag{1.24}$$

i.e. the standard deviation divided by the mean. Whenever the units of measurement are changed, the effect upon the mean and the standard deviation is the same, hence the coefficient of variation is unchanged. For the wealth distribution its value is 238.333/146.984 = 1.621, i.e. the standard deviation is 162% of the mean. This may be compared directly with the coefficient of variation of a different wealth distribution to see which exhibits a greater relative degree of dispersion.

Independence of units of measurement

It is worth devoting a little attention to this idea that some summary measures are independent of the units of measurement and some are not, as it occurs quite often in statistics and is not often appreciated at first. A statistic that is independent of the units of measurement is one which is unchanged even when the units of measurement are changed. It is therefore more useful in general than a statistic which is not independent, since one can use it to make comparisons, or judgements, without worrying about how it was measured.

The mean is not independent of the units of measurement. If we are told the average income in the UK is 20 000, for example, we need to know whether it is measured in pounds sterling, euros or even dollars. The underlying level of income is the same, of course, but it is measured differently. By contrast, the rate of growth (described in detail shortly) is independent of the units of measurement. If we are told it is 3% per annum, it would be the same whether it were calculated in pounds, euros or dollars. If told that the rate of growth in the US is 2% per annum, we can immediately conclude that the UK is growing faster, no further information is needed.

Most measures we have encountered so far, such as the mean and variance, do depend on units of measurement. The coefficient of variation is one that does not. We now go on to describe another means of measuring dispersion that avoids the units of measurement problem.

The standard deviation of the logarithm

Another solution to the problem of different units of measurement is to use the logarithm[6] of wealth rather than the actual value. The reason why this works can best be illustrated by an example. Suppose that between 1997 and 2003 each individual's wealth doubled, so that $X_i^{2003} = 2X_i^{1997}$, where X_i^t indicates the wealth of individual i in year t. It follows that the standard deviation of wealth in 2003, X^{2003}, is therefore exactly twice that of 1997, X^{1997}. Taking logs, we have $\ln X_i^{2003} = \ln 2 + \ln X_i^{1997}$, so it follows that the distribution of $\ln X^{2003}$ is the same as that of $\ln X^{1997}$, except that it is shifted to the right by $\ln 2$ units. The variances (and hence standard deviations) of the two logarithmic distributions must therefore be the same, indicating no change in the *relative* dispersion of the two wealth distributions.

The standard deviation of the logarithm of wealth is calculated from the data in Table 1.10. The variance turns out to be

Table 1.10 The calculation of the standard deviation of the logarithm of wealth

Range	Mid-point x (£000)	ln (x)	Frequency, f	fx	fx^2
0–	5.0	1.609	2448	3939.9	6341.0
10 000–	17.5	2.862	1823	5217.8	14 934.4
25 000–	32.5	3.481	1375	4786.7	16 663.7
40 000–	45.0	3.807	480	1827.2	6955.5
50 000–	55.0	4.007	665	2664.9	10 679.0
60 000–	70.0	4.248	1315	5586.8	23 735.4
80 000–	90.0	4.500	1640	7379.7	33 207.2
100 000–	125.0	4.828	2151	10 385.7	50 145.4
150 000–	175.0	5.165	2215	11 440.0	59 085.2
200 000–	250.0	5.521	1856	10 247.8	56 583.0
300 000–	400.0	5.991	1057	6333.0	37 943.8
500 000–	750.0	6.620	439	2906.2	19 239.3
1 000 000–	1500.0	7.313	122	892.2	6524.9
2 000 000–	3000.0	8.006	50	400.3	3205.1
Totals			17 636	74 008.2	345 243.0

Note: Use the 'ln' key on your calculator or the = LN() function in a spreadsheet to obtain natural logarithms of the data. You should obtain ln 5 = 1.609, ln 17.5 = 2.862, etc.

---

[6] See Appendix 1C if you are unfamiliar with logarithms. Note that we use the natural logarithm here, but the effect would be the same using logs to base 10.

$$\sigma^2 = \frac{345\,243.0}{17\,636} = \left(\frac{74\,008.2}{17\,636}\right)^2 = 1.966$$

and the standard deviation $\sigma = 1.402$.

For comparison, the standard deviation of log income in 1979 (discussed in more detail later on) is 1.31, so there appears to have been a slight increase in relative dispersion over this time period.

Measuring deviations from the mean: z-scores

Imagine the following problem. A man and a woman are arguing over their career records. The man says he earns more than she does, so is more successful. The woman replies that women are discriminated against and that, relative to women, she is doing better than the man is, relative to other men. Can the argument be resolved?

Suppose the data are as follows: the average male salary is £19 500, the average female salary £16 800. The standard deviation of male salaries is £4750, for women it is £3800. The man's salary is £31 375 while the woman's is £26 800. The man is therefore £11 875 above the mean, the woman £10 000. However, women's salaries are less dispersed than men's, so the woman has done well to reach £26 800.

One way to resolve the problem is to calculate the *z-score*, which gives the salary in terms of the *number of standard deviations from the mean*. Thus for the man, the z-score is

$$z = \frac{X - \mu}{\sigma} = \frac{31\,375 - 19\,500}{4750} = 2.50 \tag{1.25}$$

Thus the man is 2.5 standard deviations above the male mean salary. For the woman the calculation is

$$z = \frac{26\,800 - 16\,800}{3800} = 2.632 \tag{1.26}$$

The woman is 2.632 standard deviations above her mean and therefore wins the argument – she is nearer the top of her distribution than is the man and so is more of an outlier. Actually, this probably will not end the argument, but is the best the statistician can do! The z-score is an important concept which will be used again later in the book when we cover hypothesis testing (Chapter 5).

Chebyshev's inequality

Use of the z-score leads on naturally to Chebyshev's inequality, which tells us about the proportion of observations that fall into the tails of any distribution, regardless of its shape. The theorem is expressed as follows

> At least $(1 - 1/k^2)$ of the observations in any distribution
> lie within k standard deviations of the mean $\tag{1.27}$

If we take the female wage distribution given above, we can ask what proportion of women lie beyond 2.632 standard deviations from the mean (in both tails of the distribution). Setting $k = 2.632$, then $(1 - 1/k^2) = (1 - 1/2.632^2) = 0.8556$.

So at least 85% of women have salaries within ±2.632 standard deviations of the mean, i.e. between £6 800 (= 16 800 − 2.632 × 3800) and £26 800 (= 16 800 + 2.632 × 3800). 15% of women therefore lie outside this range.

Chebyshev's inequality is a very conservative rule since it applies to *any* distribution; if we know more about the shape of a particular distribution (for example, men's heights follow a Normal distribution – see Chapter 3) then we can make a more precise statement. In the case of the Normal distribution, over 99% of men are within 2.632 standard deviations of the average height, because there is a concentration of observations near the centre of the distribution.

We can also use Chebyshev's inequality to investigate the inter-quartile range. The formula (1.27) implies that 50% of observations lie within $\sqrt{2} = 1.41$ standard deviations of the mean, a more conservative value than our previous 1.3.

Exercise 1.4

(a) For the data in Exercise 2, calculate the inter-quartile range, the variance and the standard deviation.

(b) Calculate the coefficient of variation.

(c) Check if the relationship between the IQR and the standard deviation stated in the text is approximately true for this distribution.

(d) Approximately how much of the distribution lies within one standard deviation either side of the mean? How does this compare with the prediction from Chebyshev's inequality?

Measuring skewness

The **skewness** of a distribution is the third characteristic that was mentioned earlier, in addition to location and dispersion. The wealth distribution is heavily skewed to the right, or **positively** skewed; it has its long tail in the right-hand end of the distribution. A measure of skewness gives a numerical indication of how asymmetric is the distribution.

One measure of skewness, known as the **coefficient of skewness**, is

$$\frac{\sum f(x - \mu)^3}{N\sigma^3} \tag{1.28}$$

and it is based upon *cubed* deviations from the mean. The result of applying formula (1.28) is positive for a right-skewed distribution (such as wealth), zero for a symmetric one, and negative for a left-skewed one. Table 1.11 shows the calculation for the wealth data (some rows are omitted for brevity). From this we obtain

$$\frac{\sum f(x - \mu)^3}{N} = \frac{1\,563\,796\,357\,499}{17\,636} = 88\,670\,693.89$$

and dividing by σ^3 gives $\dfrac{88\,670\,693.89}{13\,537\,964} = 6.550$, which is positive, as expected.

The measure of skewness is much less useful in practical work than measures of location and dispersion, and even knowing the value of the coefficient does not always give much idea of the shape of the distribution: two quite different distributions can share the same coefficient. In descriptive work it is probably better to draw the histogram itself.

Table 1.11 Calculation of the skewness of the wealth data

Range	Mid-point x (£000)	Frequency f	Deviation $x - \mu$	$(x - \mu)^3$	$f(x - \mu)^3$
0	5.0	2448	−142.0	−2 862 304	−7 006 919 444
10 000	17.5	1823	−129.5	−2 170 929	−3 957 603 101
:		:		:	:
1 000 000	1500.0	122	1353.0	2 476 903 349	302 182 208 638
2 000 000	3000.0	50	2853.0	23 222 701 860	1 161 135 092 991
Totals		17 636	4457.2	25 927 167 232	1 563 796 357 499

Comparison of the 2003 and 1979 distributions of wealth

Some useful lessons may be learned by comparing the 2003 distribution with its counterpart from 1979. This covers the period of Conservative government starting with Mrs Thatcher in 1979 up until the first six years of Labour administration. This shows how useful the various summary statistics are when it comes to comparing two different distributions. The wealth data for 1979 are given in Problem 1.5 below, where you are asked to confirm the following calculations.

Average wealth in 1979 was £16 399, about one-ninth of its 2003 value. The average increased substantially therefore (at about 10% per annum, on average), but some of this was due to inflation rather than a real increase in the quantity of assets held. In fact, between 1979 and 2003 the retail price index rose from 52.0 to 181.3, i.e. it increased approximately three and a half times. Thus the nominal[7] increase (i.e. in cash terms, before any adjustment for rising prices) in wealth is made up of two parts: (i) an inflationary part which more than tripled measured wealth and (ii) a real part, consisting of a 2.5 fold increase (thus $3.5 \times 2.5 = 9$, approximately). Price indexes are covered in Chapter 10 where it is shown more formally how to divide a nominal increase into price and real (quantity) components. It is likely that the extent of the real increase in wealth is overstated here due to the use of the retail price index rather than an index of asset prices. A substantial part of the increase in asset values over the period is probably due to the very rapid rise in house prices (houses form a significant part of the wealth of many households).

The standard deviation is similarly affected by inflation. The 1979 value is 25 552 compared to 2003's 238 333, which is about nine times larger. The spread of the distribution appears to have increased therefore (even if we take account of the general price effect). Looking at the coefficient of variation, however, shows that it has increased from 1.56 to 1.62 which is a modest difference. The spread of the distribution *relative to its mean* has not changed by much. This is confirmed by calculating the standard deviation of the logarithm: for 1979 this gives a figure of 1.31, slightly smaller than the 2003 figure (of 1.40).

The measure of skewness for the 1979 data comes out as 5.723, smaller that the 2003 figure (of 6.550). This suggests that the 1979 distribution is less skewed

---

[7] This is a different meaning of the term 'nominal' from that used earlier to denote data measured on a nominal scale, i.e. data grouped into categories without an obvious ordering. Unfortunately, both meanings of the word are in common (statistical) usage, although it should be obvious from the context which use is meant.

than is the 1994 one. Again, these two figures can be directly compared because they do not depend upon the units in which wealth is measured. However, the relatively small difference is difficult to interpret in terms of how the shape of the distribution has changed.

Summary

- Descriptive statistics are useful for summarising large amounts of information, highlighting the main features but omitting the detail.
- Different techniques are suited to different types of data, e.g. bar charts for cross-section data and rates of growth for time series.
- Graphical methods, such as the bar chart, provide a picture of the data. These give an informal summary but they are unsuitable as a basis for further analysis.
- Important graphical techniques include the bar chart, frequency distribution, relative and cumulative frequency distributions, histogram and pie chart. For time-series data a time-series chart of the data is informative.
- Numerical techniques are more precise as summaries. Measures of location (such as the mean), of dispersion (the variance) and of skewness form the basis of these techniques.
- Important numerical summary statistics include the mean, median and mode; variance, standard deviation and coefficient of variation; coefficient of skewness.
- For bivariate data the scatter diagram (or XY graph) is a useful way of illustrating the data.
- Data are often transformed in some way before analysis, for example by taking logs. Transformations often make it easier to see key features of the data in graphs and sometimes make summary statistics easier to interpret. For example, with time-series data the average rate of growth may be more appropriate than the mean of the series.

Key terms and concepts

bar chart	mode
box and whiskers plot	outliers
coefficient of variation	pie chart
compound growth	quantiles
cross-section data	relative and cumulative frequencies
cross-tabulation	scatter diagram (XY chart)
data transformation	skewness
frequencies	standard deviation
frequency table	time-series data
histogram	variance
mean	z-score
median	

Reference

Atkinson, A. B. *The Economics of Inequality*, 1983, 2nd edn., Oxford University Press.

2

Probability

Learning outcomes

By the end of this chapter you should be able to:

- understand the essential concept of the probability of an event occurring;

- appreciate that the probability of a combination of events occurring can be calculated using simple arithmetic rules (the addition and multiplication rules);

- understand that a probability can depend upon the outcome of other events (conditional probability);

- know how to make use of probability theory to help make decisions in situations of uncertainty.

Complete your diagnostic test for Chapter 2 now to create your personal study plan. Exercises with an icon ⁇ are also available for practice in MathXL with additional supporting resources.

Probability theory and statistical inference

In October 1985 Mrs Evelyn Adams of New Jersey, USA, won $3.9 m in the State lottery at odds of 1 in 3 200 000. In February 1986 she won again, although this time only (!) $1.4 m at odds of 1 in 5 200 000. The odds against both these wins were calculated at about 1 in 17 300 bn. Mrs Adams is quoted as saying 'They say good things come in threes, so . . .'.

The above story illustrates the principles of probability at work. The same principles underlie the theory of statistical inference, which is the task of drawing conclusions (inferences) about a population from a sample of data drawn from that population. For example, we might have a survey which shows that 30% of a sample of 100 families intend to take a holiday abroad next year. What can we conclude from this about *all* families? The techniques set out in this and subsequent chapters show how to accomplish this.

Why is knowledge of probability necessary for the study of statistical inference? In order to be able to say something about a population on the basis of some sample evidence we must first examine how the sample data are collected. In many cases, the sample is a random one, i.e. the observations making up the sample are chosen at random from the population. If a second sample were selected it would almost certainly be different from the first. Each member of the population has a particular probability of being in the sample (in simple random sampling the probability is the same for all members of the population). To understand sampling procedures, and the implications for statistical inference, we must therefore first examine the theory of probability.

As an illustration of this, suppose we wish to know if a coin is fair, i.e. equally likely to fall heads or tails. The coin is tossed 10 times and 10 heads are recorded. This constitutes a random sample of tosses of the coin. What can we infer about the coin? *If* it is fair, the probability of getting ten heads is 1 in 1024, so a fairly unlikely event seems to have happened. We might reasonably infer therefore that the coin is biased towards heads.

The definition of probability

The first task is to define precisely what is meant by probability. This is not as easy as one might imagine and there are a number of different schools of thought on the subject. Consider the following questions:

- What is the probability of 'heads' occurring on the toss of a coin?
- What is the probability of a driver having an accident in a year of driving?
- What is the probability of a country such as Peru defaulting on its international loan repayments (as Mexico did in the 1980s)?

We shall use these questions as examples when examining the different schools of thought on probability.

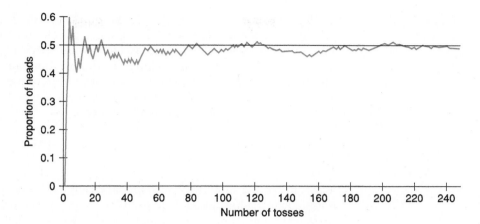

Figure 2.1
The proportion of
heads in 250 tosses
of a fair coin

The frequentist view

Considering the first question above, the frequentist view would be that the probability is equal to the proportion of heads obtained from a coin in the long run, i.e. if the coin were tossed many times. The first few results of such an experiment might be

H, T, T, H, H, H, T, H, T, . . .

After a while, the proportion of heads settles down at some particular fraction and subsequent tosses will individually have an insignificant effect upon the value. Figure 2.1 shows the result of tossing a coin 250 times and recording the proportion of heads (actually, this was simulated on a computer: life is too short to do it for real).

This shows the proportion settling down at a value of about 0.50, which indicates an unbiased coin (or rather, an unbiased computer in this case!). This value is the probability, according to the frequentist view. To be more precise, the probability is defined as the proportion of heads obtained as the number of tosses *approaches infinity*. In general we can define Pr(H), the probability of event H (in this case heads) occurring, as

$$\Pr(H) = \frac{\text{number of occurrences of } H}{\text{number of trials}}, \text{ as the number of trials approaches infinity.}$$

In this case, each toss of the coin constitutes a trial.

This definition gets round the obvious question of how many trials are needed before the probability emerges, but means that the probability of an event cannot strictly be obtained in finite time.

Although this approach appears attractive in theory, it does have its problems. One could not actually toss the coin an infinite number of times. Or, what if one took a different coin, would the results from the first coin necessarily apply to the second?

Perhaps more seriously, the definition is of less use for the second and third questions posed above. Calculating the probability of an accident is not too problematic: it may be defined as the proportion of all drivers having an accident during the year. However, this may not be relevant for a *particular* driver, since drivers vary so much in their accident records. And how would you answer the third question? There is no long run that we can appeal to. We cannot re-run history over and over again to see in what proportion of cases the country defaults. Yet this is what lenders want to know and credit-rating agencies have to assess. Maybe another approach is needed.

The subjective view

According to the subjective view, probability is a degree of belief that someone holds about the likelihood of an event occurring. It is inevitably subjective and therefore some argue that it should be the degree of belief that it is *rational* to hold, but this just shifts the argument to what is meant by 'rational'. Some progress can be made by distinguishing between prior and posterior beliefs. The former are those held before any evidence is considered; the latter are the modified probabilities in the light of the evidence. For example, one might initially believe a coin to be fair (the prior probability of heads is one-half), but not after seeing only five heads in fifty tosses (the posterior probability would be less than a half).

Although it has its attractions, this approach (which is the basis of Bayesian statistics) also has its drawbacks. It is not always clear how one should arrive at the prior beliefs, particularly when one really has no prior information. Also, these methods often require the use of sophisticated mathematics, which may account for the limited use made of them. The development of more powerful computers and user-friendly software may increase the popularity of the Bayesian approach.

There is not universal agreement therefore as to the precise definition of probability. We do not have space here to explore the issue further, so we will ignore the problem! The probability of an event occurring will be defined as a certain value and we will not worry about the precise origin or meaning of that value. This is an axiomatic approach: we simply state what the probability is, without justifying it, and then examine the consequences.

Exercise 2.1

(a) Define the probability of an event according to the frequentist view.

(b) Define the probability of an event according to the subjective view.

Exercise 2.2

For the following events, suggest how their probability might be calculated. In each case, consider whether you have used the frequentist or subjective view of probability (or possibly some mixture).

(a) The Republican party winning the next US election.

(b) The number 5 being the first ball drawn in next week's lottery.

(c) A repetition of the 2004 Asian tsunami.

(d) Your train home being late.

Probability theory: the building blocks

We start with a few definitions, to establish a vocabulary that we will subsequently use.

- An experiment is an action such as flipping a coin, which has a number of possible outcomes or events, such as heads or tails.
- A trial is a single performance of the experiment, with a single outcome.
- The sample space consists of all the possible outcomes of the experiment. The outcomes for a single toss of a coin are {heads, tails}, for example, and these constitute the sample space for a toss of a coin. The outcomes in the sample space are mutually exclusive, which means that the occurrence of one rules out all the others. One cannot have both heads and tails in a single toss of a coin. As a further example, if a single card is drawn at random from a pack, then the sample space may be drawn as in Figure 2.2. Each point represents one card in the pack and there are 52 points altogether. (The sample space could be set out in alternative ways. For instance, one could write a list of all the cards: ace of spades, king of spades, . . . , two of clubs. One can choose the representation most suitable for the problem at hand.)
- With each outcome in the sample space we can associate a probability, which is the chance of that outcome occurring. The probability of heads is one-half; the probability of drawing the ace of spades from a pack of cards is one in 52, etc.

There are restrictions upon the probabilities we can associate with the outcomes in the sample space. These are needed to ensure that we do not come up with self-contradictory results; for example, it would be odd to arrive at the conclusion that we could expect heads more than half the time *and* tails more than half the time. To ensure our results are always consistent, the following rules apply to probabilities:

- The probability of an event must lie between 0 and 1, i.e.

$$0 \leq \Pr(A) \leq 1, \text{ for any event } A \tag{2.1}$$

The explanation is straightforward. If A is certain to occur it occurs in 100% of all trials and so its probability is 1. If A is certain not to occur then its probability is 0, since it never happens however many trials there are. As one cannot be more certain than certain, probabilities of less than 0 or more than 1 can never occur, and equation (2.1) follows.

- The sum of the probabilities associated with all the outcomes in the sample space is 1. Formally

$$\sum P_i = 1 \tag{2.2}$$

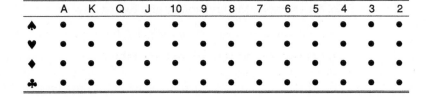

Figure 2.2
The sample space for drawing from a pack of cards

where P_i is the probability of event i occurring. This follows from the fact that one, and only one, of the outcomes *must* occur, since they are mutually exclusive and also exhaustive, i.e. they define all the possibilities.

- Following on from equation (2.2) we may define the complement of an event as everything in the sample space apart from that event. The complement of heads is tails, for example. If we write the complement of A as not-A then it follows that $\Pr(A) + \Pr(\text{not-}A) = 1$ and hence

$$\Pr(\text{not-}A) = 1 - \Pr(A) \tag{2.3}$$

Compound events

Most practical problems require the calculation of the probability of a set of outcomes rather than just a single one, or the probability of a series of outcomes in separate trials. For example, the probability of drawing a spade at random from a pack of cards encompasses 13 points in the sample space (one for each spade). This probability is 13 out of 52, or one-quarter, which is fairly obvious; but for more complex problems the answer is not immediately evident. We refer to such sets of outcomes as compound events. Some examples are getting a five *or* a six on a throw of a die or drawing an ace *and* a queen to complete a 'straight' in a game of poker.

It is sometimes possible to calculate the probability of a compound event by examining the sample space, as in the case of drawing a spade above. However, in many cases this is not so, for the sample space is too complex or even impossible to write down. For example, the sample space for three draws of a card from a pack consists of over 140 000 points! (A typical point might be, for example, the ten of spades, eight of hearts and three of diamonds.) An alternative method is needed. Fortunately there are a few simple rules for manipulating probabilities which help us to calculate the probabilities of compound events.

If the previous examples are examined closely it can be seen that outcomes are being compounded using the words 'or' and 'and': '. . . five *or* six on a single throw . . .'; '. . . an ace *and* a queen . . .'. 'And' and 'or' act as operators, and compound events are made up of simple events compounded by these two operators. The following rules for manipulating probabilities show how to use these operators and thus how to calculate the probability of a compound event.

The addition rule

This rule is associated with 'or'. When we want the probability of one outcome *or* another occurring, we add the probabilities of each. More formally, the probability of A or B occurring is given by

$$\Pr(A \text{ or } B) = \Pr(A) + \Pr(B) \tag{2.4}$$

So, for example, the probability of a five or a six on a roll of a die is

$$\Pr(5 \text{ or } 6) = \Pr(5) + \Pr(6) = 1/6 + 1/6 = 1/3 \tag{2.5}$$

This answer can be verified from the sample space, as shown in Figure 2.3. Each dot represents a simple event (one to six). The compound event is made up of two of the six points, shaded in Figure 2.3, so the probability is 2/6 or 1/3.

Figure 2.3
The sample space for
rolling a die

Figure 2.4
The sample space for
drawing a queen or
a spade

However, equation (2.4) is not a general solution to this type of problem, i.e. it does not *always* work, as can be seen from the following example. What is the probability of a queen or a spade in a single draw from a pack of cards? $Pr(Q) = 4/52$ (four queens in the pack) and $Pr(S) = 13/52$ (13 spades), so applying equation (2.4) gives

$$Pr(Q \text{ or } S) = Pr(Q) + Pr(S) = 4/52 + 13/52 = 17/52 \qquad (2.6)$$

However, if the sample space is examined, the correct answer is found to be 16/52, as in Figure 2.4. The problem is that one point in the sample space (the one representing the queen of spades) is double-counted, once as a queen and again as a spade. The event 'drawing a queen *and* a spade' is possible, and gets double-counted. Equation (2.4) has to be modified by subtracting the probability of getting a queen *and* a spade, to eliminate this double counting. The correct answer is obtained from

$$Pr(Q \text{ or } S) = Pr(Q) + Pr(S) - Pr(Q \text{ and } S) \qquad (2.7)$$
$$= 4/52 + 13/52 - 1/52$$
$$= 16/52$$

The general rule is therefore

$$Pr(A \text{ or } B) = Pr(A) + Pr(B) - Pr(A \text{ and } B) \qquad (2.8)$$

Rule (2.4) worked for the die example because $Pr(5 \text{ and } 6) = 0$ since a five and a six cannot simultaneously occur. The double counting did not affect the calculation of the probability.

In general, therefore, one should use equation (2.8), but when two events are mutually exclusive the rule simplifies to equation (2.4).

The multiplication rule

The multiplication rule is associated with use of the word 'and' to combine events. Consider a mother with two children. What is the probability that they are both boys? This is really a compound event: a boy on the first birth *and* a boy on the second. Assume that in a single birth a boy or girl is equally likely, so $Pr(boy) = Pr(girl) = 0.5$. Denote by $Pr(B1)$ the probability of a boy on the first birth and by $Pr(B2)$ the probability of a boy on the second. Thus the question asks for $Pr(B1 \text{ and } B2)$ and this is given by

$$Pr(B1 \text{ and } B2) = Pr(B1) \times Pr(B2) = 0.5 \times 0.5 \qquad (2.9)$$
$$= 0.25$$

Intuitively, the multiplication rule can be understood as follows. One-half of mothers have a boy on their first birth and of these, one-half will again have a boy on the second. Therefore a quarter (a half of one-half) of mothers have two boys.

Like the addition rule, the multiplication rule requires slight modification before it can be applied generally and give the right answer in all circumstances. The example assumes first and second births to be independent events, i.e. that having a boy on the first birth does not affect the probability of a boy on the second. This assumption is not always valid.

Write $Pr(B2|B1)$ to indicate the probability of the event $B2$ *given* that the event $B1$ has occurred. (This is known as the conditional probability, more precisely the probability of $B2$ conditional upon $B1$.) Let us drop the independence assumption and suppose the following

$$Pr(B1) = Pr(G1) = 0.5 \qquad (2.10)$$

i.e. boys and girls are equally likely on the first birth, and

$$Pr(B2|B1) = Pr(G2|G1) = 0.6 \qquad (2.11)$$

i.e. a boy is more likely to be followed by another boy, and a girl by another girl. (It is easy to work out $Pr(B2|G1)$ and $Pr(G2|B1)$. What are they?)

Now what is the probability of two boys? Half of all mothers have a boy first, and of these, 60% have another boy. Thus 30% (60% of 50%) of mothers have two boys. This is obtained from the rule

$$Pr(B1 \text{ and } B2) = Pr(B1) \times Pr(B2|B1) \qquad (2.12)$$
$$= 0.5 \times 0.6$$
$$= 0.3$$

Thus in general we have

$$Pr(A \text{ and } B) = Pr(A) \times Pr(B|A) \qquad (2.13)$$

which simplifies to

$$Pr(A \text{ and } B) = Pr(A) \times Pr(B) \qquad (2.14)$$

if A and B are independent.

Independence may therefore be defined as follows: two events, A and B, are independent if the probability of one occurring is not influenced by the fact of the other having occurred. Formally, if A and B are independent then

$$Pr(B|A) = Pr(B|\text{not } A) = Pr(B) \qquad (2.15)$$

and

$$Pr(A|B) = Pr(A|\text{not } B) = Pr(A) \qquad (2.16)$$

The concept of independence is an important one in statistics, as it usually simplifies problems considerably. If two variables are known to be independent then we can analyse the behaviour of one without worrying about what is happening to the other variable. For example, sales of computers are independent of temperature, so if one is trying to predict sales next month one does not need to worry about the weather. In contrast, ice cream sales do depend on the weather, so predicting sales accurately requires one to forecast the weather first.

Intuition does not always work with probabilities!

Counter-intuitive results frequently arise in probability, which is why it is wise to use the rules to calculate probabilities in tricky situations, rather than rely on intuition. Take the following questions:

- What is the probability of obtaining two heads (HH) in two tosses of a coin?
- What is the probability of obtaining tails followed by heads (TH)?
- If a coin is tossed until either HH or TH occurs, what are the probabilities of each sequence occurring first?

The answers to the first two are easy: $\frac{1}{2} \times \frac{1}{2} = \frac{1}{4}$ in each case. You might therefore conclude that each sequence is equally likely to be the first observed, but you would be wrong!

Unless HH occurs on the first two tosses, then TH *must* occur first. HH is therefore the first sequence *only* if it occurs on the first two tosses, which has a probability of $\frac{1}{4}$. The probability that TH is first is therefore $\frac{3}{4}$. The probabilities are unequal, a strange result. Now try the same thing with HHH and THH and three tosses of a coin.

Combining the addition and multiplication rules

More complex problems can be solved by suitable combinations of the addition and multiplication formulae. For example, what is the probability of a mother having one child of each sex? This could occur in one of two ways: a girl followed by a boy or a boy followed by a girl. It is important to note that these are two different routes to the same outcome. Therefore we have (assuming non-independence according to equation (2.11))

$$\begin{aligned}
\text{Pr}(1 \text{ girl}, 1 \text{ boy}) &= \text{Pr}((G1 \text{ and } B2) \text{ or } (B1 \text{ and } G2)) \\
&= \text{Pr}(G1) \times \text{Pr}(B2|G1) + \text{Pr}(B1) \times \text{Pr}(G2|B1) \\
&= (0.5 \times 0.4) + (0.5 \times 0.4) \\
&= 0.4
\end{aligned}$$

The answer can be checked if we remember equation (2.2) stating that probabilities must sum to 1. We have calculated the probability of two boys (0.3) and of a child of each sex (0.4). The only other possibility is of two girls. This probability must be 0.3, the same as two boys, since boys and girls are treated symmetrically in this problem (even with the non-independence assumption). The sum of the three possibilities (two boys, one of each or two girls) is therefore $0.3 + 0.4 + 0.3 = 1$, as it should be. This is often a useful check to make, especially if one is unsure that one's calculations are correct.

Note that the problem would have been different if we had asked for the probability of the mother having one girl with a younger brother.

Tree diagrams

The preceding problem can be illustrated using a tree diagram, which often helps to clarify a problem. A tree diagram is an alternative way of enumerating

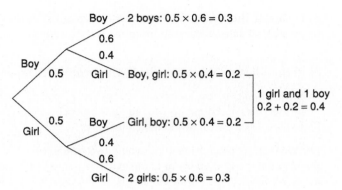

Figure 2.5
Tree diagram for a
family with two children

all possible outcomes in the sample space, with the associated probabilities. The diagram for two children is shown in Figure 2.5.

The diagram begins at the left and the first node shows the possible alternatives (boy, girl) at that point and the associated probabilities (0.5, 0.5). The next two nodes show the alternatives and probabilities for the second birth, given the sex of the first child. The final four nodes show the possible results: {boy, boy}; {boy, girl}; {girl, boy}; and {girl, girl}.

To find the probability of two girls, using the tree diagram, follow the lowest path, multiplying the probabilities along it to give $0.5 \times 0.6 = 0.3$. To find the probability of one child of each sex it is necessary to follow all the routes which lead to such an outcome. There are two in this case: leading to boy, girl and to girl, boy. Each of these has a probability of 0.2, obtained by multiplying the probabilities along that branch of the tree. Adding these together (since either one *or* the other leads to the desired outcome) yields the answer, giving $0.2 + 0.2 = 0.4$. This provides a graphical alternative to the formulae used above and may help comprehension.

The tree diagram can obviously be extended to cover third and subsequent children although the number of branches rapidly increases (in geometric progression). The difficulty then becomes not just the calculation of the probability attached to each outcome, but sorting out which branches should be taken into account in the calculation. Suppose we consider a family of five children of whom three are girls. To simplify matters we again assume independence of probabilities. The appropriate tree diagram has $2^5 = 32$ end-points, each with probability 1/32. How many of these relate to families with three girls and two boys, for example? One can draw the diagram and count them, yielding the answer 10, but it takes considerable time and is prone to error. Far better would be to use a formula. To develop this, we use the ideas of **combinations** and **permutations**.

Combinations and permutations

How can we establish the number of ways of having three girls and two boys in a family of five children? One way would be to write down all the possible orderings:

GGGBB   GGBGB   GGBBG   GBGGB   GBGBG
GBBGG   BGGGB   BGGBG   BGBGG   BBGGG

This shows that there are 10 such orderings, so the probability of three girls and two boys in a family of five children is 10/32. In more complex problems this soon becomes difficult or impossible. The record number of children born to a British mother is 39 (!) of whom 32 were girls. The appropriate tree diagram has over five thousand billion 'routes' through it, and drawing one line (i.e. for one child) per second would imply 17 433 years to complete the task! Rather than do this, we use the combinatorial formula to find the answer. Suppose there are n children, r of them girls, then the number of orderings, denoted nCr, is obtained from[1]

$$nCr = \frac{n!}{r!(n-r)!}$$

$$= \frac{n \times (n-1) \times \ldots \times 1}{\{r \times (r-1) \times \ldots \times 1\} \times \{(n-r) \times (n-r-1) \times \ldots \times 1\}} \tag{2.17}$$

In the above example $n = 5$, $r = 3$ so the number of orderings is

$$5C3 = \frac{5 \times 4 \times 3 \times 2 \times 1}{\{3 \times 2 \times 1\} \times \{2 \times 1\}} = 10 \tag{2.18}$$

If there were four girls out of five children then the number of orderings or combinations would be

$$5C4 = \frac{5 \times 4 \times 3 \times 2 \times 1}{\{4 \times 3 \times 2 \times 1\} \times 1} = 5 \tag{2.19}$$

This gives five possible orderings, i.e. the single boy could be the first, second, third, fourth or fifth born.

Why does this formula work? Consider five empty places to fill, corresponding to the five births in chronological order. Take the case of three girls (call them Amanda, Bridget and Caroline for convenience) who have to fill three of the five places. For Amanda there is a choice of five empty places. Having 'chosen' one, there remain four for Bridget, so there are $5 \times 4 = 20$ possibilities (i.e. ways in which these two could choose their places). Three remain for Caroline, so there are $60 (= 5 \times 4 \times 3)$ possible orderings in all (the two boys take the two remaining places). Sixty is the number of permutations of three *named* girls in five births. This is written $5P3$ or in general nPr. Hence

$$5P3 = 5 \times 4 \times 3$$

or in general

$$nPr = n \times (n-1) \times \ldots \times (n-r+1) \tag{2.20}$$

A simpler formula is obtained by multiplying and dividing by $(n-r)!$

$$nPr = \frac{n \times (n-r) \times \ldots \times (n-r+1) \times (n-r)!}{(n-r)!} = \frac{n!}{(n-r)!} \tag{2.21}$$

---

[1] $n!$ is read 'n factorial' and is defined as the product of all the integers up to and including n. Thus, for example, $3! = 3 \times 2 \times 1 = 6$.

What is the difference between *nPr* and *nCr*? The latter does not distinguish between the girls; the two cases Amanda, Bridget, Caroline, boy, boy and Bridget, Amanda, Caroline, boy, boy are effectively the same (three girls followed by two boys). So *nPr* is larger by a factor representing the number of ways of ordering the three girls. This factor is given by $r! = 3 \times 2 \times 1 = 6$ (any of the three girls could be first, either of the other two second, and then the final one). Thus to obtain *nCr* one must divide *nPr* by *r!*, giving (2.17).

Exercise 2.3

(a) A dart is thrown at a dartboard. What is the sample space for this experiment?

(b) An archer has a 30% chance of hitting the bull's eye on the target. What is the complement to this event and what is its probability?

(c) What is the probability of two mutually exclusive events both occurring?

(d) A spectator reckons there is a 70% probability of an American rider winning the Tour de France and a 40% probability of Frenchman winning. Comment.

Exercise 2.4

(a) For the archer in Exercise 2.3(b) what is the probability that she hits the target with one (and only one) of two arrows?

(b) What is the probability that she hits the target with both arrows?

(c) Explain the importance of the assumption of independence for the answers to both parts (a) and (b) of this exercise.

(d) If the archer becomes more confident after a successful shot (i.e. her probability of a shot on target rises to 50%) and less confident (probability falls to 20%) after a miss, how would this affect the answers to parts (a) and (b)?

Exercise 2.5

(a) Draw the tree diagrams associated with Exercise 2.4. You will need one for the case of independence of events, one for non-independence.

(b) Extend the diagram (assuming independence) to a third arrow. Use this to mark out the paths with two successful shots out of three. Calculate the probability of two hits out of three shots.

(c) Repeat part (b) for the case of non-independence. For this you may assume that a hit raises the problem of success with the next arrow to 50%. A miss lowers it to 20%.

Exercise 2.6

(a) Show how the answer to Exercise 2.5(b) may be arrived at using algebra, including the use of the combinatorial formula.

(b) Repeat part (a) for the non-independence case.

Bayes' theorem

Bayes' theorem is a factual statement about probabilities, which in itself is uncontroversial. However, the use and interpretation of the result is at the heart of the difference between classical and Bayesian statistics. The theorem itself is easily derived from first principles. Equation (2.22) is similar to equation (2.13) covered earlier when discussing the multiplication rule

$$Pr(A \text{ and } B) = Pr(A|B) \times Pr(B) \tag{2.22}$$

hence

$$Pr(A|B) = \frac{Pr(A \text{ and } B)}{Pr(B)} \tag{2.23}$$

Expanding both top and bottom of the right-hand side

$$Pr(A|B) = \frac{Pr(B|A) \times Pr(A)}{Pr(B|A) \times Pr(A) + Pr(B|\text{not } A) \times Pr(\text{not } A)} \tag{2.24}$$

Equation (2.24) is known as Bayes' theorem and is a statement about the probability of the event A, conditional upon B having occurred. The following example demonstrates its use.

Two bags contain red and yellow balls. Bag A contains six red and four yellow balls, bag B has three red and seven yellow balls. A ball is drawn at random from one bag and turns out to be red. What is the probability that it came from bag A? Since bag A has relatively more red balls to yellow balls than does bag B, it seems bag A ought to be favoured. The probability should be more than 0.5. We can check if this is correct.

Denoting

$$Pr(A) = 0.5 \quad \text{(the probability of choosing bag } A \text{ at random)} = Pr(B)$$

$$Pr(R|A) = 0.6 \quad \text{(the probability of selecting a red ball from bag } A\text{), etc.}$$

we have

$$Pr(A|R) = \frac{Pr(R|A) \times Pr(A)}{Pr(R|A) \times Pr(A) + Pr(R|B) \times Pr(B)} \tag{2.25}$$

using Bayes' theorem. Evaluating this gives

$$Pr(A|R) = \frac{0.6 \times 0.5}{0.6 \times 0.5 + 0.3 \times 0.5} \tag{2.26}$$

$$= {}^2/_3$$

(You can check that $Pr(B|R) = {}^1/_3$ so that the sum of the probabilities is 1.) As expected, this result is greater than 0.5.

Bayes' theorem can be extended to cover more than two bags: if there are five bags, for example, labelled A to E, then

$$Pr(A|R) = \frac{Pr(R|A) \times Pr(A)}{Pr(R|A) \times Pr(A) + Pr(R|B) \times Pr(B) + \ldots + Pr(R|E) \times Pr(E)} \tag{2.27}$$

In Bayesian language, $Pr(A)$, $Pr(B)$, etc., are known as the prior (to the drawing of the ball) probabilities, $Pr(R|A)$, $Pr(R|B)$, etc., are the likelihoods and $Pr(A|R)$, $Pr(B|R)$, etc., are the posterior probabilities. Bayes' theorem can alternatively be expressed as

$$\text{posterior probability} = \frac{\text{likelihood} \times \text{prior probability}}{\Sigma(\text{likelihoods} \times \text{prior probabilites})} \tag{2.28}$$

This is illustrated below, by reworking the above example.

	Prior probabilities	Likelihoods	Prior × likelihood	Posterior probabilities
A	0.5	0.6	0.30	0.30/0.45 = 2/3
B	0.5	0.3	0.15	0.15/0.45 = 1/3
Total			0.45	

The general version of Bayes' theorem may be stated as follows. If there are n events labelled $E_1, \ldots, E_n$ then the probability of the event E_i occurring, given the sample evidence S, is

$$\Pr(E_i|S) = \frac{\Pr(S|E_i) \times \Pr(E_i)}{\sum (\Pr(S|E_i) \times \Pr(E_i))} \tag{2.29}$$

As stated earlier, dispute arises over the interpretation of Bayes' theorem. In the above example there is no difficulty because the probability statements can be interpreted as relative frequencies. If the experiment of selecting a bag at random and choosing a ball from it were repeated many times, then of those occasions when a red ball is selected, in two-thirds of them bag A will have been chosen. However, consider an alternative interpretation of the symbols:

A: a coin is fair;
B: a coin is unfair;
R: the result of a toss is a head.

Then, given a toss (or series of tosses) of a coin, this evidence can be used to calculate the probability of the coin being fair. But this makes no sense according to the frequentist school: either the coin is fair or not; it is not a question of probability. The calculated value must be interpreted as a degree of belief and be given a subjective interpretation.

Exercise 2.7

(a) Repeat the 'balls in the bag' exercise from the text, but with bag A containing five red and three yellow balls, bag B containing one red and two yellow balls. The single ball drawn is red. Before doing the calculation, predict which bag is more likely to be the source of the drawn ball. Explain why.

(b) Bag A now contains 10 red and six yellow balls (i.e. twice as many as before, but in the same proportion). Does this alter the answer you obtained in part (a)?

(c) Set out your answer to part (b) in the form of prior probabilities and likelihoods, in order to obtain the posterior probability.

Summary

- The theory of probability forms the basis of statistical inference: the drawing of inferences on the basis of a random sample of data. The reason for this is the probability basis of random sampling.
- A convenient definition of the probability of an event is the number of times the event occurs divided by the number of trials (occasions when the event could occur).

- For more complex events, their probabilities can be calculated by combining probabilities, using the addition and multiplication rules.
- The probability of events *A* or *B* occurring is calculated according to the addition rule.
- The probability of *A* and *B* occurring is given by the multiplication rule.
- If *A* and *B* are not independent, then $\Pr(A \text{ and } B) = \Pr(A) \times \Pr(B|A)$, where $\Pr(B|A)$ is the probability of *B* occurring given that *A* has occurred (the conditional probability).
- Tree diagrams are a useful technique for enumerating all the possible paths in series of probability trials, but for large numbers of trials the huge number of possibilities makes the technique impractical.
- For experiments with a large number of trials (e.g. obtaining 20 heads in 50 tosses of a coin) the formulae for combinations and permutations can be used.
- The combinatorial formula *nCr* gives the number of ways of combining *r* similar objects among *n* objects, e.g. the number of orderings of three girls (and hence implicitly two boys also) in five children.
- The permutation formula *nPr* gives the number of orderings of *r* distinct objects among *n*, e.g. three named girls among five children.
- Bayes' theorem provides a formula for calculating a conditional probability, e.g. the probability of someone being a smoker, given they have been diagnosed with cancer. It forms the basis of Bayesian statistics, allowing us to calculate the probability of a hypothesis being true, based on the sample evidence and prior beliefs. Classical statistics disputes this approach.
- Probabilities can also be used as the basis for decision making in conditions of uncertainty, using as decision criteria expected value maximisation, maximin, maximax or minimax regret.

Key terms and concepts

addition rule	minimax
Bayes' theorem	minimax regret
combinations	multiplication rule
complement	mutually exclusive
compound event	outcome or event
conditional probability	permutations
exhaustive	probability experiment
expected value of perfect information	probability of an event
frequentist approach	sample space
independent events	subjective approach
maximin	tree diagram

3

Probability distributions

Learning outcomes

By the end of this chapter you should be able to:

- recognise that the result of most probability experiments (e.g. the score on a die) can be described as a random variable;

- appreciate how the behaviour of a random variable can often be summarised by a probability distribution (a mathematical formula);

- recognise the most common probability distributions and be aware of their uses;

- solve a range of probability problems using the appropriate probability distribution.

Complete your diagnostic test for Chapter 3 now to create your personal study plan. Exercises with an icon ? are also available for practice in MathXL with additional supporting resources.

Introduction

In this chapter the probability concepts introduced in Chapter 2 are generalised by using the idea of a probability distribution. A probability distribution lists, in some form, all the possible outcomes of a probability experiment and the probability associated with each one. For example, the simplest experiment is tossing a coin, for which the possible outcomes are heads or tails, each with probability one-half. The probability distribution can be expressed in a variety of ways: in words, or in a graphical or mathematical form. For tossing a coin, the graphical form is shown in Figure 3.1, and the mathematical form is

$$\Pr(H) = \tfrac{1}{2}$$
$$\Pr(T) = \tfrac{1}{2}$$

The different forms of presentation are equivalent, but one might be more suited to a particular purpose.

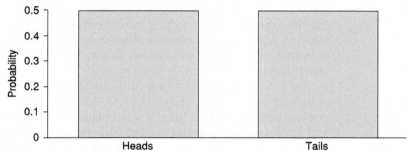

Figure 3.1
The probability distribution for the toss of a coin

Some probability distributions occur often and so are well known. Because of this they have names so we can refer to them easily; for example, the Binomial distribution or the Normal distribution. In fact, each constitutes a *family* of distributions. A single toss of a coin gives rise to one member of the Binomial distribution family; two tosses would give rise to another member of that family. These two distributions differ in the number of tosses. If a biased coin were tossed, this would lead to yet another Binomial distribution, but it would differ from the previous two because of the different probability of heads.

Members of the Binomial family of distributions are distinguished either by the number of tosses or by the probability of the event occurring. These are the two parameters of the distribution and tell us all we need to know about the distribution. Other distributions might have different numbers of parameters, with different meanings. Some distributions, for example, have only one parameter. We will come across examples of different types of distribution throughout the rest of this book.

In order to understand fully the idea of a probability distribution a new concept is first introduced, that of a random variable. As will be seen later in the chapter, an important random variable is the sample mean, and to understand how to draw inferences from the sample mean it is important to recognise it as a random variable.

Random variables

Examples of random variables have already been encountered in Chapter 2, for example, the result of the toss of a coin, or the number of boys in a family of five children. A random variable is one whose outcome or value is the result of chance and is therefore unpredictable, although the range of possible outcomes and the probability of each outcome may be known. It is impossible to know in advance the outcome of a toss of a coin for example, but it must be either heads or tails, each with probability one-half. The number of heads in 250 tosses is another random variable, which can take any value between zero and 250, although values near 125 are the most likely. You are very unlikely to get 250 heads from tossing a fair coin!

Intuitively, most people would 'expect' to get 125 heads from 250 tosses of the coin, since heads comes up half the time on average. This suggests we could use the expected value notation introduced in Chapter 1 and write $E(X) = 125$, where X represents the number of heads obtained from 250 tosses. This usage is indeed valid and we will explore this further below. It is a very convenient shorthand notation.

The time of departure of a train is another example of a random variable. It may be timetabled to depart at 11.15, but it probably (almost certainly!) will not leave at exactly that time. If a sample of ten basketball players were taken, and their average height calculated, this would be a random variable. In this latter case, it is the process of taking a sample that introduces the variability which makes the resulting average a random variable. If the experiment were repeated, a different sample and a different value of the random variable would be obtained.

The above examples can be contrasted with some things which are *not* random variables. If one were to take *all* basketball players and calculate their average height, the result would not be a random variable. This time there is no sampling procedure to introduce variability into the result. If the experiment were repeated the same result would be obtained, since the same people would be measured the second time (this assumes that the population does not change, of course). Just because the value of something is unknown does not mean it qualifies as a random variable. This is an important distinction to bear in mind, since it is legitimate to make probability statements about random variables ('the probability that the average height of a sample of basketball players is over 195 cm is 60%') but not about parameters ('the probability that the Pope is over six feet is 60%'). Here again there is a difference of opinion between frequentist and subjective schools of thought. The latter group would argue that it is possible to make probability statements about the Pope's height. It is a way of expressing lack of knowledge about the true value. The frequentists would say the Pope's height is a fact that we do not happen to know; that does not make it a random variable.

The Binomial distribution

One of the simplest distributions which a random variable can have is the Binomial. The Binomial distribution arises whenever the underlying probability experiment has just two possible outcomes, for example heads or tails from the toss of a coin. Even if the coin is tossed many times (so one could end up with one, two, three . . . , etc., heads in total) the *underlying* experiment has only two outcomes, so the Binomial distribution should be used. A counter-example would be the rolling of die, which has six possible outcomes (in this case the Multinomial distribution, not covered in this book, would be used). Note, however, that if we were interested only in rolling a six or not, we *could* use the Binomial by defining the two possible outcomes as 'six' and 'not-six'. It is often the case in statistics that by suitable transformation of the data we can use different distributions to tackle the same problem. We will see more of this later in the chapter.

The Binomial distribution can therefore be applied to the type of problem encountered in the previous chapter, concerning the sex of children. It provides a general formula for calculating the probability of r boys in n births or, in more general terms, the probability of r 'successes' in n trials.[1] We shall use it to calculate the probabilities of 0, 1, . . . , 5 boys in five births.

For the Binomial distribution to apply we first need to assume independence of successive events and we shall assume that, for any birth

$$\Pr(\text{boy}) = P = \tfrac{1}{2}$$

It follows that

$$\Pr(\text{girl}) = 1 - \Pr(\text{boy}) = 1 - P = \tfrac{1}{2}$$

Although we have $P = \tfrac{1}{2}$ in this example, the Binomial distribution can be applied for any value of P between 0 and 1.

First we consider the case of $r = 5$, $n = 5$, i.e. five boys in five births. This probability is found using the multiplication rule

$$\Pr(r = 5) = P \times P \times P \times P \times P = P^5 = (\tfrac{1}{2})^5 = 1/32$$

The probability of four boys (and then implicitly one girl) is

$$\Pr(r = 4) = P \times P \times P \times P \times (1 - P) = 1/32$$

But this gives only one possible ordering of the four boys and one girl. Our original statement of the problem did not specify a particular ordering of the children. There are five possible orderings (the single girl could be in any of five positions in rank order). Recall that we can use the combinatorial formula nCr to calculate the number of orderings, giving $5C4 = 5$. Hence the probability of four boys and one girl in any order is 5/32. Summarising, the formula for four boys and one girl is

$$\Pr(r = 4) = 5C4 \times P^4 \times (1 - P)$$

---

[1] The identification of a boy with 'success' is a purely formal one and is not meant to be pejorative!

For three boys (and two girls) we obtain

$$\Pr(r = 3) = 5C3 \times P^3 \times (1 - P)^2 = 10 \times 1/8 \times 1/4 = 10/32$$

In a similar manner

$$\Pr(r = 2) = 5C2 \times P^2 \times (1 - P)^3 = 10/32$$

$$\Pr(r = 1) = 5C1 \times P^1 \times (1 - P)^4 = 5/32$$

$$\Pr(r = 0) = 5C0 \times P^0 \times (1 - P)^5 = 1/32$$

As a check on our calculations we may note that the sum of the probabilities equals 1, as they should do, as we have enumerated all possibilities.

A fairly clear pattern emerges. The probability of r boys in n births is given by

$$\Pr(r) = nCr \times P^r \times (1 - P)^{n-r}$$

and this is known as the Binomial formula or distribution. The Binomial distribution is appropriate for analysing problems with the following characteristics:

- There is a number (n) of trials.
- Each trial has only two possible outcomes, 'success' (with probability P) and 'failure' (probability $1 - P$) and the outcomes are independent between trials.
- The probability P does not change between trials.

The probabilities calculated by the Binomial formula may be illustrated in a diagram, as shown in Figure 3.2. This is very similar to the relative frequency distribution which was introduced in Chapter 1. That distribution was based on empirical data (to do with wealth) while the Binomial probability distribution is a theoretical construction, built up from the basic principles of probability theory.

As stated earlier, the Binomial is, in fact, a family of distributions and each member of this family is distinguished by two **parameters**, n and P. The Binomial is thus a distribution with two parameters, and once their values are known the distribution is completely determined (i.e. $\Pr(r)$ can be calculated for all values of r). To illustrate the difference between members of the family of the Binomial distribution, Figure 3.3 presents three other Binomial distributions, for different values of P and n. It can be seen that for the value of $P = \frac{1}{2}$ the

Figure 3.2
Probability distribution of the number of boys in five children

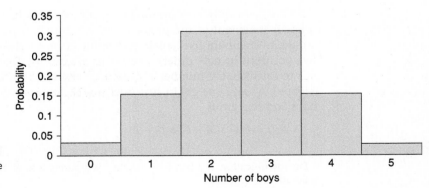

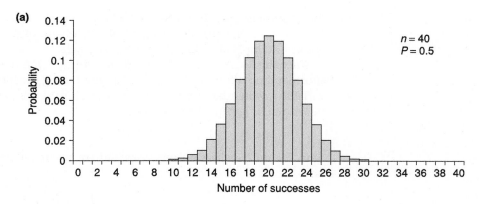

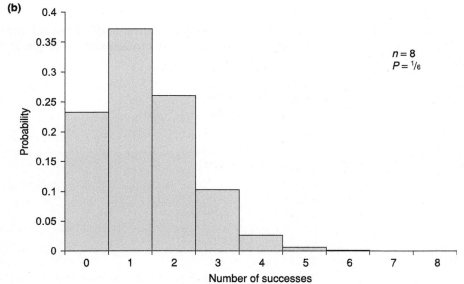

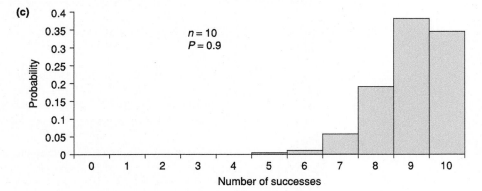

Figure 3.3
Binomial distributions
with different
parameter values

distribution is symmetric, while for all other values it is skewed to either the left or the right. Part (b) of the figure illustrates the distribution relating to the worked example of rolling a die, described below.

Since the Binomial distribution depends only upon the two values n and P, a shorthand notation can be used, rather than using the formula itself. A random variable r, which has a Binomial distribution with the parameters n and P, can be written in general terms as

$$r \sim B(n, P) \tag{3.1}$$

Thus for the previous example of children, where r represents the number of boys

$$r \sim B(5, \tfrac{1}{2})$$

This is simply a brief and convenient way of writing down the information available; it involves no new problems of a conceptual nature. Writing

$$r \sim B(n, P)$$

is just a shorthand for

$$\Pr(r) = nCr \times P^r \times (1 - P)^{n-r}$$

Teenage weapons

This is a nice example of how knowledge of the Binomial distribution can help our interpretation of events in the news.

> 'One in five teens carry weapon'. (link on main BBC news web site 23 July 2007)

Following the link to the text of the story, we read:

> 'One in five young teenagers say that their friends are carrying knives and weapons, says a major annual survey of schoolchildren's health and wellbeing'.

With concerns about knife crime among teenagers, this survey shows that a fifth of youngsters are 'fairly sure' or 'certain' that their male friends are carrying a weapon.'

Notice, incidentally, how the story subtly changes. The headline suggests 20% of teenagers carry a weapon. The text then says this is what *young* teenagers report of their *friends*. It then reveals that some are only 'fairly sure' and that it applies to boys, not girls. By now our suspicions should be aroused. What is the truth?

Note that you are more likely to know someone who carries a weapon than to carry one yourself. Let p be the proportion who truly carry a weapon. Assume also that each person has 10 friends. What is the probability that a person, selected at random, has no friends who carry a weapon? Assuming independence, this is given by $(1 - p)^{10}$. Hence the probability of at least one friend with a weapon is $1 - (1 - p)^{10}$. This is proportion of people who will report having at least one friend with a weapon. How does this vary with p? This is set out in the following table:

p	P(≥ 1 friend with weapon) $1 - (1 - p)^{10}$
0.0%	0%
0.5%	5%
1.0%	10%
1.5%	14%
2.0%	18%
2.5%	22%
3.0%	26%
3.5%	30%
4.0%	34%

Thus a true proportion of just over 2% carrying weapons will generate a report suggesting 20% know someone carrying a weapon! This is much less alarming (and less newsworthy) than in the original story.

You might like to test the assumptions. What happens if there are more than 10 friends assumed? What happens if events are not independent, i.e. having one friend with a weapon increases the probability of another friend with a weapon?

The mean and variance of the Binomial distribution

In Chapter 1 we calculated the mean and variance of a set of data, of the distribution of wealth. The picture of that distribution (Figure 1.9) looks not too dissimilar to one of the Binomial distributions shown in Figure 3.3 above. This suggests that we can calculate the mean and variance of a Binomial distribution, just as we did for the empirical distribution of wealth. Calculating the mean would provide the answer to a question such as 'If we have a family with five children, how many do we expect to be boys?'. Intuitively the answer seems clear, 2.5 (even though such a family could not exist!). The Binomial formula allows us to confirm this intuition.

The mean and variance are most easily calculated by drawing up a relative frequency table based on the Binomial frequencies. This is shown in Table 3.1 for the values $n = 5$ and $P = \frac{1}{2}$. Note that r is equivalent to x in our usual notation and $\Pr(r)$, the relative frequency, is equivalent to $f(x)/\sum f(x)$. The mean of this distribution is given by

$$E(r) = \frac{\sum r \times \Pr(r)}{\sum \Pr(r)} = \frac{80/32}{32/32} = 2.5 \tag{3.2}$$

Table 3.1 Calculating the mean and variance of the Binomial distribution

r	Pr(r)	$r \times \Pr(r)$	$r^2 \times \Pr(r)$
0	1/32	0	0
1	5/32	5/32	5/32
2	10/32	20/32	40/32
3	10/32	30/32	90/32
4	5/32	20/32	80/32
5	1/32	5/32	25/32
Totals	32/32	80/32	240/32

and the variance is given by

$$V(r) = \frac{\sum r^2 \times \Pr(r)}{\sum \Pr(r)} - \mu^2 = \frac{240/32}{32/32} - 2.5^2 = 1.25 \qquad (3.3)$$

The mean value tells us that in a family of five children we would expect, on average, two and a half boys. Obviously no single family can be like this; it is the average over all such families. The variance is more difficult to interpret intuitively, but it tells us something about how the number of boys in different families will be spread around the average of 2.5.

There is a quicker way to calculate the mean and variance of the Binomial distribution. It can be shown that the mean can be calculated as nP, i.e. the number of trials times the probability of success. For example, in a family with five children and an equal probability that each child is a boy or a girl, then we expect $nP = 5 \times \frac{1}{2} = 2.5$ to be boys.

The variance can be calculated as $nP(1 - P)$. This gives $5 \times \frac{1}{2} \times \frac{1}{2} = 1.25$, as found above by extensive calculation.

Worked example 3.1   Rolling a die

If a die is thrown four times, what is the probability of getting two or more sixes? This is a problem involving repeated experiments (rolling the die) with but two types of outcome for each roll: success (a six) or failure (anything but a six). Note that we combine several possibilities (scores of 1, 2, 3, 4 or 5) together and represent them all as failure. The probability of success (one-sixth) does not vary from one experiment to another, and so use of the Binomial distribution is appropriate. The values of the parameters are $n = 4$ and $P = 1/6$. Denoting by r the random variable 'the number of sixes in four rolls of the die' then

$$r \sim B(4, \tfrac{1}{6})$$

Hence

$$\Pr(r) = nCr \times P^r (1 - P)^{(n-r)}$$

where $P = \frac{1}{6}$ and $n = 4$. The probabilities of two, three and four sixes are then given by

$$\Pr(r = 2) = 4C2(\tfrac{1}{6})^2(\tfrac{5}{6})^2 = 0.116$$

$$\Pr(r = 3) = 4C3(\tfrac{1}{6})^3(\tfrac{5}{6})^1 = 0.015$$

$$\Pr(r = 4) = 4C4(\tfrac{1}{6})^4(\tfrac{5}{6})^0 = 0.00077$$

Since these events are mutually exclusive, the probabilities can simply be added together to achieve the desired result, which is 0.132, or 13.2%. This is the probability of two or more sixes in four rolls of a die.

This result can be illustrated diagrammatically as part of the area under the appropriate Binomial distribution, shown in Figure 3.4.

The shaded areas represent the probabilities of two or more sixes and together their area represents 13.2% of the whole distribution. This illustrates an important principle: that probabilities can be represented by areas under an appropriate probability distribution. We shall see more of this later.

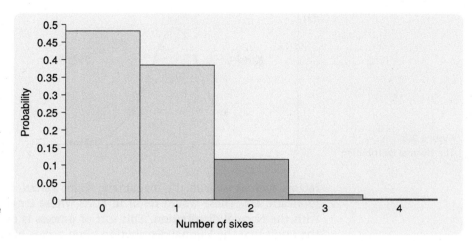

Figure 3.4
Probability of two or more sixes in four rolls of a die

Exercise 3.1

(a) The probability of a randomly drawn individual having blue eyes is 0.6. What is the probability that four people drawn at random all have blue eyes?

(b) What is the probability that two of the sample of four have blue eyes?

(c) For this particular example, write down the Binomial formula for the probability of r blue-eyed individuals, for $r = 0 \ldots 4$. Confirm that the probabilities sum to one.

Exercise 3.2

(a) Calculate the mean and variance of the number of blue-eyed individuals in the previous exercise.

(b) Draw a graph of this Binomial distribution and on it mark the mean value and the mean value +/– one standard deviation.

Having introduced the concept of probability distributions using the Binomial, we now move on to the most important of all probability distributions – the Normal.

The Normal distribution

The Binomial distribution applies when there are two possible outcomes to an experiment, but not all problems fall into this category. For instance, the (random) arrival time of a train is a continuous variable and cannot be analysed using the Binomial. There are many probability distributions in statistics, developed to analyse different types of problem. Several of them are covered in this book and the most important of them is the Normal distribution, which we now turn to. It was discovered by the German mathematician Gauss in the nineteenth century (hence it is also known as the Gaussian distribution), in the course of his work on regression (see Chapter 7).

Many random variables turn out to be Normally distributed. Men's (or women's) heights are Normally distributed. IQ (the measure of intelligence) is also Normally distributed. Another example is of a machine producing (say) bolts with a nominal length of 5 cm which will actually produce bolts of slightly varying length (these differences would probably be extremely small) due to

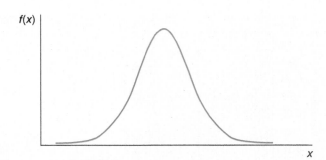

Figure 3.5
The Normal distribution

factors such as wear in the machinery, slight variations in the pressure of the lubricant, etc. These would result in bolts whose length varies, in accordance with the Normal distribution. This sort of process is extremely common, with the result that the Normal distribution often occurs in everyday situations.

The Normal distribution tends to arise when a random variable is the result of many independent, random influences added together, none of which dominates the others. A man's height is the result of many genetic influences, plus environmental factors such as diet, etc. As a result, height is Normally distributed. If one takes the height of men and women together, the result is not a Normal distribution, however. This is because there is one influence which dominates the others: gender. Men are, on average, taller than women. Many variables familiar in economics are not Normal however – incomes, for example (although the logarithm of income is approximately Normal). We shall learn techniques to deal with such circumstances in due course.

Having introduced the idea of the Normal distribution, what does it look like? It is presented below in graphical and then mathematical forms. Unlike the Binomial, the Normal distribution applies to continuous random variables such as height and a typical Normal distribution is illustrated in Figure 3.5. Since the Normal distribution is a continuous one it can be evaluated for all values of x, not just for integers. The figure illustrates the main features of the distribution:

- It is unimodal, having a single, central peak. If this were men's heights it would illustrate the fact that most men are clustered around the average height, with a few very tall and a few very short people.
- It is symmetric, the left and right halves being mirror images of each other.
- It is bell-shaped.
- It extends continuously over all the values of x from minus infinity to plus infinity, although the value of $f(x)$ becomes extremely small as these values are approached (the pages of this book being of only finite width, this last characteristic is not faithfully reproduced!). This also demonstrates that most empirical distributions (such as men's heights) can only be an approximation to the theoretical ideal, although the approximation is close and good enough for practical purposes.

Note that we have labelled the y-axis '$f(x)$' rather than 'Pr(x)' as we did for the Binomial distribution. This is because it is *areas under the curve* that represent probabilities, not the heights. With the Binomial, which is a discrete distribution, one can legitimately represent probabilities by the heights of the bars. For the Normal, although $f(x)$ does not give the probability per se, it does give an indication: you are more likely to encounter values from the middle of the distribution (where $f(x)$ is greater) than from the extremes.

In mathematical terms the formula for the Normal distribution is (x is the random variable)

$$f(x) = \frac{1}{\sigma\sqrt{2\pi}} e^{-\frac{1}{2}\left(\frac{x-\mu}{\sigma}\right)^2}$$

(3.4)

The mathematical formulation is not so formidable as it appears. μ and σ are the parameters of the distribution, such as n and P for the Binomial (though they have different meanings); π is 3.1416 and e is 2.7183. If the formula is evaluated using different values of x the values of $f(x)$ obtained will map out a Normal distribution. Fortunately, as we shall see, we do not need to use the mathematical formula in most practical problems.

Like the Binomial, the Normal is a family of distributions differing from one another only in the values of the parameters μ and σ. Several Normal distributions are drawn in Figure 3.6 for different values of the parameters.

Whatever value of μ is chosen turns out to be the centre of the distribution. As the distribution is symmetric, μ is its mean. The effect of varying σ is to narrow (small σ) or widen (large σ) the distribution. σ turns out to be the standard deviation of the distribution. The Normal is another two-parameter family of distributions like the Binomial, and once the mean μ and the standard deviation σ (or equivalently the variance, σ^2) are known the whole of the distribution can be drawn.

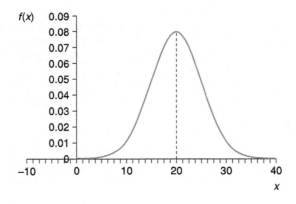

Figure 3.6(a)
The Normal distribution, $\mu = 20$, $\sigma = 5$

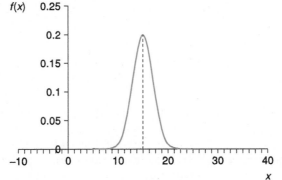

Figure 3.6(b)
The Normal distribution, $\mu = 15$, $\sigma = 2$

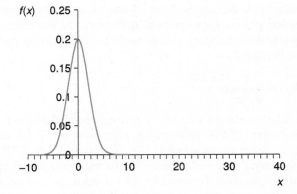

Figure 3.6(c)
The Normal distribution,
$\mu = 0$, $\sigma = 4$

The shorthand notation for a Normal distribution is

$$x \sim N(\mu, \sigma^2) \tag{3.5}$$

meaning 'the variable x is Normally distributed with mean μ and variance σ^2'. This is similar in form to the expression for the Binomial distribution, though the meanings of the parameters are different.

Use of the Normal distribution can be illustrated using a simple example. The height of adult males is Normally distributed with mean height $\mu = 174$ cm and standard deviation $\sigma = 9.6$ cm. Let x represent the height of adult males; then

$$x \sim N(174, 92.16) \tag{3.6}$$

and this is illustrated in Figure 3.7. Note that equation (3.6) contains the variance rather than the standard deviation.

What is the probability that a randomly selected man is taller than 180 cm? If all men are equally likely to be selected, this is equivalent to asking what proportion of men are over 180 cm in height. This is given by the area under the Normal distribution, to the right of $x = 180$, i.e. the shaded area in Figure 3.7. The further from the mean of 174, the smaller the area in the tail of the distribution. One way to find this area would be to make use of equation (3.4), but this requires the use of sophisticated mathematics.

Since this is a frequently encountered problem, the answers have been set out in the tables of the standard Normal distribution. We can simply look up the solution. However, since there is an infinite number of Normal distributions (one for every combination of μ and σ^2) it would be an impossible task to tabulate

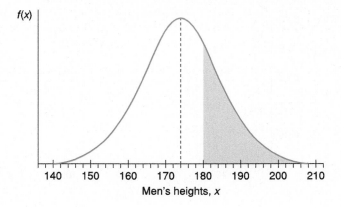

Figure 3.7
Illustration of men's
height distribution

them all. The standard Normal distribution, which has a mean of zero and variance of one, is therefore used to represent all Normal distributions. Before the table can be consulted, therefore, the data have to be transformed so that they accord with the standard Normal distribution.

The required transformation is the z score, which was introduced in Chapter 1. This measures the distance between the value of interest (180) and the mean, measured in terms of standard deviations. Therefore we calculate

$$z = \frac{x - \mu}{\sigma} \qquad (3.7)$$

and z is a Normally distributed random variable with mean 0 and variance 1, i.e. $z \sim N(0, 1)$. This transformation shifts the original distribution μ units to the left and then adjusts the dispersion by dividing through by σ, resulting in a mean of 0 and variance 1. z is Normally distributed because x is Normally distributed. The transformation in equation (3.7) retains the Normal distribution shape, despite the changes to mean and variance. If x followed some other distribution then z would not be Normal either.

It is easy to verify the mean and variance of z using the rules for E and V operators encountered in Chapter 1

$$E(z) = E\left(\frac{x - \mu}{\sigma}\right) = \frac{1}{\sigma}(E(x) - \mu) = 0 \quad \text{(since } E(x) = \mu)$$

$$V(z) = V\left(\frac{x - \mu}{\sigma}\right) = \frac{1}{\sigma^2}V(x) = \frac{\sigma^2}{\sigma^2} = 1$$

Evaluating the z score from our data we obtain

$$z = \frac{180 - 174}{9.6} = 0.63 \qquad (3.8)$$

This shows that 180 is 0.63 standard deviations above the mean, 174, of the distribution. This is a measure of how far 180 is from 174 and allows us to look up the answer in tables. The task now is to find the area under the standard Normal distribution to the right of 0.63 standard deviations above the mean. This answer can be read off directly from the table of the standard Normal distribution, included as Table A2 in the appendix to this book. An excerpt from Table A2 (see page **414**) is presented in Table 3.2.

The left-hand column gives the z score to one place of decimals. The appropriate row of the table to consult is the one for $z = 0.6$, which is shaded. For the second place of decimals (0.03) we consult the appropriate column, also shaded. At their intersection we find the value 0.2643, which is the desired area and

Table 3.2 **Areas of the standard Normal distribution (excerpt from Table A2)**

z	0.00	0.01	0.02	0.03	. . .	0.09
0.0	0.5000	0.4960	0.4920	0.4880	. . .	0.4641
0.1	0.4602	0.4562	0.4522	0.4483	. . .	0.4247
⋮	⋮	⋮	⋮	⋮	. . .	⋮
0.5	0.3085	0.3050	0.3015	0.2981	. . .	0.2776
0.6	0.2743	0.2709	0.2676	0.2643	. . .	0.2451
0.7	0.2420	0.2389	0.2358	0.2327	. . .	0.2148

therefore probability, i.e. 26.43% of the distribution lies to the right of 0.63 standard deviations above the mean. Therefore 26.43% of men are over 180 cm in height.

Use of the standard Normal table is possible because, although there is an infinite number of Normal distributions, they are all fundamentally the same, so that the area to the right of 0.63 standard deviations above the mean is the same for all of them. As long as we measure the distance in terms of standard deviations then we can use the standard Normal table. The process of standardisation turns all Normal distributions into a standard Normal distribution with a mean of zero and a variance of one. This process is illustrated in Figure 3.8.

The area in the right-hand tail is the same for both distributions. It is the standard Normal distribution in Figure 3.8(b), which is tabulated in Table A2. To demonstrate how standardisation turns all Normal distributions into the standard Normal, the earlier problem is repeated but taking all measurements in inches. The answer should obviously be the same. Taking 1 inch = 2.54 cm the figures are

$$x = 70.87 \quad \sigma = 3.78 \quad \mu = 68.50$$

What proportion of men are over 70.87 inches in height? The appropriate Normal distribution is now

$$x \sim N(68.50, 3.78^2) \tag{3.9}$$

The z score is

$$z = \frac{70.87 - 68.50}{3.78} = 0.63 \tag{3.10}$$

which is the same z score as before and therefore gives the same probability.

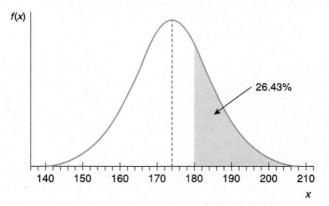

Figure 3.8(a)
The Normal distribution

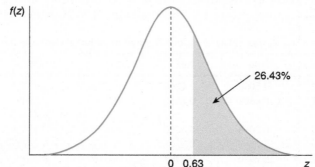

Figure 3.8(b)
The standard Normal distribution corresponding to Figure 3.8(a)

> **Worked example 3.2**
>
> Packets of cereal have a nominal weight of 750 grams, but there is some variation around this as the machines filling the packets are imperfect. Let us assume that the weights follow a Normal distribution. Suppose that the standard deviation around the mean of 750 is 5 grams. What proportion of packets weigh more than 760 grams?
>
> Summarising our information, we have $x \sim N(750, 25)$, where x represents the weight. We wish to find $\Pr(x > 760)$. To be able to look up the answer, we need to measure the distance between 760 and 750 in terms of standard deviations. This is
>
> $$z = \frac{760 - 750}{5}$$
> $$= 2.0$$
>
> Looking up $z = 2.0$ in Table A2 reveals an area of 0.0228 in the tail of the distribution. Thus 2.28% of packets weigh more than 760 grams.

Since a great deal of use is made of the standard Normal tables, it is worth working through a couple more examples to reinforce the method. We have so far calculated that $\Pr(z > 0.63) = 0.2643$. Since the total area under the graph equals one (i.e. the sum of probabilities must be one), the area to the left of $z = 0.63$ must equal 0.7357, i.e. 73.57% of men are under 180 cm. It is fairly easy to manipulate areas under the graph to arrive at any required area. For example, what proportion of men are between 174 and 180 cm in height? It is helpful to refer to Figure 3.9 at this point.

The size of area A is required. Area B has already been calculated as 0.2643. Since the distribution is symmetric the area A + B must equal 0.5, since 174 is at the centre (mean) of the distribution. Area A is therefore $0.5 - 0.2643 = 0.2357$. 23.57% is the desired result.

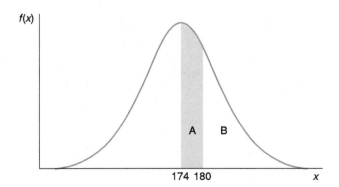

Figure 3.9
The proportion of men between 174 cm and 180 cm in height

Using software to find areas under the standard Normal distribution

If you use a spreadsheet program you can look up the z-distribution directly and hence dispense with tables. In *Excel*, for example, the function '=*NORMSDIST*(0.63)' gives the answer 0.7357, i.e. the area to the *left* of the z score. The area in the right-hand tail is then obtained by subtracting this value from 1, i.e. 1 − 0.7357 = 0.2643. Entering the formula '= 1 − *NORMSDIST*(0.63)' in a cell will give the area in the right-hand tail directly.

As a final exercise consider the question of what proportion of men are between 166 and 178 cm tall. As shown in Figure 3.10 area C + D is wanted. The only way to find this is to calculate the two areas separately and then add them together. For area D the z score associated with 178 is

$$z_D = \frac{178 - 174}{9.6} = 0.42 \tag{3.11}$$

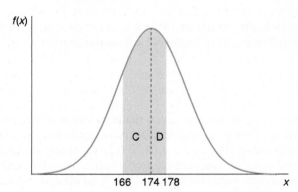

Figure 3.10
The proportion of men between 166 cm and 178 cm in height

Table A2 (see page **414**) indicates that the area in the right-hand tail, beyond z = 0.42, is 0.3372, so area D = 0.5 − 0.3372 = 0.1628. For C, the z score is

$$z_C = \frac{166 - 174}{9.6} = -0.83 \tag{3.12}$$

The minus sign indicates that it is the left-hand tail of the distribution, below the mean, which is being considered. Since the distribution is symmetric, it is the same as if it were the right-hand tail, so the minus sign may be ignored when consulting the table. Looking up z = 0.83 in Table A2 gives an area of 0.2033 in the tail, so area C is therefore 0.5 − 0.2033 = 0.2967. Adding areas C and D gives 0.1628 + 0.2967 = 0.4595. So nearly half of all men are between 166 and 178 cm in height.

An alternative interpretation of the results obtained above is that if a man is drawn at random from the adult population, the probability that he is over 180 cm tall is 26.43%. This is in line with the frequentist school of thought. Since 26.43% of the population is over 180 cm in height, that is the probability of a man over 180 cm being drawn at random.

Exercise 3.3

(a) The random variable x is distributed Normally, with x ~ N(40, 36). Find the probability that x > 50.

(b) Find Pr(x < 45).

(c) Find Pr(36 < x < 44).

Exercise 3.4

?

The mean +/− 0.67 standard deviations cuts off 25% in each tail of the Normal distribution. Hence the middle 50% of the distribution lies within +/− 0.67 standard deviations of the mean. Use this fact to calculate the inter-quartile range for the distribution $x \sim N(200, 256)$.

Exercise 3.5

?

As suggested in the text, the logarithm of income is approximately Normally distributed. Suppose the log (to the base 10) of income has the distribution $x \sim N(4.18, 2.56)$. Calculate the inter-quartile range for x and then take anti-logs to find the inter-quartile range of income.

The sample mean as a Normally distributed variable

One of the most important concepts in statistical inference is the probability distribution of the mean of a random sample, since we often use the sample mean to tell us something about an associated population. Suppose that, from the population of adult males, a random sample of size $n = 36$ is taken, their heights measured and the mean height of the sample calculated. What can we infer from this about the true average height of the population? To do this, we need to know about the statistical properties of the sample mean. The sample mean is a random variable because of the chance element of random sampling (different samples would yield different values of the sample mean). Since the sample mean is a random variable it must have associated with it a probability distribution.

We therefore need to know, first, what is the appropriate distribution and, second, what are its parameters. From the definition of the sample mean we have

$$\bar{x} = \frac{1}{n}(x_1 + x_2 + \ldots + x_n) \tag{3.13}$$

where each observation, x_i, is itself a Normally distributed random variable, with $x_i \sim N(\mu, \sigma^2)$, because each comes from the parent distribution with such characteristics. (We stated earlier that men's heights are Normally distributed.) We now make use of the following theorem to demonstrate that $\bar{x}$ is Normally distributed:

Theorem

Any linear combination of independent, Normally distributed random variables is itself Normally distributed.

A linear combination of two variables x_1 and x_2 is of the form $w_1 x_1 + w_2 x_2$ where w_1 and w_2 are constants. This can be generalised to any number of x values. It is clear that the sample mean satisfies these conditions and is a linear combination of the individual x values (with the weight on each observation equal to $1/n$). As long as the observations are independently drawn, therefore, the sample mean is Normally distributed.

We now need the parameters (mean and variance) of the distribution. For this we use the E and V operators once again

$$E(\bar{x}) = \frac{1}{n}(E(x_1) + E(x_2) + \ldots + E(x_n)) = \frac{1}{n}(\mu + \mu + \ldots + \mu) = \frac{1}{n}n\mu = \mu \tag{3.14}$$

$$V(\bar{x}) = V\left(\frac{1}{n}[x_1 + x_2 + \ldots + x_n]\right) \tag{3.15}$$

$$= \frac{1}{n^2}(V(x_1) + V(x_2) + \ldots + V(x_n))$$

$$= \frac{1}{n^2}(\sigma^2 + \sigma^2 + \ldots + \sigma^2)$$

$$= \frac{1}{n^2}n\sigma^2 = \frac{\sigma^2}{n}$$

Putting all this together, we have[2]

$$\bar{x} \sim N\left(\mu, \frac{\sigma^2}{n}\right) \tag{3.16}$$

This we may summarise in the following theorem:

Theorem

The sample mean, $\bar{x}$, drawn from a population which has a Normal distribution with mean μ and variance σ^2, has a sampling distribution which is Normal, with mean μ and variance σ^2/n, where n is the sample size.

The meaning of this theorem is as follows. First of all it is assumed that the population from which the samples are to be drawn is itself Normally distributed (this assumption will be relaxed in a moment), with mean μ and variance σ^2. From this population many samples are drawn, each of sample size n, and the mean of each sample is calculated. The samples are independent, meaning that the observations selected for one sample do not influence the selection of observations in the other samples. This gives many sample means, $\bar{x}_1$, $\bar{x}_2$, etc. If these sample means are treated as a new set of observations, then the probability distribution of these observations can be derived. The theorem states that this distribution is Normal, with the sample means centred around μ, the population mean, and with variance σ^2/n. The argument is set out diagrammatically in Figure 3.11.

Intuitively this theorem can be understood as follows. If the height of adult males is a Normally distributed random variable with mean $\mu = 174$ cm and

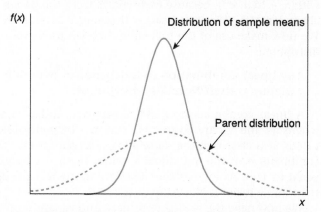

Figure 3.11
The parent distribution and the distribution of sample means

Note: The distribution of $\bar{x}$ is drawn for a sample size of $n = 9$. A larger sample size would narrow the $\bar{x}$ distribution; a smaller sample size would widen it.

---

[2] Don't worry if you didn't follow the derivation of this formula, just accept that it is correct.

variance $\sigma^2 = 92.16$, then it would be expected that a random sample of (say) nine males would yield a sample mean height of around 174 cm, perhaps a little more, perhaps a little less. In other words, the sample mean is centred around 174 cm, or the mean of the distribution of sample means is 174 cm.

The larger is the size of the individual samples (i.e. the larger n), the closer the sample mean would tend to be to 174 cm. For example, if the sample size is only two, a sample of two very tall people is quite possible, with a high sample mean as a result, well over 174 cm, e.g. 182 cm. But if the sample size were 20, it is very unlikely that 20 very tall males would be selected and the sample mean is likely to be much closer to 174. This is why the sample size n appears in the formula for the variance of the distribution of the sample mean, σ^2/n.

Note that, once again, we have transformed one (or more) random variables, the x_i values, with a particular probability distribution into another random variable, $\bar{x}$, with a (slightly) different distribution. This is common practice in statistics: transforming a variable will often put it into a more useful form, for example one whose probability distribution is well known.

The above theorem can be used to solve a range of statistical problems. For example, what is the probability that a random sample of nine men will have a mean height greater than 180 cm? The height of all men is known to be Normally distributed with mean $\mu = 174$ cm and variance $\sigma^2 = 92.16$. The theorem can be used to derive the probability distribution of the sample mean. For the population we have

$$\bar{x} \sim N(\mu, \sigma^2), \text{ i.e. } \bar{x} \sim N(174, 92.16)$$

Hence for the sample mean

$$\bar{x} \sim N(\mu, \sigma^2/n), \text{ i.e. } \bar{x} \sim N(174, 92.16/9)$$

This is shown diagrammatically in Figure 3.12.

To answer the question posed, the area to the right of 180, shaded in Figure 3.11, has to be found. This should by now be a familiar procedure. First the z score is calculated

$$z = \frac{\bar{x} - \mu}{\sqrt{\sigma^2/n}} = \frac{180 - 174}{\sqrt{92.16/9}} = 1.88 \tag{3.17}$$

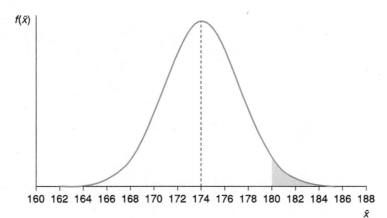

Figure 3.12
The proportion of sample means greater than $\bar{x} = 180$

Note that the z score formula is subtly different because we are dealing with the sample mean $\bar{x}$ rather than x itself. In the numerator we use $\bar{x}$ rather than x and in the denominator we use σ^2/n, not σ^2. This is because $\bar{x}$ has a variance σ^2/n, not σ^2, which is the population variance. $\sqrt{\sigma^2/n}$ is known as the **standard error**, to distinguish it from σ, the standard deviation of the population. The principle behind the z score is the same however: it measures how far is a sample mean of 180 from the population mean of 174, measured in terms of standard deviations.

Looking up the value of $z = 1.88$ in Table A2 gives an area of 0.0311 in the right-hand tail of the Normal distribution. Thus 3.11% of sample means will be greater than or equal to 180 cm when the sample size is nine. The desired probability is therefore 3.11%.

As this probability is quite small, we might consider the reasons for this. There are two possibilities:

(a) through bad luck, the sample collected is not very representative of the population as a whole;
(b) the sample is representative of the population, but the population mean is not 174 cm after all.

Only one of these two possibilities can be correct. How to decide between them will be taken up later on, in Chapter 5 on hypothesis testing.

It is interesting to examine the difference between the answer for a sample size of nine (3.11%) and the one obtained earlier for a single individual (26.43%). The latter may be considered as a sample of size one from the population. The examples illustrate the fact that the larger the sample size, the closer the sample mean is likely to be to the population mean. Thus larger samples tend to give better estimates of the population mean.

Oil reserves

An interesting application of probability distributions is to the estimation of oil reserves. The quantity of oil in an oil field is not known for certain, but is subject to uncertainty. The *proven* oil reserve of a field is the amount recoverable with probability of 90% (known as P90 in the oil industry). One can then add up the proven oil reserves around the world to get a total of proven reserves.

However, using probability theory we can see this might be misleading. Suppose we have 50 fields, where the recoverable quantity of oil is distributed as $x \sim N(100, 81)$ in each. From tables we note that $\bar{x} - 1.28s$ cuts off the bottom 10% of the Normal distribution, 88.48 in this case. This is the proven reserve for a field. Summing across the 50 fields gives 4424 as total reserves. But is there a 90% probability of recovering at least this amount?

Using the first theorem above, the total quantity of oil y is distributed Normally, with mean $E(y) = E(x_1) + \ldots + E(x_{50}) = 5000$ and variance $V(y) = V(x_1) + \ldots + V(x_{50}) = 4050$, assuming independence of the oil fields. Hence we have $y \sim N(5000, 4050)$. Again, the bottom 10% is cut off by $\bar{y} - 1.28s$, which is 4919. This is 11% larger than the 4424 calculated above. Adding up the proven reserves of each field individually underestimates the true total proven reserves. In fact, the probability of total proven reserves being greater than 4424 is almost 100%.

Note that the numbers given here are for illustration purposes and don't reflect the actual state of affairs. The principle of the calculation is correct however.

Sampling from a non-Normal population

The previous theorem and examples relied upon the fact that the population followed a Normal distribution. But what happens if it is not Normal? After all, it is not known for certain that the heights of all adult males are exactly Normally distributed, and there are many populations which are not Normal (e.g. wealth, as shown in Chapter 1). What can be done in these circumstances? The answer is to use another theorem about the distribution of sample means (presented without proof). This is known as the Central Limit Theorem:

Theorem

The sample mean $\bar{x}$, drawn from a population with mean μ and variance σ^2, has a sampling distribution which approaches a Normal distribution with mean μ and variance σ^2/n, as the sample size approaches infinity.

This is very useful, since it drops the assumption that the population is Normally distributed. Note that the distribution of sample means is only Normal as long as the sample size is infinite; for any finite sample size the distribution is only approximately Normal. However, the approximation is close enough for practical purposes if the sample size is larger than 25 or so observations. If the population distribution is itself nearly Normal then a smaller sample size would suffice. If the population distribution is particularly skewed then more than 25 observations would be desirable. Twenty-five observations constitutes a rule of thumb that is adequate in most circumstances. This is another illustration of statistics as an inexact science. It does not provide absolutely clear-cut answers to questions but, used carefully, helps us to arrive at sensible conclusions.

As an example of the use of the Central Limit Theorem, we return to the wealth data of Chapter 1. Recall that the mean level of wealth was 146.984 (measured in £000) and the variance 56 803. Suppose that a sample of $n = 50$ people were drawn from this population. What is the probability that the sample mean is greater than 160 (i.e. £160 000)?

On this occasion we know that the parent distribution is highly skewed so it is fortunate that we have 50 observations. This should be ample for us to justify applying the Central Limit Theorem. The distribution of $\bar{x}$ is therefore

$$\bar{x} \sim N(\mu, \sigma^2/n) \tag{3.18}$$

and, inserting the parameter values, this gives[3]

$$\bar{x} \sim N(146.984, 56\ 803/50) \tag{3.19}$$

To find the area beyond a sample mean of 160, the z score is first calculated

$$z = \frac{160 - 146.984}{\sqrt{56\ 803/50}} = 0.39 \tag{3.20}$$

Referring to the standard Normal tables, the area in the tail is then found to be 34.83%. This is the desired probability. So there is a probability of 34.83% of finding a mean of £160 000 or greater with a sample of size 50. This demonstrates

---

[3] Note that if we used 146 984 for the mean we would have 56 803 000 000 as the variance. Using £000 keeps the numbers more manageable. The z score is the same in both cases.

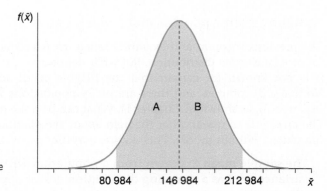

Figure 3.13
The probability of $\bar{x}$ lying within £66 000 either side of £146 984

that there is quite a high probability of getting a sample mean which is a relatively long way from £146 984. This is a consequence of the high degree of dispersion in the distribution of wealth.

Extending this example, we can ask what is the probability of the sample mean lying within, say, £66 000 either side of the true mean of £146 984 (i.e. between £80 984 and £212 984)? Figure 3.13 illustrates the situation, with the desired area shaded. By symmetry, areas A and B must be equal, so we only need find one of them. For B, we calculate the z score

$$z = \frac{212.984 - 146.984}{\sqrt{56\,803/50}} = 1.958 \tag{3.21}$$

From the standard Normal table, this cuts off approximately 2.5% in the upper tail, so area B = 0.475. Areas A and B together make up 95% of the distribution, therefore. There is thus a 95% probability of the sample mean falling within the range [80 984, 212 984] and we call this the 95% probability interval for the sample mean. We write this

$$\Pr(80\,984 \leqslant \bar{x} \leqslant 212\,984) = 0.95 \tag{3.22}$$

or, in terms of the formulae we have used[4]

$$\Pr(\mu - 1.96\sqrt{\sigma^2/n} \leqslant \bar{x} \leqslant \mu + 1.96\sqrt{\sigma^2/n}) = 0.95 \tag{3.23}$$

The 95% probability interval and the related concept of the 95% confidence interval (which will be introduced in Chapter 4) play important roles in statistical inference. We deliberately designed the example above to arrive at an answer of 95% for this reason.

Exercise 3.6

(a) If x is distributed as $x \sim N(50, 64)$ and samples of size $n = 25$ are drawn, what is the distribution of the sample mean $\bar{x}$?

(b) If the sample size doubles to 50, how is the standard error of $\bar{x}$ altered?

(c) Using the sample size of 25, (i) what is the probability of $\bar{x} > 51$? (ii) What is $\Pr(\bar{x} < 48)$? (iii) What is $\Pr(49 < \bar{x} < 50.5)$?

---

[4] 1.96 is the precise value cutting off 2.5% in each tail.

Summary

- The behaviour of many random variables (e.g. the result of the toss of a coin) can be described by a probability distribution (in this case, the Binomial distribution).

- The Binomial distribution is appropriate for problems where there are only two possible outcomes of a chance event (e.g. heads/tails, success/failure) and the probability of success is the same each time the experiment is conducted.

- The Normal distribution is appropriate for problems where the random variable has the familiar bell-shaped distribution. This often occurs when the variable is influenced by many, independent factors, none of which dominates the others. An example is men's heights, which are Normally distributed.

- The Poisson distribution is used in circumstances where there is a very low probability of 'success' and a high number of trials.

- Each of these distributions is actually a family of distributions, differing in the parameters of the distribution. Both the Binomial and Normal distributions have two parameters: n and P in the former case, μ and σ^2 in the latter. The Poisson distribution has one parameter, its mean μ.

- The mean of a random sample follows a Normal distribution, because it is influenced by many independent factors (the sample observations), none of which dominates in the calculation of the mean. This statement is always true if the population from which the sample is drawn follows a Normal distribution.

- If the population is not Normally distributed then the Central Limit Theorem states that the sample mean is Normally distributed in large samples. In this case 'large' means a sample of about 25 or more.

Key terms and concepts

Binomial distribution	probability distribution
Central Limit Theorem	random variable
Normal distribution	standard error
parameters of a distribution	standard Normal distribution
Poisson distribution	

5

Hypothesis testing

Learning outcomes

By the end of this chapter you should be able to:

- understand the philosophy and scientific principles underlying hypothesis testing;
- appreciate that hypothesis testing is about deciding whether a hypothesis is true or false on the basis of a sample of data;
- recognise the type of evidence which leads to a decision that the hypothesis is false;
- carry out hypothesis tests for a variety of statistical problems;
- recognise the relationship between hypothesis testing and a confidence interval;
- recognise the shortcomings of hypothesis testing.

Complete your diagnostic test for Chapter 5 now to create your personal study plan. Exercises with an icon ? *are also available for practice in MathXL with additional supporting resources.*

Introduction

This chapter deals with issues very similar to those of the previous chapter on estimation, but examines them in a different way. The estimation of population parameters and the testing of hypotheses about those parameters are similar techniques (indeed they are formally equivalent in a number of respects), but there are important differences in the interpretation of the results arising from each method. The process of estimation is appropriate when measurement is involved, such as measuring the true average expenditure on food; hypothesis testing is better when decision making is involved, such as whether to accept that a supplier's products are up to a specified standard. Hypothesis testing is also used to make decisions about the truth or otherwise of different theories, such as whether rising prices are caused by rising wages; and it is here that the issues become contentious. It is sometimes difficult to interpret correctly the results of hypothesis tests in these circumstances. This is discussed further later in this chapter.

The concepts of hypothesis testing

In many ways hypothesis testing is analogous to a criminal trial. In a trial there is a defendant who is *initially presumed innocent*. The *evidence* against the defendant is then presented and, if the jury finds this convincing *beyond all reasonable doubt*, he is found guilty; the presumption of innocence is overturned. Of course, mistakes are sometimes made: an innocent person is convicted or a guilty person set free. Both of these errors involve costs (not only in the monetary sense), either to the defendant or to society in general, and the errors should be avoided if at all possible. The laws under which the trial is held may help avoid such errors. The rule that the jury must be convinced 'beyond all reasonable doubt' helps to avoid convicting the innocent, for instance.

The situation in hypothesis testing is similar. First there is a maintained or null hypothesis which is initially *presumed* to be true. The empirical evidence, usually data from a random sample, is then gathered and assessed. If the evidence seems inconsistent with the null hypothesis, i.e. it has a low probability of occurring *if* the hypothesis were true, then the null hypothesis is *rejected* in favour of an alternative. Once again there are two types of error one can make, either rejecting the null hypothesis when it is really true, or not rejecting it when in fact it is false. Ideally one would like to avoid both types of error.

An example helps to clarify the issues and the analogy. Suppose that you are thinking of taking over a small business franchise. The current owner claims the weekly turnover of each existing franchise is £5000 and at this level you are willing to take on a franchise. You would be more cautious if the turnover is less than this figure. You examine the books of 26 franchises chosen at random and find that the average turnover was £4900 with standard deviation £280. What do you do?

The null hypothesis in this case is that average weekly turnover is £5000 (or more; that would be even more to your advantage). The alternative hypothesis is that turnover is strictly less than £5000 per week. We may write these more succinctly as follows

$H_0: \mu = 5000$
$H_1: \mu < 5000$

H_0 is conventionally used to denote the null hypothesis, H_1 the alternative. Initially, H_0 is presumed to be true and this presumption will be tested using the sample evidence. Note that the sample evidence is *not* used as part of the hypothesis.

You have to decide whether the owner's claim is correct (H_0) or not (H_1). The two types of error you could make are as follows:

- **Type I error** – reject H_0 when it is in fact true. This would mean missing a good business opportunity.
- **Type II error** – not rejecting H_0 when it is in fact false. You would go ahead and buy the business and then find out that it is not as attractive as claimed. You would have overpaid for the business.

The situation is set out in Figure 5.1.

Obviously a good decision rule would give a good chance of making a correct decision and rule out errors as far as possible. Unfortunately it is impossible completely to eliminate the possibility of errors. As the decision rule is changed to reduce the probability of a Type I error, the probability of making a Type II error inevitably increases. The skill comes in balancing these two types of error.

Again a diagram is useful in illustrating this. Assuming that the null hypothesis is true, then the sample observations are drawn from a population with mean 5000 and some variance, which we shall assume is accurately measured by the sample variance. The distribution of $\bar{x}$ is then given by

$$\bar{x} \sim N(\mu, \sigma^2/n) \text{ or} \tag{5.1}$$
$$\bar{x} \sim N(5000, 280^2/26)$$

Under the alternative hypothesis the distribution of $\bar{x}$ would be the same except that it would be centred on a value less than 5000. These two situations are illustrated in Figure 5.2. The distribution of $\bar{x}$ under H_1 is shown by a dashed curve to signify that its exact position is unknown, only that it lies to the left of the distribution under H_0.

A decision rule amounts to choosing a point or dividing line on the horizontal axis in Figure 5.2. If the sample mean lies to the left of this point then H_0 is rejected (the sample mean is too far away from H_0 for it to be credible) in favour of H_1 and you do not buy the firm. If $\bar{x}$ lies above this decision point then H_0 is not rejected and you go ahead with the purchase. Such a decision point is

		True situation	
		H_0 true	H_0 false
Decision	Accept H_0	Correct decision	Type II error
	Reject H_0	Type I error	Correct decision

Figure 5.1
The two different types of error

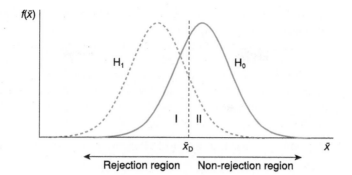

Figure 5.2
The sampling
distributions of $\bar{x}$
under H_0 and H_1

shown in Figure 5.2, denoted by $\bar{x}_D$. To the left of $\bar{x}_D$ lies the rejection (of H_0) region; to the right lies the non-rejection region.

Based on this point, we can see the probabilities of Type I and Type II errors. The area under the H_0 distribution to the left of $\bar{x}_D$, labelled I, shows the probability of rejecting H_0 given that it is in fact true: a Type I error. The area under the H_1 distribution to the right of $\bar{x}_D$, labelled II, shows the probability of a Type II error: not rejecting H_0 when it is in fact false (and H_1 is true).

Shifting the decision line to the right or left alters the balance of these probabilities. Moving the line to the right increases the probability of a Type I error but reduces the probability of a Type II error. Moving the line to the left has the opposite effect.

The Type I error probability can be calculated for any value of $\bar{x}_D$. Suppose we set $\bar{x}_D$ to a value of 4950. Using the distribution of $\bar{x}$ given in equation (5.1) above, the area under the distribution to the left of 4950 is obtained using the z score

$$z = \frac{\bar{x}_D - \mu}{\sqrt{s^2/n}} = \frac{4950 - 5000}{\sqrt{280^2/26}} = -0.91 \tag{5.2}$$

From the tables of the standard Normal distribution we find that the probability of a Type I error is 18.1%. Unfortunately, the Type II error probability cannot be established because the exact position of the distribution under H_1 is unknown. Therefore we cannot decide on the appropriate position of $\bar{x}_D$ by some balance of the two error probabilities.

The convention therefore is to set the position of $\bar{x}_D$ by using a Type I error probability of 5%, known as the significance level[1] of the test. In other words, we are prepared to accept a 5% probability of rejecting H_0 when it is, in fact, true. This allows us to establish the position of $\bar{x}_D$. From Table A2 (see page **414**) we find that $z = -1.64$ cuts off the bottom 5% of the distribution, so the decision line should be 1.64 standard errors below 5000. The value -1.64 is known as the critical value of the test. We therefore obtain

$$\bar{x}_D = 5000 - 1.64\sqrt{280^2/26} = 4910 \tag{5.3}$$

---

[1] The term **size** of the test is also used, not to be confused with the sample size. We use the term 'significance level' in this text.

Since the sample mean of 4900 lies below 4910 we reject H_0 *at the 5% significance level* or equivalently we reject *with 95% confidence*. The significance level is generally denoted by the symbol α and the complement of this, given by $1 - \alpha$, is known as the confidence level (as used in the confidence interval).

An equivalent procedure would be to calculate the z score associated with the sample mean, known as the **test statistic**, and then compare this to the critical value of the test. This allows the hypothesis testing procedure to be broken down into five neat steps.

(1)   Write down the null and alternative hypotheses:

H_0: $\mu = 5000$
H_1: $\mu < 5000$

(2)   Choose the significance level of the test, conventionally $\alpha = 0.05$ or 5%.
(3)   Look up the critical value of the test from statistical tables, based on the chosen significance level. $z^* = 1.64$ is the critical value in this case.

(4)   Calculate the test statistic

$$z = \frac{\bar{x} - \mu}{\sqrt{s^2/n}} = \frac{-100}{\sqrt{280^2/26}} = -1.82 \tag{5.4}$$

(5)   Decision rule. Compare the test statistic with the critical value: if $z < -z^*$ reject H_0 in favour of H_1. Since $-1.82 < -1.64$ H_0 is rejected with 95% confidence. Note that we use $-z^*$ here (rather than $+z^*$) because we are dealing with the left-hand tail of the distribution.

Worked example 5.1

A sample of 100 workers found the average overtime hours worked in the previous week was 7.8, with standard deviation 4.1 hours. Test the hypothesis that the average for all workers is 5 hours or less.
    We can set out the five steps of the answer as follows:

(1) H_0: $\mu = 5$
      H_1: $\mu > 5$
(2)   Significance level, $\alpha = 5\%$.
(3)   Critical value $z^* = 1.64$.
(4)   Test statistic

$$z = \frac{\bar{x} - \mu}{\sqrt{s^2/n}} = \frac{7.8 - 5}{\sqrt{4.1^2/100}} = 6.8$$

(5)   Decision rule: $6.8 > 1.64$ so we reject H_0 in favour of H_1. Note that in this case we are dealing with the right-hand tail of the distribution (positive values of z and z^*). Only high values of $\bar{x}$ reject H_0.

One-tail and two-tail tests

In the above example the rejection region for the test consisted of one tail of the distribution of $\bar{x}$, since the buyer was only concerned about turnover being less

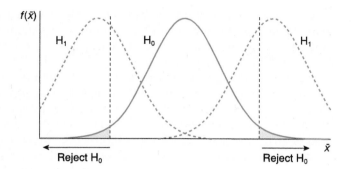

Figure 5.3
A two-tail hypothesis
test

than claimed. For this reason it is known as a one-tail test. Suppose now that an accountant is engaged to sell the franchise and wants to check the claim about turnover before advertising the business for sale. In this case she would be concerned about turnover being either below *or* above 5000.

This would now become a two-tail test with the null and alternative hypotheses being

$$H_0: \mu = 5000$$
$$H_1: \mu \neq 5000$$

Now there are two rejection regions for the test. Either a very low sample mean *or* a very high one will serve to reject the null hypothesis. The situation is presented graphically in Figure 5.3.

The distribution of $\bar{x}$ under H_0 is the same as before, but under the alternative hypothesis the distribution could be shifted either to the left or to the right, as depicted. If the significance level is still chosen to be 5%, then the complete rejection region consist of the *two* extremes of the distribution under H_0, containing 2.5% in each tail (hence 5% in total). This gives a Type I error probability of 5% as before.

The critical value of the test therefore becomes $z^* = 1.96$, the value which cuts off 2.5% in each tail of the standard Normal distribution. Only if the test statistic falls into one of the rejection regions beyond 1.96 standard errors from the mean is H_0 rejected.

Using data from the previous example, the test statistic remains $z = -1.82$ so that the null hypothesis cannot be rejected in this case, as -1.82 does not fall beyond -1.96. To recap, the five steps of the test are:

(1) $H_0: \mu = 5000$
      $H_1: \mu \neq 5000$
(2) Choose the significance level: $\alpha = 0.05$.
(3) Look up the critical value: $z^* = 1.96$.
(4) Evaluate the test statistic

$$z = \frac{-100}{\sqrt{280^2/26}} = -1.82$$

(5) Compare test statistic and critical values: if $z < -z^*$ or $z > z^*$ reject H_0 in favour of H_1. In this case $-1.82 > -1.96$ so H_0 cannot be rejected with 95% confidence.

One- and two-tail tests therefore differ only at steps 1 and 3. Note that we have come to different conclusions according to whether a one- or two-tail test was used, with the same sample evidence. There is nothing wrong with this, however, for there are different interpretations of the two results. If the investor always uses his rule, he will miss out on 5% of good investment opportunities, when sales are (by chance) low. He will never miss out on a good opportunity because the investment appears too good (i.e. sales by chance are very high). For the accountant, 5% of the firms with sales averaging £5000 will not be advertised as such, *either* because sales appear too low *or* because they appear too high.

It is tempting on occasion to use a one-tail test because of the sample evidence. For example, the accountant might look at the sample evidence above and decide that the franchise operation can only have true sales less than or equal to 5000. Therefore a one-tail test is used. This is a dangerous practice, since the sample evidence is being used to help formulate the hypothesis, which is then tested on that same evidence. This is going round in circles; the hypothesis should be chosen *independently* of the evidence, which is then used to test it. Presumably the accountant would also use a one-tail test (with $H_1: \mu > 5000$ as the alternative hypothesis) if it was noticed that the sample mean were *above* the hypothesised value. In effect therefore the 10% significance level would be used, not the 5% level, since there would be 5% in each tail of the distribution. A Type I error would be made on 10% of all occasions rather than 5%.

It is acceptable to use a one-tail test when you have *independent* information about what the alternative hypothesis should be, or you are not concerned about one side of the distribution (such as the investor) and can effectively add that into the null hypothesis. Otherwise, it is safer to use a two-tail test.

Exercise 5.1

(a) Two political parties are debating crime figures. One party says that crime has increased compared to the previous year. The other party says it has not. Write down the null and alternative hypotheses.

(b) Explain the two types of error that could be made in this example and the possible costs of each type of error.

Exercise 5.2

?

(a) We test the hypothesis $H_0: \mu = 100$ against $H_1: \mu > 100$ by rejecting H_0 if our sample mean is greater than 108. If in fact $\bar{x} \sim N(100, 900/25)$, what is the probability of making a Type I error?

(b) If we wanted a 5% Type I error probability, what decision rule should we adopt?

(c) If we knew that μ could only take on the values 100 (under H_0) or 112 (under H_1) what would be the Type II error probability using the decision rule in part (a)?

Exercise 5.3

?

Test the hypothesis $H_0: \mu = 500$ versus $H_1: \mu \neq 500$ using the evidence $\bar{x} = 530$, $s = 90$ from a sample of size $n = 30$.

The choice of significance level

We justified the choice of the 5% significance level by reference to convention. This is usually a poor argument for anything, but it does have some justification. In an ideal world we would have precisely specified null *and* alternative hypotheses (e.g. we would test $H_0: \mu = 5000$ against $H_1: \mu = 4500$, these being the only possibilities). Then we could calculate the probabilities of both Type I *and* Type II errors, for any given decision rule. We could then choose the optimal decision rule, which gives the best compromise between the two types of error. This is reflected in a court of law. In criminal cases, the jury must be convinced of the prosecution's case beyond reasonable doubt, because of the cost of committing a Type I error. In a civil case (libel, for example) the jury need only be convinced *on the balance of probabilities*. In a civil case, the costs of Type I and Type II error are more evenly balanced and so the burden of proof is lessened.

However, in practice we usually do not have the luxury of two well-specified hypotheses. As in the example, the null hypothesis is precisely specified (it has to be or the test could not be carried out) but the alternative hypothesis is imprecise (sometimes called a composite hypothesis because it encompasses a range of values). Statistical inference is often used not so much as an aid to decision making but to provide evidence for or against a particular theory, to alter one's degree of belief in the truth of the theory. For example, an economic theory might assert that rising prices are caused by rising wages (the cost–push theory of inflation). The null and alternative hypotheses would be:

H_0: there is no connection between rising wages and rising prices;
H_1: there is some connection between rising wages and rising prices.

(Note that the null has 'no connection', since this is a precise statement. 'Some connection' is too vague to be the null hypothesis.) Data could be gathered to test this hypothesis (the appropriate methods will be discussed in the chapters on correlation and regression). But what decision rests upon the result of this test? It could be thought that government might make a decision to impose a prices and incomes policy, but if every academic study of inflation led to the imposition or abandonment of a prices and incomes policy there would have been an awful lot of policies! (In fact, there *were* a lot of such policies, but not as many as the number of studies of inflation.) No single study is decisive ('more research is needed' is a very common phrase) but each does influence the climate of opinion which may eventually lead to a policy decision. But if a hypothesis test is designed to influence opinion, how is the significance level to be chosen?

It is difficult to trade off the costs of Type I and Type II errors and the probability of making those errors. A Type I error in this case means concluding that rising wages do cause rising prices when, in fact, they do not. So what would be the cost of this error, i.e. imposing a prices and incomes policy when, in fact, it is not needed? It is extremely difficult, if not impossible, to put a figure on it. It would depend on what type of prices and incomes policy were imposed – would wages be frozen or allowed to rise with productivity, how fast would prices be allowed to rise, would company dividends be frozen? The costs of the Type II error would also be problematic (not imposing a needed prices and incomes policy), for they would depend, among other things, on what alternative policies might be adopted.

The 5% significance level really does depend upon convention therefore, it cannot be justified by reference to the relative costs of Type I and Type II errors (it is too much to believe that everyone does consider these costs and independently arrives at the conclusion that 5% is the appropriate significance level!). However, the 5% convention does impose some sort of discipline upon research;

it sets some kind of standard which all theories (hypotheses) should be measured against. Beware the researcher who reports that a particular hypothesis is rejected at the 8% significance level; it is likely that the significance level was chosen so that the hypothesis could be rejected, which is what the researcher was hoping for in the first place!

The Prob-value approach

Suppose a result is significant at the 4.95% level (i.e. it just meets the 5% convention and the null hypothesis is rejected). A *very* slight change in the sample data could have meant the result being significant at only the 5.05% level, and the null hypothesis not being rejected. Would we really be happy to alter our belief completely on such fragile results? Most researchers (but not all!) would be cautious if their results were only just significant (or fell just short of significance).

This suggests an alternative approach: the significance level of the test statistic could be reported and the reader could make his own judgements about it. This is known as the `Prob-value` approach, the Prob-value being the significance level of the calculated test statistic. For example, the calculated test statistic for the investor problem was $z = -1.82$ and the associated Prob-value is obtained from Table A2 (see page **414**) as 3.44%, i.e. -1.82 cuts off 3.44% in one tail of the standard Normal distribution. This means that the null hypothesis can be rejected at the 3.44% significance level or, alternatively expressed, with 96.56% confidence.

Notice that Table A2 gives the Prob-value for a one-tail test; for a two-tail test the Prob-value should be doubled. Thus for the accountant, using the two-tail test, the significance level is 6.88% and this is the level at which the null hypothesis can be rejected. Alternatively we could say we reject the null with 93.12% confidence. This does not meet the standard 5% criterion (for the significance level) which is most often used, so would result in non-rejection of the null.

An advantage of using the Prob-value approach is that many statistical software programs routinely provide the Prob-value of a calculated test statistic. If one understands the use of Prob-values then one does not have to look up tables (this applies to any distribution, not just the Normal), which can save a lot of time.

To summarise, one rejects the null hypothesis if either:

- (Method 1) – the test statistic **is greater than** the critical value, i.e. $z > z^*$, or
- (Method 2) – the Prob-value associated with the test statistic **is less than** the significance level, i.e. $P < 0.05$ (if the 5% significance level is used).

I have found that many students initially find this confusing, because of the opposing inequality in the two versions (greater than and less than). For example, a program might calculate a hypothesis test and report the result as '$z = 1.4$ (P value $= 0.162$)'. The first point to note is that most software programs report the Prob-value for a two-tail test by default. Hence, assuming a 5% significance level, in this case we cannot reject H_0 because $z = 1.4 < 1.96$ or equivalently because $0.162 > 0.05$, against a two-tailed alternative (i.e. H_1 contains $\neq$).

If you wish to conduct a one-tailed test you have to halve the reported Prob-value, becoming 0.081 in this example. This is again greater than 5%, so the hypothesis is still accepted, even against a one-sided alternative (H_1 contains > or <). Equivalently, one could compare 1.4 with the one-tail critical value, 1.64, showing non-rejection of the null, but one has to look up the standard Normal table with this method. Computers cannot guess whether a one- or two-sided test is wanted, so take the conservative option and report the two-sided value. The correction for a one-sided test has to be done manually.

Significance, effect size and power

Researchers usually look for 'significant' results. Academic papers report that 'the results are significant' or that 'the coefficient is significantly different from zero at the 5% significance level'. It is vital to realise that the word 'significant' is used here in the *statistical* sense and not in its everyday sense of being *important*. Something can be statistically significant yet still unimportant.

Suppose that we have some more data about the business examined earlier. Data for 100 franchises have been uncovered, revealing an average weekly turnover of £4975 with standard deviation £143. Can we reject the hypothesis that the average weekly turnover is £5000? The test statistic is

$$z = \frac{4975 - 5000}{\sqrt{143^2/100}} = -1.75$$

Since this is less than $-z^* = -1.64$ the null is rejected with 95% confidence. True average weekly turnover is less than £5000. However, the difference is only £25 per week, which is 0.5% of £5000. Common sense would suggest that the difference may be unimportant, even if it is significant in the statistical sense. One should not interpret statistical results in terms of significance alone, therefore; one should also look at the size of the difference (sometimes known as the effect size) and ask whether it is important or not. This is a mistake made by even experienced researchers; a review of articles in the prestigious *American Economic Review* reported that 82% of them confused statistical significance for economic significance in some way (McCloskey and Ziliak, 2004).

This problem with hypothesis testing paradoxically grows worse as the sample size increases. For example, if 250 observations reveal average sales of 4985 with standard deviation 143, the null would (just) be rejected at 5% significance. In fact, given a large enough sample size we can virtually guarantee to reject the null hypothesis even before we have gathered the data. This can be seen from equation (5.4) for the z score test statistic: as n grows larger, the test statistic also inevitably increases.

A good way to remember this point is to appreciate that it is the *evidence* which is significant, not the size of the effect. Strictly, it is better to say '. . . there is significant evidence of difference between . . .' than '. . . there is a significant difference between . . .'.

A related way of considering the effect of increasing sample size is via the concept of the power of a test. This is defined as

Power of a test = $1 - \text{Pr(Type II error)} = 1 - \beta$ (5.5)

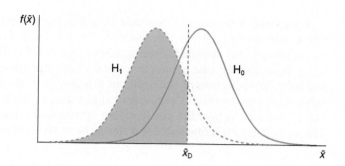

where β is the symbol conventionally used to indicate the probability of a Type II error. As a Type II error is defined as not rejecting H_0 when false (equivalent to rejecting H_1 when true), power is the probability of rejecting H_0 when false (if H_0 is false, it must be *either* accepted *or* rejected; hence these probabilities sum to one). This is one of the correct decisions identified earlier, associated with the lower right-hand box in Figure 5.1, that of correctly rejecting a false null hypothesis. The power of a test is therefore given by the area under the H_1 distribution, to the left of the decision line, as illustrated (shaded) in Figure 5.4 (for a one-tail test).

It is generally desirable to maximise the power of a test, as long as the probability of a Type I error is not raised in the process. There are essentially three ways of doing this.

- Avoid situations where the null and alternative hypotheses are very similar, i.e. the hypothesised means are not far apart (a small effect size).
- Use a large sample size. This reduces the sampling variance of $\bar{x}$ (under both H_0 and H_1) so the two distributions become more distinct.
- Use good sampling methods which have small sampling variances. This has a similar effect to increasing the sample size.

Unfortunately, in economics and business the data are very often given in advance and there is little or no control possible over the sampling procedures. This leads to a neglect of consideration of power, unlike in psychology, for example, where the experiment can often be designed by the researcher. The gathering of sample data will be covered in detail in Chapter 9.

Exercise 5.4

If a researcher believes the cost of making a Type I error is much greater than the cost of a Type II error, should they choose a 5% or 1% significance level? Explain why.

Exercise 5.5

(a) A researcher uses *Excel* to analyse data and test a hypothesis. The program reports a test statistic of $z = 1.77$ (P value = 0.077). Would you reject the null hypothesis if carrying out (i) a one-tailed test (ii) a two-tailed test? Use the 5% significance level.

(b) Repeat part (a) using a 1% significance level.

Further hypothesis tests

We now proceed to consider a number of different types of hypothesis test, all involving the same principles but differing in details of their implementation. This is similar to the exposition in the last chapter covering, in turn, tests of a proportion, tests of the difference of two means and proportions, and finally problems involving small sample sizes.

Testing a proportion

A car manufacturer claims that no more than 10% of its cars should need repairs in the first three years of their life, the warranty period. A random sample of 50 three-year-old cars found that 8 had required attention. Does this contradict the maker's claim?

This problem can be handled in a very similar way to the methods used for a mean. The key, once again, is to recognise the sample proportion as a random variable with an associated probability distribution. From Chapter 4 (equation (4.9)), the sampling distribution of the sample proportion in large samples is given by

$$p \sim N\left(\pi, \frac{\pi(1 - \pi)}{n}\right) \tag{5.6}$$

In this case $\pi = 0.10$ (under the null hypothesis, the maker's claim). The sample data are

$$p = 8/50 = 0.16$$
$$n = 50$$

Thus 16% of the sample required attention within the warranty period. This is substantially higher than the claimed 10%, but is this just because of a bad sample or does it reflect the reality that the cars are badly built? The hypothesis test is set out along the same lines as for a sample mean.

(1) H_0: $\pi = 0.10$
     H_1: $\pi > 0.10$

     (The only concern is the manufacturer not matching its claim.)
(2) Significance level: $\alpha = 0.05$.
(3) The critical value of the one-tail test at the 5% significance level is $z^* = 1.64$, obtained from the standard Normal table.
(4) The test statistic is

$$z = \frac{p - \pi}{\sqrt{\dfrac{\pi(1 - \pi)}{n}}} = \frac{0.16 - 0.10}{\sqrt{\dfrac{0.1 \times 0.9}{50}}} = 1.41$$

(5) Since the test statistic is less than the critical value, it falls into the non-rejection region. The null hypothesis is not rejected by the data. The manufacturer's claim is not unreasonable.

Note that for this problem, the rejection region lies in the *upper* tail of the distribution because of the 'greater than' inequality in the alternative hypothesis. The null hypothesis is therefore rejected in this case if $z > z*$.

Do children prefer branded goods only because of the name?

Researchers at Johns Hopkins Bloomberg School of Public Health in Maryland found young children were influenced by the packaging of foods. 63 children were offered two identical meals, save that one was still in its original packaging (from MacDonalds). 76% of the children preferred the branded French fries.

Is this evidence significant? The null hypothesis is $H_0: \pi = 0.5$ versus $H_1: \pi > 0.5$. The test statistic for this hypothesis test is

$$z = \frac{p - \pi}{\sqrt{\dfrac{\pi(1-\pi)}{n}}} = \frac{0.76 - 0.50}{\sqrt{\dfrac{0.5 \times 0.5}{63}}} = 4.12$$

which is greater than the critical value of $z* = 1.64$. Hence we conclude that children are influenced by the packaging or brand name.

[*Source: New Scientist*, 11 August 2007.]

Testing the difference of two means

Suppose a car company wishes to compare the performance of its two factories producing an identical model of car. The factories are equipped with the same machinery but their outputs might differ due to managerial ability, labour relations, etc. Senior management wishes to know if there is any difference between the two factories. Output is monitored for 30 days, chosen at random, with the following results:

	Factory 1	Factory 2
Average daily output	420	408
Standard deviation of daily output	25	20

Does this produce sufficient evidence of a real difference between the factories, or does the difference between the samples simply reflect random differences such as minor breakdowns of machinery? The information at our disposal may be summarised as

$$\bar{x}_1 = 420 \qquad \bar{x}_2 = 408$$
$$s_1 = 25 \qquad s_2 = 20$$
$$n_1 = 30 \qquad n_2 = 30$$

The hypothesis test to be conducted concerns the difference between the factories' outputs, so the appropriate random variable to examine is $\bar{x}_1 - \bar{x}_2$. From Chapter 4 (equation (4.12)), this has the following distribution, in large samples

$$\bar{x}_1 - \bar{x}_2 \sim N\left(\mu_1 - \mu_2, \frac{\sigma_1^2}{n_1} + \frac{\sigma_2^2}{n_2}\right) \tag{5.7}$$

The population variances, σ_1^2 and σ_2^2, may be replaced by their sample estimates, s_1^2 and s_1^2, if the former are unknown, as here. The hypothesis test is therefore as follows.

(1) H_0: $\mu_1 - \mu_2 = 0$
     H_1: $\mu_1 - \mu_2 \neq 0$

The null hypothesis posits no real difference between the factories. This is a two-tail test since there is no a priori reason to believe one factory is better than the other, apart from the sample evidence.

(2) Significance level: $\alpha = 1\%$. This is chosen since the management does not want to interfere unless it is really confident of some difference between the factories. In order to favour the null hypothesis, a lower significance level than the conventional 5% is set.

(3) The critical value of the test is $z^* = 2.57$. This cuts off 0.5% in each tail of the standard Normal distribution.

(4) The test statistic is

$$z = \frac{(\bar{x}_1 - \bar{x}_2) - (\mu_1 - \mu_2)}{\sqrt{\dfrac{s_1^2}{n_1} + \dfrac{s_2^2}{n_2}}} = \frac{(420 - 408) - 0}{\sqrt{\dfrac{25^2}{30} + \dfrac{20^2}{30}}} = 2.05$$

Note that this is of the same form as in the single-sample cases. The hypothesised value of the difference (zero in this case) is subtracted from the sample difference and this is divided by the standard error of the random variable.

(5) Decision rule: $z < z^*$ so the test statistic falls into the non-rejection region. There does not appear to be a significant difference between the two factories.

A number of remarks about this example should be made. First, it should be noted that it is not necessary for the two sample sizes to be equal (although they are in the example). For example, 45 days' output from factory 1 and 35 days' from factory 2 could have been sampled. Second, the values of s_1^2 and s_2^2 do not have to be equal. They are respectively estimates of σ_1^2 and σ_2^2 and, although the null hypothesis asserts that $\mu_1 = \mu_2$, it does not assert that the variances are equal. Management wants to know if the *average* levels of output are the same; it is not concerned about daily fluctuations in output. A test of the hypothesis of equal variances is set out in Chapter 6.

The final point to consider is whether all the necessary conditions for the correct application of this test have been met. The example noted that the 30 days were chosen at random. If the 30 days sampled were consecutive we might doubt whether the observations were truly independent. Low output on one day (e.g. due to a mechanical breakdown) might influence the following day's output (e.g. if a special effort were made to catch up on lost production).

Testing the difference of two proportions

The general method should by now be familiar, so we will proceed by example for this case. Suppose that, in a comparison of two holiday companies' customers, of the 75 who went with Happy Days Tours, 45 said they were satisfied, while 48 of the 90 who went with Fly by Night Holidays were satisfied. Is there a significant difference between the companies?

This problem can be handled by a hypothesis test on the difference of two sample proportions. The procedure is as follows. The sample evidence is

$$p_1 = 45/75 = 0.6 \qquad n_1 = 75$$
$$p_2 = 48/90 = 0.533 \qquad n_2 = 90$$

The hypothesis test is carried out as follows

(1) H_0: $\pi_1 - \pi_2 = 0$
     H_1: $\pi_1 - \pi_2 \neq 0$

(2) Significance level: $\alpha = 5\%$.
(3) Critical value: $z^* = 1.96$.
(4) Test statistic: The distribution of $p_1 - p_2$ is

$$p_1 - p_2 \sim N\left(\pi_1 - \pi_2, \frac{\pi_1(1 - \pi_1)}{n_1} + \frac{\pi_2(1 - \pi_2)}{n_2}\right)$$

so the test statistic is

$$z = \frac{(p_1 - p_2) - (\pi_1 - \pi_2)}{\sqrt{\dfrac{\pi_1(1 - \pi_1)}{n_1} + \dfrac{\pi_2(1 - \pi_2)}{n_2}}} \qquad (5.8)$$

However, π_1 and π_2 in the denominator of equation (5.8) have to be replaced by estimates from the samples. They cannot simply be replaced by p_1 and p_2 because these are unequal; to do so would contradict the null hypothesis that they *are* equal. Since the null hypothesis is assumed to be true (for the moment), it doesn't make sense to use a test statistic which explicitly supposes the null hypothesis to be false. Therefore π_1 and π_2 are replaced by an estimate of their common value which is denoted $\hat{\pi}$ and whose formula is

$$\hat{\pi} = \frac{n_1 p_1 + n_2 p_2}{n_1 + n_2} \qquad (5.9)$$

i.e. a weighted average of the two sample proportions. This yields

$$\hat{\pi} = \frac{75 \times 0.6 + 90 \times 0.533}{75 + 90} = 0.564$$

This, in fact, is just the proportion of all customers who were satisfied, 93 out of 165. The test statistic therefore becomes

$$z = \frac{0.6 - 0.533 - 0}{\sqrt{\dfrac{0.564 \times (1 - 0.564)}{75} + \dfrac{0.564 \times (1 - 0.564)}{90}}} = 0.86$$

(5) The test statistic is less than the critical value so the null hypothesis cannot be rejected with 95% confidence. There is not sufficient evidence to demonstrate a difference between the two companies' performance.

Are women better at multi-tasking?

The conventional wisdom is 'yes'. However, the concept of multi-tasking originated in computing and, in that domain it appears men are more likely to multi-task. Oxford Internet Surveys (http://www.oii.ox.ac.uk/microsites/oxis/) asked a sample of 1578 people if they multi-tasked while on-line (e.g. listening to music, using the phone). 69% of men said they did compared to 57% of women. Is this difference statistically significant?

The published survey does not give precise numbers of men and women respondents for this question, so we will assume equal numbers (the answer is not very sensitive to this assumption). We therefore have the test statistic

$$z = \frac{0.69 - 0.57 - 0}{\sqrt{\dfrac{0.63 \times (1 - 0.63)}{789} + \dfrac{0.63 \times (1 - 0.63)}{789}}} = 4.94$$

(0.63 is the overall proportion of multi-taskers.) The evidence is significant and clearly suggests this is a genuine difference: men are the multi-taskers!

Exercise 5.6

A survey of 80 voters finds that 65% are in favour of a particular policy. Test the hypothesis that the true proportion is 50%, against the alternative that a majority is in favour.

Exercise 5.7

A survey of 50 teenage girls found that on average they spent 3.6 hours per week chatting with friends over the internet. The standard deviation was 1.2 hours. A similar survey of 90 teenage boys found an average of 3.9 hours, with standard deviation 2.1 hours. Test if there is any difference between boys' and girls' behaviour.

Exercise 5.8

One gambler on horse racing won on 23 of his 75 bets. Another won on 34 out of 95. Is the second person a better judge of horses, or just luckier?

Hypothesis tests with small samples

As with estimation, slightly different methods have to be employed when the sample size is small ($n < 25$) and the population variance is unknown. When both of these conditions are satisfied the t distribution must be used rather than the Normal, so a t test is conducted rather than a z test. This means consulting tables of the t distribution to obtain the critical value of a test, but otherwise the methods are similar. These methods will be applied to hypotheses about sample means only, since they are inappropriate for tests of a sample proportion, as was the case in estimation.

Testing the sample mean

A large chain of supermarkets sells 5000 packets of cereal in each of its stores each month. It decides to test-market a different brand of cereal in 15 of its stores. After a month the 15 stores have sold an average of 5200 packets each, with a standard deviation of 500 packets. Should all supermarkets switch to selling the new brand?

The sample information is

$$\bar{x} = 5200, \; s = 500, \; n = 15$$

From Chapter 4 the distribution of the sample mean from a small sample when the population variance is unknown is based upon

$$\frac{\bar{x} - \mu}{\sqrt{s^2/n}} \sim t_v \qquad\qquad (5.10)$$

with $v = n - 1$ degrees of freedom. The hypothesis test is based on this formula and is conducted as follows

(1) H_0: $\mu = 5000$
    H_1: $\mu > 5000$
    (Only an improvement in sales is relevant.)
(2) Significance level: $\alpha = 1\%$ (chosen because the cost of changing brands is high).
(3) The critical value of the t distribution for a one-tail test at the 1% significance level with $v = n - 1 = 14$ degrees of freedom is $t^* = 2.62$.
(4) The test statistic is

$$t = \frac{\bar{x} - \mu}{\sqrt{s^2/n}} = \frac{5200 - 5000}{\sqrt{500^2/15}} = 1.55$$

(5) The null hypothesis is not rejected since the test statistic, 1.55, is less than the critical value, 2.62. It would probably be unwise to switch over to the new brand of cereals.

Testing the difference of two means

A survey of 20 British companies found an average annual expenditure on research and development of £3.7m with a standard deviation of £0.6m. A survey of 15 similar German companies found an average expenditure on research and development of £4.2m with standard deviation £0.9m. Does this evidence lend support to the view often expressed that Britain does not invest enough in research and development?

This is a hypothesis about the difference of two means, based on small sample sizes. The test statistic is again based on the t distribution, i.e.

$$\frac{(\bar{x}_1 - \bar{x}_2) - (\mu_1 - \mu_2)}{\sqrt{\dfrac{S^2}{n_1} + \dfrac{S^2}{n_2}}} \sim t_v \qquad\qquad (5.11)$$

where S^2 is the pooled variance (as given in equation (4.23)) and the degrees of freedom are given by $v = n_1 + n_2 - 2$.

The hypothesis test procedure is as follows:

(1) H_0: $\mu_1 - \mu_2 = 0$
    H_1: $\mu_1 - \mu_2 < 0$
(2) Significance level: $\alpha = 5\%$.

(3) The critical value of the t distribution at the 5% significance level for a one-tail test with $v = n_1 + n_2 - 2 = 33$ degrees of freedom is approximately $t^* = 1.70$.

(4) The test statistic is based on equation (5.11)

$$t = \frac{(\bar{x}_1 - \bar{x}_2) - (\mu_1 - \mu_2)}{\sqrt{\dfrac{S^2}{n_1} + \dfrac{S^2}{n_2}}} = \frac{3.7 - 4.2 - 0}{\sqrt{\dfrac{0.55}{20} + \dfrac{0.55}{15}}} = -1.97$$

where S^2 is the pooled variance, calculated by

$$S^2 = \frac{(n_1 - 1)s_1^2 + (n_2 - 1)s_2^2}{n_1 + n_2 - 2} = \frac{19 \times 0.6^2 + 14 \times 0.9^2}{33} = 0.55$$

(5) The test statistic falls in the rejection region, $t < -t^*$, so the null hypothesis is rejected. The data do support the view that Britain spends less on R&D than Germany.

Exercise 5.9

It is asserted that parents spend, on average, £540 per annum on toys for each child. A survey of 24 parents finds expenditure of £490, with standard deviation £150. Does this evidence contradict the assertion?

Exercise 5.10

A sample of 15 final-year students were found to spend on average 15 hours per week in the university library, with standard deviation 3 hours. A sample of 20 freshers found they spend on average 9 hours per week in the library, standard deviation 5 hours. Is this sufficient evidence to conclude that finalists spend more time in the library?

Summary

- Hypothesis testing is the set of procedures for deciding whether a hypothesis is true or false. When conducting the test we presume the hypothesis, termed the null hypothesis, is true until it is proved false on the basis of some sample evidence.

- If the null is proved false, it is rejected in favour of the alternative hypothesis. The procedure is conceptually similar to a court case, where the defendant is presumed innocent until the evidence proves otherwise.

- Not all decisions turn out to be correct and there are two types of error that can be made. A Type I error is to reject the null hypothesis when it is in fact true. A Type II error is not to reject the null when it is false.

- Choosing the appropriate decision rule (for rejecting the null hypothesis) is a question of trading off Type I and Type II errors. Because the alternative hypothesis is imprecisely specified, the probability of a Type II error usually cannot be specified.

- The rejection region for a test is therefore chosen to give a 5% probability of making a Type I error (sometimes a 1% probability is chosen). The critical value of the test statistic (sometimes referred to as the critical value of the test) is the value which separates the acceptance and rejection regions.

- The decision is based upon the value of a test statistic, which is calculated from the sample evidence and from information in the null hypothesis

$$\left(\text{e.g. } z = \frac{\bar{x} - \mu}{s/\sqrt{n}} \right)$$

- The null hypothesis is rejected if the test statistic falls into the rejection region for the test (i.e. it exceeds the critical value).

- For a two-tail test there are two rejection regions, corresponding to very high and very low values of the test statistic.

- Instead of comparing the test statistic to the critical value, an equivalent procedure is to compare the Prob-value of the test statistic with the significance level. The null is rejected if the Prob-value is less than the significance level.

- The power of a test is the probability of a test correctly rejecting the null hypothesis. Some tests have low power (e.g. when the sample size is small) and therefore are not very useful.

Key terms and concepts

alternative hypothesis	paired samples
critical value	power
effect size	Prob-value
independent samples	rejection region
null or maintained hypothesis	significance level
one- and two-tail tests	Type I and Type II errors

Reference

D. McCloskey, and S. Ziliak, Size matters: the standard error of regressions in the *American Economic Review*, *Journal of Socio-Economics*, 2004, **33**, 527–546.

7

Correlation and regression

Contents

Learning outcomes

By the end of this chapter you should be able to:

- understand the principles underlying correlation and regression;
- calculate and interpret a correlation coefficient and relate it to an *XY* graph of the two variables;
- calculate the line of best fit (regression line) and interpret the result;
- recognise the statistical significance of the results, using confidence intervals and hypothesis tests;
- recognise the importance of the units in which the variables are measured and of transformations to the data;
- use computer software (*Excel*) to derive the regression line and interpret the computer output.

Complete your diagnostic test for Chapter 7 now to create your personal study plan. Exercises with an icon **?** *are also available for practice in MathXL with additional supporting resources.*

Introduction

Correlation and regression are techniques for investigating the statistical relationship between two, or more, variables. In Chapter 1 we examined the relationship between investment and gross domestic product (GDP) using graphical methods (the *XY* chart). Although visually helpful, this did not provide any precise measurement of the strength of the relationship. In Chapter 6 the χ^2 test did provide a test of the significance of the association between two category-based variables, but this test cannot be applied to variables measured on a ratio scale. Correlation and regression fill in these gaps: the strength of the relationship between two (or more) ratio scale variables can be measured and the significance tested.

Correlation and regression are the techniques most often used by economists and forecasters. They can be used to answer such questions as

- Is there a link between the money supply and the price level?
- Do bigger firms produce at lower cost than smaller firms?
- Does instability in a country's export performance hinder its growth?

Each of these questions is about economics or business as much as about statistics. The statistical analysis is part of a wider investigation into the problem; it cannot provide a complete answer to the problem but, used sensibly, is a vital input. Correlation and regression techniques may be applied to time-series or cross-section data. The methods of analysis are similar in each case, although there are differences of approach and interpretation which are highlighted in this chapter and the next.

This chapter begins with the topic of correlation and simple (i.e. two variable) regression, using as an example the determinants of the birth rate in developing countries. In Chapter 8, multiple regression is examined, where a single dependent variable is explained by more than one explanatory variable. This is illustrated using time-series data pertaining to imports into the UK. This shows how a small research project can be undertaken, avoiding the many possible pitfalls along the way. Finally, a variety of useful additional techniques, tips and traps is set out, to help you understand and overcome a number of problems that can arise in regression analysis.

What determines the birth rate in developing countries?

This example follows the analysis in Michael Todaro's book, *Economic Development in the Third World* (3rd edn, pp. 197–200) where he tries to establish which of three variables (gross national product (GNP) per capita, the growth rate per capita or income inequality) is most important in determining a country's birth rate. (This analysis has been dropped from later editions of Todaro's book.) The analysis is instructive as an example of correlation and regression techniques in a number of ways. First, the question is an important one; it was discussed at the UN International Conference on Population and Development in Cairo in 1995. It is felt by many that reducing the birth rate is a vital factor in economic

Table 7.1 Todaro's data on birth rate, GNP, growth and inequality

Country	Birth rate	1981 GNP p.c.	GNP growth	Income ratio
Brazil	30	2200	5.1	9.5
Colombia	29	1380	3.2	6.8
Costa Rica	30	1430	3.0	4.6
India	35	260	1.4	3.1
Mexico	36	2250	3.8	5.0
Peru	36	1170	1.0	8.7
Philippines	34	790	2.8	3.8
Senegal	48	430	−0.3	6.4
South Korea	24	1700	6.9	2.7
Sri Lanka	27	300	2.5	2.3
Taiwan	21	1170	6.2	3.8
Thailand	30	770	4.6	3.3

Source: Adapted from Todaro, M. (1992).

development (birth rates in developed countries average around 12 per 1000 population, in developing countries around 30). Second, Todaro uses the statistical analysis to arrive at an unjustified conclusion (it is always best to learn from others' mistakes).

The data used by Todaro are shown in Table 7.1 using a sample of 12 developing countries. Two points need to be made initially. First, the sample only includes developing countries, so the results will not give an all-embracing explanation of the birth rate. Different factors might be relevant to developed countries, for example. Second, there is the important question of why these particular countries were chosen as the sample and others ignored. The choice of country was, in fact, limited by data availability, and one should ask whether countries with data available are likely to be representative of all countries. Data were, in fact, available for more than 12 countries, so Todaro was selective. You are asked to explore the implications of this in some of the problems at the end of the chapter.

The variables are defined as follows:

Birth rate: the number of births per 1000 population in 1981.
GNP per capita: 1981 gross national product p.c., in US dollars.
Growth rate: the growth rate of GNP p.c. per annum, 1961–1981.
Income ratio: the ratio of the income share of the richest 20% to that of the poorest 40%. A higher value of this ratio indicates greater inequality.

We leave aside the concerns about the sample until later and concentrate now on analysing the figures. The first thing it is useful to do is to graph the variables to see if anything useful is revealed. *XY* graphs are the most suitable in this case and they are shown in Figure 7.1. From these we see a reasonably tidy relationship between the birth rate and the growth rate, with a negative slope; there is a looser relationship with the income ratio, with a positive slope; and there is little discernible pattern (apart from a flat line) in the graph of birth rate against GNP. Todaro asserts that the best relationship is between the birth rate and income inequality. He rejects the growth rate as an important determinant of the birth rate because of the four countries at the top of the chart, which have

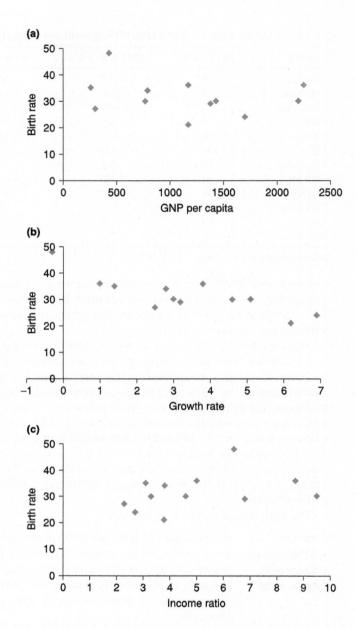

Figure 7.1
Graphs of the birth
rate against (a) GNP,
(b) growth and
(c) income ratio

very different growth rates, yet similar birth rates. In the following sections we shall see whether Todaro's conclusions are justified.

Correlation

The relationships graphed in Figure 7.1 can first be summarised numerically by measuring the correlation coefficient between any pair of variables. We illustrate this by calculating the correlation coefficient between the birth rate (*B*) and growth (*G*), although we also present the results for the other cases. Just as the mean is a number that summarises information about a single variable, so the correlation coefficient is a number which summarises the relationship between two variables.

The different types of possible relationship between any two variables, *X* and *Y*, may be summarised as follows:

- High values of *X* tend to be associated with low values of *Y* and vice versa. This is termed negative correlation, and appears to be the case for *B* and *G*.
- High (low) values of *X* tend to be associated with high (low) values of *Y*. This is positive correlation and reflects (rather weakly) the relationship between *B* and the income ratio (*IR*).
- No relationship between *X* and *Y* exists. High (low) values of *X* are associated about equally with high and low values of *Y*. This is zero, or the absence of, correlation. There appears to be little correlation between the birth rate and per capita GNP.

It should be noted that positive correlation does not mean that high values of *X* are *always* associated with high values of *Y*, but usually they are. It is also the case that correlation only represents a *linear* relationship between the two variables. As a counter-example, consider the backwards-bending labour supply curve, as suggested by economic theory (higher wages initially encourage extra work effort, but above a certain point the benefit of higher wage rates is taken in the form of more leisure). The relationship is non-linear and the measured degree of correlation between wages and hours of work is likely to be low, even though the former obviously influences the latter.

The sample correlation coefficient, *r*, is a numerical statistic which distinguishes between the types of cases shown in Figure 7.1. It has the following properties:

- It always lies between −1 and +1. This makes it relatively easy to judge the strength of an association.
- A positive value of *r* indicates positive correlation, a higher value indicating a stronger correlation between *X* and *Y* (i.e. the observations lie closer to a straight line). *r* = 1 indicates perfect positive correlation and means that all the observations lie precisely on a straight line with positive slope, as Figure 7.2 illustrates.
- A negative value of *r* indicates negative correlation. Similar to the above, a larger negative value indicates stronger negative correlation and *r* = −1 signifies perfect negative correlation.

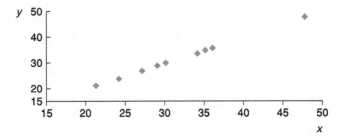

Figure 7.2
Perfect positive
correlation

Table 7.2 Calculation of the correlation coefficient, r

Country	Birth rate Y	GNP growth X	Y^2	X^2	XY
Brazil	30	5.1	900	26.01	153.0
Colombia	29	3.2	841	10.24	92.8
Costa Rica	30	3.0	900	9.00	90.0
India	35	1.4	1225	1.96	49.0
Mexico	36	3.8	1296	14.44	136.8
Peru	36	1.0	1296	1.00	36.0
Philippines	34	2.8	1156	7.84	95.2
Senegal	48	−0.3	2304	0.09	−14.4
South Korea	24	6.9	576	47.61	165.6
Sri Lanka	27	2.5	729	6.25	67.5
Taiwan	21	6.2	441	38.44	130.2
Thailand	30	4.6	900	21.16	138.0
Totals	380	40.2	12 564	184.04	1139.7

Note: In addition to the X and Y variables in the first two columns, three other columns are needed, for X^2, Y^2 and XY values.

- A value of $r = 0$ (or close to it) indicates a lack of correlation between X and Y.
- The relationship is symmetric, i.e. the correlation between X and Y is the same as between Y and X. It does not matter which variable is labelled Y and which is labelled X.

The formula[1] for calculating the correlation coefficient is given in equation (7.1)

$$r = \frac{n\sum XY - \sum X \sum Y}{\sqrt{(n\sum X^2 - (\sum X)^2)(n\sum Y^2 - (\sum Y)^2)}} \tag{7.1}$$

The calculation of r for the relationship between birth rate (Y) and growth (X) is shown in Table 7.2 and equation (7.2). From the totals in Table 7.2 we calculate

$$r = \frac{12 \times 1139.7 - 40.2 \times 380}{\sqrt{(12 \times 184.04 - 40.2^2)(12 \times 12\ 564 - 380^2)}} = -0.824 \tag{7.2}$$

This result indicates a fairly strong negative correlation between the birth rate and growth. Countries which have higher economic growth rates also tend to have lower birth rates. The result of calculating the correlation coefficient for the case of the birth rate and the income ratio is $r = 0.35$, which is positive as expected. Greater inequality (higher IR) is associated with a higher birth rate, though the degree of correlation is not particularly strong and less than the correlation with the growth rate. Between the birth rate and GNP per capita the value of r is only −0.26 indicating only a modest degree of correlation. All of this begins to cast doubt upon Todaro's interpretation of the data.

---

[1] The formula for r can be written in a variety of different ways. The one given here is the most convenient for calculation.

Exercise 7.1

(a) Perform the required calculations to confirm that the correlation between the birth rate and the income ratio is 0.35.

(b) In *Excel*, use the = CORREL() function to confirm your calculations in the previous two exercises. (For example, the function = CORREL(A1:A12,B1:B12) would calculate the correlation between a variable X in cells A1:A12 and Y in cells B1:B12.)

(c) Calculate the correlation coefficient between the birth rate and the growth rate again, but expressing the birth rate per 100 population and the growth rate as a decimal. (In other words, divide Y by 10 and X by 100.) Your calculation should confirm that changing the units of measurement leaves the correlation coefficient unchanged.

Are the results significant?

These results come from a (small) sample, one of many that could have been collected. Once again we can ask the question, what can we infer about the population (of all developing countries) from the sample? *Assuming* the sample was drawn at random (which may not be justified) we can use the principles of hypothesis testing introduced in Chapter 5. As usual, there are two possibilities.

(1) The truth is that there is no correlation (in the population) and that our sample exhibits such a large (absolute) value by chance.
(2) There really is a correlation between the birth rate and the growth rate and the sample correctly reflects this.

Denoting the true but unknown population correlation coefficient by ρ (the Greek letter 'rho') the possibilities can be expressed in terms of a hypothesis test

$H_0: \rho = 0$
$H_1: \rho \neq 0$

The test statistic in this case is not r itself but a transformation of it

$$t = \frac{r\sqrt{n-2}}{\sqrt{1-r^2}} \tag{7.3}$$

which has a t distribution with $n - 2$ degrees of freedom. The five steps of the test procedure are therefore:

(1) Write down the null and alternative hypotheses (shown above).
(2) Choose the significance level of the test: 5% by convention.
(3) Look up the critical value of the test for $n - 2 = 10$ degrees of freedom: $t^*_{10} = 2.228$ for a two-tail test.
(4) Calculate the test statistic using equation (7.3)

$$t = \frac{-0.824\sqrt{12-2}}{\sqrt{1-(-0.824)^2}} = -4.59$$

(5) Compare the test statistic with the critical value. In this case $t < -t^*_{10}$ so H_0 is rejected. There is a less than 5% chance of the sample evidence occurring if the null hypothesis were true, so the latter is rejected. There does appear to be a genuine association between the birth rate and the growth rate.

Performing similar calculations (see Exercise 7.2 below) for the income ratio and for GNP reveals that in both cases the null hypothesis cannot be rejected at the 5% significance level. These observed associations could well have arisen by chance.

Are significant results important?

Following the discussion in Chapter 5, we might ask if a certain value of the correlation coefficient is economically important as well as being significant. We saw earlier that 'significant' results need not be important. The difficulty in this case is that we have little intuitive understanding of the correlation coefficient. Is $\rho = 0.5$ important, for example? Would it make much difference if it were only 0.4?

Our understanding may be helped if we look at some graphs of variables with different correlation coefficients. Three are shown in Figure 7.3. Panel (a) of the figure graphs two variables with a correlation coefficient of 0.2. Visually there seems little association between the variables, yet the correlation coefficient is (just) significant: $t = 2.06$ ($n = 100$ and the Prob-value is 0.046). This is a significant result which does not impress much.

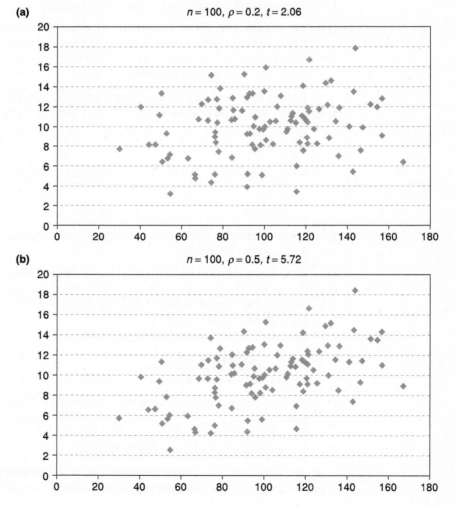

Figure 7.3
Variables with different correlations

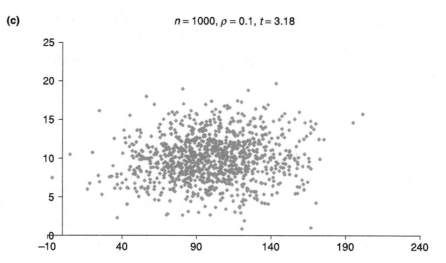

Figure 7.3
(cont'd)

In panel (b) the correlation coefficient is 0.5 and the association seems a little stronger visually, though there is still a substantial scatter of the observations around a straight line. Yet the t statistic in this case is 5.72, highly significant (Prob-value 0.000).

Finally, panel (c) shows an example where $n = 1000$. To the eye this looks much like a random scatter, with no discernable pattern. Yet the correlation coefficient is 0.1 and the t statistic is 3.18, again highly significant (Prob-value = 0.002).

The lessons from this seem fairly clear. What looks like a random scatter on a chart may in fact reveal a relationship between variables which is statistically significant, especially if there are a large number of observations. On the other hand, a high t-statistic and correlation coefficient can still mean there is a lot of variation in the data, revealed by the chart. Panel (b) suggests, for example, that we are unlikely to get a very reliable prediction of the value of y, even if we know the value of x.

Exercise 7.2

(a) Test the hypothesis that there is no association between the birth rate and the income ratio.

(b) Look up the Prob-value associated with the test statistic and confirm that it does not reject the null hypothesis.

Correlation and causality

It is important to test the significance of any result because almost every pair of variables will have a non-zero correlation coefficient, even if they are totally unconnected (the chance of the sample correlation coefficient being *exactly* zero is very, very small). Therefore it is important to distinguish between correlation coefficients which are significant and those which are not, using the t test just outlined. But even when the result is significant one should beware of the danger of 'spurious' correlation. Many variables which clearly cannot be related turn out to be 'significantly' correlated with each other. One now famous example is between the price level and cumulative rainfall. Because they both rise year after year, it is easy to see why they are correlated, yet it is hard to think of a plausible reason why they should be causally related to each other.

Apart from spurious correlation there are four possible reasons for a non-zero value of r.

(1) X influences Y.
(2) Y influences X.
(3) X and Y jointly influence each other.
(4) Another variable, Z, influences both X and Y.

Correlation alone does not allow us to distinguish between these alternatives. For example, wages (X) and prices (Y) are highly correlated. Some people believe this is due to cost–push inflation, i.e. that wage rises lead to price rises. This is case (1) above. Others believe that wages rise to keep up with the cost of living (i.e. rising prices), which is (2). Perhaps a more convincing explanation is (3), a wage–price spiral where each feeds upon the other. Others would suggest that it is the growth of the money supply, Z, which allows both wages and prices to rise. To distinguish between these alternatives is important for the control of inflation, but correlation alone does not allow that distinction to be made.

Correlation is best used therefore as a suggestive and descriptive piece of analysis, rather than a technique which gives definitive answers. It is often a preparatory piece of analysis, which gives some clues to what the data might yield, to be followed by more sophisticated techniques such as regression.

The coefficient of rank correlation

On occasion it is inappropriate or impossible to calculate the correlation coefficient as described above and an alternative approach is required. Sometimes the original data are unavailable but the ranks are. For example, schools may be ranked in terms of their exam results, but the actual pass rates are not available. Similarly, they may be ranked in terms of spending per pupil, with actual spending levels unavailable. Although the original data are missing, one can still test for an association between spending and exam success by calculating the correlation between the ranks. If extra spending improves exam performance, schools ranked higher on spending should also be ranked higher on exam success, leading to a positive correlation.

Second, even if the raw data are available, they may be highly skewed and hence the correlation coefficient may be influenced heavily by a few outliers. In this case, the hypothesis test for correlation may be misleading as it is based on the assumption of underlying Normal distributions for the data. In this case we could transform the values to ranks, and calculate the correlation of the ranks. In a similar manner to the median, described in Chapter 1, this can effectively deal with heavily skewed distributions.

In these cases, it is Spearman's coefficient of rank correlation that is calculated. (The 'standard' correlation coefficient described above is more fully known as Pearson's product-moment correlation coefficient, to distinguish it.) The formula to be applied is the same as before, though there are a few tricks to be learned about constructing the ranks and also the hypothesis test is conducted in a different manner.

Table 7.3 Calculation of Spearman's rank correlation coefficient

Country	Birth rate Y	Growth rate X	Rank Y	Rank X	Y^2	X^2	XY
Brazil	30	5.1	7	3	49	9	21
Colombia	29	3.2	9	6	81	36	54
Costa Rica	30	3.0	7	7	49	49	49
India	35	1.4	4	10	16	100	40
Mexico	36	3.8	2.5	5	6.25	25	12.5
Peru	36	1.0	2.5	11	6.25	121	27.5
Philippines	34	2.8	5	8	25	64	40
Senegal	48	−0.3	1	12	1	144	12
South Korea	24	6.9	11	1	121	1	11
Sri Lanka	27	2.5	10	9	100	81	90
Taiwan	21	6.2	12	2	144	4	24
Thailand	30	4.6	7	4	49	16	28
Totals	–	–	78	78	647.5	650	409

Note: The country with the highest growth rate (South Korea) is ranked 1 for variable X; Taiwan, the next fastest growth nation, is ranked 2, etc. For the birth rate, Senegal is ranked 1, having the highest birth rate, 48. Taiwan has the lowest birth rate and so is ranked 12 for variable Y.

Using the ranks is generally less efficient than using the original data, because one is effectively throwing away some of the information (e.g. by *how much* do countries' growth rates differ). However, there is a trade-off: the rank correlation coefficient is more robust, i.e. it is less influenced by outliers or highly skewed distributions. If one suspects this is a risk, it may be better to use the ranks. This is similar to the situation where the median can prove superior to the mean as a measure of central tendency.

We will calculate the rank correlation coefficient for the data on birth and growth rates, to provide a comparison with the ordinary correlation coefficient calculated earlier. It is unlikely that the distributions of birth or of growth rates is particularly skewed (and we have too few observations to reliably tell) so the Pearson measure might generally be preferred, but we calculate the Spearman coefficient for comparison. Table 7.3 presents the data for birth and growth rates in the form of ranks. Calculating the ranks is fairly straightforward, though there are a couple of points to note.

The country with the highest birth rate has the rank of 1, the next highest 2, and so on. Similarly, the country with the highest growth rate ranks 1, etc. One could reverse a ranking, so the lowest birth rate ranks 1, for example; the direction of ranking can be somewhat arbitrary. This would leave the rank correlation coefficient unchanged in value, but the sign would change (e.g. 0.5 would become −0.5). This could be confusing as we would now have a 'negative' correlation rather than a positive one (though the birth rate variable would now have to be redefined). It is better to use the 'natural' order of ranking for each variable.

Where two or more observations are the same, as are the birth rates of Mexico and Peru, then they are given the same rank, which is the average of the relevant ranking values. For example, both countries are given the rank of 2.5, which is the average of 2 and 3. Similarly, Brazil, Costa Rica and Thailand are all given the rank of 7, which is the average of 6, 7 and 8. The next country, Colombia, is then given the rank of 9.

Excel warning

Microsoft Excel has a *rank()* function built in, which takes a variable and calculates a new variable consisting of the ranks, similar to the above table. However, note that it deals with tied values in a different way. In the example above, Brazil, Costa Rica and Thailand would all be given a rank of 6 by *Excel*, not 7. This then gives a different correlation coefficient to that calculated here. *Excel's* method can be shown to be problematic since, if the rankings are reversed (e.g. the highest growth country is numbered 12 rather than 1) *Excel* gives a different numerical result.

We now apply formula (7.1) to the ranked data, giving

$$r_s = \frac{n\sum XY - \sum X \sum Y}{\sqrt{(n\sum X^2 - (\sum X)^2)(n\sum Y^2 - (\sum Y)^2)}}$$

$$= \frac{12 \times 409 - 78 \times 78}{\sqrt{(12 \times 650 - 78^2)(12 \times 647.5 - 78^2)}} = -0.691$$

This indicates a negative rank correlation between the two variables, as with the standard correlation coefficient ($r = -0.824$), but with a slightly smaller absolute value.

To test the significance of the result a hypothesis test can be performed on the value of ρ_s, the corresponding population parameter

$H_0: \rho_s = 0$
$H_1: \rho_s \neq 0$

This time the t distribution cannot be used (because we are no longer relying on the parent distribution being Normal), but prepared tables of the critical values for ρ_s itself may be consulted; these are given in Table A6 (see page **426**), and an excerpt is given in Table 7.4.

The critical value at the 5% significance level, for $n = 12$, is 0.591. Hence the null hypothesis is rejected if the rank correlation coefficient falls outside the

Table 7.4 Excerpt from Table A6: Critical values of the rank correlation coefficient

n	10%	5%	2%	1%
5	0.900			
6	0.829	0.886	0.943	
⋮	⋮	⋮	⋮	⋮
11	0.523	0.623	0.763	0.794
12	0.497	0.591	0.703	0.780
13	0.475	0.566	0.673	0.746

Note: The critical value is given at the intersection of the shaded row and column.

range [−0.591, 0.591], which it does in this case. Thus the null can be rejected with 95% confidence; the data do support the hypothesis of a relationship between the birth rate and growth. This critical value shown in the table is for a two-tail test. For a one-tail test, the significance level given in the top row of the table should be halved.

Exercise 7.3

(a) Rank the observations for the income ratio across countries (highest = 1) and calculate the coefficient of rank correlation with the birth rate.

(b) Test the hypothesis that $\rho_s = 0$.

(c) Reverse the rankings for both variables and confirm that this does not affect the calculated test statistic.

Worked example 7.1

To illustrate all the calculations and bring them together without distracting explanation, we work through a simple example with the following data on X and Y:

Y	17	18	19	20	27	18
X	3	4	7	6	8	5

An XY graph of the data reveals the following picture, which suggests positive correlation:

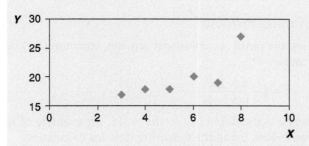

Note that one point appears to be something of an outlier. All the calculations for correlation may be based on the following table:

Obs	Y	X	Y²	X²	XY	Rank Y R_Y	Rank X R_X	R_Y^2	R_X^2	$R_X R_Y$
1	17	3	289	9	51	6	6	36	36	36
2	18	4	324	16	72	4.5	5	20.25	25	22.5
3	19	7	361	49	133	3	2	9	4	6
4	20	6	400	36	120	2	3	4	9	6
5	27	8	729	64	216	1	1	1	1	1
6	18	5	324	25	90	4.5	4	20.25	16	18
Totals	119	33	2427	199	682	21	21	90.5	91	89.5

The (Pearson) correlation coefficient r is therefore:

$$r = \frac{n\sum XY - \sum X \sum Y}{\sqrt{(n\sum X^2 - (\sum X)^2)(n\sum Y^2 - (\sum Y)^2)}}$$

$$= \frac{6 \times 682 - 33 \times 119}{\sqrt{(6 \times 199 - 33^2)(6 \times 2427 - 119^2)}} = 0.804$$

The hypothesis H_0: $\rho = 0$ versus H_1: $\rho \neq 0$ can be tested using the t test statistic:

$$t = \frac{r\sqrt{n-2}}{\sqrt{1-r^2}} = \frac{0.804 \times \sqrt{6-2}}{\sqrt{1-0.804^2}} = 2.7$$

which is compared to a critical value of 2.776, so the null hypothesis is not rejected, narrowly. This is largely attributable to the small number of observations and anyway it may be unwise to use the t-distribution on such a small sample. The rank correlation coefficient is calculated as

$$r = \frac{n\sum XY - \sum X \sum Y}{\sqrt{(n\sum X^2 - (\sum X)^2)(n\sum Y^2 - (\sum Y)^2)}}$$

$$= \frac{6 \times 89.5 - 21 \times 21}{\sqrt{(6 \times 91 - 21^2)(6 \times 90.5 - 21^2)}} = 0.928$$

The critical value at the 5% significance level is 0.886, so the rank correlation coefficient *is* significant, in contrast to the previous result. Not too much should be read into this, however; with few observations the ranking process can easily alter the result substantially.

A simpler formula

When the ranks occur without any ties, equation (7.1) simplifies to the following formula:

$$r_s = 1 - \frac{6 \times \sum d^2}{n(n^2 - 1)} \tag{7.4}$$

where d is the difference in the ranks. An example of the use of this formula is given below, using the following data for calculation

Rank Y	Rank X	d	d^2
1	5	−4	16
4	1	3	9
5	2	3	9
6	3	3	9
3	4	−1	1
2	6	−4	16
		Total	60

The differences d and their squared values are shown in the final columns of the table and from these we obtain

$$r_s = 1 - \frac{6 \times 60}{6 \times (6^2 - 1)} = -0.714 \tag{7.5}$$

This is the same answer as would be obtained using the conventional formula (7.1). The verification is left as an exercise. Remember, this formula can only be used if there are no ties in either variable.

Regression analysis

Regression analysis is a more sophisticated way of examining the relationship between two (or more) variables than is correlation. The major differences between correlation and regression are the following:

- Regression can investigate the relationships between two *or more* variables.
- A *direction* of causality is asserted, from the explanatory variable (or variables) to the dependent variable.
- The *influence* of each explanatory variable upon the dependent variable is measured.
- The *significance* of each explanatory variable can be ascertained.

Thus regression permits answers to such questions as:

- Does the growth rate influence a country's birth rate?
- If the growth rate increases, by how much might a country's birth rate be expected to fall?
- Are other variables important in determining the birth rate?

In this example we assert that the direction of causality is from the growth rate (X) to the birth rate (Y) and not vice versa. The growth rate is therefore the explanatory variable (also referred to as the independent or exogenous variable) and the birth rate is the dependent variable (also called the explained or endogenous variable).

Regression analysis describes this causal relationship by fitting a straight line drawn through the data, which best summarises them. It is sometimes called 'the line of best fit' for this reason. This is illustrated in Figure 7.4 for the birth rate and growth rate data. Note that (by convention) the explanatory variable is placed on the horizontal axis, the explained on the vertical. This regression line is downward sloping (its derivation will be explained shortly) for the same

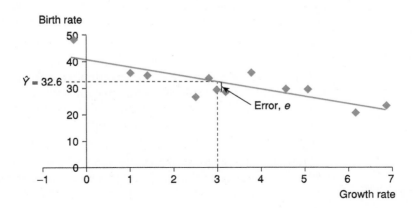

Figure 7.4
The line of best fit

reason that the correlation coefficient is negative, i.e. high values of Y are generally associated with low values of X and vice versa.

Since the regression line summarises knowledge of the relationship between X and Y, it can be used to predict the value of Y given any particular value of X. In Figure 7.4 the value of $X = 3$ (the observation for Costa Rica) is related via the regression line to a value of Y (denoted by $\hat{Y}$) of 32.6. This predicted value is close (but not identical) to the actual birth rate of 30. The difference reflects the absence of perfect correlation between the two variables.

The difference between the actual value, Y, and the predicted value, $\hat{Y}$, is called the error or residual. It is labelled e in Figure 7.4. (*Note*: The italic e denoting the error term should not be confused with the roman letter e, used as the base for natural logarithms (see Appendix 1C to Chapter 1, page **78**). Why should such errors occur? The relationship is never going to be an exact one for a variety of reasons. There are bound to be other factors besides growth which affect the birth rate (e.g. the education of women) and these effects are all subsumed into the error term. There might additionally be simple measurement error (of Y) and, of course, people do act in a somewhat random fashion rather than follow rigid rules of behaviour.

All of these factors fall into the error term and this means that the observations lie around the regression line rather than on it. If there are many of these factors, none of which is predominant, and they are independent of each other, then these errors may be assumed to be Normally distributed about the regression line.

Why not include these factors explicitly? On the face of it this would seem to be an improvement, making the model more realistic. However, the costs of doing this are that the model becomes more complex, calculation becomes more difficult (not so important now with computers) and it is generally more difficult for the reader (or researcher) to interpret what is going on. If the main interest is the relationship between the birth rate and growth, why complicate the model unduly? There is a virtue in simplicity, as long as the simplified model still gives an undistorted view of the relationship. In Chapter 10 on multiple regression the trade-off between simplicity and realism will be further discussed, particularly with reference to the problems which can arise if relevant explanatory variables are omitted from the analysis.

Calculation of the regression line

The equation of the sample regression line may be written

$$\hat{Y}_i = a + bX_i \tag{7.6}$$

where

$\hat{Y}_i$ is the predicted value of Y for observation (country) i
X_i is the value of the explanatory variable for observation i, and
a, b are fixed coefficients to be estimated; a measures the intercept of the regression line on the Y axis, b measures its slope.

This is illustrated in Figure 7.5.

The first task of regression analysis is to find the values of a and b so that the regression line may be drawn. To do this we proceed as follows. The difference between the actual value, Y_i, and its predicted value, $\hat{Y}_i$, is e_i, the error. Thus

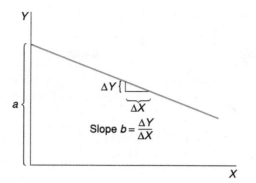

$$Y_i = \hat{Y}_i + e_i \qquad (7.7)$$

Substituting equation (7.6) into equation (7.7) the regression equation can be written

$$Y_i = a + bX_i + e_i \qquad (7.8)$$

Equation (7.8) shows that observed birth rates are made up of two components:

(1) that part explained by the growth rate, $a + bX_i$, and
(2) an error component, e_i.

In a good model, part (1) should be large relative to part (2) and the regression line is based upon this principle. The line of best fit is therefore found by finding the values of a and b which *minimise the sum of squared errors* ($\sum e_i^2$) from the regression line. For this reason, this method is known as 'the method of least squares' or simply 'ordinary least squares' (OLS). The use of this criterion will be justified later on, but it can be said in passing that the sum of the errors is not minimised because that would not lead to a unique answer for the values a and b. In fact, there is an infinite number of possible regression lines which all yield a sum of errors equal to zero. Minimising the sum of *squared* errors does yield a unique answer.

The task is therefore to

$$\text{minimise } \sum e_i^2 \qquad (7.9)$$

by choice of a and b.

Rearranging equation (7.8) the error is given by

$$e_i = Y_i - a - bX_i \qquad (7.10)$$

so equation (7.9) becomes

$$\text{minimise } \sum(Y_i - a - bX_i)^2 \qquad (7.11)$$

by choice of a and b.

Finding the solution to equation (7.11) requires the use of differential calculus, and is not presented here. The resulting formulae for a and b are

$$b = \frac{n \sum XY - \sum X \sum Y}{n \sum X^2 - (\sum X)^2} \qquad (7.12)$$

and

$$a = \bar{Y} - b\bar{X} \tag{7.13}$$

where $\bar{X}$ and $\bar{Y}$ are the mean values of X and Y respectively. The values necessary to evaluate equations (7.12) and (7.13) can be obtained from Table 7.2 which was used to calculate the correlation coefficient. These values are repeated for convenience

$$\sum Y = 380 \qquad \sum Y^2 = 12\,564$$
$$\sum X = 40.2 \qquad \sum X^2 = 184.04$$
$$\sum XY = 1139.70 \qquad n = 12$$

Using these values we obtain

$$b = \frac{12 \times 1139.70 - 40.2 \times 380}{12 \times 184.04 - 40.2^2} = -2.700$$

and

$$a = \frac{380}{12} - (-2.700) \times \frac{40.2}{12} = 40.711$$

Thus the regression equation can be written, to two decimal places for clarity, as

$$Y_i = 40.71 - 2.70X_i + e_i$$

Interpretation of the slope and intercept

The most important part of the result is the slope coefficient $b = -2.7$ since it measures the effect of X upon Y. This result implies that a unit increase in the growth rate (e.g. from 2% to 3% p.a.) would lower the birth rate by 2.7, for example from 30 births per 1000 population to 27.3. Given that the growth data refer to a 20-year period (1961 to 1981), this increase in the growth rate would have to be sustained over such a time, not an easy task. How big is the effect upon the birth rate? The average birth rate in the sample is 31.67, so a reduction of 2.7 for an average country would be a fall of 8.5% ($2.7/31.67 \times 100$). This is reasonably substantial (although not enough to bring the birth rate down to developed country levels) but would need a considerable, sustained increase in the growth rate to bring it about.

The value of a, the intercept, may be interpreted as the predicted birth rate of a country with zero growth (since $\hat{Y}_i = a$ at $X = 0$). This value of 40.71 is fairly close to that of Senegal, which actually had negative growth over the period and whose birth rate was 48, a little higher than the intercept value. Although a has a sensible interpretation in this case, this is not always so. For example, in a regression of the demand for a good on its price, a would represent demand at zero price, which is unlikely ever to be observed.

Exercise 7.4

?

(a) Calculate the regression line relating the birth rate to the income ratio.

(b) Interpret the coefficients of this equation.

Measuring the goodness of fit of the regression line

Having calculated the regression line we now ask whether it provides a good fit for the data, i.e. do the observations tend to lie close to, or far away from, the line? If the fit is poor, perhaps the effect of X upon Y is not so strong after all. Note that even if X has *no* effect upon Y we can still calculate a regression line and its slope coefficient b. Although b is likely to be small, it is unlikely to be exactly zero. Measuring the goodness of fit of the data to the line helps us to distinguish between good and bad regressions.

We proceed by comparing the three competing models explaining the birth rate. Which of them fits the data best? Using the income ratio and the GNP variable gives the following regressions (calculations not shown) to compare with our original model:

for the income ratio (IR): $B = 26.44 + 1.045 \times \text{IR} + e$
for GNP: $B = 34.72 - 0.003 \times \text{GNP} + e$
for growth: $B = 40.71 - 2.70 \times \text{GROWTH} + e$

How can we decide which of these three is 'best' on the basis of the regression equations alone? From Figure 7.1 it is evident that some relationships appear stronger than others, yet this is not revealed by examining the regression equation alone. More information is needed. (You cannot choose the best equation simply by looking at the size of the coefficients. Try to think why.)

The goodness of fit is calculated by comparing two lines: the regression line and the 'mean line' (i.e. a horizontal line drawn at the mean value of Y). The regression line *must* fit the data better (if the mean line were the best fit, that is also where the regression line would be) but the question is how much better? This is illustrated in Figure 7.6, which demonstrates the principle behind the calculation of the **coefficient of determination**, denoted by R^2 and usually more simply referred to as 'R squared'.

The figure shows the mean value of Y, the calculated sample regression line and an arbitrarily chosen sample observation (X_i, Y_i). The difference between Y_i and $\bar{Y}$ (length $Y_i - \bar{Y}$) can be divided up into:

(1) That part 'explained' by the regression line, $\hat{Y}_i - \bar{Y}$ (i.e. explained by the value of X_i).
(2) The error term $e_i = Y_i - \hat{Y}_i$.

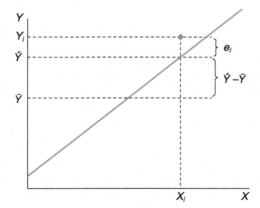

Figure 7.6
The calculation of R^2

In algebraic terms

$$Y_i - \bar{Y} = (Y - \hat{Y}_i) + (\hat{Y}_i - \bar{Y}) \tag{7.14}$$

A good regression model should 'explain' a large part of the differences between the Y_i values and $\bar{Y}$, i.e. the length $\hat{Y}_i - \bar{Y}$ should be large relative to $Y_i - \bar{Y}$. A measure of fit would therefore be $(\hat{Y}_i - \bar{Y})/(Y_i - \bar{Y})$. We need to apply this to all observations, not just a single one. Hence we need to sum this expression over all the sample observations. A problem is that some of the terms would take a negative value and offset the positive terms. To get round this problem we square each of the terms in equation (7.14) to make them all positive, and then sum over the observations. This gives

$\sum(Y_i - \bar{Y})^2$, known as the total sum of squares (TSS)
$\sum(\hat{Y}_i - \bar{Y})^2$, the regression sum of squares (RSS), and
$\sum(Y_i - \hat{Y}_i)^2$, the error sum of squares (ESS)

The measure of goodness of fit, R^2, is then defined as the ratio of the regression sum of squares to the total sum of squares, i.e.

$$R^2 = \frac{\text{RSS}}{\text{TSS}} \tag{7.15}$$

The better the divergences between Y_i and $\bar{Y}$ are explained by the regression line, the better the goodness of fit, and the higher the calculated value of R^2. Further, it is true that

$$\text{TSS} = \text{RSS} + \text{ESS} \tag{7.16}$$

From equations (7.15) and (7.16) we can then see that R^2 must lie between 0 and 1 (note that since each term in equation (7.16) is a sum of squares, none of them can be negative). Thus

$$0 \leqslant R^2 \leqslant 1$$

A value of $R^2 = 1$ indicates that all the sample observations lie exactly on the regression line (equivalent to perfect correlation). If $R^2 = 0$ then the regression line is of no use at all – X does not influence Y (linearly) at all, and to try to predict a value of Y_i one might as well use the mean $\bar{Y}$ rather than the value X_i inserted into the sample regression equation.

To calculate R^2, alternative formulae to those above make the task easier. Instead we use

$$\text{TSS} = \sum(Y_i - \bar{Y})^2 = \sum Y_i^2 - n\bar{Y}^2 = 12\,564 - 12 \times 31.67^2 = 530.667$$
$$\text{ESS} = \sum(Y_i - \hat{Y})^2 = \sum Y_i^2 - a\sum Y_i - b\sum X_i Y_i$$
$$= 12\,564 - 40.711 \times 380 - (-2.7) \times 1139.70 = 170.754$$
$$\text{RSS} = \text{TSS} - \text{ESS} = 530.667 - 170.754 = 359.913$$

This gives the result

$$R^2 = \frac{\text{RSS}}{\text{TSS}} = \frac{359.913}{530.667} = 0.678$$

This is interpreted as follows. Countries' birth rates vary around the overall mean value of 31.67. 67.8% of this variation is explained by variation in countries' growth rates. This is quite a respectable figure to obtain, leaving only 32.8% of the variation in Y left to be explained by other factors (or pure random variation). The regression seems to make a worthwhile contribution to explaining why birth rates differ.

It turns out that in simple regression (i.e. where there is only one explanatory variable), R^2 is simply the square of the correlation coefficient between X and Y. Thus for the income ratio and for GNP we have

$$\text{for IR:} \quad R^2 = 0.35^2 = 0.13$$
$$\text{for GNP:} \quad R^2 = -0.26^2 = 0.07$$

This shows, once again, that these other variables are not terribly useful in explaining why birth rates differ. Each of them only explains a small proportion of the variation in Y.

It should be emphasised at this point that R^2 is not the only criterion (or even an adequate one in all cases) for judging the quality of a regression equation and that other statistical measures, set out below, are also required.

Exercise 7.5

(a) Calculate the R^2 value for the regression of the birth rate on the income ratio, calculated in Exercise 7.4.

(b) Confirm that this result is the same as the square of the correlation coefficient between these two variables, calculated in Exercise 7.1.

Inference in the regression model

So far, regression has been used as a descriptive technique, to measure the relationship between the two variables. We now go on to draw inferences from the analysis about what the *true* regression line might look like. As with correlation, the estimated relationship is in fact a *sample* regression line, based upon data for 12 countries. The estimated coefficients a and b are random variables, since they would differ from sample to sample. What can be inferred about the true (but unknown) regression equation?

The question is best approached by first writing down a true or population regression equation, in a form similar to the sample regression equation

$$Y_i = \alpha + \beta X_i + \varepsilon_i \tag{7.17}$$

As usual, Greek letters denote true, or population, values. Thus α and β are the population *parameters*, of which a and b are (point) estimates, using the method of least squares, and ε is the population error term. If we could observe the individual error terms ε_i then we would be able to get exact values of α and β (even from a sample), rather than just estimates.

Given that a and b are estimates, we can ask about their properties: whether they are unbiased and how precise they are, compared to alternative estimators. Under reasonable assumptions (e.g. see Maddala (2001), Chapter 3) it can be shown that the OLS estimates of the coefficients are unbiased. Thus OLS provides useful point estimates of the parameters (the true values α and β). This is one reason for using the least squares method. It can also be shown that, among the class of linear unbiased estimators, OLS has the minimum variance, i.e. the method provides the most precise estimates. This is another, powerful justification for the use of OLS. So, just as the sample mean provides a more precise estimate of the population mean than does a single observation, the least squares estimates of α and β are the most precise.

Analysis of the errors

To find confidence intervals for α and β we need to know which statistical distribution we should be using, i.e. the distributions of a and b. These can be derived, based on the assumptions that the error term ε in equation (7.17) above is Normally distributed and that the errors are statistically independent of each other. Since we are using cross-section data from countries which are different geographically, politically and socially it seems reasonable to assume the errors are independent.

To check the Normality assumption we can graph the residuals calculated from the sample regression line. If the true errors are Normal it seems likely that these residuals should be approximately Normal also. The residuals are calculated according to equation (7.10) above. For example, to calculate the residual for Brazil we subtract the fitted value from the actual value. The fitted value is calculated by substituting the growth rate into the estimated regression equation, yielding $\hat{Y} = 40.712 - 2.7 \times 5.1 = 26.9$. Subtracting this from the actual value gives $Y_i - \hat{Y} = 30 - 26.9 = 3.1$. Other countries' residuals are calculated in similar manner, yielding the results shown in Table 7.5.

These residuals may then be gathered together in a frequency table (as in Chapter 1) and graphed. This is shown in Figure 7.7.

Although the number of observations is small (and therefore the graph is not a smooth curve) the chart does have the greater weight of frequencies in the centre as one would expect, with less weight as one moves into the tails of the distribution. The assumption that the true error term is Normally distributed does not seem unreasonable.

If the residuals from the sample regression equation appeared distinctly non-Normal (heavily skewed, for example) then one should be wary of constructing confidence intervals using the formulae below. Instead, one might consider transforming the data (see below) before continuing. There are more formal tests for Normality of the residuals but they are beyond the scope of this book. Drawing a graph is an informal alternative, which can be useful, but remember that graphical methods can be misinterpreted.

Table 7.5 Calculation of residuals

	Actual birth rate	Fitted values	Residuals
Brazil	30	26.9	3.1
Colombia	29	32.1	−3.1
Costa Rica	30	32.6	−2.6
⋮	⋮	⋮	⋮
Sri Lanka	27	34.0	−7.0
Taiwan	21	24.0	−3.0
Thailand	30	28.3	1.7

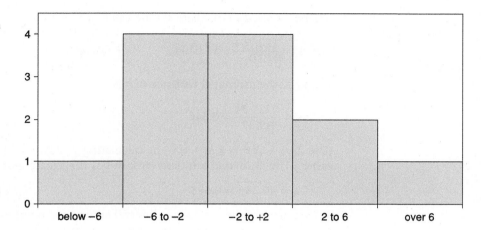

Figure 7.7
Bar chart of residuals
from the regression
equation

If one were using time-series data one should also check the residuals for **autocorrelation** at this point. This occurs when the error in period *t* is dependent in some way on the error in the previous period(s) and implies that the method of least squares may not be the best way of estimating the relationship. In this example we have cross-section data, so it is not appropriate to check for autocorrelation, since the ordering of the data does not matter. Chapter 8, on multiple regression, covers this topic.

Confidence interval estimates of α and β

Having checked that the residuals appear reasonably Normal we can proceed with inference. This means finding interval estimates of the parameters α and β and, later on, conducting hypothesis tests. As usual, the 95% confidence interval is obtained by adding and subtracting approximately two standard errors from the point estimate. We therefore need to calculate the standard error of *a* and of *b* and we also need to look up tables to find the precise number of standard errors to add and subtract. The principle is just the same as for the confidence interval estimate of the sample mean, covered in Chapter 4.

The estimated sampling variance of *b*, the slope coefficient, is given by

$$s_b^2 = \frac{s_e^2}{\sum (X_i - \bar{X})^2} \tag{7.18}$$

where

$$s_e^2 = \frac{\sum e_i^2}{n - 2} = \frac{\text{ESS}}{n - 2} \tag{7.19}$$

is the **estimated variance of the error term**, ε.

The sampling variance of *b* measures the uncertainty associated with the estimate. Note that the uncertainty is greater (i) the larger the error variance s_e^2 (i.e. the more scattered the points around the regression line) and (ii) the lower the dispersion of the *X* observations. When *X* does not vary much it is then more difficult to measure the effect of changes in *X* upon *Y*, and this is reflected in the formula.

First we need to calculate s_e^2. The value of this is

$$s_e^2 = \frac{170.754}{10} = 17.0754 \qquad (7.20)$$

and so the estimated variance of b is

$$s_b^2 = \frac{17.0754}{49.37} = 0.346 \qquad (7.21)$$

(Use $\sum(X_i - \bar{X})^2 = \sum X_i^2 - n\bar{X}^2$ in calculating (7.21) – it makes the calculation easier.) The estimated standard error of b is the square root of (7.21),

$$s_b = \sqrt{0.346} = 0.588 \qquad (7.22)$$

To construct the confidence interval around the point estimate, $b = -2.7$, the t distribution is used (in regression this applies to all sample sizes, not just small ones). The 95% confidence interval is thus given by

$$[b - t_v s_b,\ b + t_v s_b] \qquad (7.23)$$

where t_v is the (two-tail) critical value of the t distribution at the appropriate significance level (5% in this case), with $v = n - 2$ degrees of freedom. The critical value is 2.228. Thus the confidence interval evaluates to

$$[-2.7 - 2.228 \times 0.588,\ -2.7 + 2.228 \times 0.588] = [-4.01, -1.39]$$

Thus we can be 95% confident that the true value of β lies within this range. Note that the interval only includes negative values: we can rule out an upwards-sloping regression line.

For the intercept a, the estimate of the variance is given by

$$s_a^2 = s_e^2 \times \left(\frac{1}{n} + \frac{\bar{X}^2}{\sum(X_i - \bar{X})^2} \right) = 17.0754 \times \left(\frac{1}{12} + \frac{3.35^2}{49.37} \right) = 5.304 \qquad (7.24)$$

and the estimated standard error of a is the square root of this, 2.303. The 95% confidence interval for α, again using the t distribution, is

$$[40.71 - 2.228 \times 2.303,\ 40.71 + 2.228 \times 2.303] = [35.57, 45.84]$$

The results so far can be summarised as follows

$$Y_i = 40.711 - 2.70X_i + e_i$$
$$\text{s.e. } (2.30) \qquad (0.59)$$
$$R^2 = 0.678 \qquad n = 12$$

This conveys, at a glance, all the necessary information to the reader, who can then draw the inferences deemed appropriate. Any desired confidence interval (not just the 95% one) can be quickly calculated with the aid of a set of t tables.

Testing hypotheses about the coefficients

As well as calculating confidence intervals, one can use hypothesis tests as the basis for statistical inference in the regression model. These tests are quickly and easily explained given the information already assembled. Consider the following hypothesis

$H_0: \beta = 0$
$H_1: \beta \neq 0$

This null hypothesis is interesting because it implies no influence of X upon Y at all (i.e. the slope of the true regression line is flat and Y_i can be equally well predicted by $\bar{Y}$). The alternative hypothesis asserts that X does in fact influence Y.

The procedure is in principle the same as in Chapter 5 on hypothesis testing. We measure how many standard deviations separate the observed value of b from the hypothesised value. If this is greater than an appropriate critical value we reject the hypothesis. The test statistic is calculated using the formula

$$t = \frac{b - \beta}{s_b} = \frac{-2.7 - 0}{0.588} = -4.59 \qquad (7.25)$$

Thus the sample coefficient b differs by 4.59 standard errors from its hypothesised value $\beta = 0$. This is compared to the critical value of the t distribution, using $n - 2$ degrees of freedom. Since $t < -t_{10}^*$ $(= -2.228)$, in this case the null hypothesis is rejected with 95% confidence. X does have some influence on Y. Similar tests using the income ratio and GDP to attempt to explain the birth rate show that in neither case is the slope coefficient significantly different from zero, i.e. neither of these variables appears to influence the birth rate.

Rule of thumb for hypothesis tests

A quick and reasonably accurate method for establishing whether a coefficient is significantly different from zero is to see if it is at least twice its standard error. If so, it is significant. This works because the critical value (at 95%) of the t distribution for reasonable sample sizes is about 2.

Sometimes regression results are presented with the t statistic (as calculated above), rather than the standard error, below each coefficient. This implicitly assumes that the hypothesis of interest is that the coefficient is zero. This is not always appropriate: in the consumption function a test for the marginal propensity to consume being equal to 1 might be of greater relevance, for example. In a demand equation, one might want to test for unit elasticity. For this reason, it is better to present the standard errors rather than the t statistics.

Note that the test statistic $t = -4.59$ is exactly the same result as in the case of testing the correlation coefficient. This is no accident, for the two tests are equivalent. A non-zero slope coefficient means there is a relationship between X and Y which also means the correlation coefficient is non-zero. Both null hypotheses are rejected.

Testing the significance of R^2: the F test

Another check of the quality of the regression equation is to test whether the R^2 value, calculated earlier, is significantly greater than zero. This is a test using the F distribution and turns out once again to be equivalent to the two previous tests $H_0: \beta = 0$ and $H_0: \rho = 0$, conducted in previous sections, using the t distribution.

The null hypothesis for the test is $H_0: R^2 = 0$, implying once again that X does not influence Y (hence equivalent to $\beta = 0$). The test statistic is

$$F = \frac{R^2/1}{(1 - R^2)/(n - 2)} \tag{7.26}$$

or equivalently

$$F = \frac{\text{RSS}/1}{\text{ESS}/(n - 2)} \tag{7.27}$$

The F statistic is therefore the ratio of the regression sum of squares to the error sum of squares, each divided by their degrees of freedom (for the RSS there is one degree of freedom because of the one explanatory variable, for the ESS there are $n - 2$ degrees of freedom). A high value of the F statistic rejects H_0 in favour of the alternative hypothesis, $H_1: R^2 > 0$. Evaluating (7.26) gives

$$F = \frac{0.678/1}{(1 - 0.678)/10} = 21.078 \tag{7.28}$$

The critical value of the F distribution at the 5% significance level, with $v_1 = 1$ and $v_2 = 10$, is $F^*_{1,10} = 4.96$. The test statistic exceeds this, so the regression as a whole is significant. It is better to use the regression model to explain the birth rate than to use the simpler model which assumes all countries have the same birth rate (the sample average).

As stated before, this test is equivalent to those carried out before using the t distribution. The F statistic is, in fact, the square of the t statistic calculated earlier ($-4.59^2 = 21.078$) and reflects the fact that, in general

$$F_{1,n-2} = t^2_{n-2}$$

The Prob-value associated with both statistics is the same (approximately 0.001 in this case) so both tests reject the null at the same level of significance. However, in multiple regression with more than one explanatory variable, the relationship no longer holds and the tests do fulfil different roles, as we shall see in the next chapter.

Exercise 7.6

(a) For the regression of the birth rate on the income ratio, calculate the standard errors of the coefficients and hence construct 95% confidence intervals for both.

(b) Test the hypothesis that the slope coefficient is zero against the alternative that it is not zero.

(c) Test the hypothesis $H_0: R^2 = 0$.

Interpreting computer output

Having shown how to use the appropriate formulae to derive estimates of the parameters, their standard errors and to test hypotheses, we now present all these results as they would be generated by a computer software package, in this case *Excel*. This removes all the effort of calculation and allows us to concentrate on more important issues such as the interpretation of the results. Table 7.6 shows the computer output.

Table 7.6 **Regression analysis output using** *Excel*

	A	B	C	D	E	F	G	H
25								
26								
27								
28		*Regression Statistics*						
29		Multiple R	0.824					
30		R square	0.678					
31		Adjusted R square	0.646					
32		Standard error	4.132					
33		Observations	12					
34								
35		ANOVA						
36			*df*	*SS*	*MS*	*F*	*Significance F*	
37		Regression	1	359.913	359.913	21.078	0.001	
38		Residual	10	170.754	17.075			
39		Total	11	530.667				
40								
41			*Coefficients*	*Standard Error*	*t Stat*	*P-value*	*Lower 95%*	*Upper 95%*
42		Intercept	40.71	2.30	17.68	7.15E-09	35.58	45.84
43		GR	−2.70	0.59	−4.59	0.001	−4.01	−1.39
44								
45								
46								
47								

The table presents all the results we have already derived, plus a few more.

- The regression coefficients, standard errors and *t* ratios are given at the bottom of the table, suitably labelled. The column headed '*P value*' (this is how *Excel* refers to the *Prob-value*, discussed in Chapter 5) gives some additional information – it shows the significance level of the *t* statistic. For example, the slope coefficient is significant at the level of 0.1%,[2] i.e. there is this probability of getting such a sample estimate by chance. This is much less than our usual 5% criterion, so we conclude that the sample evidence did not arise by chance.
- The program helpfully calculates the 95% confidence interval for the coefficients also, which were derived above in equation (7.23).
- Moving up the table, there is a section headed ANOVA (Analysis of Variance). This is similar to the ANOVA covered in Chapter 6. This table provides the sums of squares values (RSS, ESS and TSS, in that order) and their associated degrees of freedom in the '*df*' column. The '*MS*' ('mean square') column calculates the sums of squares each divided by their degrees of freedom, whose ratio gives the *F* statistic in the next column. This is the value calculated in equation (7.28). The '*Significance F*' value is similar to the *P value* discussed previously: it shows the level at which the *F* statistic is significant (0.1% in this case) and saves us looking up the *F* tables.
- At the top of the table is given the R^2 value and the standard error of the error term, s_e, labelled 'Standard Error', which we have already come across. 'Multiple R' is simply the square root of R^2; 'Adjusted R^2' (sometimes called '*R*-bar squared' and written $\bar{R}^2$) adjusts the R^2 value for the degrees of freedom. This is an alternative measure of fit, which is not affected by the number of explanatory variables, unlike R^2. See Maddala (2001) Chapter 4 for a more detailed explanation.

---

[2] This is the area in *both* tails, so it is for a two-tail test.

Prediction

Earlier we showed that the regression line could be used for prediction, using the figures for Costa Rica. The point estimate of Costa Rica's birth rate is calculated simply by putting its growth rate into the regression equation and assuming a zero value for the error, i.e.

$$\hat{Y} = 40.711 - 2.7 \times 3 + 0 = 32.6$$

This is a point estimate, which is unbiased, around which we can build a confidence interval. There are, in fact, two confidence intervals we can construct, the first for the position of the *regression line* at $X = 3$, the second for an *individual observation* (on Y) at $X = 3$. Using the 95% confidence level, the first interval is given by the formula

$$\left[\hat{Y} - t_{n-2} \times s_e \sqrt{\frac{1}{n} + \frac{(X_P - \bar{X})^2}{\Sigma(X - \bar{X})^2}}, \ \hat{Y} + t_{n-2} \times s_e \sqrt{\frac{1}{n} + \frac{(X_P - \bar{X})^2}{\Sigma(X - \bar{X})^2}} \right] \tag{7.29}$$

where X_P is the value of X for which the prediction is made. t_{n-2} denotes the critical value of the t distribution at the 5% significance level (for a two-tail test) with $n - 2$ degrees of freedom. This evaluates to

$$\left[32.6 - 2.228 \times 4.132 \sqrt{\frac{1}{12} + \frac{(3 - 3.35)^2}{49.37}}, \right.$$

$$\left. 32.6 + 2.228 \times 4.132 \sqrt{\frac{1}{12} + \frac{(3 - 3.35)^2}{49.37}} \right]$$

$$= [29.90, 35.30]$$

This means that we predict with 95% confidence that the *average* birth rate of all countries growing at 3% p.a. is between 29.9 and 35.3.

The second type of interval, for the value of Y itself at $X_P = 3$, is somewhat wider, because there is an additional element of uncertainty: individual countries do not lie on the regression line, but around it. This is referred to as the 95% prediction interval. The formula for this interval is

$$\left[\hat{Y} - t_{n-2} \times s_e \sqrt{1 + \frac{1}{n} + \frac{(X_P - \bar{X})^2}{\Sigma(X - \bar{X})^2}}, \right.$$

$$\left. \hat{Y} + t_{n-2} \times s_e \sqrt{1 + \frac{1}{n} + \frac{(X_P - \bar{X})^2}{\Sigma(X - \bar{X})^2}} \right] \tag{7.30}$$

Note the extra '1' inside the square root sign. When evaluated, this gives a 95% prediction interval of [23.01, 42.19]. Thus we are 95% confident that an individual country growing at 3% p.a. will have a birth rate within this range.

The two intervals are illustrated in Figure 7.8. The smaller confidence interval is shown in a darker shade, with the wider prediction interval being about twice as big. Note from the formulae that the prediction is more precise (the interval is smaller)

- the closer the sample observations lie to the regression line (smaller s_e);
- the greater the spread of sample X values (larger $\Sigma(X - \bar{X})^2$);

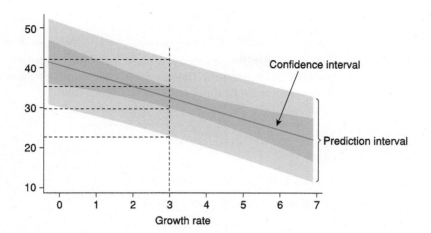

Figure 7.8
Confidence and prediction intervals

● the larger the sample size;
● the closer to the mean of X the prediction is made (smaller $X_P - \bar{X}$).

This last characteristic is evident in the diagram, where the intervals are narrower towards the centre of the diagram.

There is an additional danger of predicting far outside the range of sample X values, if the true regression line is not linear as we have assumed. The linear sample regression line might be close to the true line within the range of sample X values but diverge substantially outside. Figure 7.9 illustrates this point.

In the birth rate sample, we have a fairly wide range of X values; few countries grow more slowly than Senegal or faster than Korea.

Exercise 7.7   Use *Excel*'s regression tool to confirm your answers to Exercises 7.4 to 7.6.

Exercise 7.8   (a) Predict (point estimate) the birth rate for a country with an income ratio of 10.

(?)

(b) Find the 95% confidence interval prediction for a typical country with IR = 10.

(c) Find the 95% confidence interval prediction for an individual country with IR = 10.

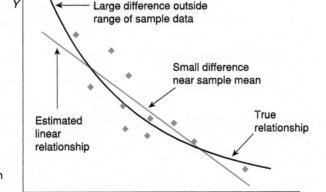

Figure 7.9
The danger of prediction outside the range of sample data

Worked example 7.2

We continue the previous worked example, completing the calculations needed for regression. The previous table contains most of the preliminary calculations. To find the regression line we use

$$b = \frac{n \sum XY - \sum X \sum Y}{n \sum X^2 - (\sum X)^2} = \frac{6 \times 682 - 33 \times 119}{6 \times 199 - 33^2} = 1.57$$

and

$$a = 19.83 - 1.57 \times 5.5 = 11.19$$

Hence we obtain the equation

$$Y_i = 11.19 + 1.57X_i + e_i$$

For inference, we start with the sums of squares:

$$\text{TSS} = \sum(Y_i - \bar{Y})^2 = \sum Y_i^2 - n\bar{Y}^2 = 2427 - 6 \times 19.83^2 = 66.83$$
$$\text{ESS} = \sum(Y_i - \hat{Y}_i)^2 = \sum Y_i^2 - a \sum Y_i - b \sum X_i Y_i$$
$$= 2427 - 11.19 \times 119 - 1.57 \times 682 = 23.62$$
$$\text{RSS} = \text{TSS} - \text{ESS} = 66.83 - 23.62 = 43.21$$

We then obtain $R^2 = \text{RSS}/\text{TSS} = 43.21/66.83 = 0.647$ or 64.7% of the variation in Y explained by variation in X.

To obtain the standard errors of the coefficients, we first calculate the error variance as $s_e^2 = \text{ESS}/(n - 2) = 23.62/4 = 5.905$ and the estimated variance of the slope coefficient is

$$s_b^2 = \frac{s_e^2}{\sum(X - \bar{X})^2} = \frac{5.905}{17.50} = 0.338$$

and the standard error of b is therefore $\sqrt{0.338} = 0.581$.

Similarly for a we obtain

$$s_a^2 = s_e^2 \times \left(\frac{1}{n} + \frac{\bar{X}^2}{\sum(X - \bar{X})^2} \right) = 5.905 \times \left(\frac{1}{6} + \frac{5.5^2}{17.50} \right) = 11.19$$

and the standard error of a is therefore 3.34.

Confidence intervals for a and b can be constructed using the critical value of the t distribution, 2.776 (5%, $v = 4$), yielding $1.57 \pm 2.776 \times 0.581 = [-0.04, 3.16]$ for b and $[1.90, 20.47]$ for a. Note that zero is inside the confidence interval for b. This is also reflected in the test of $H_0: \beta = 0$ which is

$$t = \frac{1.57 - 0}{0.581} = 2.71$$

which falls short of the two-tailed critical value, 2.776. Hence H_0 cannot be rejected.

The F statistic, to test $H_0: R^2 = 0$ is

$$F = \frac{\text{RSS}/1}{\text{ESS}/(n - 2)} = \frac{43.21/1}{23.62/(6 - 2)} = 7.32$$

which compares to a critical value of $F(1,4)$ of 7.71 so, again, the null cannot be rejected (remember that this and the t test on the slope coefficient are equivalent in simple regression).

We shall predict the value of Y for a value of $X = 10$, yielding $\hat{Y} = 11.19 + 1.57 \times 10 = 26.90$. The 95% confidence interval for this prediction is calculated using equation (7.29), which gives

$$\left[\begin{array}{c} 26.90 - 2.776 \times 2.43 \sqrt{\dfrac{1}{6} + \dfrac{(10 - 5.5)^2}{17.50}}, \\[2ex] 26.90 + 2.776 \times 2.43 \sqrt{\dfrac{1}{6} + \dfrac{(10 - 5.5)^2}{17.50}} \end{array} \right] = [19.14, 34.66].$$

The 95% prediction interval for an actual observation at $X = 10$ is given by (7.30), resulting in

$$\left[\begin{array}{c} 26.90 - 2.776 \times 2.43 \sqrt{1 + \dfrac{1}{6} + \dfrac{(10 - 5.5)^2}{17.50}}, \\[2ex] 26.90 + 2.776 \times 2.43 \sqrt{1 + \dfrac{1}{6} + \dfrac{(10 - 5.5)^2}{17.50}} \end{array} \right] = [16.62, 37.18].$$

Units of measurement

The measurement and interpretation of the regression coefficients depends upon the units in which the variables are measured. For example, suppose we had measured the birth rate in births per *hundred* (not *thousand*) of population; what would be the implications? Obviously nothing fundamental is changed; we ought to obtain the same qualitative result, with the same interpretation. However, the regression coefficients cannot remain the same: if the slope coefficient remained $b = -2.7$, this would mean that an increase in the growth rate of one percentage point reduces the birth rate by 2.7 births *per hundred*, which is clearly wrong. The right answer should be 0.27 births per hundred (equivalent to 2.7 per thousand) so the coefficient should change to $b = -0.27$. Thus, in general, the sizes of the coefficients depend upon the units in which the variables are measured. This is why one cannot judge the importance of a regression equation from the size of the coefficients alone.

It is easiest to understand this in graphical terms. A graph of the data will look exactly the same, except that the scale on the Y-axis will change; it will be divided by 10. The intercept of the regression line will therefore change to $a = 4.0711$ and the slope to $b = -0.27$. Thus the regression equation becomes

$$Y_i = 4.0711 - 0.27X_i + e_i'$$
$$(e_i' = e_i/10)$$

Since nothing fundamental has altered, any hypothesis test must yield the same test statistic. Thus t and F statistics are unaltered by changes in the units of measurement; nor is R^2 altered. However, standard errors will be divided by 10 (they have to be to preserve the t statistics; see equation (7.25) for example). Table 7.7 sets out the effects of changes in the units of measurement upon the

Table 7.7 The effects of data transformations

| Factor (k) multiplying . . . | | Effect upon | | | |
Y	X	a	s_a	b	s_b
k	1	⟵———— All multiplied by k ————⟶			
1	k	Unchanged		Divided by k	
k	k	Multiplied by k		Unchanged	

coefficients and standard errors. In the table it is assumed that the variables have been multiplied by a constant k; in the above case $k = 1/10$ was used.

It is important to be aware of the units in which the variables are measured. If not, it is impossible to know how large is the effect of X upon Y. It may be statistically significant but you have no idea of how important it is. This may occur if, for instance, one of the variables is presented as an index number (see Chapter 10) rather than in the original units.

How to avoid measurement problems: calculating the elasticity

A neat way of avoiding the problems of measurement is to calculate the **elasticity**, i.e. the *proportionate* change in Y divided by the *proportionate* change in X. The proportionate changes are the same whatever units the variables are measured in. The proportionate change in X is given by $\Delta X/X$, where ΔX indicates the *change* in X. Thus if X changes from 100 to 110, the proportionate change is $\Delta X/X = 10/100 = 0.1$ or 10%. The elasticity, η, is therefore given by

$$\eta = \frac{\Delta Y/Y}{\Delta X/X} = \frac{\Delta Y}{\Delta X} \times \frac{X}{Y} \qquad (7.31)$$

The second form of the equation is more useful, since $\Delta Y/\Delta X$ is simply the slope coefficient b. We simply need to multiply this by the ratio X/Y, therefore. But what values should be used for X and Y? The convention is to use the means, so we obtain the following formula for the elasticity, from a linear regression equation

$$\eta = b \times \frac{\bar{X}}{\bar{Y}} \qquad (7.32)$$

This evaluates to $-2.7 \times 3.35/31.67 = -0.29$. This is interpreted as follows: a 1% increase in the growth rate would lead to a 0.29% decrease in the birth rate. Equivalently, and perhaps a little more usefully, a 10% rise in growth (from say 3% to 3.3% p.a.) would lead to a 2.9% decline in the birth rate (e.g. from 30 to 29.13). This result is the same whatever units the variables X and Y are measured in.

Note that this elasticity is measured at the means; it would have a different value at different points along the regression line. Later on we show an alternative method for estimating the elasticity, in this case the elasticity of demand which is familiar in economics.

Non-linear transformations

So far only *linear* regression has been dealt with, that is fitting a straight line to the data. This can sometimes be restrictive, especially when there is good reason

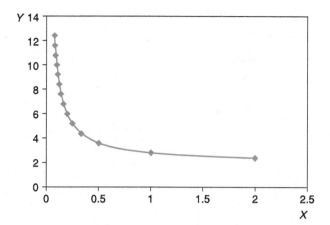

Figure 7.10
Graph of *Y* against *X*

to believe that the true relationship is non-linear (e.g. the labour supply curve). Poor results would be obtained by fitting a straight line through the data in Figure 7.10, yet the shape of the relationship seems clear at a glance.

Fortunately this problem can be solved by transforming the data, so that when graphed a linear relationship between the two variables appears. Then a straight line can be fitted to these transformed data. This is equivalent to fitting a curved line to the original data. All that is needed is to find a suitable transformation to 'straighten out' the data. Given the data represented in Figure 7.10, if *Y* were graphed against 1/*X* the relationship shown in Figure 7.11 would appear.

Thus, if the regression line

$$Y_i = a + b\frac{1}{X_i} + e_i \tag{7.33}$$

were fitted, this would provide a good representation of the data in Figure 7.10. The procedure is straightforward. First, calculate the reciprocal of each of the *X* values and then use these (together with the original data for *Y*), using exactly the same methods as before. This transformation appears inappropriate for the birth rate data (see Figure 7.1) but serves as an illustration. The transformed *X*

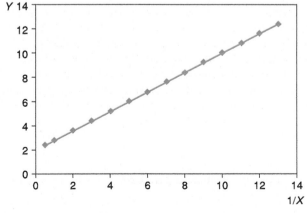

Figure 7.11
Figure 7.10 transformed:
Y against 1/*X*

values are 0.196 (= 1/5.1) for Brazil, 0.3125 (= 1/3.2) for Colombia, etc. The resulting regression equation is

$$Y_i = 31.92 - 3.96\frac{1}{X_i} + e_i \tag{7.34}$$

s.e. (1.64)   (1.56)
$R^2 = 0.39$, $F = 6.44$, $n = 12$

This appears worse than the original specification (the R^2 is low and the slope coefficient is not significantly different from zero) so the transformation does not appear to be a good one. Note also that it is difficult to calculate the effect of X upon Y in this equation. We can see that a unit increase in $1/X$ reduces the birth rate by 3.96, but we do not have an intuitive feel for the inverse of the growth rate. This latest result also implies that a *fall* in the growth rate (hence $1/X$ rises) lowers the birth rate – the converse of our previous result. In the next chapter, we deal with a different example where a non-linear transformation does improve matters.

Table 7.8 presents a number of possible shapes for data, with suggested data transformations which will allow the relationship to be estimated using linear regression. In each case, once the data have been transformed, the methods and formulae used above can be applied.

It is sometimes difficult to know which transformation (if any) to apply. A graph of the data is unlikely to be as tidy as the diagrams in Table 7.8.

Table 7.8 Data transformations

Name	Graph of relationship	Original relationship	Transformed relationship	Regression
Double log	$b>1$ $0<b<1$ $b<0$	$Y = aX^b e$	$\ln Y = \ln a + b \ln X + \ln e$	$\ln Y$ on $\ln X$
Reciprocal	$b>0$ $b<0$	$Y = a + b/X + e$	$Y = a + b\dfrac{1}{X} + e$	Y on $\dfrac{1}{X}$
Semi-log		$e^Y = aX^b e$	$Y = \ln a + b \ln X + \ln e$	Y on $\ln X$
Exponential	$b>0$ $b<0$	$Y = e^{a+bX+e}$	$\ln Y = a + bX + e$	$\ln Y$ on X

Economic theory rarely suggests the form which a relationship should follow, and there are no simple statistical tests for choosing alternative formulations. The choice can sometimes be made after visual inspection of the data, or on the basis of convenience. The double log transformation is often used in economics as it has some very convenient properties. Unfortunately it cannot be used with the growth rate data here because Senegal's growth rate was negative. It is impossible to take the logarithm of a negative number. We therefore postpone the use of the log transformation in regression until the next chapter.

Exercise 7.9 	(a) Calculate the elasticity of the birth rate with respect to the income ratio, using the results of previous exercises. (b) Give a brief interpretation of the meaning of this figure.
Exercise 7.10 	Calculate a regression relating the birth rate to the inverse of the income ratio $1/IR$.

Summary

- Correlation refers to the extent of association between two variables. The (sample) correlation coefficient is a measure of this association, extending from $r = -1$ to $r = +1$.

- Positive correlation ($r > 0$) exists when high values of X tend to be associated with high values of Y and low X values with low Y values.

- Negative correlation ($r < 0$) exists when high values of X tend to be associated with low values of Y and vice versa.

- Values of r around 0 indicate an absence of correlation.

- As the sample correlation coefficient is a random variable we can test for its significance, i.e. test whether the true value is zero or not. This test is based upon the t distribution.

- The existence of correlation (even if 'significant') does not necessarily imply causality. There can be other reasons for the observed association.

- Regression analysis extends correlation by asserting a causality from X to Y and then measuring the relationship between the variables via the regression line, the 'line of best fit'.

- The regression line $Y = a + bX$ is defined by the intercept a and slope coefficient b. Their values are found by minimising the sum of squared errors around the regression line.

- The slope coefficient b measures the responsiveness of Y to changes in X.

- A measure of how well the regression line fits the data is given by the coefficient of determination, R^2, varying between 0 (very poor fit) and 1 (perfect fit).

- The coefficients a and b are unbiased point estimates of the true values of the parameters. Confidence interval estimates can be obtained, based on the t distribution. Hypothesis tests on the parameters can also be carried out using the t distribution.

336   Introduction to Quantitative Methods and Finance

- A test of the hypothesis $R^2 = 0$ (implying the regression is no better at predicting Y than simply using the mean of Y) can be carried out using the F distribution.

- The regression line may be used to predict Y for any value of X by assuming the residual to be zero for that observation.

- The measured response of Y to X (given by b) depends upon the units of measurement of X and Y. A better measure is often the elasticity, which is the proportionate response of Y to a proportionate change in X.

- Data are often transformed prior to regression (e.g. by taking logs) for a variety of reasons (e.g. to fit a curve to the original data).

Key terms and concepts

autocorrelation	intercept
correlation coefficient	prediction
coefficient of determination (R^2)	regression line or equation
coefficient of rank correlation	regression sum of squares
dependent (endogenous) variable	slope
elasticity	standard error
error sum of squares	t ratio
error term (or residual)	total sum of squares
independent (exogenous) variable	

References

G. S. Maddala, *Introduction to Econometrics*, 2001, 3rd edn., Wiley.
M. P. Todaro, *Economic Development for a Developing World*, 1992, 3rd edn., Financial Times Prentice Hall.

Problems

Some of the more challenging problems are indicated by highlighting the problem number in colour.

7.1   The other data which Todaro might have used to analyse the birth rate were:

Country	Birth rate	GNP	Growth	Income ratio
Bangladesh	47	140	0.3	2.3
Tanzania	47	280	1.9	3.2
Sierra Leone	46	320	0.4	3.3
Sudan	47	380	−0.3	3.9
Kenya	55	420	2.9	6.8
Indonesia	35	530	4.1	3.4
Panama	30	1910	3.1	8.6
Chile	25	2560	0.7	3.8
Venezuela	35	4220	2.4	5.2
Turkey	33	1540	3.5	4.9
Malaysia	31	1840	4.3	5.0
Nepal	44	150	0.0	4.7
Malawi	56	200	2.7	2.4
Argentina	20	2560	1.9	3.6

For *one* of the three possible explanatory variables (in class, different groups could examine each of the variables):

(a) Draw an *XY* chart of the data above and comment upon the result.

(b) Would you expect a line of best fit to have a positive or negative slope? Roughly, what would you expect the slope to be?

(c) What would you expect the correlation coefficient to be?

(d) Calculate the correlation coefficient, and comment.

(e) Test to see if the correlation coefficient is different from zero. Use the 95% confidence level.

(Analysis of this problem continues in Problem 7.5.)

7.2   The data below show consumption of margarine (in ounces per person per week) and its real price, for the UK.

Year	Consumption	Price	Year	Consumption	Price
1970	2.86	125.6	1980	3.83	104.2
1971	3.15	132.9	1981	4.11	95.5
1972	3.52	126.0	1982	4.33	88.1
1973	3.03	119.6	1983	4.08	88.9
1974	2.60	138.8	1984	4.08	97.3
1975	2.60	141.0	1985	3.76	100.0
1976	3.06	122.3	1986	4.10	86.7
1977	3.48	132.7	1987	3.98	79.8
1978	3.54	126.7	1988	3.78	79.9
1979	3.63	115.7			

(a) Draw an *XY* plot of the data and comment.

(b) From the chart, would you expect the line of best fit to slope up or down? *In theory*, which way should it slope?

(c) What would you expect the correlation coefficient to be, approximately?

(d) Calculate the correlation coefficient between margarine consumption and its price.

(e) Is the coefficient significantly different from zero? What is the implication of the result?

(The following totals will reduce the burden of calculation: $\sum Y = 67.52$; $\sum X = 2101.70$; $\sum Y^2 = 245.055$; $\sum X^2 = 240\,149.27$; $\sum XY = 7299.638$; Y is consumption, X is price. If you wish, you could calculate a logarithmic correlation. The relevant totals are: $\sum y = 23.88$; $\sum x = 89.09$; $\sum y^2 = 30.45$; $\sum x^2 = 418.40$; $\sum xy = 111.50$, where $y = \ln Y$ and $x = \ln X$.)

(Analysis of this problem continues in Problem 7.6.)

7.3 What would you expect to be the correlation coefficient between the following variables? Should the variables be measured contemporaneously or might there be a lag in the effect of one upon the other?

(a) Nominal consumption and nominal income.

(b) GDP and the imports/GDP ratio.

(c) Investment and the interest rate.

7.4 As Problem 7.3, for:

(a) real consumption and real income;

(b) individuals' alcohol and cigarette consumption;

(c) UK and US interest rates.

7.5 Using the data from Problem 7.1, calculate the rank correlation coefficient between the variables and test its significance. How does it compare with the ordinary correlation coefficient?

7.6 Calculate the rank correlation coefficient between price and quantity for the data in Problem 7.2. How does it compare with the ordinary correlation coefficient?

7.7 (a) For the data in Problem 7.1, find the estimated regression line and calculate the R^2 statistic. Comment upon the result. How does it compare with Todaro's findings?

(b) Calculate the standard error of the estimate and the standard errors of the coefficients. Is the slope coefficient significantly different from zero? Comment upon the result.

(c) Test the overall significance of the regression equation and comment.

(d) Taking your own results and Todaro's, how confident do you feel that you understand the determinants of the birth rate?

(e) What do you think will be the result of estimating your equation using all 26 countries' data? Try it! What do you conclude?

7.8 (a) For the data given in Problem 7.2, estimate the sample regression line and calculate the R^2 statistic. Comment upon the results.

(b) Calculate the standard error of the estimate and the standard errors of the coefficients. Is the slope coefficient significantly different from zero? Is demand inelastic?

(c) Test the overall significance of the regression and comment upon your result.

7.9 From your results for the birth rate model, predict the birth rate for a country with *either* (a) GNP equal to $3000, (b) a growth rate of 3% p.a. *or* (c) an income ratio of 7. How does your prediction compare with one using Todaro's results? Comment.

7.10 Predict margarine consumption given a price of 70. Use the 99% confidence level.

7.11 (Project) Update Todaro's study using more recent data.

7.12 Try to build a model of the determinants of infant mortality. You should use cross-section data for 20 countries or more and should include both developing and developed countries in the sample.

   Write up your findings in a report which includes the following sections: discussion of the problem; data gathering and transformations; estimation of the model; interpretation of results. Useful data may be found in the Human Development Report (use Google to find it online).

Answers to exercises

Exercise 7.1

(a) The calculation is:

	Birth rate Y	Income ratio X	Y^2	X^2	XY
Brazil	30	9.5	900	90.25	285
Colombia	29	6.8	841	46.24	197.2
Costa Rica	30	4.6	900	21.16	138
India	35	3.1	1225	9.61	108.5
Mexico	36	5	1296	25	180
Peru	36	8.7	1296	75.69	313.2
Philippines	34	3.8	1156	14.44	129.2
Senegal	48	6.4	2304	40.96	307.2
South Korea	24	2.7	576	7.29	64.8
Sri Lanka	27	2.3	729	5.29	62.1
Taiwan	21	3.8	441	14.44	79.8
Thailand	30	3.3	900	10.89	99
Totals	380	60	12 564	361.26	1964

$$r = \frac{12 \times 1964 - 60 \times 380}{\sqrt{(12 \times 361.26 - 60^2)(12 \times 12\,564 - 380^2)}} = 0.355$$

(c) As for (a) except $\Sigma X = 0.6$, $\Sigma Y = 38$, $\Sigma X^2 = 0.036126$, $\Sigma Y^2 = 125.64$, $\Sigma XY = 1.964$. Hence

$$r = \frac{12 \times 1.964 - 0.6 \times 38}{\sqrt{(12 \times 0.036126 - 0.6^2)(12 \times 125.64 - 38^2)}} = 0.355$$

Exercise 7.2

(a) $t = \dfrac{0.355\sqrt{12 - 2}}{\sqrt{1 - (0.355)^2}} = 1.20$

(b) The Prob-value, for a two-tailed test is 0.257 or 25%, so we do not reject the null of no correlation.

Exercise 7.3

(a) The calculation is:

	Birth rate Y	Income ratio X	Rank of Y	Rank of X	Y^2	X^2	XY
Brazil	30	9.5	7	1	49	1	7
Colombia	29	6.8	9	3	81	9	27
Costa Rica	30	4.6	7	6	49	36	42
India	35	3.1	4	10	−16	100	40
Mexico	36	5	2.5	5	−6.25	25	12.5
Peru	36	8.7	2.5	2	6.25	4	5
Philippines	34	3.8	5	7.5	−25	56.25	37.5
Senegal	48	6.4	1	4	−1	16	4
South Korea	24	2.7	11	11	121	121	121
Sri Lanka	27	2.3	10	12	−100	144	120
Taiwan	21	3.8	12	7.5	144	56.25	90
Thailand	30	3.3	7	9	−49	81	63
Totals			78	78	647.5	649.5	569

$$r_s = \frac{12 \times 569 - 78^2}{\sqrt{(12 \times 649.5 - 78^2)(12 \times 647.5 - 78^2)}} = 0.438$$

(b) This is less than the critical value of 0.591 so the null of no rank correlation cannot be rejected.

(c) Reversing the rankings should not alter the result of the calculation.

Exercise 7.4

(a) Using the data and calculations in the answer to Exercise 7.1 we obtain:

$$b = \frac{12 \times 1964 - 60 \times 380}{12 \times 361.26 - 60^2} = 1.045$$

$$a = \frac{380}{12} - (1.045) \times \frac{60}{12} = 26.443$$

(b) A unit increase in the measure of inequality leads to approximately one additional birth per 1000 mothers. The constant has no useful interpretation. The income ratio cannot be zero (in fact, it cannot be less than 0.5).

Exercise 7.5

(a) $\text{TSS} = \Sigma(Y_i - \bar{Y})^2 = \Sigma Y_i^2 - n\bar{Y}^2 = 12\,564 - 12 \times 31.67^2 = 530.667$

$\begin{aligned}\text{ESS} &= \Sigma(Y_i - \hat{Y}_i)^2 = \Sigma Y_i^2 - a\,\Sigma Y_i - b\,\Sigma X_i Y_i\\ &= 12\,564 - 26.443 \times 380 - 1.045 \times 1139.70 = 463.804\end{aligned}$

$\text{RSS} = \text{TSS} - \text{ESS} = 530.667 - 463.804 = 66.863$

$R^2 = 0.126.$

(b) This is the square of the correlation coefficient, calculated earlier as 0.355.

Exercise 7.6

(a) $s_e^2 = \dfrac{463.804}{10} = 46.3804$

and so

$s_b^2 = \dfrac{46.3804}{61.26} = 0.757$

and

$s_b = \sqrt{0.757} = 0.870$

For a the estimated variance is

$$s_a^2 = s_e^2 \times \left(\frac{1}{n} + \frac{\bar{X}^2}{\Sigma(X_i - \bar{X})^2}\right) = 46.3804 \times \left(\frac{1}{12} + \frac{5^2}{61.26}\right) = 22.793$$

and hence $s_a = 4.774$. The 95% CIs are therefore $1.045 \pm 2.228 \times 0.87 = [-0.894, 2.983]$ for b and $26.443 \pm 2.228 \times 4.774 = [15.806, 37.081]$.

(b) $t = \dfrac{1.045 - 0}{0.870} = 1.201$

Not significant.

(c) $F = \dfrac{\text{RSS}/1}{\text{ESS}/(n-2)} = \dfrac{66.863/1}{463.804/(12-2)} = 1.44$

Exercise 7.7

Excel should give the same answers.

Exercise 7.8

(a) $\hat{BR} = 26.44 + 1.045 \times 10 = 36.9$.

(b) $\left[36.9 - 2.228 \times 6.81\sqrt{\dfrac{1}{12} + \dfrac{(10-5)^2}{61.26}},\ 36.9 + 2.228 \times 6.81\sqrt{\dfrac{1}{12} + \dfrac{(10-5)^2}{61.26}}\right]$

$= [26.3,\ 47.5]$

(c) $\left[36.9 - 2.228 \times 6.81\sqrt{1 + \dfrac{1}{12} + \dfrac{(10-5)^2}{61.26}},\ 36.9 + 2.228 \times 6.81\sqrt{1 + \dfrac{1}{12} + \dfrac{(10-5)^2}{61.26}}\right]$

$= [18.4,\ 55.4]$

Exercise 7.9

(a) $e = 1.045 \times \dfrac{5}{31.67} = 0.165$

(b) A 10% rise in the inequality measure (e.g. from 4 to 4.4) raises the birth rate by 1.65% (e.g. from 30 to 30.49).

Exercise 7.10

$$BR = 38.82 - 29.61 \times \frac{1}{IR} + e$$

s.e.   (19.0)

$R^2 = 0.19$, $F(1,10) = 2.43$.

The regression is rather poor and the F statistic is not significant.

Chapter 1

INTRODUCTION

Learning objectives

After studying this chapter you should be able to:

1 Understand that short-term and long-term interest rates, stock indices and foreign exchange rates are all related, and affect both bonds and stocks prices.

2 Understand the potential profits and losses of stocks with reference to the recent collapse of the Nasdaq index.

3 Understand the important role of the European and American capital markets in the world capital market.

4 Compare the historical average rates of return on various assets and the forecast of the average rates of return for the years 1999–2025.

5 Understand the growing role of online trading.

6 Compare and contrast corporate finance and investments.

7 Understand the difference between investments in real assets and investments in financial assets (securities).

8 State some good reasons for the study of investments.

9 Summarize the overall investment process.

INVESTMENT IN THE NEWS

Market falls are worst in decade

By Alex Skorecki in London and Gary Silverman in New York

The curtain came down yesterday on the worst year in a decade for world stock markets.

The Dow Jones Industrial Average, the leading US index, has fallen 6 per cent from its opening level of 11,497 on January 1, its worst performance in 20 years.

The total return on the Standard & Poor's 500 stocks was minus 10 per cent – the worst performance since 1977.

In Frankfurt, Germany's benchmark Xetra Dax index has been relatively resistant to decline, but is still 20 per cent off its March peak. And the high-technology Neuer Markt has fallen by about two thirds.

The Paris CAC 40 index of blue chip shares has closed at much the same level as it started 2000, despite its high exposure to technology, media and telecommunications shares (TMTs), reflecting the strength of the French economy. Nonetheless, it is about 15 per cent off its peak for the year.

In London, the FTSE 100 index closed at 6,222.5, 10 per cent lower on the year. The last time it fell more sharply was in 1990.

▶

INVESTMENT IN THE NEWS

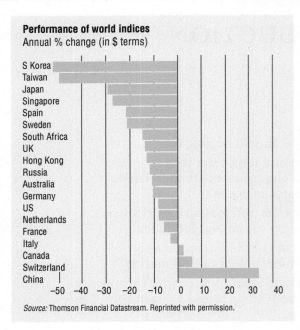

Performance of world indices
Annual % change (in $ terms)

S Korea
Taiwan
Japan
Singapore
Spain
Sweden
South Africa
UK
Hong Kong
Russia
Australia
Germany
US
Netherlands
France
Italy
Canada
Switzerland
China

-50 -40 -30 -20 -10 0 10 20 30 40

Source: Thomson Financial Datastream. Reprinted with permission.

Tokyo's benchmark index, the Nikkei 225 average, had its worst year of the decade, falling more than 27 per cent and closing yesterday at 13,785.

It is all a far cry from the buoyant mood in which the year began, in the midst of a frenzied rush for TMT shares and wide-spread optimism about the sustaining power of the US-led economic boom.

Nasdaq, the US market dominated by high-technology shares, surged until early March, but ended the worst year in its three-decade life 39 per cent down and 51.8 per cent off its peak.

The decline has been a two-stage process, according to Theodore Varelas, equity strategist at ABN Amro in London. 'First, we had the bursting of the TMT bubble as the high equity valuations proved to be unsustainable. Then in the second half of the year we saw the US economy slowing down.'

The best performer among markets in developed economies has been Copenhagen, though it made a mere 3 per cent gain. It was followed by Zurich on 2 per cent. At the other end of the spectrum was Wellington in New Zealand, with a fall of 33 per cent.

The rise and fall was sharper in Europe than the US, with European markets packing the same order of growth into six months that US markets had seen over 18 months. Europe's telecoms companies and telecoms equipment markers, such as Nokia and Ericsson, were the focus of huge inflows of capital, pegged to the prospects for third-generation mobile phones.

The constituents of the FTSE 100 index reflected the boom-bust picture. In March nine TMT stocks, including Freeserve and Psion, were added to the blue chip index, but they and others were ejected at quarterly revisions because their market capitalisations had fallen so far.

In Asia, where markets are also driven strongly by technology and electronics shares, there was a spring surge followed by bitter disappointment. Tokyo share prices are down to the level of two years ago while Seoul has halved over 12 months. Hong Kong fared relatively well, thanks to a balance of new and old economy stocks, but is still down 12 per cent.

As the gloom deepened, investors retreated to less volatile sectors. Larry Wachtel, market analyst at Prudential Securities in New York, said: 'The areas that flourished this year were the defensive stocks like drugs, energy and utilities.'

Source: Financial Times, 30 December 2000, p.1. Reprinted with permission.

INVESTMENT IN THE NEWS

Exhibit 1.1(a) Equity market developments

Exhibit 1.1(b) International short- and long-term interest rates

Weekly averages, in percentages

Exhibit 1.1(c) Bilateral exchange rates

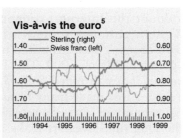

[1] Weekly averages; indexed to the average for the first week of 1994.
[2] IFC indices in US dollar terms; indexed to the month-end observation for December 1993.
[3] Three-month euromarket interest rates.
[4] Yields in annual terms on the basis of 10-year benchmark government bonds.
[5] ECC before 1999.

Sources: (a) International Finance Corporation (IFC); BIS; (b) and (c) Thomson Financial Datastream; BIS.

INVESTMENT IN THE NEWS

Exhibit 1.2 Short-term interest rates in various currencies

Period average	UK	USA
1990	14.76	8.28
1991	11.51	5.98
1992	9.63	3.83
1993	5.92	3.30
1994	5.50	4.75
1995	6.70	6.04
1996	6.05	5.51
1997	6.87	5.74
1998	7.35	5.56
1999	5.44	5.41
1999		
July	5.07	5.31
August	5.15	5.45
September	5.33	5.57
October	5.94	6.18
November	5.76	6.10
December	5.95	6.13
2000		
January	6.05	6.04
February	6.14	6.10
March	6.14	6.20
April	6.19	6.31
May	6.19	6.75
June	6.11	6.79
July	6.09	6.73
August	6.13	6.69

Source: Thomson Financial Datastream. Reprinted with permission.

Exhibit 1.3 The euro vs. other currencies

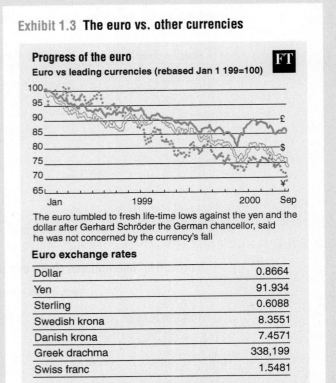

Progress of the euro

Euro vs leading currencies (rebased Jan 1 199=100)

Jan 1999 2000 Sep

The euro tumbled to fresh life-time lows against the yen and the dollar after Gerhard Schröder the German chancellor, said he was not concerned by the currency's fall

Euro exchange rates

Dollar	0.8664
Yen	91.934
Sterling	0.6088
Swedish krona	8.3551
Danish krona	7.4571
Greek drachma	338,199
Swiss franc	1.5481

Source: Thomson Financial Datastream. Reprinted with permission.

No doubt the Internet, communications and new inventions have pushed the Western economy to new heights. For example, the Nasdaq[1] index, which is composed of many such firms and new start-ups, jumped from 1,000 points in 1999 to 5,048 points in March 2000. This large profit was almost completely wiped out when the Nasdaq index dropped from 5,048 points in March 2000 to 1,820.6 in March 2001.[2] Such a loss made many firms and individuals much less willing to spend money, which in turn raised fears of a recession in the US and in the Western world.

In the long run, investors make a substantial gain in the stock market above what they can make by investing their money in bonds, or depositing their money in the bank.

---

[1] Nasdaq Index – National Association of Securities Dealers' Automated Quotations. Nasdaq is a computerized system that provides brokers and dealers with price quotations for securities traded over the counter as well as on the New York Stock Exchange.

[2] It is interesting to notice how volatile was the Nasdaq in that period: it fell by more than 5% in one day 17 times during that year and it rose by more than 5% 15 times during the year.

However, the investment in stocks is very risky, as the *Investment in the news* article reveals. The year 2000 was one of the worst in the stock market, and this phenomenon was felt across most countries. It is interesting that China was the outlier with a positive rate of return of more than 30% in that year (see the bar chart in the article).

These fears induced the chairman of the US Federal Reserve Bank to cut the interest rate from 6.5% to 5% to jump-start the economy. In April 2001, another half per cent cut in interest rate was announced (to 4.5%), and the Nasdaq index reacted with an 8% jump in one day. The drop in interest rate continued and in August 2001 it was reduced to 3.5% (in January 2002 it was 1.75%). With this drop the stock market reacted with a decrease in prices. From these events we see that interest rates, recession and stock prices are all related factors. Also, while there is a potential large profit on these new inventions or so-called start-ups, a large loss may also show its ugly face when these start-ups do not fulfil expectations or fail completely.

The figures that follow illustrate the main issues which are important to investors and which are extensively dealt with in this book.

The following is a sample of questions raised by looking at these figures:

1 What are stock indices and what do they measure? Why do some of the indices rise and some fall? (See Exhibit 1.1(a).)

2 Why interest rates may vary across time? Why are short-term interest rates generally lower than long-term interest rates (see Exhibit 1.1(b))? Does the interest rate difference reflect risk? Expected inflation? As an investor who would like to invest in bonds, should you invest in long-term higher interest rate investments rather than short-term lower interest rate investments? We will explain in this book why such a conclusion may be wrong. Apart from interest, the bonds investor is also exposed to possible capital gains and capital losses. In addition, the short-term interest rate in the UK dropped from 14.76% in 1990 to only 6.13% in March 2001! In the US there was a decline from 8.28% in 1990 to about 1.75% in January 2002. What induced such a large drop in short-term interest rates? Why is there such a big difference in the drop in the two countries? How is this related to the rate of inflation? To currency exchange rates?

3 How can one explain the differences in interest rates across countries? Given these interest rate differences, why not borrow in Japan at almost zero interest rate and deposit the money in the UK or the US and make the interest rate difference (see Exhibit 1.1(b))?

4 Related to question 3 above, the figures given in Exhibit 1.1(c) reveal that the exchange rates are not fixed across time. Thus, borrowing in Japan and depositing the money in the UK may be risky to the British investor because the British pound may be weaker, which will eat up all the profit from the interest rate difference. Moreover, investors can also induce a money loss on such transactions. To see this, assume that the British investor borrows 100,000 yen, exchanges them to pounds and deposits the pounds in the UK. He or she may find that when converting the pounds back to yen (in order to pay back the loan), a much larger number of pounds has to be paid for the 100,000 yen; hence, a loss occurred on the transaction.

The euro is a relatively new currency. On 1 January 1999 the following European countries introduced the euro: Germany, France, Italy, Spain, Portugal, Finland, Ireland, Belgium, Luxembourg, the Netherlands and Austria. The euro thus supersedes the German mark, French franc, Italian lira, Spanish peseta, Portuguese escudo, Finnish markka, Irish punt, Belgian and Luxembourg franc, Dutch guilder and Austrian schilling. The conversion rate of each of these currencies was decided in advance (see Appendix 1A). In 2002 these European national currencies continue to exist in parallel with the euro. The timetable for the euro can be seen in Appendix 1A. In September

2000, the Danish voted for not joining the euro. The people of the UK will probably decide on this issue after 2002. Unfortunately, the euro turned out to be very weak relative to the other currencies. Exhibit 1.3 shows what happened to an investor who decided to invest in the euro in 1999. The euro fell by 15% against sterling, by about 20% against the US dollar and by more than 30% against the yen. This situation caused the European Central Bank to intervene in the market, as you can see in the press release from 22 September 2000 shown in the box.

PRESS-SERVICE 22 September 2000

The ECB announces joint intervention in the exchange markets

On the initiative of the European Central Bank, the monetary authorities of the United States and Japan joined with the European Central Bank in concerted intervention in exchange markets because of their shared concern about the potential implications of recent movements in the euro exchange rate for the world economy.

European Central Bank: Internet: http://www.ecb.int

---

5 Exhibits 1.1(a) and (b) reveal that as the long-term interest rate declines, the stock markets respond with a sharp rise, with the exception of the Nikkei index (the Japanese stock index). What is the relationship between interest rates and stock prices? It is not that simple. In January and March 2001, Mr Alan Greenspan, Chairman of the American Federal Reserve Bank, announced a decrease in the interest rate from 6% to 5%. Despite these interest cuts, the Dow Jones index dropped by 12% and the Nasdaq index dropped by 25% in the first quarter of 2001. On the other hand, in April 2001 when Greenspan surprised the market with another half per cent cut, which was announced on an earlier date than expected, the Nasdaq reacted by a jump of 8.2% on one day. We will argue that it is important to compare the *expected* interest rate changes to the actual changes. In the case of the recent cut in interest rate in the US, it is possible that investors were disappointed because they expected a larger interest rate cut.

6 How does the decline in long-term interest rates affect bond prices?

Most of this book deals with valuation of stocks, bonds and derivatives; a large portion of the book is devoted to answering questions like the six described above. For example, we see that interest rates fluctuate over time: in the US, the *long-term* interest rate fell to about 4.3% in January 1999 and jumped back to about 6.25% in August 1999[3] (not shown in the graph). Generally, when the US Federal Reserve Bank or any national bank in Europe changes the interest rate, this also affects stock and bond prices, as well as foreign exchange rates. We discuss in this book how changes in interest rates affect bond and stock prices as well as foreign exchange rates.

Nowadays, we have a global capital market with almost completely free movement of capital across countries, with a low transaction cost due to Internet trading. Thus, any macro-economic change (in inflation, interest rate, etc.) in one major country directly affects other countries' markets because investors can buy assets in most major capital markets, and by switching capital from one market to another, they affect asset prices as well as foreign exchange rates.

---

[3] In August 2000 the long-term interest rate fell to 5.92%. It continued to fall during 2001 and in January 2002 the rate was 5.46%.

There are other macro-economic factors which affect the stock and bond market. One crucial factor is the expected rate of inflation. For example, in August 1999, fears of an increase in inflation in the US forced the Federal Reserve Bank to increase the interest rate. In August 1999, data revealed that the wage per hour increased by 3.5% on an annual basis, less than the expected 3.8% rate. As a result, the fears of an inflation and interest rate hike faded out, the Dow Jones industrial index jumped by 2% and the Nasdaq index jumped by 4% in one day. Similarly, the interest rate on long-term bonds fell from 6.18% to 6.02%, and the price of the bonds jumped by 1.8% on that same day. In 2001 fears of a recession prevailed, triggering a series of interest rate cuts.

Exhibit 1.2 shows that such an effect also occurred in the UK. The Bank of England raised the interest rate in the second half of 1999 (which was about 5%) by more than 1%.

Thus, we can see that many macro-economic factors affect inflation and interest rate expectation, and hence also stock and bond prices.

The above figures are related to macro-economic factors. This does not mean that a firm's specific performance is not important for stock and bond valuation. Allocating assets between stocks and bonds and the allocation of funds to various foreign countries is greatly affected by the macro-economic factors illustrated above. However, selecting the stocks to be included in the stock portion of the portfolio is determined mainly by the firm's specific factors, e.g. expected future rate of return and risk. Thus, macro-economic factors determine the *asset allocation*, and firms' specific factors determine the *stock selectivity*, or the composition of the equity component of the portfolio. We deal in this book with both macro-economic factors as well as a firm's specific factors.

1.1   A FEW FACTS ON THE CAPITAL MARKET

First, the US market is by far the largest, and in the US the New York Stock Exchange (NYSE) is the largest. Exhibit 1.4 shows the stock market capitalization (i.e. equity) at the end of 1998. NYSE, Nasdaq and Chicago account for 62% of the world market capitalization. It is interesting that Japan accounts for only 10%; before the collapse of the Nikkei index (which in the past had reached almost 40,000 points, compared to about 10,000 points in January 2002) it had a much bigger portion of the market capitalization.

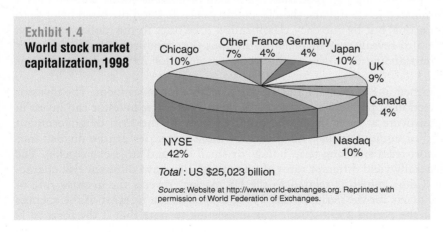

Exhibit 1.4
World stock market capitalization, 1998

Chicago 10%
Other 7%
France 4%
Germany 4%
Japan 10%
UK 9%
Canada 4%
Nasdaq 10%
NYSE 42%

Total : US $25,023 billion

Source: Website at http://www.world-exchanges.org. Reprinted with permission of World Federation of Exchanges.

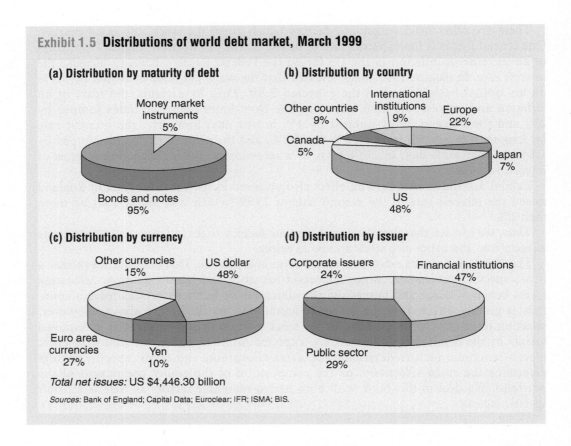

Exhibit 1.5 Distributions of world debt market, March 1999

(a) Distribution by maturity of debt

Money market instruments 5%

Bonds and notes 95%

(b) Distribution by country

Other countries 9%

International institutions 9%

Europe 22%

Canada 5%

Japan 7%

US 48%

(c) Distribution by currency

Other currencies 15%

US dollar 48%

Euro area currencies 27%

Yen 10%

(d) Distribution by issuer

Corporate issuers 24%

Financial institutions 47%

Public sector 29%

Total net issues: US $4,446.30 billion

Sources: Bank of England; Capital Data; Euroclear; IFR; ISMA; BIS.

Exhibit 1.5 reveals the stock of the various issues of the outstanding debt at the end of March 1999. Exhibit 1.5(a) distinguishes between short-term money market instruments and long-term bonds and notes. It reveals that the debt market is mainly long-term (more than one year), with bonds and notes making up about 95% of the debt market.

Exhibit 1.5(b) provides a breakdown of the debt market by countries. Here we see that Europe accounts for 22% of the outstanding debt and the US accounts for 48%. Exhibit 1.5(c) provides the breakdown of the debt by currency showing the central role that the US dollar plays in the debt market. Note that if a British firm issues bonds in London and the bonds are nominated in US dollars, then by country classification the bond belongs to the category of 'Europe' but by currency classification it belongs to the 'dollar' category. Finally, Exhibit 1.5(d) reveals that financial institutions (i.e. commercial banks) account for 47% of the outstanding debt, the public sector accounts for 29% and corporations account for 24%.

The assets described in Exhibits 1.4 and 1.5 are available for investment. The investor has to make a selection of portfolios composed of these assets. The investor can invest in bonds (which constitute a 'debt' from the point of view of the firm or government issuing the bonds) or equity (stocks). Also, each of these categories can be divided into subgroups (i.e. short-term and long-term bonds, or small cap and large cap stocks). The various assets generally yield different rates of return and also have different risk characteristics. Exhibit 1.6(a), which is related to the US market, reveals the *average* rate of return on various assets for the period 1926–1998, as well as the forecast of the average rates of return for the period 1999–2025. It is interesting to note that if the forecast is

Exhibit 1.6(a) **Average rate of return for the period 1926–1998 and forecast for the period 1999–2025**

	1926–1998	1999–2025
Forecast total return of small cap Stocks	12.4%	12.5%
Forecast total return of large cap Stocks	13.2%	11.6%
Forecast total return of government bonds	5.7% (long-term)	4.7%
Forecast total return of treasury bills	3.8%	4.5%
Forecast of inflation	3.2%	3.1%

Source: Website at http://www.ibbotson.com/news/dow.forecast.asp and *Stocks, Bonds, Bills and Inflation* ® *Yearbook*, © Ibbotson Associates, Inc. Based on copyrighted works by Ibbotson and Sinquefield. All rights reserved. Used with permission.

correct, the Dow Jones index is expected to be at 120,362 points in the year 2025 (compared to about 11,000 in 1999 and 9,800 in January 2002).

Exhibit 1.6(b) shows the returns for the UK (FTSE 100), Germany (DAX) and France (CAC 40) stock indices in the last 10–15 years (up to June 2000).

Past performance as well as future forecasts have one thing in common: they are both characterized by a high average rate of return on stocks. Bonds, on the other hand, and in particular Treasury bonds, hardly beat inflation.

Does this mean that investment in stocks is better than investment in bonds? Not necessarily so. Stocks are also riskier than bonds. When you invest, say, for one year, you get the realized return for this year but you do not receive the 'average' return. Thus, you may lose a lot of money despite the reported high average returns. For example, investors around the world lost more than 20% on stock investment in October 1987 in only one day. Such losses do not generally occur with bond investment. For the investors who needed their money in October 1987, the 'average' return was not very appealing.

Up to March 1999, investing in the Nasdaq was far better than the other investment. Can we recommend investing in the Nasdaq in the future?

Exhibit 1.6(c) shows the rate of return of some major indexes against the US Nasdaq index in the period January 2001–December 2001. The crash in the Nasdaq was more severe than the crash of other indexes. Thus, a profit in one period does not necessarily indicate a success in the future. The boxed article 'Investors: Is the worst over?' (on p. 13) shows that the Internet stocks crash raised a lot of questions about the future of investment in the stock markets.

Thus, in this book we consider average returns as well as risk of the various assets, with the goal of constructing a portfolio of assets which generally includes stocks (for their relatively high return) as well as bonds (for their relatively high safety).

Sometimes you wish to take a position with a potentially high reward, but you do not wish to be exposed to a high risk. For example, consider an American investor who is bullish on UK stocks, and hence wishes to invest in UK stocks but does not wish to be exposed to foreign exchange currency risk. Derivatives can be employed to reduce this risk. In our specific example, currency options can be bought or currency swaps can be employed. Exhibit 1.7 shows the growing role of derivatives (not including stock options), increasing from a $196 billion daily turnover in 1995 to a $362 billion daily turnover in 1998.

The derivatives in the international market are very colourful with currency and interest rate swaps, interest rate and currency options, and forward agreements (FRAs), which are swap-of-cash-flows agreements that will start sometime in the future, say

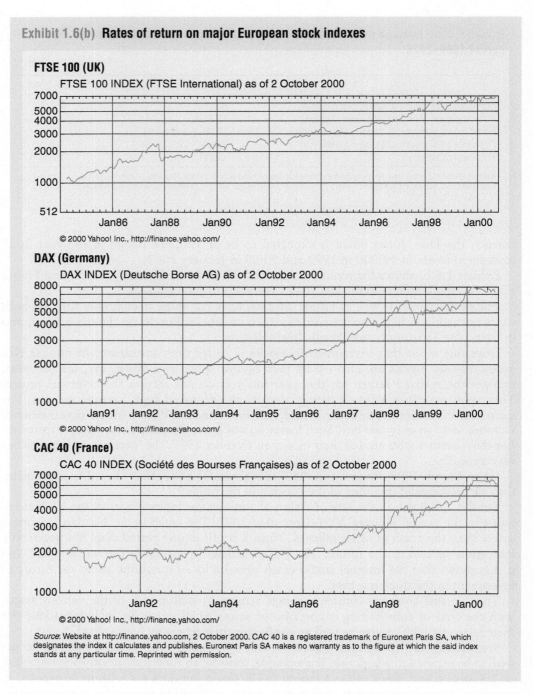

Exhibit 1.6(b) **Rates of return on major European stock indexes**

FTSE 100 (UK)

FTSE 100 INDEX (FTSE International) as of 2 October 2000

© 2000 Yahoo! Inc., http://finance.yahoo.com/

DAX (Germany)

DAX INDEX (Deutsche Borse AG) as of 2 October 2000

© 2000 Yahoo! Inc., http://finance.yahoo.com/

CAC 40 (France)

CAC 40 INDEX (Société des Bourses Françaises) as of 2 October 2000

© 2000 Yahoo! Inc., http://finance.yahoo.com/

Source: Website at http://finance.yahoo.com, 2 October 2000. CAC 40 is a registered trademark of Euronext Paris SA, which designates the index it calculates and publishes. Euronext Paris SA makes no warranty as to the figure at which the said index stands at any particular time. Reprinted with permission.

two years from now. Two chapters of this book are devoted to derivatives, which have nowadays become a very important investment vehicle (see Chapters 12 and 13).

The capital market is full of surprises and unexpected events. There are two basic approaches to handling these events:

(a) Trying to forecast future events, e.g. a cut in the interest rate by the Federal Reserve Bank or the National Central Bank, and capitalizing on it if the forecast is correct.
(b) Constructing a portfolio of assets to reduce risk of unforeseen future events.

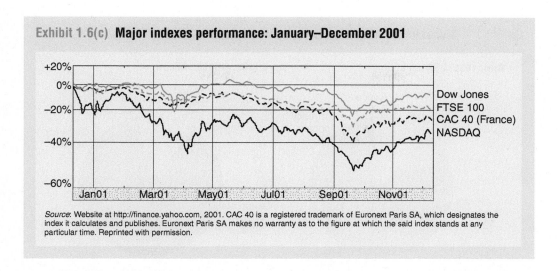

Exhibit 1.6(c) Major indexes performance: January–December 2001

Source: Website at http://finance.yahoo.com, 2001. CAC 40 is a registered trademark of Euronext Paris SA, which designates the index it calculates and publishes. Euronext Paris SA makes no warranty as to the figure at which the said index stands at any particular time. Reprinted with permission.

Investors: Is the worst over?

By Pierre Belec

NEW YORK (Reuters) – They're Wall Street's walking wounded, the masses of investors in shock after the stock market went from slow correction to freefall frenzy. Twelve months after 'The Big One' started, people are only now beginning to ask themselves 'What could I have been thinking?'

Many have lost their shirts after throwing money into 'New Economy' stocks, those technology high-flyers.

A lot of tech stocks have crashed and some have burned. Internet stocks that went through the roof two years ago are now selling for pennies a share after having their 15 minutes of fame.

The optimists say the technology-laced Nasdaq market, which has been the hardest hit, appears to have hit bottom and they think that months from now Wall Streeters will be kicking themselves for not scooping up stocks after the tumble. They say the bullish ingredients are coming together, i.e., the media have discovered that there is a bear market, which is usually a good time to start buying.

But there's the scary realization the market is still overpriced, despite its heart-stopping drop.

Source: Website at http://biz.yahoo.com/rb/010324/business_markets_stocks_dc_330.html, 25 March 2001.

Exhibit 1.8 reveals 20 unexpected events which occurred in 1998 that were totally unpredicted. Russia's default, the loss on derivatives, the Long-Term Capital Management (LTCM) which was near collapse, the Nikkei index sharp decline, and a negative interest on yen deposits, are only a few examples demonstrating the risk involved in investing in the capital market all over the world. Of course, if such events are forecast, the investor can be wealthy. However, given that it is hard, if not impossible, to predict such events, we teach you in this book how to protect yourself from possible negative events. For example, the Long-Term Capital Management (LTCM) near bankruptcy (due to speculation on changes in interest rates on various types of bonds) could be avoided if one would adhere to the principle of diversification: if you speculate on some change in interest rates, take into account the possibility that you may be wrong. Hence, allocate only a limited proportion of your investment to this position. This is the main idea of portfolio diversification, advocating not to 'put all your eggs in one basket'. By similar reasoning, if you invest some proportion of your assets in Japan and some in the UK or the US, the unpredicted losses in Japan may be offset by the gains from investing in other countries. Thus, international diversification may stabilize your portfolio, without necessarily reducing the average

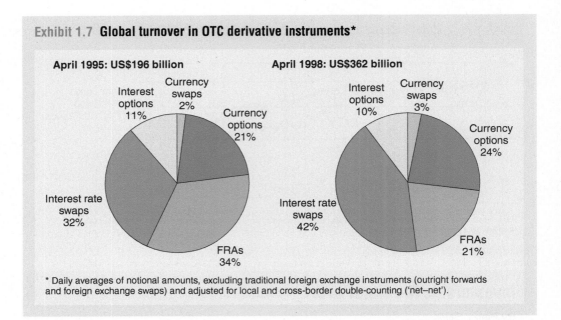

Exhibit 1.7 Global turnover in OTC derivative instruments*

April 1995: US$196 billion

- Interest options 11%
- Currency swaps 2%
- Currency options 21%
- Interest rate swaps 32%
- FRAs 34%

April 1998: US$362 billion

- Interest options 10%
- Currency swaps 3%
- Currency options 24%
- Interest rate swaps 42%
- FRAs 21%

* Daily averages of notional amounts, excluding traditional foreign exchange instruments (outright forwards and foreign exchange swaps) and adjusted for local and cross-border double-counting ('net–net').

Exhibit 1.8 Twenty unexpected events of 1998

Capital Markets Risk Advisors, a New York risk management consultant, keeps an informal list of 'first-time' market events – events that risk models relying on historical data can't foresee. Normally, four or five such events occur each year. In 1998 CMRA recorded 77. Here are some that had the greatest impact on markets.

Apr 7	Citicorp and Travelers agree to a $82.9 billion merger.
May 18	Indonesia's rupiah collapses, to 17,000 to the US dollar.
Aug 17	Russia defaults on some debt; rouble collapses.
Aug 31	The Dow plunges 512.61 points, or 6.37%.
July–Sept	US banks suffer worst derivatives losses ever – $445 million.
Sept 24	Hedge fund Long Term Capital Management is bailed out to the tune of $3.6 billion.
Sept 27	Japan Leasing files for bankruptcy with $17.9 billion in liabilities – biggest financial failure since World War II.
Oct 5	30-year US treasury yield hits record 4.74% low.
Oct 7	The US dollar plunges 7.8% against the yen, largest one-day loss in 12 years.
Oct 8	China's yuan soars to an all-time high of 8.2777 to the US dollar.
Oct 9	Japan's Nikkei Index sinks to 11,542, lowest since 1984.
Oct 13	London's FTSE-100 index soars a record 214.2 points.
Nov 2	The US savings rate sinks to a miserably low 0.2%.
Nov 5	Some leading Western banks cut yen deposit rates to below zero – a negative interest rate.
Nov 11	Shares of the globe.com skyrocket more than tenfold in first day of trading.
Nov 23	7 M&A megadeals ($1 billion plus) are announced the same day.
Nov 30	US mortgage rates fall to 6.64%, lowest since 1967.
Dec 3	11 European countries cut interest rates simultaneously.
Dec 4	Exxon and Mobil announce $86.3 billion merger, largest industrial deal ever.
Dec 10	World oil prices slide below $10 a barrel, lowest since 1986.

Source: Global Finance, March 1999.

portfolio return. We devote Chapters 6 and 14 to this diversification idea, and Chapter 15 to international diversification.

1.2 ONLINE TRADING

The trading system has been through a revolution. Online trading has grown rapidly since its onset. You can sit at home in front of your computer and sell and buy stocks several times a day (hence the name day-trader). You do not need to call your broker, and after opening an account with your broker, with a push of a button you conduct a transaction. Online trading reduces transaction costs and has attracted many new investors to the stock market.

Exhibit 1.9(a) shows that the proportion of online investors increased from 1997 to 1999 with a forecast for a continuation of this growth up to 2002. For example, in 2002, there is an expectation that out of about 80 million investors, 20 million will be online investors. Exhibit 1.9(b) explains the reasons why investors choose to invest online.

In this introduction we mention the fascinating revolution that is taking place in the trading system. Chapter 3 is devoted to the various trading mechanisms employed in the capital market.

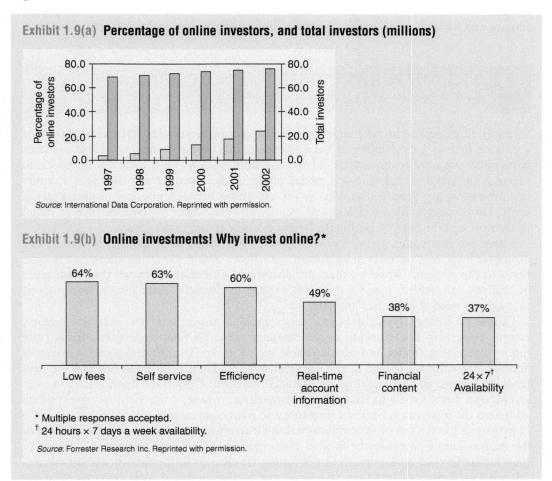

Exhibit 1.9(a) **Percentage of online investors, and total investors (millions)**

Source: International Data Corporation. Reprinted with permission.

Exhibit 1.9(b) **Online investments! Why invest online?***

* Multiple responses accepted.
† 24 hours × 7 days a week availability.

Source: Forrester Research Inc. Reprinted with permission.

1.3 FACTORS AFFECTING ASSET PRICES

In this book we examine models for determining the value of various financial assets (for example, bonds and stocks) and show how changes in expected earnings, dividends and risk, or changes in inflation rate and in the interest rate, affect the current price of these assets.

Thus, what affects the asset's value is a firm's specific factors (earnings and risk), as well as macro-economic factors such as inflation, interest rate, etc. Generally, academics and practitioners agree on the effects of the most important economic factors on the prices of stocks and bonds. For example, almost all agree that when the Federal Reserve cuts interest rates *more than expected*, or when it announces no increase in the interest rate when such an increase is expected, the overall stock market will go up. If the Federal Reserve cuts interest rates less than expected, the overall stock market will go down. Similarly, investors routinely observe that when a firm announces greater-than-expected quarterly earnings and dividends, the stock price of the firm goes up. The only questionable issue is the extent to which such news will or should affect prices. Indeed, the valuation models presented in the following chapters attempt to evaluate both stock and bond prices and the effect of various levels of interest rates, dividends, earnings and risk on these prices.

Some of the information in this book will be familiar to readers from studies in other classes – particularly corporate finance. In the next section, we compare corporate finance and investments. We then compare investments in physical and financial assets.

1.4 THE DIFFERENCE BETWEEN CORPORATE FINANCE AND INVESTMENTS

Virtually all students who take an investments course are required to have had at least one corporate finance (or principles of finance) course. In a corporate finance course, students have some exposure to investment-related concepts, such as yield to maturity, portfolio variance and the dividend valuation model. Students often wonder why they need to study investments again. Specifically, what is the difference between physical project analysis studied in corporate finance classes and security analysis? After all, both involve an initial investment and the hope of getting the largest possible return in the future.

There are many similarities between project analysis and investment analysis. For example, both rely on estimating future cash flows and discounting these future cash flows to the present. However, there are also many differences between these two types of analysis. Therefore, specific tools are needed in financial asset investment analysis that are not needed in project analysis.

Corporate finance typically covers issues such as project analysis, capital structure, capital budgeting and working capital management. To finance projects, firms raise money by issuing stocks and bonds. These securities are bought and sold by investors and are subsequently traded in the financial market. Thus, both investors and the firm have an interest in the workings of financial markets. Corporate finance involves the interaction between firms and financial markets, whereas the field of investments addresses the interaction between investors and financial markets.

Investment is the use of financial capital in an effort to create more financial capital in the future. That is, an investor forgoes consumption today in an attempt to achieve an even higher level of consumption in the future. Investment in the money market (securities with maturities of less than one year) can be distinguished from investment in the

---

Exhibit 1.10 Examples of financial securities by market classification

---

Money market securities

- Treasury bills
- Commercial paper
- Negotiable certificates of deposit
- Eurodollars
- Banker's acceptance
- Repurchase agreements

Capital market securities

- Fixed-income securities: debt instruments by the European Treasury, federal agencies, municipalities, and corporations
- Equity securities: common stock and preferred stock

Derivative market securities

- Options
- Future contracts

---

capital market (securities with maturities greater than one year). Exhibit 1.10 provides examples of the securities in each of the three main market categories.

Some investments are speculative, meaning they involve a high degree of risk. However, many investors in speculative vehicles undertake strategies to hedge against the risk of a major loss. Hedging is a technique used to limit loss potential. Risk reduction can also be achieved by holding a portfolio of assets or by investing in derivative assets. A portfolio is a group of securities that are held together in an effort to achieve a maximum future consumption (or rate of return) for a given level of risk.

The primary focus of this book is on the relationship between financial markets and investors. Hence, issues related to corporate finance will be addressed only to the extent that they influence prices and perceptions of riskiness in financial markets. The basic formulas employed in both areas – corporate finance and investments – are covered. In fact, some of the same techniques used to evaluate assets in project analysis are used in financial assets analysis. Therefore, Appendix A at the end of the book reviews the basic formulas – present value, internal rate of return and so forth – that you studied in your corporate finance course. This review will serve as a bridge between the two courses and will help later, because stock and bond valuation formulas are based on present value and internal rate of return methods.

1.5 THE DIFFERENCE BETWEEN PHYSICAL AND FINANCIAL ASSETS

There are two categories of assets: financial assets, which are intangible, such as corporate stocks and bonds, and physical assets, also called real assets or tangible assets. Examples of tangible assets are precious metals, real estate and textile machines. Although financial assets are typically represented by tangible certificates of ownership, the financial asset itself is intangible. Financial assets are also called securities. A key distinction between financial and real (physical) assets is that real assets are income-generating assets used to produce goods or services. Financial assets, in contrast, represent claims against the income generated by real assets.

Investment in real assets differs from investment in financial assets in several ways. Investing in the capital market typically involves a commitment of money to various financial assets, such as bonds and stocks, as opposed to real assets, such as machines. The use of the term *investment* in this book is confined strictly to investments in financial assets.

Financial assets are divisible, i.e. you can buy a few shares of BMW on the German exchange. Physical assets are not divisible: you cannot buy some fraction of a machine. Financial assets are marketable, i.e. they can be easily bought and sold. You can sell stocks that you hold with a phone call to your broker, but it is difficult to quickly sell a physical asset, e.g. a house. Marketability refers to the ease with which you convert the asset into cash, while liquidity reflects the feasibility of converting an asset into cash quickly and without significantly affecting its price. Stocks with a large number of outstanding shares that are actively traded are very liquid. These securities are preferred by investors who trade large quantities of securities, because their trading activity will have no (or minimal) impact on the security's price. Many financial assets are very easy to buy and sell. However, most real assets are not very liquid and hence are described as illiquid. An investor who owns textile machines and who wants to sell them will generally have difficulty doing so.

Financial assets can be held for a relatively short period of time. But when investors acquire a real asset, they normally plan to hold it for a relatively long period. Buying new steel-producing machines, for example, requires large installation costs. Therefore, no-one would plan to hold these machines for a month or even just a year. However, the transaction costs of buying securities are relatively low, and investing for a month or a year may be reasonable. Thus, the planned holding period of securities can be much shorter than the corresponding holding period of most real assets.

Finally, there is a difference in information availability. There is plenty of information on financial assets, while on physical assets there is much less information. For example, suppose you enquire about buying an oil-drilling machine. Where would you get information on the value of the machine? What are the transportation and installation costs of the machine? Probably only a few people in the oil industry have the information to determine these costs. The situation is different with stocks and bonds. Anyone can open the *Financial Times* or call a broker to find out how much a share of BMW stock costs. Similarly, a person who wants to buy shares of BMW stock can obtain information (at almost no cost) on earnings, dividends and so forth. Today, almost every large firm has an Internet site, and an investor can obtain all needed information free of charge with just the push of a button. Because this information is publicly available, the impact of many published factors on the value of the financial asset can be analyzed. This type of analysis cannot be easily done with real assets.

Four factors – divisibility, marketability (also called liquidity), holding period and information availability – make investments in financial assets different from investments in real assets. Thus, we need different tools to analyze these types of investments. In particular, because of the divisibility property of financial assets, this book will focus on how to build portfolios of securities.

1.6   THE BENEFITS OF STUDYING INVESTMENTS

Studying investment can lead to a rewarding career. As the financial markets become increasingly complex, job opportunities for professional investors increase. Even though

Exhibit 1.11 Job opportunities in investments

Title	Typical firms	Description
Broker, registered representative, account executive	Brokerage firms, financial institutions	Provide sales and financial planning services
Analyst	Brokerage firms, financial institutions	Conduct research and security analysis
Financial planner	Private firms, certified public accountant (CPA) firms	Advise individual investors
Portfolio manager	Mutual fund groups, pension funds, money managers	Perform asset allocation and security selection
Asset/liability and risk manager	Insurance companies, financial institutions, banks	Perform research, actuarial work and asset allocation
Auditor	All firms	Monitor and devise internal controls
Regulator	Government agencies, exchanges	Oversee and police market activity
Surveillance	Exchanges	Oversee and monitor trading behaviour

job opportunities declined after the October 1987 stock market crash, the overall trend has been expansion. Increasingly, firms are looking for people with specialized skills. In 1999, the stock indices in the United States hit an all-time high, with the Dow Jones index passing the 11,000-point mark. This bull market increases the demand for finance majors with specialized skills. Exhibit 1.11 provides a sampling of job opportunities in the investments field, and Exhibit 1A.3 in Appendix 1A lists some job opportunities that were available at the European Central Bank.

1.7 THE INVESTMENT PROCESS

The study of investments is never completed. The investment process is dynamic and ongoing. Thus, the job of the investment analyst is never finished. However, there are always five basic components in the investment process: investor characteristics, investment vehicles, strategy development, strategy implementation and strategy monitoring.

1.7.1 Investor characteristics

Exhibit 1.12 shows the relationship of the components in the investment process. The first element in the investment process is the investor. The investor may be an individual or an institutional investor, such as a manager of an employee retirement account or bank trust department. The investor should first establish the investment policy, a written document detailing the objectives and constraints (characteristics) of the investor.

The investment policy should have specific objectives regarding the return requirement and risk tolerance. For example, the investment policy may state that the portfolio's target average return should exceed 8% and the portfolio should avoid exposure to more than

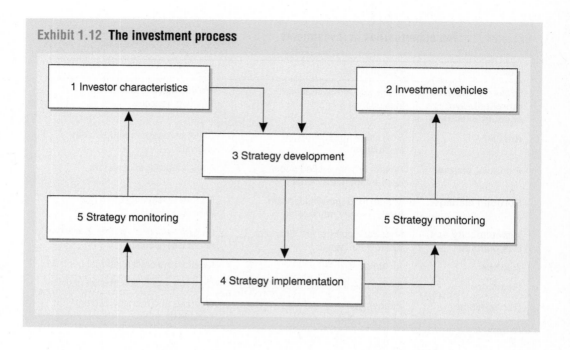

Exhibit 1.12 **The investment process**

10% in losses. Typically, identifying the tolerance for risk is the most important objective, because every investor would like to earn the greatest return possible. The investment policy should also state any constraints that will affect the day-to-day management of the funds. Constraints include any liquidity needs, projected time horizons, tax considerations, and legal and regulatory considerations.

1.7.2 Investment vehicles: the trade-off between risk and return

After an assessment has been made of the investor's characteristics, the available investment opportunities can be explored. Financial assets are broadly classified as money market capital market and derivative market securities.

Let us look at three categories of investment vehicles: bonds, stocks and derivative securities. Bonds are financial assets that represent a creditor relationship with an entity. They are debt instruments of a firm. Stocks represent an ownership position in a corporation. Derivative securities (also called contingent claims), such as options and futures, are tied to the performance of another security (hence the term derivative). Of the three categories, bonds are generally the least risky and also offer the lowest return. Stocks offer a higher return on average; however, they are generally riskier than bonds. Derivative securities have the highest potential risk level, as well as the highest potential return. Exhibit 1.13 describes these three major classes of investment opportunities and gives some general information about them. Of course, the information in Exhibit 1.13 is general and therefore not true for every security.

1.7.3 Strategy development

The next element in the investment process is to optimize the competing constraints of the various investment vehicles and the investor's characteristics. Investors generally

Exhibit 1.13 Summary of investment vehicles

Vehicle	Potential risks	Potential return	Marketability	Dividend and interest cash flows
Bonds	Low	Low	Low/moderate	High
Stocks	Moderate/high	Moderate/high	Usually good	Low
Derivative securities	Very high	Potentially high	Low	None

seek an investment strategy that provides the highest possible expected return within the constraints of the desired cash flow, risk level and other important variables (such as liquidity).

The precise strategy developed depends on the investor's perception of how good capital markets are at processing information. If the capital markets process information quickly and accurately, we say that the markets are efficient. An efficient market is one in which stock prices reflect all relevant information about the stock.

If an investor believes that the market is efficient, the investment focus will be on designing well-diversified portfolios. (The investor sees no benefit in trying to uncover mispriced securities.) However, the investor who does not believe that the markets are efficient may wish to acquire all of the latest information and attempt to buy underpriced securities and sell overpriced securities.

Chapters 6 and 14 of this book address the development of strategies when the investor believes that the market is efficient. Chapters 9, 10 and 18 address the development of strategies when the investor does not believe that the market is efficient. Most investors fall somewhere between these two extreme views. They typically believe the market is somewhat efficient, so they diversify and try to design optimal portfolios, as discussed in Chapter 6. However, investors are ever watchful for securities that may be temporarily mispriced due to some unforeseen event.

When developing a strategy, some investors like to avoid as much risk as possible. For example, investors who need money to pay tuition next year would put all their money in very safe securities, such as short-term bonds. Some investors who are not willing to miss a possible high return are willing to expose themselves to the risk and put all or most of their money in stocks or derivative securities. However, it is not necessary to go to the extreme and put all available money in one security. The investor can buy a little of each category of asset. By doing so, the investor may benefit from a relatively high return but not be exposed to a very high risk. This concept is known as asset allocation.

Asset allocation is the apportioning of an investment portfolio among various asset categories, such as cash, bonds, stocks and real estate. Asset allocation plays a key role in investment management. Securities within each asset class – for example, stocks – tend to move together over time. This co-movement is called correlation. Thus, asset allocation is essential, because assets in different classes do not tend to move together. This lack of co-movement helps reduce portfolio risk.

After the asset allocation decision has been made, the investor can turn to the task of individual security selection. Security selection is the decision-making process used to determine the specific securities within each asset class that are most suitable for a client's needs.

1.7.4 Strategy implementation

After a strategy has been developed, the asset allocation decisions are implemented and the specific securities selected. Successful implementation of the asset allocation decision is difficult in practice, because it involves changing securities in the portfolio frequently. One problem is transaction costs: changing the asset allocation decision is costly because it requires liquidating many securities.[4] These costs directly reduce the benefits expected from the allocation strategy.

A second problem is changing economic and market factors. Economies and markets are in constant flux, which changes the optimal allocation strategy. These changes result in assets either being allocated in a suboptimal fashion or incurring transaction costs induced by the need to change the asset allocation. Thus, constantly changing circumstances result in the need of investors to constantly change their asset allocations.

A third problem is changing investor objectives and constraints. Over time, the needs of an individual or fund change, requiring reallocation of assets. For example, an investor's degree of aversion to risk may change if he or she inherits a large sum of money.

An investor must also decide the best course of day-to-day strategy implementation – that is, the most cost-effective way to acquire the desired financial assets.

1.7.5 Strategy monitoring

Once the investment process has begun, it is important to periodically re-evaluate the approach. This monitoring is necessary because financial markets change, tax laws change, and other events alter stated goals. For example, in 1997, a reduction in the capital gains tax from 28% to 20% took place. How should this reduction affect an investor's asset allocation strategy? Perhaps a much better security than was previously available is created. Investors must regularly examine and question their strategy to make sure it is the best. Primarily, they need to monitor goals and objectives and review the available financial assets.

1.8 WHERE DO WE GO FROM HERE? A BRIEF OVERVIEW OF THE BOOK

This book has six parts. The remainder of Part I provides an overview of the investment environment. Chapter 2 introduces the basic securities used in the investment process: stocks, bonds and derivative securities. Chapter 3 surveys the security markets, focusing on the practical issues investors encounter when they actually implement an investment strategy.

Part II focuses on the basic components of risk and return. Chapter 4 surveys the methods used for calculating the historical rates of return, focusing on the professionally

---

[4] A recent solution to avoiding these costs is to use futures and options contracts on broad-based indices. Also, the recently implemented Internet trading sharply reduces these transaction costs.

accepted standards. Chapter 5 reviews the calculation of future rates of return and variability based on some objective or subjective probability beliefs. The chapter examines different attitudes towards risk and its influence on returns. Chapter 6 explains how one can reduce risk by holding a portfolio of various assets as well as the riskless asset.

With this background in portfolio management, Part III turns to security analysis. Chapters 7 and 8 are devoted to bonds, and Chapters 9 and 10 are devoted to stocks. Chapter 11 introduces overall market analysis, the question of whether to invest in bonds or stocks, as well as industry analysis.

Part IV covers derivative securities, with Chapter 12 devoted to forwards and futures, and Chapter 13 devoted to options. Part V of the book is devoted to the equilibrium risk–return relationship and to the gain from international diversification. Finally, Part VI discusses the concept of efficient markets (Chapter 16), mutual funds (trusts) and how to measure their performance (Chapter 17), and technical analysis (Chapter 18), i.e. to the investment methods employed by technicians and chartists who don't believe that the market is efficient.

SUMMARY

■ *Demonstrate the interrelationship between interest rates and stock prices.*
Generally, when interest rates drop, stock market indexes rise. However, the drop in interest rates is not relevant, but the drop (or the increase) relative to what investors expected will be the change.

■ *Demonstrate the relationship between various economic factors across countries.*
A low interest rate in Japan and a high interest rate in the UK does not imply that it is profitable to borrow in Japan and deposit the money in the UK. The reason is that a fluctuation (in our case of yen against sterling) may wash out such apparent profits and even induce a loss.

■ *Demonstrate the role of the various assets in the market.*
One can invest in stocks, bond derivatives, etc. Each asset has its risk–return profile. The risks are very large, and unpredictable events may occur. Diversification, or not 'putting all one's eggs in one basket', is key advice to avoid disasters such as occurred to LTCM.

■ *Demonstrate that there is no 'free lunch'.*
Stocks are, *on average*, more profitable than bonds and particularly short-term bonds, but we do not recommend buying only stocks because they are more risky – e.g. compare the Nasdaq at the end of 2000 and the beginning of 2001.

■ *Compare and contrast corporate finance and investments.*
Corporate finance typically covers project analysis, capital structure, capital budgeting, and working capital management. Corporate finance addresses the relationship between the financial markets and firms, whereas the field of investments addresses the relationship between investors and the financial markets. The investments field typically covers issues related to security analysis. It also covers issues unique to investments in securities, such as portfolio diversification and hedging.

■ *Differentiate between investments in real assets and investments in financial assets (securities).*
The differences include the divisibility of investment in securities (you can buy a small fraction of a firm); marketability (you can sell a $100,000 investment in stock with one

phone call to a broker); the investment holding period (which can be shorter for financial assets); and the more abundant information available on financial assets as compared with real assets.

■ *Summarize the overall investment process.*

The investment process consists of five components: investor characteristics, investment vehicles, strategy development, strategy implementation and strategy monitoring.

KEY TERMS

Asset	Holding period	Physical asset
Asset allocation	Information availability	Portfolio
Capital market	Investment	Real asset
Correlation	Investment policy	Security
Derivatives	Liquidity	Security selection
Divisible	Long-term capital	Speculative
Efficient market	management (LTCM)	Tangible asset
Financial asset	Marketability	
Hedge	Money market	

SELECTED REFERENCES

Ayling, David E. *The Internationalisation of Stockmarkets*. Brookfield, VT: Gower Publishing, 1986.

de Caires, Bryan, and David Simmonds, (eds). *The GT Guide to World Equity Markets 1989*. London: Euromoney Publications, 1989.

Downes, John, and Jordan Elliot Goodman. *Dictionary of Finance and Investment Terms*, 2nd edn. New York: Barron's Educational Series, 1987.

Eatwell, John, Murray Milgate, and Peter Newman (eds). *New Palgrave Dictionary of Money and Finance*. New York: W.W. Norton, 1989.

Erb, Claude B., Campbell R. Harvey, and Tadas E. Viskanta. 'Expected return and volatility in 135 countries'. *Journal of Portfolio Management*, Spring 1996, pp. 46–58.

Global Finance, 'What if Wall Street crashed?', January 2000, Vol. 14, No. 1.

Global Finance, 'What if the EMU falls apart?', January 2000, Vol. 14, No. 1.

Global Finance, 'What if emerging markets dollarized?', January 2000, Vol. 14, No. 1.

Global Finance, 'What if the Internet bubble burst?', January 2000, Vol. 14, No. 1.

Huang, Roger D., and Hans R. Stoll. *Major World Equity Markets: Current Structure and Prospects for Change*. Monograph Series in Finance and Economics, Monograph 1991–3. New York: New York University Salomon Center, 1991.

Johnson, Mark, 'The euro gets physical as the ECB prepares new coins and notes', *Global Finance*, July 2001.

Malkiel, Burton. *A Random Walk Down Wall Street*, 5th edn. New York: W.W. Norton, 1991.

Appendix 1A   THE INTRODUCTION OF THE EURO

Exhibit 1A.1 **Euro conversion rates for currencies participating in EMU**

1 euro equals:	
1.95583	German marks
6.55957	French francs
1936.27	Italian lira
166.386	Spanish pesetas
200.482	Portuguese escudos
5.94573	Finnish markka
0.787564	Irish punt
40.3399	Belgian/Luxembourg francs
2.20371	Dutch guilders
13.7603	Austrian schillings

Source: Website at http://www.euro.gov.uk/rate.html, 10 October 2000. © Crown Copyright 1999. Crown copyright material is reproduced with the permission of the Controller of Her Majesty's Stationery Office and the Queen's Printer for Scotland.

Exhibit 1A.2 **Timetable for countries that introduced the euro on 1 January 1999**

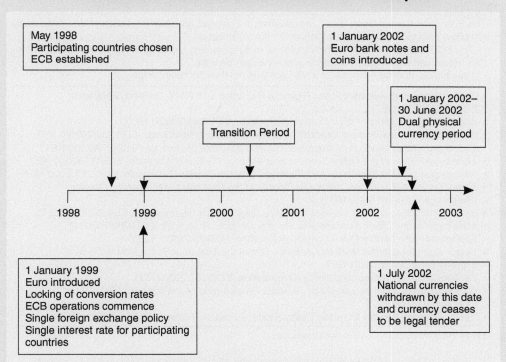

May 1998
Participating countries chosen
ECB established

1 January 2002
Euro bank notes and coins introduced

1 January 2002–
30 June 2002
Dual physical
currency period

Transition Period

1998   1999   2000   2001   2002   2003

1 January 1999
Euro introduced
Locking of conversion rates
ECB operations commence
Single foreign exchange policy
Single interest rate for participating
countries

1 July 2002
National currencies
withdrawn by this date
and currency ceases
to be legal tender

Source: Website at http://www.euro.gov.uk/will/time.html, 10 October 2000. © Crown Copyright 1999. Crown copyright material is reproduced with the permission of the Controller of Her Majesty's Stationery Office and the Queen's Printer for Scotland.

The changeover can be divided into three distinct phases:

- **Spring 1998–31 December 1998** – Phase 1 started with the decision in May by EU governments on which countries qualify to join. The European Central Bank (ECB) was then set up.
- **1 January 1999–31 December 2001: the 'transition period'** – The conversion rates between currencies of qualifying countries and the euro were legally fixed on 1 January 1999. The euro then became the legal currency in those countries. The ECB became responsible for interest rates. National currencies continued to exist in parallel to the euro, but changed in status. They are temporary 'denominations' or 'units' of the euro. No euro banknotes or coins are available, so national banknotes and coins are being used for all cash transactions.
- **1 January 2002–30 June 2002 (at the latest): the 'dual circulation period'** – Euro banknotes and coins will be introduced in participating countries on 1 January 2002. They will circulate alongside national currency banknotes and coins. By the end of the period, national banknotes and coins will be withdrawn from circulation. Old national banknotes will remain convertible into euros according to national practice.

Source: Website at http://www.euro.gov.uk/will/time.html, 10 October 2000. © Crown copyright 1999.

Exhibit 1A.3 Job opportunities at the European Central Bank

The European Central Bank (ECB), established in Frankfurt am Main on 1 June 1998, is currently recruiting staff to fill existing vacancies within the organisation.

The ECB has its own terms and conditions of employment, including a competitive salary structure, retirement plan, health insurance and relocation benefits.

Candidates must be nationals of a Member State of the European Union.

- *Senior Accounting Assistant in the Financial Reporting and Policy Division* (Reference: ECB/221/2000/II NET)
- *Economist in the Middle Office Division* (Reference: ECB/229/2000/II NET)
- *Accountants in the Financial Reporting and Policy Division* (Reference: ECB/234/2000/II NET)
- *Economist-Statistician in the Directorate General Statistics* (Reference: ECB/278/2000 NET)
- *Messenger/Driver in the Office Services and Security Division* (Reference: ECB/279/2000 NET)
- *Research Analyst in the Money and Banking Statistics Division* (Reference: ECB/280/2000 NET)
- *Senior Organisation Expert / Strategic Planner in the Organisational Planning Division* (Reference: ECB/281/2000 NET)
- *System Integrator in the IT Business Development Division* (Reference: ECB/282/2000 NET)
- *Messenger in the Office Services and Security Division* (Reference: ECB/283/2000 NET)
- *Economist in the Middle Office Division* (Reference: ECB/284/2000 NET)
- *Senior Economist in the Monetary Analysis Unit of the Monetary Policy Stance Division* (Reference: ECB/285/2000 NET)
- *Bookkeeper in the Accounting Division* (Reference: ECB/287/2000 NET)
- *German Translator in the Language Services Division* (short-term position) (Reference: ECB/288/2000 NET)
- *Senior Economist in the Monetary Policy Strategy Division* (Reference: ECB/289/00 NET)

Source: Website at European Central Bank, 2 October 2000.

Chapter 2

BONDS, STOCKS AND OTHER FINANCIAL SECURITIES

Learning objectives

After studying this chapter you should be able to:

1 Describe basic characteristics and types of bonds and stocks.
2 Explain how to read the securities quotes.
3 Compare different types of derivative securities.
4 Explain the risks involved in bond and stock investment.
5 Describe investment opportunities in international securities and mutual funds.

INVESTMENT IN THE NEWS

Treasuries lower on price data

Bond prices fell yesterday after the Labor Department reported that consumer prices posted their largest gain in 10 months in January, raising some concerns that inflation might not be as mild as many had thought.

But losses were modest as stock prices continued to slide, and analysts said inflation was not enough of a threat to keep the Federal Reserve from cutting interest rates further.

The Consumer Price Index, the benchmark gauge of inflation, rose 0.6 percent last month as energy costs soared after a gain in December of just 0.2 percent.

Inflation erodes the value of long-term securities, and 30-year bonds shed more than half a point by late afternoon. But economists maintained that the risk of a recession – not inflation – represented the greatest threat to the economy.

Of more immediate concern, traders said, slumping equity markets might be expected to stem losses by Treasuries ...

Source: The New York Times, Thursday 22 February 2001.

Inflation erodes the value of long-term bonds. Also stocks (the equity market) are affected by inflation. And as we see, the price of 10-year Treasury notes fell but their yield rose.

What are bonds and stocks, and how are their prices related to inflation? And why, when bond prices fall, does the yield rise?

This chapter describes the basic characteristics of bonds and stocks, describes the cash flows attached to each of these two important securities, discusses inflation, and shows why low inflation is expected to have a positive effect on bond prices and relatively high inflation has a negative effect on bond prices. This chapter also illustrates how to read the financial quotes as they appear in the financial media. We show the relationship between yield and bond prices. We discuss options in this chapter only briefly; separate chapters in Part IV (Chapters 12 and 13) discuss the valuation and management of options, and forward and futures contracts, as well as providing more detailed analyses of each.

2.1 BONDS

A bond is a financial contract.[1] The bond issuer, such as a corporation, will pay the bond's buyer periodic interest. Then, at the end of the specified term, the issuer pays the principal, also called the par value. In return, the bondholder pays the firm a given sum of money today. Bonds are traded in the bond market and have a market price that may change over time. A bond is a security that is basically an IOU from the issuer. It carries no corporate ownership privileges. For example, a 10-year AT&T bond gives you the right to receive periodic coupon (interest) payments and the principal (or face value) at maturity. As a bondholder, you have no voice in the affairs of the corporation. Most bonds are fixed-rate bonds or fixed-income securities, because the stated payments are contractual and constant over time. However, some bonds pay variable income and are referred to as floating-rate bonds. For example, in July 1999, Ford Unit (Ford Motor Credit Co.) launched the largest corporation bond issue in US history ($8.6 billion) at a floating rate which holds for 32 years at 140 basis points (i.e. 1.4%) over the Treasury rates. Shorter maturity bonds were issued by Ford 26 basis points (0.26%) over the three-month LIBOR (see Section 2.1.2) rate. With a floating-rate or fixed-rate bond, the issuer is obligated to pay the bondholder specified amounts of money at specified dates. As long as the maturity of the bond is not too long, and there is no risk of bankruptcy (e.g. government bonds and gilts), the risks of bonds are generally low, with correspondingly low returns. Bonds are usually less liquid than stocks and generate relatively high periodic cash flows (to the bondholders in the form of interest payments).

Bonds are interest-bearing obligations of governments or corporations. With every passing day, investors are offered new types of bonds with different characteristics. Among the newest types of bonds are century bonds, which mature in 100 years. Dresser Industries issued $200 million worth of century bonds in 1996, which will mature in 2096.[2] On 23 March 2001, the Grantite Company issued 350 million bonds nominated in sterling that will mature in January 2041. This section examines common characteristics of bonds and the most popular types of bonds traded today.

---

[1] It is common to make a distinction between bonds and fixed-income securities. Fixed-income securities include all interest-bearing securities, whereas bonds refer only to securities that are long-term.
[2] *Barron's*, 17 May 1999, p. MW54.

2.1.1 **Basic characteristics of bonds**

Bonds have three major identifying characteristics. First, they are typically securities issued by a corporation or governmental unit. Second, they usually pay fixed periodic interest instalments, called coupon payments. Also available are variable coupon payment bonds, or bonds whose coupon payment changes as market interest rates change. Third, bonds pay a lump sum at maturity that is called the par value, face value or principal.

Bonds are typically classified into two groups based on their length of time to maturity. Money market securities are short-term (less than 1 year) obligations (e.g. Treasury bills) and usually require a minimum of $25,000 to purchase. In contrast, capital market securities are long-term securities (more than 1 year) such as Treasury bonds (usually having initial maturities in excess of 10 years). The term *capital market securities* also applies to stock.

Exhibit 2.1(a) shows the cash flow characteristics of a bond in general. Exhibit 2.1(b) shows an example of cash flows from a particular bond. The downward-pointing arrows in Exhibit 2.1 depict the cash payments from the investor, and the upward-pointing arrows depict cash receipts to the investor. Hence, by investing the current market price of the bond today ($Price), there is a promised stream of cash receipts in the future, called coupon payments ($C), and principal payment (or par value, $Par).

The bond price today is the present value of its future coupons and par value. Note that if inflation increases the discount rate will increase and the present value of the future cash flows ($C and $Par) will decrease, thus decreasing the price of the bond. The

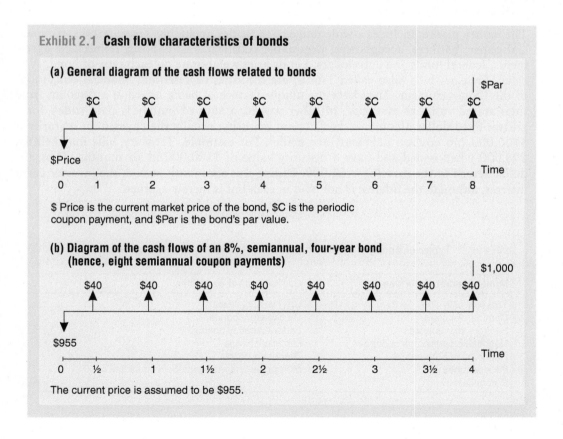

Exhibit 2.1 Cash flow characteristics of bonds

(a) General diagram of the cash flows related to bonds

$ Price is the current market price of the bond, $C is the periodic coupon payment, and $Par is the bond's par value.

(b) Diagram of the cash flows of an 8%, semiannual, four-year bond (hence, eight semiannual coupon payments)

The current price is assumed to be $955.

opposite holds when the interest rate decreases. For example, on 23 March 2001, the bonds of IBM with $8^3/_8\%$ interest (coupon) and maturity in 2013 were traded at $\$115^1/_2$ while the par value is only $100. Due to a decrease in the interest rates, the discount rate decreases and the present value of future cash flows on IBM's bonds increases, which explains the gap between the market value and par value of these bonds. Thus, bond prices are sensitive to interest rate changes. The larger the change in the interest rate, the larger the potential losses or gains. However, as the *Investment in the news* article reveals, stocks are also sensitive to changes in rates induced by interest changes.

The advantages of bonds to an investor relative to stocks are that they are good sources of current income, at least for short-term bonds, and their investment is relatively safe from large losses (unless, of course, the bonds have a large risk of default by the issuing company). Another advantage is that bondholders receive their payments before shareholders can be compensated. A major disadvantage of bonds relative to stocks is that the potential profit is limited.

2.1.2 Types of bonds

Several types of bonds are available to investors, including short term and long term, high risk and low risk, and taxable and nontaxable. Exhibit 2.2 lists the different types of bonds, classified by whether they are money market securities or capital market securities. The following section provides a brief description of various types of bonds.

■ **Money market securities**

The money market includes a wide range of securities, including Treasury bills, commercial paper, bankers' acceptances, negotiable certificates of deposit, repurchase agreements, federal funds and eurodollars. Let us briefly elaborate on each type of bond.

US Treasury bills (also called T-bills) are securities representing financial obligations of the US government. They have the unique feature of being issued at a discount from their stated value at maturity. In other words, a sum of money is paid today for a greater fixed dollar amount in the future at maturity; usually the payment at maturity is $100,000 (no coupon payments are made). For example, Treasury bills may sell for $98,000 when issued and have a maturity value of $100,000 in six months. Thus, the dollar return to the investor is $2,000. During this six-month period, the investor earns interest, although the interest is not paid in cash but is merely accrued.

Exhibit 2.2 **Types of bonds**

Money market securities	Capital market securities
Treasury bills	US Treasury notes
Commercial paper	US Treasury bonds
Bankers' acceptances	Federal agency bonds
Negotiable certificates of deposit	Municipal bonds
Repurchase agreements	Corporate bonds
Federal funds	Mortgages and mortgage-backed securities
Eurodollars	

Exhibit 2.3(a) US Treasury bills

Maturity		Days to Mat.	Bid	Asked	Fri. Chg.	Ask Yld.
Jul	05 '01	3	3.07	2.99	− 0.19	3.03
Jul	12 '01	10	3.38	3.30	+ 0.02	3.35
Jul	19 '01	17	3.41	3.33	−	3.38
Jul	26 '01	24	3.38	3.30	− 0.03	3.35
Aug	02 '01	31	3.41	3.37	+ 0.03	3.43
Aug	09 '01	38	3.44	3.40	+ 0.01	3.46
Aug	16 '01	45	3.46	3.42	−	3.48
Aug	23 '01	52	3.50	3.46	− 0.04	3.53
Aug	30 '01	59	3.53	3.49	− 0.03	3.56
Sep	06 '01	66	3.58	3.56	+ 0.02	3.63
Sep	13 '01	73	3.57	3.55	+ 0.02	3.63
Sep	20 '01	80	3.57	3.55	+ 0.02	3.63
Sep	27 '01	87	3.57	3.56	+ 0.02	3.64
Oct	04 '01	94	3.57	3.55	+ 0.03	3.63
Oct	04 '01	94	3.57	3.56	+ 0.03	3.64
Oct	11 '01	101	3.56	3.54	+ 0.02	3.63
Oct	18 '01	108	3.56	3.54	+ 0.02	3.63
Oct	25 '01	115	3.56	3.54	+ 0.02	3.63
Nov	01 '01	122	3.55	3.53	+ 0.01	3.62
Nov	08 '01	129	3.53	3.51	− 0.01	3.60
Nov	15 '01	136	3.53	3.51	−	3.61
Nov	23 '01	144	3.53	3.51	−	3.61
Nov	29 '01	150	3.54	3.52	−	3.62
Dec	06 '01	157	3.53	3.51	−	3.61
Dec	13 '01	164	3.52	3.50	− 0.01	3.61
Dec	20 '01	171	3.51	3.49	− 0.03	3.60
Dec	27 '01	178	3.52	3.51	−	3.62
Jan	02 '02	184	3.53	3.52	+ 0.02	3.63
Feb	28 '02	241	3.51	3.50	+ 0.04	3.62

Source: *Barron's*, 2 July 2001, p. 29. Barron's Online by *Barron's*. © 2001 by Dow Jones & Co., Inc. Reproduced with permission of Dow Jones & Co., Inc. in the format *Fundamentals of Investments* via Copyright Clearance Center.

Treasury bills have maturities of less than one year. T-bills are issued on an auction basis. The US Treasury accepts competitive bids and allocates bills to those offering the highest prices. Noncompetitive bids are also accepted. A noncompetitive bid is an offer to purchase the bills at a price that equals the average of the competitive bids. The yields on T-bills are closely watched in the money market for signs of interest rate trends. Many floating rate loans have interest rates tied to the yield on T-bills. By the end of 1998, the short-term Treasury securities market exceeded $370 billion.[3]

Gilts are bonds issued by the British government and are equivalent to the Treasury securities in the US in that they are perceived to have no risk or default.

Exhibit 2.3(a) shows recent quotes for US Treasury bills. The first two columns give the maturity date and the number of days left to maturity. Next, the bid and asked discount rates are given, followed by the change from the previous day. Note that the bid and ask discount rates, as well as the yield (see Ask Yld.), are on an annual basis. The bid rate is the discount rate at which you, the investor, can sell a T-bill. The asked rate is the discount rate at which you can buy it from a dealer. The higher the discount

---

[3] *Economic Report of the President* (Washington, DC: US Government Printing Office, 1999), p. 398.

Exhibit 2.3(b) **London Stock Exchange benchmark government bonds** **FT**

Mar 23	Red Date	Coupon	Bid Price	Bid Yield	Day chg yield	Wk chg yield	Month chg yld	Year chg yld
Australia	10/02	10.000	107.9219	4.62	+ 0.10	+ 0.15	− 0.26	− 1.65
	06/11	5.750	105.0780	5.10	−	+ 0.01	− 0.29	− 1.32
Austria	05/02	4.625	100.2500	4.39	+ 0.02	− 0.05	− 0.36	− 0.16
	01/10	5.500	104.1100	4.91	+ 0.02	− 0.05	− 0.24	− 0.55
Belgium	06/02	8.750	105.2900	4.25	+ 0.02	− 0.12	− 0.37	− 0.35
	09/10	5.750	105.7400	4.97	+ 0.01	− 0.06	− 0.23	− 0.51
Canada	12/02	6.000	102.4000	4.49	+ 0.08	− 0.04	− 0.43	− 1.47
	06/10	5.500	101.9900	5.22	+ 0.08	+ 0.03	− 0.25	− 0.67
Denmark	11/02	6.000	101.9500	4.71	+ 0.02	− 0.08	− 0.31	− 0.19
	11/09	6.000	107.6700	4.88	+ 0.03	− 0.03	− 0.25	− 0.67
Finland	09/01	10.000	102.4500	4.37	+ 0.03	− 0.16	− 0.28	+ 0.06
	02/11	5.750	106.7400	4.87	+ 0.02	− 0.05	− 0.21	− 0.53
France	07/03	4.500	100.6000	4.21	+ 0.05	− 0.11	− 0.37	− 0.22
	01/06	5.000	102.7350	4.35	+ 0.03	− 0.09	− 0.33	− 0.75
	10/10	5.500	105.5000	4.77	+ 0.02	− 0.04	− 0.23	− 0.54
	04/29	5.500	102.3600	5.34	−	− 0.07	− 0.14	− 0.28
Germany	09/02	5.000	101.1300	4.17	+ 0.02	− 0.15	− 0.36	− 0.23
	08/05	5.000	102.8896	4.26	+ 0.02	− 0.11	− 0.35	− 0.86
	01/11	5.250	104.8000	4.63	+ 0.03	− 0.05	− 0.23	− 0.57
	01/31	5.500	103.7599	5.25	−	− 0.06	− 0.12	− 0.28
Greece	02/03	5.900	102.7200	4.34	− 0.04	− 0.14	− 0.40	− 1.87
	05/10	6.000	105.7000	5.20	+ 0.01	− 0.04	− 0.20	− 0.94
Ireland	10/02	2.750	97.7300	4.27	+ 0.01	− 0.12	− 0.35	− 0.21
	04/10	4.000	93.8781	4.85	+ 0.01	− 0.05	− 0.22	− 0.58
Italy	01/03	4.500	100.4300	4.25	+ 0.03	− 0.13	− 0.39	− 0.30
	12/05	5.250	103.0500	4.52	+ 0.02	− 0.12	− 0.33	− 0.55
	11/10	5.500	103.8500	4.99	+ 0.01	− 0.07	− 0.21	− 0.43
	05/31	6.000	104.8000	5.67	+ 0.01	− 0.05	− 0.10	− 0.10
Japan	12/02	4.800	108.1500	0.07	+ 0.02	−	− 0.16	− 0.27
	03/06	3.100	112.6380	0.52	+ 0.07	+ 0.05	− 0.22	− 0.71
	12/10	1.800	106.4204	1.10	+ 0.07	−	− 0.29	− 0.70
	12/20	2.500	116.0200	1.55	+ 0.07	− 0.01	− 0.33	− 0.74
Netherlands	02/03	4.750	100.9100	4.23	+ 0.03	− 0.13	− 0.39	− 0.23
	07/10	5.500	105.4818	4.75	+ 0.01	− 0.06	− 0.23	− 0.62
New Zealand	03/02	10.000	104.0620	5.59	+ 0.08	+ 0.11	− 0.28	− 1.26
	11/11	6.000	100.0680	5.99	+ 0.03	+ 0.14	− 0.12	− 0.94
Norway	10/02	9.500	103.7500	6.88	−	− 0.12	+ 0.07	+ 0.51
	05/09	5.500	96.9500	5.98	−	− 0.07	− 0.08	− 0.06
Portugal	04/03	4.812	101.0000	4.29	+ 0.02	− 0.16	− 0.41	− 0.21
	05/10	5.850	106.1000	5.00	−	− 0.06	− 0.23	− 0.50
Spain	01/03	3.000	97.8600	4.23	+ 0.02	− 0.14	− 0.39	− 0.39
	07/11	5.400	101.5800	4.98	+ 0.02	− 0.06	− 0.22	− 0.45
Sweden	04/02	5.500	101.6071	3.88	+ 0.02	− 0.08	− 0.26	− 1.11
	03/11	5.250	104.4930	4.67	+ 0.02	− 0.05	− 0.26	− 0.07
Switzerland	07/02	4.500	101.8500	2.99	− 0.05	− 0.10	− 0.28	− 0.43
	08/10	3.500	102.5000	3.19	+ 0.04	− 0.05	− 0.28	− 0.76
UK	06/02	7.000	102.4300	4.88	+ 0.03	− 0.08	− 0.34	− 1.43
	12/05	8.500	115.5600	4.76	+ 0.03	− 0.07	− 0.40	− 1.15
	12/09	5.750	107.5500	4.68	+ 0.05	+ 0.02	− 0.31	− 0.53
	06/32	4.250	97.5600	4.39	+ 0.02	+ 0.05	− 0.07	−
US	11/02	5.625	102.1242	4.29	+ 0.08	− 0.03	− 0.38	− 2.22
	11/05	5.750	105.2578	4.48	+ 0.10	−	− 0.43	− 1.92
	08/10	5.750	106.2699	4.91	+ 0.09	+ 0.03	− 0.35	− 1.18
	05/30	6.250	112.3750	5.40	+ 0.05	+ 0.02	− 0.24	− 0.51

Source: Financial Times, 26 March 2001, p. 30. Reprinted with permission.

rate, the lower the price. The difference between the bid and asked rates is called the bid-asked spread. The bid discount rates exceed asked discount rates, because dealers are willing to sell only at prices higher than they are willing to buy. The final column gives the internal rate of return of the asked price of the T-bill.

Exhibit 2.3(b) lists the government bonds traded at the London Stock Exchange.

Another type of money market security is commercial paper, which is a vehicle of short-term borrowing by large corporations. Large, well-established corporations have found that borrowing directly from investors via commercial paper is cheaper than relying solely on bank loans. The lenders are generally investors with temporarily idle cash. Commercial paper is unsecured notes of corporations, usually issued at a discount. *Unsecured* means that these loans are not backed by specific assets. That is, the only thing backing the loans is the 'full faith and credit' of the firm. Commercial paper is issued either directly from the firm to the investor or through an intermediary.

Issuers of commercial paper are typically corporations that have a high credit rating. However, other firms can use the commercial paper market if they 'enhance' the credit quality of the commercial paper. Firms can enhance their credit by purchasing a guarantee from another, more well-established firm or by pledging collateral of quality assets with the issue.

Commercial paper is riskier than Treasury bills, because there is a greater risk of default by a corporation. (There is virtually zero probability of default by the federal government.) Also, commercial paper is not easily bought and sold after it is issued, because most investors in commercial paper hold it until maturity. The majority of investors in this market are institutions such as money market mutual funds and pension funds. By the end of September 1998, the commercial paper market in the United States exceeded $715 billion.[4]

Bankers' acceptances are short-term obligations that are based on a customer's request to pay a supplier at a future date. Bankers' acceptances arise from the financial needs of corporations engaged mainly in international commerce. The supplier desires immediate payment, and the customer desires to pay once the goods are delivered and inspected. A bankers' acceptance allows both the supplier's and the customer's desires to be achieved, but not without cost.

To demonstrate how a firm and its customer use bankers' acceptances, suppose a US firm ships a 3-ton engine to a UK firm, and delivery takes two months. The US firm would like payment from the sale today, and the UK firm wants to wait until the engine is delivered. Neither the US firm's bank nor the UK firm's bank wants to provide the capital for this loan. The Swiss firm's bank provides the UK firm with a short-term loan. The bank pays the US firm a discounted amount now. The UK bank (which will be paid by the UK firm in two months) could then sell this short-term loan contract to an outside party, recouping its initial outlay. This short-term loan contract, called a banker's acceptance, will typically have a higher interest rate than similar money market securities, making it attractive to investors. Because of its complexity, the market for bankers' acceptances does not have active trading of its securities. Its market, which is much smaller than that for commercial paper, was only about $14 billion in October 1998.[5]

Negotiable certificates of deposit (CDs) are debt instruments issued by banks and usually pay interest. Most CDs cannot be traded, and they incur penalties for early withdrawal. To accommodate large money market investors, financial institutions allow

---

[4] *Economic Report of the President*, p. 379.
[5] *Ibid.*

their large-denomination CD deposits to be traded as negotiable CDs. Negotiable CDs can be as small as $100,000, but tend to trade in increments of $5 million. The maturity ranges from a few weeks to several years. The largest investors in this market are money market mutual funds and investment companies. By the end of 1998, the large-denomination CD market was approximately $624 billion.[6]

The repurchase agreements (repos) market affords additional liquidity to the money market. Firms are able to raise additional capital by selling securities held in inventory to another institution with an agreement to buy them back at a specified higher price at a specified time. The securities are usually government securities. In effect, a repurchase agreement is a short-term loan. Because of concerns about default risk, the length of maturity of a repurchase agreement is usually very short. Typically, repos are used for overnight borrowing needs.

As an example of how repos work, suppose that for cash management purposes, Ford Motor Corporation holds $4 million in three-month US Treasury bills yielding 5%. Now Ford has an immediate need for $4 million so it can purchase a specialized piece of equipment being offered at a bankruptcy liquidation. Ford's cash manager also knows that in a week, Ford will receive a $4 million payment for auto sales in Canada. What can Ford do?

One solution would be to take a bank loan at, say, 11%. Ford could also sell the T-bills and buy them back in one week. Ford would incur two transaction costs when the bills had to be repurchased. In addition, there would be a price risk in this transaction: the price of the T-bills could rise in a week. Alternatively, Ford could enter into a repurchase agreement using its T-bills. Ford could sell the T-bills to an outside firm with a guarantee to buy them back in two weeks at a specified price. From the difference between the sale price and the purchase price, an implied interest rate, known as the *repo rate*, can be computed. Obviously, Ford should employ the transaction that is the cheapest after all transaction costs are considered.

There are many variations in the design of repurchase agreements. A term repo has a longer holding period. A reverse repo is the opposite of a repo. In this transaction, a corporation buys the securities with an agreement to sell them at a specified price and time. The repo market was about $283 billion at the end of 1998.[7]

The firm that holds short-term financial assets and, in particular, bank deposits can invest in the repo market. The firm can make more money than it can earn in deposit accounts, and with a lower risk. How is this possible? Security dealers who need to borrow money are not allowed to enter the deposit market. Therefore, they are willing to pay a firm that lends them money in a repo agreement at a relatively high interest rate. In addition, a firm that lends money to dealers holds the securities as collateral, whereas the deposits in the bank are uninsured. Thus, a higher return and a lower risk on the firm's money is obtained compared with a bank deposit. For example, by investing in repos, Dupont/Canoco reports an annual income increase of $2 million.

The federal funds market helps banks place reserves on deposit at the Federal Reserve Bank. Banks that do not have sufficient funds on reserve can borrow from other banks that have excess reserves. Most of this borrowing is for one day, although some agreements are for as long as six months.

Finally, eurodollars are US dollar deposits held outside the United States. These deposits are not subject to the same regulations as bank deposits held within the United

---

[6] *Ibid.*
[7] *Ibid.*

Exhibit 2.4 **Money rates (%)**

	US	UK
Discount rate	1.25	3.75
Prime rate	4.75	4.00
T-bills rate (3-month)	1.68	$3^{29}/_{32}$
CDs rate (6 months)	1.87	$4^{1}/_{32}$
Commercial paper rate (3 months)	1.71	$4^{1}/_{8}$
LIBOR rate (6 months)	1.92	4.10875

Sources: Wall Street Journal Europe, 24 January 2002, p. 21, and Financial Times, 25 January 2002, p. 23.

States. Hence, the interest rate offered on eurodollar deposits is typically different from the rate offered in the United States. The interest rate quoted for these deposits between major banks is referred to as the LIBOR, or London Interbank Offer Rate. It is the rate that one bank asks from another bank for borrowing. London is the main trading centre for eurodollars. The LIBID, or London Interbank Bid Rate, is the rate at which major banks will offer eurodollars as deposits to other banks. The interest on loans is sometimes linked to the LIBOR. Quotes such as 'LIBOR +1%' or 'LIBOR +2%' are very common, where the riskier the borrower, the higher the increase in the interest rate above the LIBOR.

Exhibit 2.4 provides the various short-term interest rates in the US and UK. The differences between the rates reflect the risk difference as well as market imperfection; namely, the bank lends at a higher rate than it borrows in order to earn money.

The discount rate is the interest rate the Federal Reserve charges member banks for loans (with collateral usually in the form of government securities). This is the lowest interest rate on the floor, since banks set their loan rate a notch above the discount rate. When the Federal Reserve changes the discount rate, the other market rates adjust in the same direction. The prime rate is the interest rate banks charge their most creditworthy customers. Thus, for less creditworthy customers, the interest rate is high, e.g. prime + 2%, prime + 3%, etc. When the banks borrow from customers by selling CDs, they pay the investors in the CDs only 1.87%, and the difference between the prime rate and the CDs rate accounts for the banks' costs and profit. Individuals who buy stocks on margin borrow part of their investment from their brokers. The broker loan call rate is the rate at which the brokers borrow from banks to finance these loans to the customers. Because these loans are callable by the banks on a 24-hour notice, they are called call rates.

Capital market securities

Like T-bills, US Treasury notes and US Treasury bonds are government securities used to finance the government debt. In contrast to T-bills, which have maturities of less than 1 year, US Treasury notes and bonds have maturities greater than 1 year at the time they are issued. They pay stated coupon amounts semiannually and are exempt from state and local taxes. When first issued, *notes have maturities of 2 to 10 years, and bonds have maturities of more than 10 years*. The minimum denomination is $1,000.

Exhibit 2.5 illustrates Treasury bond and Treasury note quotes. The bid price of the August 2001 bond is quoted as 100:14, which means $100\frac{14}{32}$ of par value. (Recall that par value is the lump sum paid at maturity.) If par is $1,000 (which is standard), then

Exhibit 2.5 US notes and bonds

Rate	Mo/Yr	Bid	Asked	Fri. Chg	Ask Yld.
$5^1/_2$	Jul 01n	100:04	100:06	...	3.08
$6^5/_8$	Jul 01n	100:07	100:09	...	3.02
$7^7/_8$	Aug 01n	100:16	100:18	...	3.14
$13^3/_8$	Aug 01	101:06	101:08	−1	2.91
$5^1/_2$	Aug 01n	100:08	100:10	...	3.51
$6^1/_2$	**Aug 01n**	**100:14**	**100:16**	**...**	**3.34**
$5^5/_8$	Sep 01n	100:14	100:16	...	3.52
$6^3/_8$	Sep 01n	100:19	100:21	−1	3.62
$5^7/_8$	Oct 01n	100:21	100:23	−1	3.63
$6^1/_4$	Oct 01n	100:25	100:27	−1	3.61
$7^1/_2$	Nov 01n	101:12	101:14	...	3.53
$15^3/_4$	Nov 01	104:13	104:15	−1	3.43
$5^7/_8$	Nov 01n	100:27	100:29	−1	3.63
$6^1/_8$	Dec 01n	101:05	101:07	...	3.62
$6^1/_4$	Jan 02n	101:13	101:15	...	3.66
$6^3/_8$	Jan 02n	101:15	101:17	−1	3.68
$5^1/_2$	May 09n	100:30	101:00	−12	5.34
$9^1/_8$	May 04–09	111:19	111:23	−7	4.71
6	Aug 09n	104:01	104:03	−13	5.37
$10^3/_8$	**Nov 04–09**	**116:23**	**116:27**	**−14**	**4.89**
$4^1/_4$	Jan 10i	105:29	105:30	−18	3.44
$6^1/_2$	Feb 10n	107:15	107:17	−13	5.40
$11^3/_4$	Feb 05–10	122:14	122:20	−9	4.86
10	May 05–10	117:10	117:14	−13	4.99
$5^3/_4$	Aug 10n	102:15	102:16	−11	5.40
$12^3/_4$	Nov 05–10	129:29	130:03	−15	4.99

Source: Barron's, 2 July 2001, p. MW47. Barron's Online by *Barron's*. © 2001 by Dow Jones & Co., Inc. Reproduced with permission of Dow Jones & Co., Inc. in the format *Fundamentals of Investments* via Copyright Clearance Center.

this quote results in a price of $1,004.3 because $\frac{14}{32} = 0.43$. Thus, the price is 100.43% of par when 100 is the par. Because the par value is $1,000, if we buy the bond we pay $(100.43/100) \times \$1,000 = 1,004.3$ today and get only $1,000 in the future. We do not lose money, because we also receive coupon payments every semiannual period up to the maturity date. Note, however, that the price of bonds as quoted in the financial media is not equal to the cash flow the investor has to pay for the bond. The investor also has to pay the accrued interest because bond prices are quoted without the accrued interest. Accrued interest is found by multiplying the fraction of the semiannual coupon period that has elapsed by the coupon payment. For example, if 142 days have elapsed since the last coupon has been paid and the semiannual coupon is worth $45, one has to add to the quoted price of a bond $(142/184) \times \$45 = \$34.73$, where 184 days represent half a year. Investors sometimes neglect the fact that the bond is worth more than the quoted price, and hence may lose money in financial deals. The following story taken from *Barron's* illustrates such an error made by investors:

'...For example, a group known as KN Financial tendered for the bonds of May Department Stores. The group offered to pay 104.75, according to one person who had seen the offering documents. And at first glance, such a bid doesn't seem bad, considering that the bonds were trading around 104.375.

It's only by reading the fine print that investors would realize that they're getting less than meets the eye. KN's offer includes accrued interest. But the bonds are quoted in the market without accrued interest, as is the convention.

And wouldn't you know, an interest payment is due in just a few weeks. With that accrued interest added in, a fair value for the bond would be closer to 108. All of which means KN financial would be able to turn a quick $40 profit (per $1,000) on any tendered bond, with very little risk ....'

(See 'The return of mini-tenders at micro prices: Just for Feet's bondholders feel down at the heel', by Jacqueline Doherty, *Barron's*, 31 May 1999, p. MW17.)

Thus, when you buy or sell bonds, always remember that the accrued interest should be added.

A callable bond can be bought back by the issuing entity at a stated price in the future. The notation 04–09 for the November $10^3/_8$ bond in Exhibit 2.5 means that the bond is first callable in 2004 (i.e. 04) and, if not called, it matures in November 2009. The Change (Chg) column is in 32nds. Hence, the bond decreases $^{14}/_{32}$ from the previous day.

The US government also issues also *Inflation Indexed Treasury Securities*. The coupons and the principal (the par value) are linked to the cost of living index. For example, on 2 July 2001, *Barron's* reports that this linked bond which matures on 29 April had a yield of 3.875%. This means that this is the real annual rate of return the investor will get. No wonder, then, that the yield is relatively low, because with inflation of 2–3% per year the nominal yield will be about 6–7%.

The Federal National Mortgage Association (FNMA – pronounced 'Fannie Mae') issues federal agency bonds. Publicly owned and sponsored by the government, it was chartered in 1938 to purchase mortgages from lenders and resell them to investors. They are usually in $100,000 denominations.

Agency securities differ from Treasury securities. Agency securities are issued by federal government-sponsored corporations, such as the Federal Home Loan Banks, and not directly from the US government. Agency securities are perceived to be slightly more risky than Treasuries from a default risk viewpoint. The US government may not be as likely to come to the rescue of an agency as it would be for securities issued by the US Treasury.

State and local governments issue municipal bonds to finance highways, water systems, schools and other capital projects. There are two basic types of municipal bonds: general obligation bonds and revenue bonds. General obligation bonds are backed by the full faith and power of the municipality. Revenue bonds are backed by the income generated from a specific project, such as a toll bridge. The income from these bonds is exempt from federal, state and local taxes if the investor lives in that locality, but the income is subject to state and local taxes if the investor does not live in the locality issuing the bonds. Because investors are interested in after-tax returns, we would not anticipate the yields to be as high as those from their fully taxable counterparts. Everything else being equal, investors would prefer a tax-free bond.

Corporate bonds are issued to finance investment in new plant equipment (real assets). These bonds usually have a par or face value of $1,000. Corporate bonds vary in their riskiness and their returns to investors. Some highly rated bonds are very safe but pay low interest. Junk bonds, in contrast, are very risky and thus pay much higher interest. For such bonds, there is a higher risk that the firm will go bankrupt and the investor will lose the entire investment – hence the name junk bonds.

Some bonds do not pay any interest and are called zero-coupon bonds. For example, Alza Zr 14 is a bond which does not have any coupons. Thus, this bond matures in

Exhibit 2.6 Corporate bond quotes

52-Wk High	Low	Name and Coupon	Cor yld	Sales	Weekly High	Low	Last	Net Chg
101	$88^7/_8$	AES Cp 8s8	8.2	540	$98^1/_8$	96	98	$-1^5/_8$
109	100	AMR 9s16	8.7	107	$107^1/_2$	$103^5/_8$	$103^5/_8$	$-\ ^3/_8$
$101^{31}/_{32}$	$98^1/_8$	ATT $7^1/_8$02	7.1	128	101	$100^5/_8$	$100^5/_8$	$-\ ^1/_{32}$
$103^1/_8$	$97^1/_4$	ATT $6^1/_2$02	6.4	83	$102^1/_8$	$101^1/_8$	$101^1/_2$	$-\ ^3/_4$
$103^1/_8$	$96^1/_2$	ATT $6^3/_4$04	6.6	165	$102^5/_8$	$101^5/_8$	$102^1/_8$	$+\ ^1/_4$
$100^3/_4$	$93^3/_8$	ATT $5^5/_8$04	5.6	386	$100^3/_4$	$99^1/_2$	$99^7/_8$	$-\ ^3/_4$
104	$96^5/_8$	ATT 7s05	6.8	116	$103^7/_8$	$103^1/_2$	$103^3/_4$	$+\ ^1/_8$
$106^7/_8$	$97^1/_2$	ATT $7^1/_2$06	7.2	42	105	$103^1/_4$	$104^1/_2$	$-\ ^1/_2$
$106^7/_8$	$99^1/_8$	ATT $7^3/_4$07	7.4	442	$106^1/_8$	105	$105^1/_4$	$-\ ^1/_4$
$95^1/_2$	$86^1/_2$	ATT 6s09	6.4	761	$95^1/_4$	$93^1/_2$	$93^1/_2$	$-1^3/_8$
103	$91^5/_8$	ATT $8^1/_8$22	8.0	412	102	$101^1/_8$	$101^1/_4$	-1
$103^3/_4$	$92^1/_4$	ATT $8^1/_8$24	8.0	443	$102^1/_8$	$101^5/_8$	$101^7/_8$	$-\ ^1/_8$
$104^1/_2$	95	ATT 8.35s25	8.1	1177	$103^7/_8$	$102^5/_8$	$102^5/_8$	-1
90	78	ATT $6^1/_2$29	7.7	2054	$87^1/_4$	$84^7/_8$	$84^7/_8$	$-2^1/_4$
$105^1/_4$	95	ATT $8^5/_8$31	8.4	339	$104^1/_8$	$103^3/_8$	$103^3/_8$	$-\ ^7/_8$
134	70	Alza zr14	...	4	134	134	134	$+2^1/_4$
61	$56^1/_8$	AForP 5s30	8.5	2	59	59	59	-1
80	63	ARetire $5^3/_4$02	cv	175	78	76	76	-2
105	$101^1/_8$	Apache $9^1/_4$02	8.9	25	$104^1/_2$	$103^1/_4$	$104^1/_2$	$+1^1/_2$
104	$16^1/_2$	vjArmW $9^3/_4$08f	...	31	48	44	44	$+1^1/_2$
$123^7/_8$	$113^5/_8$	ARch $10^7/_8$05	8.9	2	$122^1/_2$	$122^1/_2$	$122^1/_2$	$+4$
105	$97^3/_4$	BkOne $7^1/_4$04	7.0	15	$103^1/_2$	$103^1/_2$	$103^1/_2$	$+\ ^1/_2$
...	...	...	...	...	...	...	...	...
...	...	...	...	...	...	...	...	...
...	...	...	...	...	...	...	...	...

Source: Barron's, 2 July 2001, p. MW48. Barron's Online by Barron's. © 2001 by Dow Jones & Co., Inc. Reproduced with permission of Dow Jones & Co., Inc. in the format Fundamentals of Investments via Copyright Clearance Center.

2014 (see Exhibit 2.6). Bonds that make coupon payments during the life of the bond are coupon-bearing bonds. For example, 'ATT 7s05' denotes ATT's 7% semiannual coupon-bearing bonds that mature in 2005. This means that AT&T pays coupons at a rate of 2.5% of the stated maturity value each semiannual period. Other bonds, such as the Aretire bonds listed in Exhibit 2.6, are convertible into common stock. Convertible bonds (denoted by CV) are discussed in more detail below.

Mortgages are bonds in which the borrower (the mortgagor) provides the lender (the mortgagee) collateral, which is usually real estate.[8] You are probably most familiar with mortgages on homes. In the US, default risk related to mortgages can be insured either privately or through government insurance agencies such as the Federal Housing Authority (FHA) or the Veterans Administration (VA). Mortgages are typically pooled (packaged together in portfolios) and sold. These pools of securities are called mortgage-backed securities. The originator of the mortgage will sell the mortgage through another firm (called a conduit), such as the Federal National Mortgage Association (FNMA). Mortgage-backed securities may or may not be backed by a federal agency. The most difficult aspect of managing a mortgage portfolio is assessing the risk that the mortgages will be prepaid. Mortgage holders generally prepay when interest rates are down.

---

[8] Other mortgage bonds are collateralized by corporate assets, such as property and equipment.

2.2 STOCKS

This section covers the basic characteristics of common and preferred stock. It compares and contrasts the different types of stock issues and concludes with a description of published stock quotations.

2.2.1 Basic characteristics of common stock

A common stock represents part ownership in a firm. A stock certificate is evidence of this ownership share. Common stocks are also referred to as *common shares* or *equity*. Typically, each common stock owned entitles an investor to one vote in corporate stockholders' meetings. Stockholders vote on such issues as who will be in senior management positions, who will be the outside auditor, and what to do with merger offers. Historically, common stocks on the whole have provided a higher return than bonds, but they also have higher risk. For example, in the stock market crash of 19 October 1987, the overall value of the market declined more than 20% in one day.

With common stocks, the ownership of the firm is residual; that is, common stockholders receive what is left over after all other claims on the firm have been satisfied. Because they are residual claims, common stocks have no stated maturity. In other words, unlike corporate bonds, common stocks do not have a date on which the corporation must buy them back. If you own common stock and wish to sell it, you must find a willing buyer.

Also, cash dividends are paid to stockholders only after other liabilities such as interest payments have been paid. Cash dividends are cash payments made to stockholders from the firm that issued the stock. The stockholder receives these residual benefits in the form of dividends, capital gains or both. Typically, the firm does not pay all its earnings in cash dividends. Usually the firm will retain some of its earnings to reinvest in other projects in an effort to enhance the firm's value. For example, a pharmaceutical company will take some of its earnings and invest them in research and development in an effort to discover new and better drugs, thereby earning future profits.

Corporations try to maintain a constant dividend payment, because this situation tends to enhance share prices (or at least it is perceived by some investors to do so). An investor earns capital gains (the difference between the asset's purchase price and selling price, when this difference is positive) when he or she sells stocks at a price higher than the purchase price. If the stock is sold at a price below the purchase price, a capital loss is incurred. The tax consequences of capital gains are discussed in Appendix 2A.

Several dates are important when investing in dividend-paying common stock. Dividends are typically paid quarterly, although there are many other payment methods. The declaration date is the day when the board of directors actually announces that stockholders on the date of record will receive a dividend. The date of record is the day on which the stockholder must actually own the shares to be able to receive the dividend. The date of record is usually several weeks after the declaration date. The ex-dividend date is the first day on which, if the stock is purchased, stockholders are no longer entitled to receive the dividend. Stocks on the New York Stock Exchange (NYSE) go ex-dividend four trading days before the date of record. This allows for the official records to be adjusted. The payment date is the day that the company actually mails the dividend cheques to its stockholders. The payment date is about three weeks after the ex-dividend date. Finally, some corporations pay cash to their stockholders by purchasing their own shares. These are known as buyback shares.

2.2.2 **Classifications of common stocks**

Stocks are usually classified using the following categories: (1) growth, (2) income, (3) blue chip, (4) speculative, (5) cyclical, and (6) defensive. A stock may be classified in more than one category. For example, WalMart stock is rated as both growth and blue chip. Some stocks may fall into only one or two categories, and other stocks may avoid classification because of their unique features.

Growth stocks are usually common stocks of firms having sales and earnings growth in excess of the industry average. The company pays very low or no dividends and reinvests its earnings for expansion. For example, Microsoft Corporation had recorded sales and earnings growth rates in excess of 20% per year from 1988 to 1998. To date, Microsoft has not paid any cash dividends.

Income stocks are common stocks of older, more mature firms that pay high dividends and are not growing rapidly. Stocks of utility companies are examples of income stocks. Income stocks are usually in low-risk industries, and their price increases little, if at all. For example, Duke Power Company has paid dividends consistently for at least the last 20 years without ever decreasing the amount paid. In the last 10 years, Duke has consistently increased its dividends at a rate of about 5% per year.[9] Hence, Duke Power Company has been a solid source of income and a very stable firm.

Blue chip stocks are common stocks of large, financially sound corporations with a good history of dividend payments and consistent earnings growth. These stocks tend to have very little risk of default. Blue chip stocks typically have more capital gains potential than do income stocks. For years, IBM has been well known as a blue-chip stock.

Speculative stocks are the opposite of blue chip stocks. These are stocks with a higher than average possibility of gain or loss, due to the fact that they are very risky and have considerable short-term volatility. Generally, stocks with a big difference between the high and the low price corresponding to the last 52 weeks are considered speculative stocks.

Cyclical stocks are common stocks that tend to move with the business cycle. When the economy is doing well, these stocks do well. When the country is in recession, these stocks do poorly. Ford Motor Company is a cyclical stock, as are other automobile makers. Automobile sales are typically a leading indicator of economic activity. Hence, as the economy slips into a recession, so do the earnings of automobile companies. Ford recorded large income gains during the expansion years in the late 1980s, but the company experienced sizable losses in the recession of the early 1990s.

Defensive stocks are the opposite of cyclical stocks, in a sense. Defensive stocks tend to do relatively well in recessionary periods but do not do very well when the economy is booming. These stocks are more difficult to find than cyclical stocks. Stocks of automobile-parts makers may be defensive. When the economy is in a recession, consumers are much more likely to attempt to maintain their motor vehicles rather than purchase new ones. Hence, sales by auto-parts makers tend to increase in recessions and decrease in expansions.

2.2.3 **Preferred stocks**

Preferred stocks typically pay a stated dividend and have preference over the payments to common stockholders. Thus, preferred stock is a 'hybrid security' that has some properties of bonds and some properties of stocks. Investors are attracted to this type of

---

[9] This means that if Duke paid a $1 dividend last year, then on average, it will pay $1.05 this year.

investment, but they sometimes overlook the risk. It is true that preferred stocks may provide a relatively high yield, but this high yield is not guaranteed. Also, if the firm goes bankrupt, the preferred stockholder stands in the credit line behind bondholders. A company's failure to pay preferred stock dividends, however, does not result in bankruptcy. Sometimes the firm can even call back the preferred stock, thus avoiding the high dividend. Finally, owners of preferred stock do not enjoy the same benefits as owners of common stock when the firm is doing well. That is, the common stock price could increase sharply, offering stockholders high capital gains. However, the preferred stock price gains are limited, much like the earning potential of bonds.

Cumulative preferred stocks are preferred stocks whose dividends accumulate if they are not paid. That is, before common shareholders can receive a dividend, the preferred shareholders receive all prior dividends that are due. Participating preferred stocks are preferred stocks whose dividends are tied to the success of the firm according to some stated formula in the earnings of the firm.

Dividends on preferred shares are not tax deductible. However, in 1995, the Internal Revenue Service (IRS) approved a new type of preferred shares whose dividends are tax deductible. Thus, the firm can enjoy a cheaper source of obtaining funds to finance operations.[10]

2.2.4 Reading the stock pages

Exhibit 2.7(a) shows a stock page from the financial pages of a newspaper. The first two columns give the 52-week high and low stock prices, followed in the third column by the company's abbreviated name. For example, AT&T had a 52-week high of 35.19 and a 52-week low of 16.50. The *s* by AMCOL means the firm has recently had a stock split. A stock split occurs when a company issues more new shares in return for existing shares. For example, a 2-for-1 split means that a company issues two new shares for every one share currently outstanding. Stock splits are a method that firms use to control the per-share price of its stock. After a 2-for-1 split, a firm's stock will trade at about half of its previous value.

Notice that in the explanatory notes in Exhibit 2.7(b) *pr* stands for *preference shares*, and *pf* stands for *preferred stock*. Preference shares are preferred stocks with a higher claim to any dividend payments than other preferred stock issues. That is, in hard times these shares' dividends are paid before any other dividends are paid (see ABN stock in Exhibit 2.7(a)).

The fourth column in Exhibit 2.7(a) gives the company's unique ticker symbol. The fifth column gives the volume of shares trading in 100s, and the sixth column gives the dividend yield. The dividend yield is found by dividing the annual (52-week) dollar dividend, D, by the closing price per share (denoted by P, see Column 10). The dividend yield is stated as a percentage. For example, the dividend yield = $(D/P) \times 100$ for ASA (see Exhibit 2.7(a)) is 3%.

The seventh column gives the price/earnings (P/E) ratio, which is the closing price divided by the past four quarters' earnings per share. The P/E ratio is a widely used ratio in evaluating common stocks. A firm that is expected to experience significant growth in the future will have a higher P/E ratio. That is, the current price will reflect this perceived growth, but the earnings per share, E, does not reflect this growth (because it is last year's earnings per share). Therefore, a relatively high P/E ratio is expected to be found in growth firms.

---

[10] See Andrew Bary, 'What a deal: new breed of preferred issues helps everybody but the tax man', *Barron's*, 27 February 1995.

Exhibit 2.7(a) Extract from *Barron's* Stock Tables

Mkt Sym	52-Wk High	Low	Name	Tick Sym.	Vol. 100s	Yld	P/E	Week's High	Low	Last	Net. Chg	Dividend Rec.Date
							A					
▲	17.10	9.75	**AAR**	AIR	3448	2.0	25	17.10	14.50	17.10	+ 2.55	05–01–01
	38.20	21.75	ABM Indus	ABM	4922	1.8	19	37.75	34.00	37.25	− 0.03	07–13–01
	26.50	16.81	ABN Am ADR	ABN	5305	4.3	...	19.10	18.32	18.93	+ 0.54	05–11–01
▲X	25.60	21.13	**ABN Am pfA**		4145	7.5	...	25.60	25.02	25.10	+ 0.15	06–29–01
▲X	25.65	20.25	ABN Am pfB		5764	7.3	...	25.65	24.50	24.55	+ 0.15	06–29–01
X	28.50	23.50	ACE CapTr		151	8.4	...	27.00	26.01	26.56	+ 0.12	06–29–01
X	43.94	27.13♣	ACE Ltd	ACE	51489	1.5	19	40.00	36.05	39.09	+ 1.75	06–29–01
	89.00	59.75	ACE LtdPRIDES		625	5.1	...	80.55	78.00	80.55	+ 4.30	05–15–01
▲	8.89	7.13	ACM GvtFd	ACG	15560	9.6	...	8.89	8.68	8.72	+ 0.03	07–06–01
▲	9.00	6.75	ACM OppFd	AOF	491	8.3	...	9.00	8.65	8.70	− 0.20	07–06–01
	9.38	6.19	ACM MgdDlr	ADF	2231	12.7	...	8.12	7.81	8.05	+ 0.15	07–06–01
	6.56	4.35	ACM MgdInco	AMF	1659	10.9	...	4.86	4.61	4.66	− 0.10	07–06–01
	13.50	11.50	ACM MuniSec	AMU	361	6.7	...	12.97	12.81	12.97	+ 0.07	07–06–01
	72.81	39.95♣	AES Cp	AES	109220	...	36	44.50	40.75	43.05	+ 1.99	...
	110.00	64.01	AES Tr		3712	4.9	...	70.50	65.41	69.00	+ 2.60	07–13–01
s	37.47	22.53	AFLAC	AFL	78823	.6	24	33.16	30.50	31.49	− 0.96	05–17–01
	13.25	7.90	AGCO Cp	AG	23117	.4	65	9.15	8.14	9.15	+ 0.84	02–15–01
n	25.15	24.85	AGL Cap TruPs		1640	...	...	25.15	25.00	25.15	+ 0.10	...
	24.25	15.63	AGL Res	ATG	7089	4.5	12	24.00	22.51	23.75	+ 0.80	05–18–01
	20.00	10.44	AgSvcAm	ASV	208	...	12	14.06	13.25	13.45	− 0.52	...
	19.74	11.25	AICI Cap Tr pf		155	13.2	...	17.25	17.00	17.10	− 0.19	06–15–01
▲	46.75	15.00	AIPC	PLB	5498	...	30	46.75	40.57	46.40	+ 5.94	...
	15.00	7.50♣	AK Steel	AKS	28485	2.0	15	13.46	12.00	12.54	− 0.72	05–01–01
	49.00	38.13♣	AK Steel pfB		2	7.7	...	47.00	47.00	47.00	...	06–01–01
	26.06	22.50♣	AMB Prop	AMB	8461	6.1	17	25.80	25.29	25.76	+ 0.56	07–05–01
▲	25.25	20.38♣	AMP Prof pfA		177	8.5	...	25.25	25.06	25.16	+ 0.06	07–05–01
s	7.81	2.50	**AMCOL**	ACO	3323	1.0	1	6.10	5.15	6.00	...	05–28–01
	25.31	20.13♣	AMLI Resdntl	AML	2579	7.6	9	24.60	24.00	24.60	+ 0.45	05–11–01
	43.94	26.00	AMR	AMR	71837	...	9	36.22	32.50	36.13	+ 1.77	03–15–00
	25.05	21.31	AMR PINES		383	7.9	...	25.04	24.75	24.89	− 0.03	07–15–01
X	25.69	21.75	ANZ pf		1026	8.0	...	25.57	24.95	25.14	+ 0.29	07–01–01
X	25.75	21.88	ANZ II pf		1031	8.0	...	25.65	25.12	25.18	− 0.09	07–01–01
	63.25	31.50	AOL Time	AOL	608358	...	dd	53.84	51.51	53.00	− 0.10	...
	5.31	2.63	APT Satelt	ATS	282	5.5	...	4.12	3.85	3.85	− 0.15	05–15–01
n	49.88	5.00♣	APW		8107	...	...	10.15	8.54	10.15	+ 0.95	...
	22.90	14.06♣	**ASA**	ASA	1935	3.1	...	19.80	18.80	19.14	+ 0.37	05–18–01
	29.56	15.29	AT&T Wrls	AWE	307900	...	...	16.79	15.45	16.35	+ 0.15	...
X	35.19	16.50	**AT&T**	T	470319	.7	dd	22.00	20.50	22.00	+ 1.03	06–29–01
	26.35	23.63	AT&T 8 1/4 PNS		536	8.0	...	26.05	25.37	25.65	− 0.30	07–03–01
	25.88	23.63	AT&T 8 1/8 PNS		1297	8.0	...	25.55	25.33	25.33	− 0.27	04–30–01
	31.75	15.13♣	AVX Cp	AVX	13729	.7	7	21.00	18.00	21.00	+ 3.08	05–04–01
s	40.47	24.58	AXA ADS	AXA	11135	1.8	...	29.34	27.40	28.17	− 0.22	...
▲	25.00	14.63	AZZ	AZZ	663	.6	15	25.00	22.52	25.00	+ 2.40	04–13–01
	4.00	0.44	AamesFnl	AAM	375	...	dd	1.44	1.25	1.35	+ 0.08	...
	19.50	11.47	AaronRent	RNT	2339	.2	12	17.50	15.86	17.00	− 0.50	06–01–01
	16.50	12.13	AaronRent A	RNTA	5	.3	12	15.87	15.87	15.87	− 0.13	06–01–01
...	...	...	...	...	...	...	...	...	...	...	...	...
...	...	...	...	...	...	...	...	...	...	...	...	...
...	...	...	...	...	...	...	...	...	...	...	...	...

Source: Barron's, 2 July 2001, p. MW17. Barron's Online by *Barron's*. © 2001 by Dow Jones & Co., Inc. Reproduced with permission of Dow Jones & Co., Inc. in the format *Fundamentals of Investments* via Copyright Clearance Center.

The current P/E ratio is 25 for AAR; in other words, the stock price is 25 times larger than the annual earnings per share. With the P/E ratio and the closing price, we can infer an earnings per share (EPS). That is,

$$P/E = P/EPS$$

and therefore

$$EPS = P/(P/E)$$

Exhibit 2.7(b) **How to read *Barron's* Stock Tables**

The stock tables reflect issues that changed hands during last week's trading through 4 p.m. Eastern Time. Stock ticker symbol codes appear for common stock listings. Sales volume figures are the unofficial weekly total for shares traded, quoted in hundreds. The 52-week high/low range columns show the highest and lowest intraday stock price. These ranges are adjusted to reflect stock dividends of 1% or more and cash dividends of 10% or more.

Yield is determined by dividing the company's latest 12-month dividend by the last current market price.

The price-earnings ratio is determined by dividing the closing market price by the company's diluted per-share earnings, as available, for the most recent four quarters. Charges and other adjustments usually are excluded when they qualify as extraordinary items under generally accepted accounting rules. The price/earnings ratio (P/E) reflects the relative value of a company by showing the number of times its latest 12-month earnings would have to be multiplied to equal its stock price.

As a general rule, to be eligible to receive a newly declared cash dividend or stock dividend of less than 25% on a listed security, shareholders must have purchased their stock before the ex-dividend date, which is two business days (days on which the exchanges *and* banks are open) prior to the record date.

For distributions of 25% or more, the ex-dividend date is still one business day after the payment date (the day when the new shares begin trading).

All securities listed in the Nasdaq system are identified by a four- or five-letter symbol. The fifth letter indicates the issues that aren't common or capital shares, or are subject to restrictions or special conditions. Below is a rundown of stock ticker code symbol fifth letter identifiers and a description of what they represent.

Stock ticker code symbols

A Class A.
B Class B.
C Exempt from Nasdaq listing qualifications for a limited period.
D New issue.
E Delinquent in required filings, with SEC, as determined by the National Association of Securities Dealers.
F Foreign.
K Non-voting.
L Miscellaneous situations, second class units, third class warrants or sixth class preferred stock.
M Fourth preferred, same company.
N Third preferred, same company.
O Second preferred, same company.
P First preferred, same company.
Q In bankruptcy proceedings.
R Rights.
S Shares of beneficial interest.
T With warrants or rights.
U Units.
V When issued and when distributed.
W Warrants.
Z Miscellaneous situations, including second class of warrants, fifth class preferred stock and any unit, receipt or certificate representing a limited partnership interest.

Market transaction symbols

▲ Indicates a new high intraday price for the preceding 52 weeks.
▼ Indicates a new low intraday price for the preceding 52 weeks.
cc P/E Ratio is 100 or more.
cld Called.
dd Indicates loss in the most recent four quarters.
f Indicates two zeros are omitted from volume figure.
g Indicates the dividend or earnings is expressed in Canadian money. The stock trades in U.S. dollars. No yield or price/earnings ratio is shown unless stated in U.S. money.
gg Special sales condition; no regular trading.
h Indicates a temporary exception to Nasdaq qualification.
n Indicates new stock listing issue within the past trailing 52-weeks. The high-low price range begins with the start of trading and does not cover the entire 52-week period.
nt Not traded this week.
pf Preferred stock.
pp Holder owes installment(s) of purchase price.
pr Preference shares.
rt Rights.
s Indicates a stock split or stock dividend amounting to 10% or more within the past trailing 52 weeks. The high-low price range is adjusted from the old stock.
un Units.
v Trading halted on primary market.
vj In bankruptcy or receivership or being reorganized under the Bankruptcy Code, or securities assumed by such companies.
wd When distributed.
wi When-issued trading for new issues, stock splits, or large stock dividends where the settlement date is determined after the securities become available.
wt Warrant.
ww With warrants.
x Ex-dividend or ex-rights. Shareholders must have purchased their stock before the ex-dividend date to receive a newly declared dividend – the price of the share drops automatically by the amount of the dividend and the week's net change for the share price is exclusive of the ex-dividend.
xw Without warrants.
z Sales in full, not in hundreds.
♣ Free annual/quarterly report or prospectus available. See details below

Dividend Rec. Date **06-14-01** Boldface and underline indicates a revised or recently reported dividend.

Source: Barron's, 2 July 2001. p. MW16. Barron's Online by *Barron's*. © 2001 by Dow Jones & Co., Inc. Reproduced with permission of Dow Jones & Co., Inc. in the format *Fundamentals of Investments* via Copyright Clearance Center.

For example, we find AAR EPS to be

$$EPS = \$17.10/25 \cong \$0.68$$

Thus, AAR's EPS over the past year is approximately $0.68. This is an approximation, because the reported P/E is rounded. When the earnings are negative or very close to zero, the P/E ratio is meaningless and hence not reported. Columns 9 and 10 give the previous day's high and low prices, respectively. Column 11 gives the closing price, which is the price of the last trade. Column 12 gives the change from the previous trading day, and the final column gives the date of the recently reported dividend.

When you wish to know whether the stock market is tending to go up or down, you cannot look at prices of one stock but should rely on an index of stocks or some average price of many stocks. There are many indices that measure the changes in the price of various groups of stocks. Probably the most well-known indices you hear on the daily news are the Dow Jones index, the Standard & Poor's index, the FTSE 100 and the Nasdaq index. Exhibit 2.8(a) shows that on 23 March 2001 the closing price of the FTSE 100 was 5402.3. Exhibit 2.8(b) lists the other FTSE indices. Exhibit 2.8(c) shows the major US indices such as the Dow Jones index (DJI), the S&P, the Nasdaq, etc.

Originally, the DJI average was calculated as a simple average of the stock prices included in the average, because when there is a stock split or stock dividends, the stock price artificially falls. In order to correct for this technical decline in price, the sum of all the 30 prices is divided by a number smaller than 30, such that the average will not change due to splits and stock dividends. The denominator which adjusts over time is called the *divisor*.

The DJI is a *price-weighted index* because the rate of return on the index is the rate of return that would be obtained if one share of each of the 30 stocks will be held in a portfolio. The Standard and Poor's 500 Index (S&P 500) is a *value-weighted index* rather than a price-weighted one. It measures the rate of return that would be earned on a portfolio of the 500 stocks held in proportion to their market values.

Similarly, the New York Stock Exchange index, the NYSE index, is a value-index of all listed NYSE stocks; and the American Stock Exchange index, derived from

Exhibit 2.8 Some stock market indices

(a) FTSE 100 and other FTSE indices   **FT**

	Mar. 23	Mar 22	Mar 21	Mar 20	Mar 19	2000/01 High	Low	Since comp High	Low
FTSE 100	5402.30	5314.80	5540.70	5646.80	5551.60	**6798.10**	5314.80	**6930.20**	986.90
FTSE 250	5943.80	5929.70	6104.20	6218.90	6219.40	**7149.60**	5929.70	**7149.60**	1379.40
FTSE 250 ex IT	6040.40	6037.60	6208.00	6322.60	6330.90	**7166.20**	5987.20	**7166.20**	1378.30
FTSE 350	2658.30	2620.10	2726.90	2778.90	2738.40	**3325.30**	2620.10	**3546.40**	664.50
FTSE SmallCap	2869.14	2859.34	2931.38	2979.85	2975.87	**3629.06**	2859.34	**3629.06**	1363.79
FTSE SmallCap ex IT	2860.47	2857.14	2919.96	2963.54	2960.52	**3575.63**	2857.14	**5554.10**	1363.79
FTSE All-Share	2609.40	2573.07	2676.31	2727.15	2688.78	**3265.95**	2573.07	**3265.95**	61.92

Source: Financial Times, 26 March 2001, p. 28. Reprinted with permission.

Exhibit 2.8 (continued)

(b) FTSE share indices (European series)

Mar 23	Euro Index	Day's %	change points	Yield% gross	xd adj ytd	Total retn (Euro) ¤
FTSE Eurotop 300	1308.65	+ 2.32	+ 29.68	2.21	4.89	1403.42
FTSE E300 Eurobloc	1437.26	+ 2.76	+ 38.66	2.05	2.49	1520.95
FTSE E300 Ex-Eurobloc	1190.82	+ 1.83	+ 21.37	2.39	7.07	1291.96
FTSE E300 Ex-UK	1400.87	+ 2.74	+ 37.30	2.00	1.98	1476.32
FTSE Eurotop 100	2972.87	+ 2.43	+ 70.64	2.13	10.80	1107.86
FTSE Eurobloc 100	1176.30	+ 2.84	+ 32.45	2.06	1.85	1237.17
FTSE EuroMid	1346.06	+ 1.15	+ 15.27	2.51	3.90	1474.70
FTSE EuroMid Eurobloc	1257.97	+ 1.35	+ 16.75	2.31	1.50	1357.01
FTSE EuroMid Ex-UK	1291.47	+ 1.45	+ 18.50	2.20	2.24	1380.07
FTSE Eurotop 300 Industry Sectors						
RESOURCES	1283.78	− 1.85	− 24.21	2.63	5.05	1417.03
Mining	1629.83	+ 2.45	+ 39.05	3.11	31.44	1812.45
Oil & Gas	1212.19	− 2.23	− 27.69	2.58	3.04	1307.28
BASIC INDUSTRIES	1213.15	+ 0.21	+ 2.50	2.95	6.77	1312.69
Chemicals	951.94	+ 0.22	+ 2.09	2.91	2.30	1023.81
Construction & Bld Matls	1115.62	+ 1.01	+ 11.11	2.58	1.36	1174.02
Forestry & Paper	1112.08	− 3.09	− 35.47	4.79	53.31	1314.44
GENERAL INDUSTRIALS	1253.23	+ 3.44	+ 41.72	2.31	4.80	1333.17
Aerospace & Defence	713.49	+ 1.27	+ 8.94	1.99	0.00	759.06
Diversified Industrials	872.31	+ 3.20	+ 27.06	2.91	0.00	930.53
Electronic & Elect Equip	1605.23	+ 4.60	+ 70.60	1.80	8.77	1666.08
Engineering & Machinery	827.52	+ 2.13	+ 17.26	3.35	7.52	892.37
CYCLICAL CONS GOODS	1193.57	+ 2.07	+ 24.20	2.69	0.87	1282.51
Automobiles & Parts	796.67	+ 2.05	+ 16.01	3.08	0.82	845.52
Household Goods & Texts	1782.25	+ 2.12	+ 36.92	1.72	0.00	1855.82
NON-CYC CONS GOODS	1368.12	+ 1.72	+ 23.09	1.72	4.25	1458.26
Beverages	1052.33	− 1.40	− 14.90	2.62	8.35	1143.20
Food Producers & Procesrs	1005.68	+ 0.78	+ 7.83	2.00	1.67	1057.10
Health	1110.44	+ 0.79	+ 8.69	1.49	0.00	1160.47
Personal Care & Hse Prods	1394.80	+ 2.90	+ 39.25	0.97	2.59	1437.73
Pharmaceuticals	1241.44	+ 2.35	+ 28.46	1.42	2.07	1288.09
Tobacco	1760.66	+ 1.14	+ 19.77	5.09	54.76	2005.77
CYCLICAL SERVICES	1155.36	+ 1.90	+ 21.58	2.02	3.09	1235.95
Distributors	1021.47	+ 3.90	+ 38.38	2.18	0.00	1090.97
General Retailers	873.30	+ 0.90	+ 7.81	2.40	1.07	930.85
Leisure Entertmt & Hotels	909.80	+ 1.62	+ 14.47	2.45	6.24	971.29
Media & Photography	1367.42	+ 2.37	+ 31.60	1.76	4.18	1424.12
Support Services	886.33	+ 4.00	+ 34.08	1.30	1.67	920.25
Transport	733.19	− 0.18	− 1.31	2.75	0.00	793.41
NON-CYCLICAL SERVS	1219.18	+ 2.97	+ 35.16	1.77	0.41	1283.88
Food & Drug Retailers	1218.07	− 0.07	− 0.88	1.86	0.00	1280.04
Telecommunication Servs	1163.46	+ 3.59	+ 40.29	1.76	0.47	1205.94
UTILITIES	1361.60	+ 2.12	+ 28.24	3.64	9.63	1551.88
Electricity	982.67	+ 1.99	+ 19.19	3.91	8.44	1095.67
Gas Distribution	1320.67	+ 2.60	+ 33.44	2.30	2.37	1507.52
Water	810.50	+ 2.22	+ 17.64	4.22	0.00	974.48
FINANCIALS	1382.51	+ 3.13	+ 41.92	2.61	7.90	1491.78
Banks	977.18	+ 2.94	+ 27.88	2.97	8.36	1050.95
Insurance	1070.87	+ 3.42	+ 35.41	1.79	1.04	1119.38
Life Assurance	1005.66	+ 3.21	+ 31.24	2.65	0.00	1057.10
Investment Companies	1524.24	+ 1.81	+ 27.07	1.85	0.00	1617.27
Real Estate	767.75	+ 0.40	+ 3.05	3.68	0.00	846.12
Speciality & Other Fin	1208.40	+ 7.51	+ 84.40	1.31	2.26	1273.02
INFORMATION TECH	1392.42	+ 7.62	+ 98.65	0.84	4.51	1417.91
Information Tech Hardware	1678.07	+ 8.40	+ 129.99	0.96	6.99	1711.91
Software & Computer Serv	708.66	+ 5.28	+ 35.52	0.48	0.24	717.37

Source: *Financial Times*, 26 March 2001, p. 28. Reprinted with permission.

Exhibit 2.8 (continued)

(c) The major US stock market indices

	12-Month		Weekly		Friday		Weekly	12-Month		Change From	
	High	Low	High	Low	Close	Chg.	% Chg.	Chg.	% Chg.	12/31	% Chg.
Dow Jones Averages											
30 Indus	11337.92	9389.48	10566.21	10434.84	10502.40	-102.19	-0.96	54.51	0.52	-284.45	-2.64
20 Transp	3145.65	2368.65	2833.56	2643.49	2833.56	157.07	5.87	188.19	7.11	-113.04	-3.84
15 Utilities	416.11	306.91	359.68	352.57	359.34	2.84	0.80	52.43	17.08	-52.82	-12.82
65 Comp	3392.23	2882.28	3143.60	3083.60	3143.60	24.93	0.80	152.76	5.11	-173.81	-5.24
US Tot. Mkt	358.00	252.46	284.75	280.69	284.75	1.45	0.51	-54.44	-16.05	-22.13	-7.21
Internet	326.99	54.21	84.41	79.96	84.41	6.40	8.20	-203.74	-70.71	-52.08	-38.16
New York Stock Exchange											
Comp	677.58	566.35	621.76	616.00	621.76	-3.61	-0.58	-21.17	-3.29	-35.11	-5.35
Indus	851.94	696.58	767.50	760.82	765.92	-7.35	-0.95	-57.91	-7.03	-37.37	-4.65
Utilities	504.91	365.58	376.61	365.58	376.61	7.36	1.99	-102.96	-21.47	-63.93	-14.51
Transp	494.71	379.37	469.65	443.16	469.65	21.34	4.76	84.97	22.09	6.89	1.49
Finan	657.52	520.11	627.21	620.55	626.65	-5.36	-0.85	106.54	20.48	-20.30	-3.14
American Stock Exchange											
Amex Corp	974.18	832.24	917.80	902.88	917.80	11.82	1.30	-18.09	-1.93	20.05	2.23
Major Mkt	1110.28	941.21	1054.49	1043.09	1051.15	-12.51	-1.18	23.56	2.29	-26.41	-2.45
Standard & Poor's Indexes											
100 Index	829.83	560.99	635.58	626.69	632.02	-4.13	-0.65	-158.23	-20.02	-54.43	-7.93
500 Index	1520.77	1103.25	1226.20	1211.07	1224.42	-0.93	-0.08	-230.18	-15.82	-95.86	-7.26
Indus	1874.50	1260.17	1410.09	1392.44	1407.46	1.08	0.08	-411.18	-22.61	-120.40	-7.88
Transp	764.16	563.43	713.55	661.59	713.55	35.66	5.26	150.12	26.64	15.90	2.28
Utilities	353.03	256.96	303.12	295.40	303.12	4.73	1.59	46.16	17.96	-47.49	-13.54
Finan	168.30	131.06	159.53	157.49	159.24	-2.06	-1.28	28.18	21.50	-5.48	-3.33
MidCap	548.60	433.70	519.12	503.06	519.12	13.03	2.57	37.35	7.75	2.36	0.46
SmallCap	236.76	192.86	232.41	217.90	232.41	12.97	5.91	21.72	10.31	12.82	5.84
Nasdaq Stock Market											
Comp	4274.67	1638.80	2160.54	2050.87	2160.54	125.70	6.18	-1805.57	-45.52	-309.98	-12.55
100 Index	4099.30	1370.75	1832.75	1743.90	1832.75	105.28	6.09	-1931.04	-51.31	-508.95	-21.73
Indus	2319.28	1114.27	1516.53	1434.35	1516.53	91.96	6.46	-590.03	-28.01	33.54	2.26
Insur	2314.75	1700.16	2295.45	2258.67	2277.93	24.47	1.09	577.77	33.98	84.56	3.86
Banks	2108.94	1497.35	2108.94	2062.41	2108.94	35.18	1.70	611.59	40.84	169.49	8.74
Computer	2538.43	779.72	1083.72	1024.01	1083.72	78.81	7.84	-1260.25	-53.77	-211.25	-16.31
Telecom	935.90	280.27	311.18	292.79	311.18	17.29	5.88	-559.52	-64.26	-152.26	-32.85
NNM Comp	1946.26	744.04	981.66	931.73	981.66	57.25	6.19	-823.54	-45.62	-142.84	-12.70
NNM Indus	957.32	458.13	624.60	590.70	624.60	37.99	6.48	-243.94	-28.09	12.31	2.01
Russell Indexes											
1000	813.71	577.85	647.22	638.78	646.93	0.86	0.13	-122.75	-15.95	-53.16	-7.59
2000	545.18	425.74	513.13	484.19	513.13	24.48	5.01	-4.11	-0.79	29.60	6.12
3000	841.47	601.74	677.36	667.71	677.36	3.31	0.49	-119.08	-14.95	-48.39	-6.67
Value-v	609.20	527.09	583.80	577.72	583.80	-2.07	-0.35	45.39	8.43	-12.75	-2.14
Growth-v	919.26	470.23	554.97	544.93	553.61	4.57	0.83	-318.11	-36.49	-93.10	-14.40
MidCap	667.87	534.19	610.97	594.91	610.97	12.96	2.17	-2.57	-0.42	-16.65	-2.65
Others											
Value Line-a	1306.62	1045.40	1254.80	1203.81	1254.80	46.37	3.84	192.04	18.07	130.03	11.56
Value Line-g	439.78	346.50	399.93	384.68	399.93	13.58	3.51	-7.92	-1.94	6.46	1.64
Wilshire 5000	14329.94	10068.63	11407.15	11229.02	11407.15	94.69	0.84	-2211.35	-16.24	-768.73	-6.31
Wilshire SC	905.05	629.27	763.29	727.73	763.29	30.49	4.16	-81.66	-9.66	11.10	1.48

a-Arithmetic Index. G-Geometric Index. V-Value 1000 and Growth 1000.

Source: *Barron's,* 2 July 2001, p. MW55. *Barron's Online by Barron's.* © 2001 by Dow Jones & Co., Inc. Reproduced with permission of Dow Jones & Co., Inc. in the format *Fundamentals of Investments* via Copyright Clearance Center.

stock listed in the AMEX and the Nasdaq index, relates to about 3,000 stocks which are traded over the counter (OTC). There is a broader index called the Wilshire 5,000 index which includes stocks of the NYSE and AMEX plus many stocks traded OTC.

2.3 DERIVATIVE SECURITIES

A derivative security is one whose value depends directly on, or is derived from, the value of another asset. Four types of derivative securities are stock options, convertible bonds, futures and swaps.

2.3.1 Stock options

A call option on common stock gives the holder of the option (the buyer) the right to buy a specified stock at a specified price on or before a specified date. A put option gives the holder the right to sell a specified stock at a specified price on or before a specified date. Investors buy call options in the hope that the stock price will rise so they may buy the stock at a discount. Investors buy put options hoping that the stock price will fall so they may sell the stock at a premium.

For example, the following data corresponding to options on Motorola stock was reported in *Barron's*, 2 July 2001:

Call option

Strike	Call price
$15	$2.0

Put option

Strike	Put price
$15	$0.35

This means that you could buy a call option on Motorola stock for $2. This option entitled you to buy, up to the end of July, Motorola stock for $15. The market price of Motorola on this date was $16.56. Thus, if the stock price had increased until July, say to $19, you would have bought the stock for only $15 (i.e. exercised the call option) and earned $4 less than the price you had paid for the call option, giving you a profit of $4 − $2 = $2. If you had bought a put option, and paid $0.35, it would have given you the right to sell the stock for $15. If the stock price of Motorola had dropped to, say, $10, you would have gained $5 less than the price paid for the put option ($0.35).

The advantage of call options is that when stock prices rise, these options provide a much higher return than the comparable return from stock ownership. However, there is a risk that the call option will expire worthless if the stock price falls, and a put option may expire worthless if the stock price rises. In these cases you lose all your investment, i.e. − 100% rate of return. Options are useful tools in managing the risks of a portfolio. For example, options can be used to insure the downside risk of a stock portfolio. We examine this issue in Chapter 13.

2.3.2 **Convertible bonds**

Convertible bonds provide a unique investment opportunity. A convertible bond is a corporate bond with an option to convert the bond into stock. The bondholder receives coupon payments that generally have a higher yield than the dividend yield of the underlying stock but lower than the yield on nonconvertible bonds with the same risk. Because the bond is convertible, it provides the opportunity to participate in any rise in stock price. In essence, a convertible bond is an ordinary bond with a call option attached.

Suppose Cray Research $6^1/_8$, 2011 convertible bonds were trading at $85^3/_4$. That is, the bonds offer a $6^1/_8\%$ coupon and will mature in 2011. The price of $85^3/_4$ refers to the percentage of par. The par value of the bonds is \$1,000; hence, the quoted price of the bond is \$857.50 (or $0.8575 \times \$1,000$).

To understand the price of the Cray Research bond, we need more information. We need the conversion ratio, the number of common shares a bondholder will receive if the bond is tendered for conversion. For Cray Research convertible bonds, the conversion ratio is 12.82. That is, each bond with \$1,000 par is convertible into 12.82 shares of stock. The conversion price is the par value of a bond divided by the conversion ratio, which for Cray is about \$78 (that is, \$1,000/12.82). Cray Research stock is currently trading at \$42 per share. The conversion value is the current value of a bond if it is converted. If we converted the Cray bonds, our equity would be worth \$538.44 (that is, $\$42 \times 12.82$), which is far less than the bonds' current trading price of \$857.50. The conversion premium is the value of the option to convert the bond into stocks, which is the difference between the current market value of the bonds and the comparable market price of a nonconvertible bond. In this case, the option to convert the bond to stocks at price of \$78, when the stock is presently trading at \$42, is not worth very much. We will study how to value such an option in Chapter 13.

2.3.3 **Futures**

A futures contract is a security that *obligates* one to buy or sell a specified amount of an asset at a stated price on a particular date. For example, the buyer of a 50,000 libras cotton futures contract that matures in three months agrees to buy 50,000 libras of a specified grade of cotton at a specific location at a specific price (the futures price).

For example, on 2 July 2001, the price of cotton futures in March 2002 was 44.20 cents per libra. This means that if you buy a 50,000 lb (which is the minimum in the case of cotton) contract, you are obligated to pay on the delivery date $50,000 \times \$0.4420 \cong \$22,100$ regardless of the cotton price which will prevail in March 2002.

Futures contracts exist on most major commodities: metals, energy products, interest rates, currencies, and various (mainly stock) indices. Futures are used to hedge financial price risk and to speculate on the direction of future prices. For example, a multinational corporation that has large accounts receivable in Japanese yen may sell yen futures contracts to hedge against a weakening yen relative to the dollar. A speculator who believes the dollar will weaken against the yen may buy yen futures in the hope of profiting. Thus, futures provide the ability to transfer financial price risk from the hedger to the speculator. Futures will be discussed in Chapter 12.

2.3.4 Swaps

A newer type of financial security is the swap. A swap is an agreement to exchange specific assets at future points in time. For example, a currency swap is an agreement to exchange currencies – say, US dollars for euros – at specific dates and for specific amounts in the future. The first major swap occurred between IBM and the World Bank in 1981. IBM held fixed-rate debt in German marks (DM) and Swiss francs (SF). Because of recent changes in the foreign exchange rates, IBM wanted to convert its DM and SF liabilities to US dollar liabilities. In August 1981, the World Bank issued fixed-rate bonds in dollars with the exact maturities of the IBM debt. The World Bank and IBM then agreed to 'swap' the interest payments. The interest payments were calculated based on the par value of the bonds. This par value is referred to as the notional principal. The net result of these transactions was that the World Bank would, in effect, make IBM's debt payments in DM and SF, and IBM would make the World Bank's debt payments in US dollars. Thus, IBM eliminated its currency risk. Why did the World Bank take this currency risk? Probably, it had assets in Germany and Switzerland that generated DM and SF cash flow. These assets could then be used to pay the World Bank's debts with no concern about changes in exchange rates. Thus, both sides of this transaction benefited.

2.4 RISKS OF BONDS AND STOCKS

Exhibit 2.9 compares the risk and average (or expected) return characteristics of the financial securities introduced in this chapter. If held in isolation, options and futures are the most risky, but they also provide the highest potential return. Short-term government bonds are the safest, but they also offer the smallest return. Between these two extremes are securities offering different levels of risk and return. Although stocks are typically riskier than bonds, they also offer a higher return on average. Long-term bonds have a higher risk and generally also a higher return than short-term bonds. Finally,

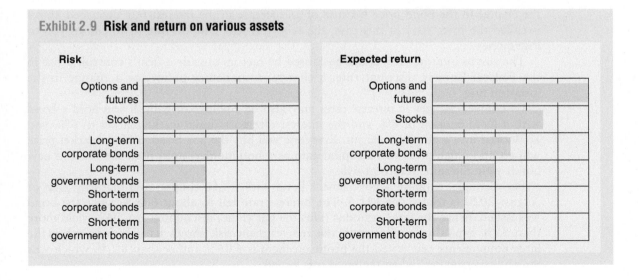

Exhibit 2.9 **Risk and return on various assets**

corporate bonds must offer a higher return on average to induce investors to take on default risk.

Investing in bonds and stocks has nine major sources of risk. (The order of coverage here does not suggest priority of risks, as risks vary among different securities.) The risk sources follow.

1 Default risk

One risk that affects bond investors is that of default. The municipality or corporation may fail to pay either the coupon payment or face value at maturity. Bond investors in the Seabrook Nuclear Power Plant suffered from default risk when the plant's owner, the New Hampshire Power Company, failed to pay the coupon payments. Firms may default if they have too much debt (relative to the cash flows they generate). In this event, both stockholders and bondholders may lose. Of course, federal government bonds do not have default risk, because the Treasury Department can print money. Corporate bonds, municipal bonds and stocks are exposed to default risk.

2 Interest rate risk

A second source of risk to bond investors is that of a change in interest rates. Would you want to buy a bond offering an annual 8% coupon rate when the market is paying 10% on newly issued bonds? Recall that bonds typically have a fixed coupon. If you have an 8% coupon bond, it is an agreement to pay you 8% of par value every year. Now suppose interest rates increase to 10%, and you are locked into a bad agreement; then you lose money. To be more specific, investors will sell the 8% bond and buy the 10% bond, causing the price of the 8% bonds to fall. The falling price will result in rising yields. For example, if an 8% coupon bond is selling for 90% of the price of the new 10% bond, for the same investment you can buy more of the old bond and earn more interest. The selling will continue until both the old and new bonds yield 10%. These higher yields imply that you can reinvest the coupon payment at a higher yield. However, if the interest goes down, the coupon reinvestment rate will be smaller and hence the terminal value of the investment will be smaller. This possible decrease in the reinvestment rate is called the reinvestment rate risk. In contrast, the change in the bond price because of an increase in the interest rate described above is called the price risk. In this case, the relatively low coupon rate (8%) causes you to lose money.

The rise in interest rates could be caused by factors outside a firm's control: a rise in the Federal Reserve discount rate, a change in monetary policy, or a change in the inflation rate.

Of course, changes in interest rates may also be a source of gain. If you hold a bond with a fixed coupon of 8% and the interest rate goes down in the market to 6%, you are locked into a good agreement. Everyone will buy the 8% bond, and its market price will go up (which gives you a capital gain as a bondholder) until both the old and new bonds yield the same return of 6%.

For example, suppose a government bond with $8^3/_4$% coupon and maturity date of August 2020 is traded for 131.5. The interest rate fell to about 6.06% since the bond was issued, hence the large coupons (plus the par value) discounted at 6.06% yield more than 31% capital gain. However, the reinvestment risk shows its ugly face: when the large coupons are reinvested the profit on them is 6.06% rather than $8^3/_4$% which was the reinvestment rate when the bond was issued.

Although changes in the interest rate may result in a gain for bondholders, interest rate changes are usually referred to as *interest rate risk*, because the uncertainty caused by these changes in general is undesirable to investors. In other words, if investors could buy one of two bonds, where the first bond's price did not change and the second bond's price would have a $50 gain or a $50 loss with equal probability, most investors would choose the first bond.

Stockholders also can lose or win when interest rates change. Specifically, higher interest rates make bonds relatively more attractive, causing some investors to sell stocks and buy bonds. This stock selling results in lower stock prices.

3 Inflation rate risk

Interest rate changes may be caused by many factors that are very hard to predict. One of these factors is a change in the inflation rate, which is referred to as the *inflation rate risk* or *purchasing power risk*. These terms refer to the risk of losing the purchasing power of future cash receipts. That is, the value of the dollars received in the future in real terms decreases, hence the investor is unable to purchase as many goods and services as anticipated.

For example, suppose a one-year bond is offering a 5% yield, but inflation is 6%. At the end of the year, investors would be able to buy *less* with the bond's proceeds than they could with the initial investment at the beginning of the year. Inflation is a threat to the future benefits provided from investing. Inflation risk also affects stocks; generally, an increase in inflation induces an increase in the interest rate which, in turn, induces a decline in stock prices.

Recently, new bonds called inflation-indexed Treasury securities, discussed above, have been issued. The interest and principal of the bonds are linked to the cost of living index, which shields these bonds from inflation rate risk.

4 Risk of call

Another potential risk to bondholders is the risk of call. Many bonds contain a call provision that allows the issuing firm to repurchase its bonds at a stated price after a stated date. The purchase price is usually the face value plus one year of coupon payments. This call provision can adversely affect the value of the bonds if interest rates decline dramatically.

For example, an 8% coupon bond with a face value of $1,000 that matures in 15 years may have a call provision after eight years. According to the call provision, the firm could repurchase the bonds any time after the eighth year if it is willing to pay the face value ($1,000) plus one year of interest ($80), or $1,080.

If interest rates fall to 5%, a non-callable bond gains from having an 8% coupon. However, for a callable bond there is a risk that the bond will be taken away from the investor, who then will not fully benefit from the drastic change in the interest rate. The firm could call the bonds and issue new ones at 5%, saving 3% per year. Thus, in the case of a sharp decrease in interest rate, the callable bonds will not provide the capital gain as will the non-callable bonds, because they can be called back at $1,080. Also, the investor faces an investment decision of what to do with the proceeds from the bond at the time the firm chooses to buy the bond back. Bonds are typically called after interest rates have fallen substantially. Thus, bond investors will be reinvesting the proceeds at a time when rates are low.

On the one hand, a callable bond, like all other bonds, also suffers losses when interest rates go up (because the price falls). On the other hand, as shown above, a callable bond's price will not go up in the same way as a noncallable bond's price. Thus, why would anyone want to buy such bonds, which seem to be an inferior investment? The reason is simple. The firm issuing the bonds must issue them at a higher interest rate than the rate for noncallable bonds; otherwise a rational investor will not buy the callable bonds. Thus, in the event that the interest rate does not go down and the bonds are not called, the bondholder enjoys a relatively high interest rate.

5 Liquidity risk

Another risk of investing in certain bonds and stocks is that they may not be liquid. That is, if the bonds or stocks have to be sold unexpectedly, it could be very costly to the investor. There may be no-one who wishes to buy the securities at that time. To get a buyer quickly, the investor may have to sell the security at an unreasonably low price relative to its true value and thus incur a substantial price concession. Investors typically do not have a liquidity risk problem with government bonds and actively traded bonds of larger corporations, such as those issued by AT&T and GM. However, investors must anticipate a liquidity risk with the bonds or stocks of small firms, because they are not actively traded. To compensate for the lack of liquidity, small firms must offer investors a higher yield on bonds and a higher expected return on the stock. No one would buy them otherwise.

6 Political and regulatory risk

Bonds and stocks are also exposed to political risk. This risk refers to unforeseen changes in the tax or legal environment that have an impact on stock and bond prices. For example, suppose Congress decided to double the income tax rate and cut the capital gains tax rate in half. What impact would this have on coupon-bearing bonds? In such a case, the tax liabilities of the coupon payments would double, and investors would have an incentive to buy stocks rather than bonds because the change in capital gains tax would favour stocks. Therefore, coupon-bearing bonds would decline in value as a result of the new tax laws.

The collapse of the Soviet Union illustrates a case of a political risk. In such a case, the government may be unable to or may refuse to pay its foreign debt, which induces a loss to a foreign investor who buys Soviet bonds.

7 Business risk

Stocks and corporate bond prices are influenced greatly by the prosperity of the particular company, as well as by the economy in general. Stock and bond prices are directly influenced by how well a company is performing. Furthermore, because the firm is often involved with risky research and development projects, stocks are influenced by company performance much more than bonds. The higher volatility of sales and profit of the firm, the higher the business risk. Company performance is usually directly linked to the performance of the overall economy.

8 Market risk

Much of the research conducted on securities markets has documented that the prices of all securities in a particular market tend to move together. For example, the US Treasury bond market exhibits a high level of co-movement of its bond prices. This principle is also true for corporate bonds and stocks. Even a good stock tends to perform poorly when the overall market is going down.

■ 9 Exchange rate risk

As an American investor, why would you buy US bonds yielding only 4.12% when you could earn 10.15% in the United Kingdom? The answer is simple: when you invest in the United Kingdom, you have to convert your US dollars to sterling. However, when you want your money back – say, at the end of the year – you must sell the UK bonds for sterling and then convert the proceeds to US dollars. Of course, there is a risk that for each pound you receive, you may get fewer dollars because of changes in the exchange rate. In dollars, you may end up with a yield much lower than 10.15%; indeed, the yield may be even less than the 4.12% that you can get on the US bonds. Thus, the high yield of 10.15% may be an illusion. Bonds are bought and sold in local currencies, not in US dollars. This exchange rate risk adds one more layer of risk for the international investor.

The risks of investing in government and corporate bonds, as well as in common stocks, are summarized in Exhibit 2.10. Corporate bonds of similar maturities to government bonds have a higher yield because of default risk. Stocks do not induce default risk, because not paying dividends does not cause the firm to be declared in default. However, stockholders are exposed to risk of default by the firm from other factors (for example, a big financial loss or lawsuit).

Exhibit 2.10 Risk exposure for bonds and stocks

Risks	Government bonds	Corporate bonds	Common stocks
Default	No	Yes	Yes
Overall level of interest rates in the economy	Yes	Yes	Yes
Inflation rate	Yes	Yes	Yes
Call	Some issues	Most issues	No
Liquidity	Little	Yes	Yes
Political and regulatory	Yes	Yes	Yes
Business	No	Yes	Yes
Market	Yes	Yes	Yes
Foreign exchange rate	Yes	Yes	Yes

Yes: Investors in bonds or stocks of this category are exposed to this risk.
No: Investors in bonds or stocks of this category are not exposed to this risk.
Little: Investors in bonds of this category are exposed to some, but not much, of this risk.

Changes in interest rates influence both the bond market and the stock market. Typically, if the interest rates fall, both the bond market and the stock market rally. Inflation risk has exactly the same influence as interest rate risk. Stocks are not callable, whereas most corporate bonds are. The call feature introduces an *opportunity loss* if interest rates fall. Liquidity risk is present in all securities; however, the government market is the most liquid. Political and regulatory risk, market risk and foreign exchange risk are present in both the bond and the stock markets. However, business risk applies only to corporate securities, not to securities issued by governments.

PRACTICE BOX

Problem

A government bond sold at $1,000. It pays an annual interest of 5% a year at the end of each year, and it matures in exactly two years. The par value is $1,000, and the bond has a yield of 5%. What is the capital gain if interest rates go down to 3%? What is the capital loss if interest rates go up to 7%? How would your results change if the bonds had 10 years to maturity? Which bond is riskier, the two-year bond or the 10-year bond?

Solution

Using present value tables, a calculator or software, we calculate the present value of the bonds' cash flows. The results are:

Interest rates (discount rate)	Market price of two-year bond	Market price of 10-year bond
3%	$1,038	$1,171
5%	$1,000	$1,000
7%	$964	$860

Thus, the two-year bond provides a $38 capital gain when rates fall to 3%, whereas the 10-year bond provides a $171 capital gain. However, the loss differences are similar in magnitude to the gain differences ($36 and $140, respectively), making the 10-year bond riskier.

2.5 INTERNATIONAL SECURITIES

International securities include stocks and bonds issued in foreign countries by foreign firms (e.g. a Japanese firm issues in the US) as well as securities issued by some domestic firms that pay interest or dividends in a different currency. For example, McDonald's Corporation issued bonds that pay interest in New Zealand dollars. International securities are increasing in importance for several reasons. First, as technologies are improving, the costs of trading international securities are declining. These costs include the cost of actual trading, taxes and other market impediments. Second, markets are dominated more and more by institutional investors. Institutional investors – such as banks, pension funds, insurance companies, endowments and mutual funds – trade large quantities of securities. These larger firms have the economies of scale to invest the energy needed to explore foreign markets. Third, technological advances in communications have been astounding. Fibre-optic telecommunication lines now link several trading firms directly to each other, as well as to multiple securities exchanges. Nowadays, with the Internet, detailed information on most major firms is available. These lines allow information to be communicated at a rate nearing the speed of light.

The major benefits of investing in international securities include the possibility of higher returns and diversification. For example, many international bonds offer a higher yield than similar US bonds. However, the investor must also consider how the bond's price will change over time, as well as how changes in the foreign exchange rate will influence the return on international bonds.

People can invest in international securities in three ways. First, investors can buy foreign bonds or stocks directly in their own markets traded in foreign currency. Second, many domestic exchanges trade American Depository Receipts (ADRs),[11] which are receipts for foreign shares held in a US bank. ADR holders are entitled to the dividends and capital gains of the foreign shares. ADRs trade just like shares of common stock. For example, ADRs trade on the NYSE for Honda Motor Company, a Japanese-based automobile manufacturer. Honda Motor's ADRs trade on the NYSE with ticker symbol HMC, and Honda Motor also trades on the Tokyo Stock Exchange (TSE) in yen. Each ADR allows the holder the rights to two common shares. For example, on a given day HMC was trading at $61^7/_8$ on the NYSE, and Honda Motor was trading at 3,630 yen on the TSE. The price difference can be explained in the following fashion. On this particular day, the dollar exchange rate for yen was 0.00846 dollar per yen. Because one ADR equals two common shares, the dollar value of two Honda common shares is about $61.42 \cong 2 \times 3,630$ yen $\times$ $0.00846. Although stock in Honda Motor can be bought in two ways, either on the TSE or on the NYSE, the price is about the same.[12] Finally, some mutual funds specialize in international markets. It is now possible to buy a portfolio of international securities with one phone call.

2.6 MUTUAL FUNDS/TRUSTS

Many investors choose to invest their money in mutual funds, which receive money from investors with the common objective of pooling the funds and then investing them in securities. There are many different types of mutual funds, as well as a range of ways to classify them. For example, there are open-end funds, which can issue additional shares upon demand and eliminate shares when they are redeemed. The shares of the open-end funds are not traded in the market, hence the investor buys and sells shares from the mutual funds themselves. The price is not determined by demand and supply but rather by the net asset value (NAV) per share. Investors can buy or sell shares of open-end funds like any other stock in the market. Conversely, closed-end funds cannot increase or decrease the number of shares easily.[13] Closed-end funds sell their shares on stock exchanges.

Some open-end funds are no-load (NL), and some are load. The load is a sales charge paid by an investor who buys a share in a load mutual fund. A fund that does not charge this fee is called a no-load fund. On a closed-end fund, the investor pays transaction costs exactly as paid on stocks bought in the stock market.

Exhibit 2.11 provides a sampling of data for mutual funds. The most important figure in the exhibit is the NAV, which is similar to the price quotation for other assets, such as stocks. 'NAV' stands for net asset value, which is the current market value of the assets per share (based on the market value of the underlying securities in the mutual fund). For example, the NAV of Brinson Global Fund is $11.16 million dollars

---

[11] American Depository Receipts are also sometimes referred to as American Depository Shares, or ADSs.

[12] Also, there are enough traders watching the relationship between these securities. In their desire to make any possible profit from price differences, these traders, who are known as *arbitrageurs*, ensure that the pricing differences will not be too great. By trading large blocks between markets, arbitrageurs influence prices, drawing them closer together.

[13] A closed-end fund, with shareholder approval, can undertake a new issue or change the nature of the fund (for example, change it to an open-end fund).

Exhibit 2.11 Sample of mutual funds data

52 Week High	Low	Fund Name	Close NAV	Wk's Chg.	—% Return — YTD	3-Yrs
		BlackRock Funds A:				
21.27	14.06	BalanceA p	14.86	− 0.16	− 7.4	+ 2.9
29.13	21.15	IndexEqA p	23.50	NA	NA	NA
15.51	13.16	LgCpValA p	14.38	− 0.02	− 3.4	+ 8.5
47.91	18.29	MicroCapA p	23.42	+ 1.72	− 6.3	+ 227.6
36.41	13.37	SmCpGrA p	15.50	+ 0.76	− 19.1	+ 23.1
		BlackRock Funds B&C:				
21.09	13.94	BalanceB t	14.73	− 0.14	− 7.8	+ 0.5
28.75	20.83	IndexEqB t	23.12	NA	NA	NA
28.75	20.82	IndexEqC t	23.11	NA	NA	NA
25.59	8.16	MdCpGrB t	8.85	+ 0.19	− 25.1	+ 52.8
47.15	17.78	MicroCapB t	22.73	+ 1.67	− 6.6	+ 220.6
47.13	17.77	MicroCapC t	22.72	+ 1.67	− 6.6	+ 220.5
21.94	12.14	SelectB t	13.22	− 0.06	− 13.2	− 7.6
34.94	12.53	SmCpGrB t	14.18	NA	NA	NA
		BlackRock Funds Svc:				
21.30	14.07	BalancedS	14.87	− 0.17	− 7.4	+ 3.3
9.85	9.20	CoreBd	9.63	− 0.13	+ 2.9	+ 18.6
29.16	21.17	IndexEqS	23.51	NA	NA	NA
15.44	9.29	IntlEqS	9.50	− 0.03	− 14.9	− 10.2
26.37	10.56	LgCpGrS	11.84	+ 0.09	− 24.4	− 13.6
15.53	13.18	LgCpValS	14.39	− 0.03	− 3.3	+ 8.9
10.46	9.75	ManagedS	10.23	− 0.15	+ 3.2	+ 17.7
22.46	12.55	SelEqS	13.70	− 0.06	− 12.8	− 5.0
36.84	13.63	SmCpGrS	15.47	NA	NA	NA
		BNY Hamilton Instit:				
18.19	13.11	EqInc	14.09	− 0.04	− 9.9	+ 12.6
15.70	10.21	IntEq	10.58	− 0.04	− 15.4	− 4.0
10.06	9.37	IntmGvt	9.85	− 0.13	+ 2.8	+ 17.6
10.32	9.76	IntlnGrd	10.09	− 0.12	+ 2.6	+ 15.8
10.20	9.62	Int TE	10.11	− 0.01	+ 3.0	+ 14.0
19.10	10.43	LgCapGth	11.45	− 0.04	− 17.4	+ 16.3
26.98	14.35	SmCapGth	17.19	+ 0.78	− 3.6	+ 89.5
29.42	24.23	BostonBalanced n	25.28	− 0.30	− 3.3	+ 5.5
		Boston Partners:				
13.19	10.81	MidValInst	12.82	+ 0.25	+ 6.6	+ 5.3
32.48	22.07 ♣	BramwellGr n	23.23	NA	NA	NA
23.91	16.62	BrandesInstlE	17.23	+ 0.07	− 7.2	+ 55.4
		Brandywine Funds:				
41.47	22.88	BlueFd n	24.21	− 0.24	− 12.2	+ 33.6
51.06	24.31	Brandywine n	26.26	+ 0.12	− 10.6	+ 41.0
		Brazos Funds:				
27.46	16.02	MicroCap	20.89	+ 1.77	+ 11.5	+ 142.6
13.94	9.73	MidCap Y	11.81	+ 0.26	− 4.2	NS
21.47	14.66	MultiCap	17.31	+ 0.45	− 4.6	NS
10.45	8.92	ReEst	10.45	+ 0.08	+ 8.0	+ 11.7
23.99	15.78	SmCap	19.50	+ 0.65	− 4.9	+ 34.4
10.22	9.61	BremerBd n	10.07	− 0.11	+ 3.8	+ 16.9
19.40	13.89	BermerGrStk n	15.46	+ 0.03	− 7.2	+ 16.1
44.71	31.20	BridgesInvest n	33.81	NA	NA	NA
		Bridgeway Funds:				
58.03	35.75	AggrGrwth n	41.94	+ 0.50	− 3.3	+ 159.0
		Brinson Fnds:				
11.63	**10.68**	**Global**	**11.16**	**NA**	**NA**	**NA**
9.48	7.84	HiYldl	7.90	+ 0.01	+ 1.6	+ 3.1
13.70	10.12	IntlEq	10.64	− 0.05	− 11.4	− 2.0
10.61	9.98	USBond	10.36	− 0.12	+ 3.5	+ 18.8
17.24	14.34	USEqty	16.00	+ 0.13	+ 2.2	+ 6.1
		Brinson Fnds Class A:				
33.57	24.17	FnSvA p	28.33	− 0.41	− 2.8	+ 3.7
9.60	5.24	StrtgyA p	5.99	+ 0.01	− 14.6	NS
35.65	25.03	TctAllA p	27.81	− 0.02	− 7.0	+ 16.7
		Brinson Fnds Class B:				
32.25	22.99	FnSvB t	26.88	− 0.40	− 3.2	+ 1.3
9.55	5.18	StrtgyB p	5.91	+ 0.01	− 15.1	NS
34.98	24.59	TctAllB p	27.27	− 0.02	− 7.3	+ 14.1

Exhibit 2.11 **(continued)**

| 52 Week | | | | | —% Return — | |
High	Low	Fund Name	Close NAV	Wk's Chg.	YTD	3-Yrs
		Brinson Fnds Class C:				
35.19	24.76	TctAllC	27.46	− 0.02	− 7.4	+ 14.1
9.55	5.19	StrtgyC p	5.91	+ 0.01	− 15.1	NS
		Brinson Fnds Class Y:				
35.98	25.26	TctAllY	28.08	− 0.03	− 6.9	+ 17.7
16.16	8.61	BrownlASmCpGr n	12.54	+ 1.02	+ 1.0	NS
34.06	24.94	BrownSmColnst	32.61	+ 1.85	+ 4.4	+ 79.0
24.24	17.04	BrundgEq xn	18.34	+ 0.01	− 8.9	+ 21.0
		Baffalo Funds:				
18.48	13.99	SmCap n	18.48	+ 0.79	+ 21.3	+ 123.2
14.73	13.88	BldProLoan	14.37	− 0.17	+ 2.9	+ 14.9
50.77	31.78	Burnhm p	35.40	− 0.07	− 8.5	+ 30.1

Source: *Barron's*, 2 July 2001, p. F8. Barron's Online by *Barron's*. © 2001 by Dow Jones & Co., Inc. Reproduced with permission of Dow Jones & Co., Inc. in the format *Fundamentals of Investments* via Copyright Clearance Center.

(see Exhibit 2.11). Investors will receive the net asset value if they sell an open-end mutual fund share. From time to time, detailed data on mutual funds is published, including data on performance in the last five years.

In closed-end funds, market supply and demand drive the trading prices. Closed-end funds trade at a premium above, or at a discount below, net asset value, depending on a range of factors (including how well the fund is run, the expenses charged, and the particular focus of the fund). Mutual funds are discussed in more detail in Chapter 17.

New investment vehicles have recently begun to compete with mutual funds. On January 1998, the American Stock Exchange began trading unit trusts called Diamonds. Each of these unit trusts represents a stake in the 30 stocks that make up the Dow Jones index. In effect, Diamonds turn the Dow into publicly trading stock, thus enabling investors to buy and sell the index at any time during the trading day. Each Diamond is sold for the equivalent of 1% of the value of the index. Thus, if the index is traded for, say, 8,000, the Diamond price is determined as $80. Diamonds complement the Amex's popular Spiders, which are unit trusts based on the stocks included in the Standard & Poor's 500 Index. Diamonds and Spiders provide a solid alternative to mutual funds.

SUMMARY

■ *Describe basic characteristics and types of bonds and stocks.*
Bonds are instruments that are useful primarily when investors have specific income requirements, whereas stocks are purchased primarily for growth potential. Money market securities are short-term obligations, including Treasury bills, commercial paper, bankers' acceptances, negotiable certificates of deposit, repurchase agreements, federal funds and eurodollars. Capital market securities are long-term obligations, including Treasury notes and bonds, federal agency bonds, municipal bonds, corporate bonds, mortgages and mortgage-backed securities, and stocks.

■ *Compare different types of derivative securities.*

A derivative security is a security whose value is derived from the value of another asset. Examples of derivative securities include stock options, convertible bonds, futures and swaps. A call option gives the holder the right to buy, whereas a put option gives the holder the right to sell, a specified stock at a specified price on or before a specified date (for an American option). A convertible bond is just like a regular bond, but with an added feature: if you own a convertible bond, you can convert the bond into a specified number of stocks. A futures contract is a security that obligates the investor to buy or sell a specified amount of an asset at a stated price on a particular date. A swap is an agreement to exchange specific assets at future points in time.

■ *Explain the risks involved in bond and stock investment.*

There are nine categories of risks related to bonds and stocks: default risk, interest rate risk, inflation rate risk, risk of call, liquidity risk, political and regulatory risk, business risk, market risk and exchange rate risk. US government bonds do not have default risk or business risk. Common stocks are not callable. Understanding the risks related to investments is an important first step in successful money management.

■ *Describe investment opportunities in international securities and mutual funds.*

International securities increase the investor's opportunities. International securities can be purchased directly from an international stock exchange, indirectly through an American Depository Receipt, or indirectly through a mutual fund. Mutual funds receive money from investors with common objectives, pool the funds together, and then invest them in securities. Shares of open-end funds are purchased and sold exclusively with the fund, whereas shares of closed-end funds are traded on stock exchanges.

KEY TERMS

American Depository Receipt (ADR)	Cumulative preferred stock	Notional principal
Asked rate	Cyclical stock	Open-end fund
Bankers' acceptance	Date of record	Par value
Bid rate	Declaration date	Participating preferred stock
Bid-ask spread	Defensive stock	Payment date
Blue chip stock	Diamonds	Preference share
Bond	Discount rate	Price risk
Buyback shares	Eurodollar	Prime rate
Call option	Ex-dividend date	Principal
Callable bond	Face value	Put option
Capital gains	Federal agency bond	Reinvestment rate risk
Capital loss	Federal funds	Repurchase agreement (repo)
Capital market security	Fixed-rate bond	Revenue bond
Cash dividend	Floating-rate bond	Reverse repo
Closed-end fund	General obligation bond	Speculative stock
Commercial paper	Growth stock	Spiders
Common stock	Income stock	Stock split
Conduit	Junk bond	Swap
Conversion premium	Money market security	T-bill
Conversion price	Mortgage	Term repo
Conversion ratio	Mortgage-backed security	US Treasury bill
Conversion value	Municipal bond	US Treasury bond
Convertible bond	Mutual fund	US Treasury note
Corporate bond	Negotiable certificate of deposit	Zero-coupon bond
Coupon-bearing bond	Net asset value	
Coupon payment		

QUESTIONS

2.1 What are the advantages and disadvantages of investing in bonds?

2.2 What are the major identifying characteristics of bonds?

2.3 Explain what is meant by the statement: 'The ownership of the firm is residual in nature'.

2.4 Explain the dates that are important in relation to the dividends paid on common stocks.

2.5 What is the P/E ratio, and how is it calculated?

2.6 What is a derivative security?

2.7 Give an example of how futures are used to hedge financial price risk and to speculate on the direction of future prices.

2.8 Why are international securities increasing in importance?

2.9   Joe-Bob from L.A. decided to invest $950 (price) in a 12% semiannual, 3-year bond. What is the yield to maturity (internal rate of return or IRR) if the par value is $1,000?

2.10 A bond is sold for $700 and matures in 5 years. It pays $20 at the end of the year. The par value is $1,000. Calculate the yield to maturity (IRR) on the bond using a calculator or software.

2.11 A junk bond is trading for $800 and matures exactly one year from now at $1,000. There is no interest paid between now and maturity.

(a) Calculate the yield to maturity on the bond.
(b) How do you explain your results, knowing that the interest rate on government bonds is only 5% a year?

2.12 The bid and asked yields on zero-coupon bonds with a $1,000 par value are 6.2% and 6%, respectively. The maturity is 5 years. What are the implied bid and asked prices of these two bonds? (Assume annual interest compounding.)

2.13 You have two different bonds, both of which were just issued for 10-year maturities: (1) a zero-coupon bond with a par value of $1,000, and (2) a bond that pays $50 interest at the end of each year with a par value of $1,000. Both of these bonds have the same 10% annual yield to maturity.

(a) Calculate the market price of these two bonds, and explain your results.
(b) Suppose that immediately after the issue of the bonds, the interest rate goes up to 12%. Which bond will suffer larger losses? Why?

2.14 The P/E ratio of a stock is 10. The price is $100 per share. What is the implied earnings per share?

2.15 The net asset value of a mutual fund is $12. The share price is $13.

(a) Is it an open-end fund or a closed-end fund?
(b) Calculate the premium or discount.

2.16 The dividend yield on IBM stock is 2%. The yield to maturity on IBM bonds is 8%. Does this mean that you will be better off buying the bonds than buying the stock?

2.17 A municipal bond and a corporate bond offer you the same yield of 8%. Both have the same risk of default.

(a) Which bond would you prefer if you were a tax-exempt investor?
(b) Which bond would you prefer if you pay 31% tax on interest received? Explain.

2.18 Suppose you buy a stock for $100. You receive $4 as a cash dividend at the end of the year. The stock price at the end of the year is $95.

(a) What is the rate of return on your investment?
(b) What is the dividend yield as measured at the beginning of the year? At the end of the year?
(c) What is your total dollar return on this investment?

2.19 Suppose you buy a stock on 1 January for 100 and consider selling it on 20 December. The stock price is $150. Your income tax rate is 31%. Is it worthwhile for you to wait a few days before selling? How many days should you wait, assuming the stock price will remain at $150? What will be your gain from waiting?

2.20 You have the following data regarding two firms (all numbers are in millions):

	Firm A		Firm B	
Year	Earnings	Dividends	Earnings	Dividends
1	$1.0	$0	$100	$50
2	1.2	0	101	50
3	1.5	0	98	50
4	1.7	0	100	55

Which firm would be classified as a growth firm, and which would not? Calculate the annual growth rate of earnings and dividends of each of these two firms.

2.21 Suppose you buy a bond that matures in one year, pays no interest, and has a par value of $1,000. You buy the bond for $950. The inflation rate was 10% for this year. What did you earn on this bond? Explain.

2.22 You hold a bond that matures in 20 years. The yield to maturity is 10%, and the coupon rate is 10%. The market, as well as the face value of the bond, is $1,000. Suppose the yield to maturity drops to 5% after you buy the bond. Determine your immediate gain under the following conditions:

(a) If the bond is not callable.
(b) If the bond is callable at $1,100 and the firm does call the bond whenever the price is above $1,100.

SELECTED REFERENCES

Fabozzi, Frank J., and D. Fabozzi. *Bond Market Analysis and Strategies*. Englewood Cliffs, NJ: Prentice-Hall, 1989.

Fabozzi, Frank J., and Irving M. Pollack (eds). *Handbook of Fixed Income Securities*. Homewood, IL: Dow Jones–Irwin, 1987.

Kelly, Jonathan M., Luis F. Martin, and John H. Carlson. 'The relationship between bonds and stocks in emerging markets'. *Journal of Portfolio Management*, Spring 1998, pp. 110–22.

Kihn, John. 'To load or not to load? A study of the marketing and distribution changes of mutual funds'. *Financial Analysts Journal*, May/June 1996, pp. 28–37.

Lederman, Jess, and Keith Park (eds). *Global Bond Markets*. Chicago: Probus, 1991.

Lederman, Jess, and Keith Park (eds). *Global Equity Markets*. Chicago: Probus, 1991.

Stigum, Marcia. *The Money Market*, 3rd edn. Homewood, IL: Dow Jones–Irwin, 1989.

SUPPLEMENTARY REFERENCES

Caglayan, Mustafa Onur, and R. Edwards Franklin. 'Hedge fund and commodity fund investments in bull and bear markets'. *The Journal of Portfolio Management*, Summer 2001, Vol. 27, No. 4.

Carrieri, F. 'The effects of liberalization on market and currency risk in the European Union'. *European Financial Management*, 2001, Vol. 7.

Schwartz, Roberta, and Daniel G. Weaver. 'What we think about the quality of our equity markets'. *The Journal of Portfolio Management*, Summer 2001, Vol. 27, No. 4.

Appendix 2A TAXES

In 1997 a new US tax law was completed after long discussion in Congress. The main item in the new law is a reduction in capital gains tax from 28% to 20%. If an asset is held for 5 years before it is sold, the capital gains tax is reduced, according to the new law, to only 18%.

Taxes are an important consideration in the investment process, because they affect an investor's net income. Investments differ in how they determine an investor's tax bill. For example, selling a stock that has greatly appreciated in price and buying a different stock will result in an investor's having to pay tax on the stock that has appreciated. No taxes would have to be paid yet, if the investor did not sell the stock.

Unfortunately, taxes are very complicated. Tax rules change often and typically the tax rates are determined more by political negotiation than by economic forces. This appendix briefly reviews some of the major tax consequences of investing in bonds and stocks.

Although there are many different taxes, the most significant tax is the federal income tax. State and local income taxes take a smaller percentage of an investor's return.

The tax rate applied to investment profits depends on whether the profits are classified as ordinary income (or loss) or capital gain (or loss). Most profits related to interest or cash dividend payments are considered ordinary income. If you own 1,000 shares of CWE, Inc., which paid $3 per share in cash dividends, then you have $3,000, or $3 × 1,000, in ordinary income. Most profits or losses related to price changes are considered capital gains or losses. If you purchased 100 shares of ABM at $30 and subsequently sold them at $35, you have a capital gain of ($35 − $30) × 100 = $500 or $5 per share (ignoring commissions).

Capital gains and losses are further divided into short-term and long-term gains and losses. If a security is held for no longer than 18 months (according to the new 1997 law), the proceeds are classified as a short-term capital gain or loss. If a security is held for more than 18 months, it is classified as a long-term capital gain or loss. Before the new 1997 law was employed, net long-term gains were taxed at a maximum rate of 28%. If your ordinary income tax rate was lower than 28%, net long-term capital gains were taxed at the ordinary income tax rate. Short-term capital gains are taxed at the ordinary income tax rate. With the new 1997 tax law, the 28% rate was reduced to 20% (or 18% if the investment is held for 5 years or more).

Commissions paid to brokers for making security transactions are deducted only after a security is sold. Commissions paid to buy a stock, for example, are considered a increasing the purchase price of the security. If 200 shares purchased at $30 resulted in a $60 commission then the price, including commission (known as the *basis*), is

$$\text{Basis} = \frac{(\$30 \times 200) + \$60}{200} = \$30.30 \text{ per share}$$

If an investor sells 100 shares for $33 (with a $30 commission) after four weeks, the investor's short-term capital gain is

$$(\$33 \times 100) - \$30 - (\$30.30 \times 100) = \$240$$

Exhibit 2A.1 lists the marginal tax rates – the amount of tax imposed on an additional dollar of income – for the four different categories of taxpayers, as well as the corporate tax rates. The tax rates are progressive, because they increase with a taxpayer's income. Hence, tax planning increases in importance as income increases. Exhibit 2A.2 lists the maximum capital gains for various holding periods. The investor can use these various rates to help decide what the holding period should be.

Exhibit 2A.1 Individual and corporate US tax rates

(a) Tax rates for individual investors in 1997

Single—Schedule X

If line 5 is: Over—	But not over—	The tax is:	of the amount over—
$0	$24,650	....................15%	$0
24,650	59,750	$3,697.50 + 28%	24,650
59,750	124,650	13,525.50 + 31%	59,750
124,650	271,050	33,644.50 + 36%	124,650
271,050	....	86,348.50 + 39.6%	271,050

Married filing jointly or Qualifying widow(er)—Schedule Y-1

If line 5 is: Over—	But not over—	The tax is:	of the amount over—
$0	$41,200	....................15%	$0
41,200	99,600	$6,180.00 + 28%	41,200
99,600	151,750	22,532.00 + 31%	99,600
151,750	271,050	38,698.50 + 36%	151,750
271,050	....	81,646.50 + 39.6%	271,050

Head of household—Schedule Z

If line 5 is: Over—	But not over—	The tax is:	of the amount over—
$0	$33,050	....................15%	$0
33,050	85,350	$4,957.50 + 28%	33,050
85,350	138,200	19,601.50 + 31%	85,350
138,200	271,050	35,985.00 + 36%	138,200
271,050	....	83,811.00 + 39.6%	271,050

Married filing separately—Schedule Y-2

If line 5 is: Over—	But not over—	The tax is:	of the amount over—
$0	$20,600	....................15%	$0
20,600	49,800	$3,090.00 + 28%	20,600
49,800	75,875	11,266.00 + 31%	49,800
75,875	135,525	19,349.25 + 36%	75,875
135,525	....	40,823.25 + 39.6%	135,525

Source: US Internal Revenue Service.

(b) US corporate tax rate schedule for 1997

Tax rate	Taxable income
15%	$0–50,000
25%	$50,001–$75,000
34%	$75,001–$100,000
39%[a]	$100,001–$335,000
34%	$335,001–$10,000,000
35%	$10,000,001–$15,000,000
38%[b]	$15,000,001–$18,333,333
35%	Over $18,333,333

[a] Includes additional 5% recapture tax under 1986 law.
[b] Includes additional 3% recapture tax under 1993 law.
Source: US Internal Revenue Service.

2A.1 Bonds

In general, bond coupon payments are considered ordinary income for tax purposes. When a bond is sold before maturity, the bond price changes are treated as capital gains and losses. However, not all bonds are taxable. The most important consideration is whether the bond's coupon payments are subject to federal income taxes. Municipal bonds are exempt from federal income tax. Because of this exemption, municipal bonds typically trade at higher prices (lower yields) than comparable corporate bonds (see

Exhibit 2A.2 US Capital Gains Tax summary*

Holding period of asset or stock	Maximum Capital Gains Tax as of 1997	Maximum Capital Gains Tax prior to 1997
If held between 0 and 12 months	39.6%	39.6%
If held between 12 and 18 months	28%	28%
If held between 18 and 60 months	20%	28%
If held more than 60 months but acquired after 2000	18%	28%

* The 20% rate applies to assets sold between 6 May 1997 and 29 July 1997 and held for between 12 and 18 months. Investors should confirm the applicable tax rates relevant to their situation with the Internal Revenue Service Tax Code.

Chapter 7). Investors in the highest tax bracket may find municipal bonds attractive on an after-tax basis.

Numerous other minor issues should be examined. For example, municipal bonds are typically also exempt from state or local income taxes in the locality where they are issued. Municipal bonds issued by, say, the state of Alabama are exempt from Alabama income tax. Also, investment in some bonds issued at a deep discount (for example, zero-coupon bonds) requires that income tax be paid on the interest accrued each year, even though the interest is not paid until the bond matures. The worst of both worlds can occur with such bonds. An investor might buy a 20-year zero-coupon bond, pay taxes each year on the implied interest (even though the investor receives no interest), and then have the bond default in the last year.

2A.2 Stocks

The cash dividends received from stocks are considered ordinary income. However, stock splits are not considered ordinary income. When a stock splits (say, two shares for each one share owned), the cost basis is adjusted.

For example, if you purchase 100 shares of Microsoft for $90 per share and pay a $50 brokerage commission, your cost basis is

$$\text{Basis} = (\$90 \times 100) + \$50 = \$9,050$$

or $90.50 ($9,050/100) per share. If Microsoft splits 2-for-1, you receive two new shares for every old share. The new basis per share is $45.25($9,050/200), and you own 200 shares. If 100 shares are sold after nine months at $50 per share (with a commission of $30), you will have the following short-term capital gain:

$$\text{Capital gain} = (100 \times \$50) - \$30 - (100 \times \$45.25)$$
$$= \$5,000 - \$30 - \$4,525$$
$$= \$45$$

Like dividends on common stocks, preferred stock dividends are not tax deductible for the company (whereas interest payments are tax deductible). However, 70% of the dividend on preferred stocks is tax exempt to most corporate owners. Thus, companies that purchase preferred shares do not have to pay taxes on 70% of the preferred dividends, although individuals must pay the full income tax rate. Therefore, corporations have an incentive to hold preferred stock, and preferred stock is most suitable for corporate clients.

This appendix has described only the major tax consequences of investment in bonds and stocks. For more information, see Ray Sommerfeld's *Essentials of Taxation* (Reading, Ma: Addison-Wesley, 1989).

Chapter 3

SECURITY MARKETS

Learning objectives

After studying this chapter you should be able to:

1 Describe the function of security markets.
2 Contrast the primary and secondary markets.
3 Explain how the investor can trade, in particular the growing role of Internet trading.
4 Summarize the operation of the secondary market.
5 Describe the basic structure of security markets.
6 Survey world security markets.

INVESTMENT IN THE NEWS

Investing in the future: Charging the net
Merrill to join online brokers it once derided

. . . By July 12, Merrill will introduce a relationship account, with an asset-based fee (minimum $1,500), offering a broker's advice and unlimited trading via the Internet, phone or broker, plus various other perks. By December 1, clients will be able to open accounts with no asset-based fee and no advisor, and be able to trade on the 'Net for as little as $29.99 per transaction.

The move puts Merrill toe-to-toe with Charles Schwab, the leading online broker, with good reason: In the first quarter, Merrill brought in $9 billion of new U.S. client assets versus $28 billion for Schwab. No doubt some of Schwab's gains were Merrill's losses.

In 18 months, John "Launny" Stefens, Merrill's vice chairman and brokerage chief, expects the firm to open 200,000 accounts under the $29.99 trading option and 200,000–300,000 relationship accounts, using the $1,500 fee option. The source: Merrill's existing base of five million accounts and new clients.

"The relationship account, I think, is revolutionary, and it has gotten very little press," says Steffens. "The $29.99 offer is just 10% of the story and it has taken 95% of the press so far."

The relationship account includes services that Stefens values at $600–$800. In addition to unlimited trades, investors get among other things: conventional or online cash-management accounts, which usually cost $100; a Visa signature card allowing no-fee ATM transactions worldwide; access to Merrill Lynch OnLine, and a financial planning package that evaluates an investor's retirement, estate and education needs, which normally costs $250.

Yes, the man who once called online trading hazardous to one's financial health has embraced the World Wide Web. "I can't be the father protectorate," says Stefens. But he maintains that "excessive trading isn't good, whether it's online or anywhere else." . . .

Source: Jacqueline Doherty, *Barron's*, 7 June 1999, p. 13.

Commission fees are one of the main sources of income of brokerage houses. Buying stocks with Merrill Lynch as a broker in the past, you had to pay about a 2% commission fee. Thus, with a $100,000 transaction, paying a fee of $2,500 was very common. High fees have been relegated to history. With the Internet service, Merrill Lynch suggests a commission fee of $29.99 per transaction. No wonder the brokerage firms and, in particular, Merrill Lynch objected in the past to online electronic trading. However, competition is the name of the game. Merrill lost business to brokers such as Charles Schwab and had no choice but to join the Internet trading revolution.

This chapter is a study of security markets – the markets where investors buy and sell the financial assets described in Chapter 2. This task is not as simple as it might seem, because security markets have changed dramatically as technology has improved and Internet investing is increasing. In a sense, learning about security markets is like aiming at a moving target.

As this chapter's *Investment in the news* illustrates, Internet investing is taking off. In many ways the Internet is ideal technology for investment tasks. It's *dynamic*: an investor can get stock quotes that are ahead of those on the 'crawler' ticker at the bottom of the television screen and daily NAVs before they are printed in the next morning's paper. The Internet is *inexpensive*: brokerages often offer lower trade commissions online, because it is cheaper for them to accept trades that way. It's *automated*: normal office hours do not apply, which is crucial in an era when everyone leads hectic lives. It's *searchable*: you can find a wealth of free, sophisticated information that was once available only to wealthy individuals, investment analysts and larger corporations.

Regardless of the changes in security markets, these markets are designed to allow firms to raise funds for growth and capital investment. They are the arenas in which investors – both individual investors and institutional investors – execute their buying and selling decisions. It is this aspect of security markets that we study in this chapter.

Our investigation of markets begins with Section 3.1, a discussion of the reasons why markets exist and the benefits they offer to society. Sections 3.2 and 3.3 explain the institutional structure of security markets. They describe the primary market, where securities are first sold, and the secondary market, where securities are subsequently traded. Section 3.4 describes and compares different methods of trading. In Section 3.5, world security markets are discussed. Finally, security markets are viewed in terms of historical development.

3.1   THE ROLE OF SECURITY MARKETS

A market is the means by which products and services are bought and sold, directly or through an agent. A market need not be a physical location. Indeed, it can be a computer network or a telecommunications system, as described in *Investment in the news*. In a security market, you do not have to possess the security you wish to sell; you can sell a security that you do not own but that you can borrow.

A security market that functions effectively provides society with two benefits. First, it allocates scarce resources – in this case, investors' funds – to those firms that will make the best economic use of them. That is, a well-functioning security market helps suppliers of funds find those who demand funds and will make the best use of them. For example, consider two firms that both need several hundred million dollars for investment. Firm A can make 20% on this investment, whereas Firm B can make only 15% (assume the risk is similar). Suppose there is a limited supply of funds. If the market is efficient and all information is available to potential investors, these investors will be more inclined to buy Stock A than Stock B. Therefore, more money will be allocated to the more profitable firm. Second, a well-functioning security market will reduce the cost of moving in and out of securities, which in turn enlarges the set of investors willing to supply funds; hence, firms will have more funds to invest in production.

A well-functioning security market also benefits buyers and sellers in three ways: by making information available, by establishing prices, and by increasing the liquidity of the assets being bought or sold.

3.1.1 Information availability

Buyers and sellers must be able to communicate with each other and have access to timely and accurate information in a well-functioning security market. Notice that neither criterion requires the buyer and seller (or their representatives) to meet at a physical location.

3.1.2 Price setting

In a well-functioning security market, prices should reflect all the available information. That is, the market price should not misrepresent known information. Price setting has its costs, and for a market to function well, these costs should be minimal. We call these costs of price setting execution costs, and they include *transaction costs, market impact effects* and *inaccurate price discovery*.

Transaction costs include the costs related to communication systems, the costs related to the party who is willing to buy or sell the securities, and any other fees or expenses. When transaction costs are low, more investors are willing to participate in the market.

Market impact effects are price changes that result from buying or selling pressure. For example, a stock may be quoted at $100, but if it has to fall to $90 for an investor to be able to sell 10,000 shares, this market impact effect represents a major cost to the investor.

Inaccurate price discovery refers to securities trading at prices that do not reflect true value. Clearly, buying a stock that is 10% overpriced will be costly. In a well-functioning security market, prices adjust quickly to new information, and securities are correctly priced. If there is a lag between the time when information is available and a price change, price discovery will be inaccurate during this period.

3.1.3 Liquidity

The liquidity of a security market is the ease with which securities can be purchased or sold without a dramatic impact on their prices. When markets are liquid, transactions are completed quickly. For example, the market for US Treasury bills is more liquid than the market for real estate, because $10 million in US Treasury bills can be traded in seconds at their fair market price, whereas trading real estate may take months. The market for stocks and bonds of big companies is more liquid than the market for securities of smaller firms. When markets are liquid, market participants execute trades at existing prices or at prices which are very close to the existing prices. This certainty of quoted prices is called price continuity. If prices are fairly certain and only small changes occur when a trade takes place, we say we have price continuity.

We can measure the liquidity of different security markets by looking at the depth, breadth and resiliency of transactions that occur in each market. If a sufficient number of orders exist at prices above and below the price at which shares are currently trading, the transaction has depth.[1] Otherwise the market is shallow. If a large volume of orders exist at prices above and below the current price, the transaction has breadth. Otherwise, it is called a thin market. If new orders come into the market rapidly when prices change due to an imbalance of orders, the transaction has resiliency.[2]

Exhibit 3.1 illustrates this concept when the current price is assumed to be 99^1/_8$. The exhibit shows hypothetical stock orders at various bid prices as they appear in the Market Maker limit order book. (The concepts of bid price, market maker and limit order will be explained later in the chapter.) Column A demonstrates a thin and shallow market; Column B, a thin and deep market; Column C, a broad and shallow market; and Column D, a broad and deep market. If the market for a given stock is broad and deep, as well as resilient, it is considered to be a relatively liquid market. A transaction can be made in such a market quickly, with no significant price change.

3.2   THE PRIMARY SECURITY MARKET

Securities are traded on two basic markets: the primary market and the secondary market. The primary market is the mechanism through which a firm can raise additional capital by selling stocks, bonds and other securities. All securities are first traded in the primary market, and the proceeds from the sale of securities go to the issuing firm. The issuers of new securities include both corporate and government entities. The secondary market is where previously issued securities trade among investors. Note that the issuing firm does not receive any funds when its securities are traded in the secondary market. However, the secondary market provides liquidity for the newly issued securities in the

Exhibit 3.1 Hypothetical stock orders*

| | Alternative hypothetical orders | | | |
Bid price	A	B	C	D
$100	100	100	1,000	1,000
99$^1/_8$	100	100	1,000	1,000
99$^3/_4$	10	50	0	1,200
99$^5/_8$	5	20	0	1,400
99$^1/_2$	0	10	0	1,500
99$^1/_8$	0	5	0	1,600
99	0	5	0	1,700
Market condition	thin and shallow	thin and deep	broad and shallow	broad and deep

* For simplicity of the discussion, all orders are assumed to be of equal volume. Hence the larger the number of orders, the larger also the volume of orders.

[1] These orders are known as *limit orders* and are covered in Section 3.4.7.
[2] For more information, see Robert A. Schwartz, *Equity Markets: Structure, Trading, and Performance* (New York: Harper & Row, 1988).

primary market. Investors are much more willing to buy securities in the primary market when they know there will be a market in which to trade them in the future. The existence of a well-functioning secondary market thus makes buying securities in the primary market more appealing.

Historically, new issues have been a profitable investment over the short run. To attract willing investors, new issues have been underpriced; that is, they have been sold at a small discount from their fair market value. Thus, the appeal of buying securities in the primary market over the secondary market is the potential for making above-average returns.

Securities traded in the primary market for the very first time are referred to as initial public offerings (IPOs). A company can have only one IPO. If a company has sold stock previously, a new stock offering is called a primary offering or a seasoned new issue. After the initial trading, the securities move to the secondary market. To issue securities in the primary market, a firm must provide a prospectus, a legal document containing the business plan and other information that will help investors make prudent investment decisions.

3.2.1 Investment bankers and underwriting

Security issues in the primary market are usually handled by investment bankers, who assist firms needing funds by locating individuals and firms wanting to invest funds. Investment bankers act as underwriters of a new issue – intermediaries between the buyers and sellers of a new issue, who may also provide a guarantee (for a certain fee) that the new issue is successful.

Underwriters perform different services to firms. Of course, the more services they provide, the larger the underwriting fee. Underwriters may do the following:

1 *Give advice.* Underwriters provide advice as to the type and terms of security to offer and the timing of the issue.
2 *Provide a firm commitment.* In this arrangement the underwriter buys the issue at a predetermined price from the issuing corporation with the expectation of reselling shares of the issue at a higher price.
3 *Make a best effort.* In this arrangement the underwriter markets the new issue as best it can and takes no price risk. The underwriter does not take ownership of the securities.
4 *Issue a standby commitment.* In this arrangement the underwriter buys the remainder of an issue that could not be sold above a specified price. The price that the underwriter must pay is substantially less than the market price; hence, the standby commitment is less risky than the firm commitment (see below).

The largest underwriters are listed in Exhibit 3.2(a). In terms of equity capital, Morgan Stanley/Dean Witter are the largest; however, Goldman Sachs earned the highest profit in 1996. Exhibit 3.2(b) lists some of the new issues brokers in the UK.

Underwriters generate revenues from the firm commitment arrangement, through the difference between the firm commitment price (P_{FC}) and the price received when issued (P_I). The difference between these two prices is referred to as the gross spread (GS) or the underwriter's discount. Thus,

Gross spread = price received by the issue − firm commitment price

or

$$GS = P_I - P_{FC} \qquad (3.1)$$

Exhibit 3.2(a) **How they stack up: profits at some of Wall Street's biggest securities firms (in billions)**

Firm	1996 Profit	Equity capital
Goldman	$2.60[a]	$5.40
Morgan Stanley, Dean Witter	1.96[b]	12.20
Merrill Lynch	1.62	7.30
Salomon	0.62	5.90
Bear Stearns	0.58[c]	3.28
Lehman	0.42	4.10
Paine Webber	0.36	1.84

[a] Goldman profits are stated before taxes and payments to partners.
[b] Morgan Stanley, Dean Witter's profits have been restated to reflect the 1997 merger.
[c] Annualized net income for the 12 months ended 31 December 1996.

Source: *Wall Street Journal*, 5 August 1997, p. C1. Wall Street Journal (Online) by *Wall Street Journal*. © 1997 by Dow Jones & Co., Inc. Reproduced with permission of Dow Jones & Co., Inc. in the format *Fundamentals of Investments* via Copyright Clearance Center.

Exhibit 3.2(b) **Some new issues brokers on the London Stock Exchange in May 2001**

Brewin Dolphin Securities Ltd
Capital International Ltd
Charles Stanley & Co Ltd
Durlacher Ltd
Fyshe Horton Finney Limited
Goodbody Stockbrokers
I A Pritchard Stockbrokers Ltd
Keith, Bayley, Rogers & Co
Kyte Securities, a division of The Kyte Group Ltd
Lloyds TSB Stockbrokers Ltd
Numis Securities Ltd
Peel, Hunt plc
Rathbone Neilson Cobbold Ltd
Redmayne-Bentley
Robson Cotterell Ltd
St Paul's Square Stockbrokers Ltd
Stocktrade, a division of Brewin Dolphin Securities Ltd
The Share Centre Limited
Walker, Crips, Weddle, Beck plc
Wilkinform Stockbrokers Ltd
Wise Speke, a division of Brewin Dolphin Securities Ltd

Source: Website at http://www.londonstockexchange.com/newissues/brokers/brokers.asp, 27 May 2001. © London Stock Exchange 2001. Reprinted with permission.

To illustrate how an investment banker profits from a firm commitment, consider the following example. Morgan Stanley helped issue 100,000 $1,000 par Gulf Stages Inc. 20-year bonds. The firm commitment price was 98.5% of par ($P_{FC} = \$985$), and the issuing price turned out to be 100.50% of par ($P_I = \$1,005.00$). The gross spread per bond was $GS = \$1,005 - \$985 = \$20$, or $2,000,000 for the issue ($20 × 100,000).

The gross spread, given as a percentage of the total proceeds to the firm, varies with the type of issue and its size. The gross spread for IPOs of bonds is about 14% for small issues (less than $1 million) and drops to about 1% for large issues ($50 million or more). For preferred stocks, the range (for the corresponding issue size) is 1.5% to 17%; for common stocks the range is 4% to 22%. If the issue has already traded in the market, the gross spread is much smaller: for stocks, about 15% for an issue of less than

$1 million and about 4% for large issues of more than $50 million. For stock right issues, the fees are much smaller: about 8% for small issues and 4% for large issues. (A stock right issue is an issue of a common stock to existing shareholders at a discount from the market price.) The reason why the spread is smaller for right issues is that rights are offered to the public at a price much lower than the current market price; hence, the underwriter's risk is relatively small. If the stocks are sold as best efforts, the underwriter does not take any risk, and the fee is about one-third (or much less, for large issues) of the gross fee. Usually, even a relatively small fee covers the administrative costs of handling the issue and makes a profit for the investment bank. The main risk faced by underwriters with firm commitments is the possibility of enormous losses between the time the underwriter makes a firm commitment and the time the underwriter sells the securities to the public. If the underwriter is wrong in the anticipated issue price, it could prove costly. Exhibit 3.3 lists the entry fees in the major US stock exchanges.

In an IPO there is no market price of the stock, hence the underwriter may be very wrong in the estimate of the value of the firm, and is therefore vulnerable to a big loss.

Exhibit 3.3 Entry fee comparison: major US stock markets

Number of Shares	Nasdaq National Market	NYSE	Amex	The Nasdaq SmallCap Market
Up to 1 million	$34,525	$51,550	$10,000	$6,000
1+ to 2 million	$38,750	$51,550 – $66,300	$15,000	$6,000 – $7,000
2+ to 3 million	$48,750	$66,300 – $73,700	$20,000	$7,000 – $8,000
3+ to 4 million	$53,750	$73,700 – $81,100	$22,500	$8,000 – $9,000
4+ to 5 million	$60,000	$81,100 – $84,600	$25,000	$9,000 – $10,000
5+ to 6 million	$63,725	$84,600 – $88,100	$27,500	$10,000
6+ to 7 million	$66,875	$88,100 – $91,600	$30,000	$10,000
7+ to 8 million	$69,375	$91,600 – $95,100	$32,500	$10,000
8+ to 9 million	$72,875	$95,100 – $98,600	$35,000	$10,000
9+ to 10 million	$75,625	$98,600 – $102,100	$37,500	$10,000
10+ to 11 million	$78,875	$102,100 – $105,600	$42,500	$10,000
11+ to 12 million	$81,625	$105,600 – $109,100	$42,500	$10,000
12+ to 13 million	$84,875	$109,100 – $112,600	$42,500	$10,000
13+ to 14 million	$87,000	$112,600 – $116,100	$42,500	$10,000
14+ to 15 million	$88,500	$116,100 – $119,600	$42,500	$10,000
15+ to 16 million	$90,500	$119,600 – $123,100	$50,000	$10,000
16+ to 20 million	$95,000	$123,100 – $137,100	$50,000	$10,000
20+ to 25 million	$95,000	$137,100 – $154,600	$50,000	$10,000
25+ to 50 million	$95,000	$154,600 – $242,100	$50,000	$10,000
50+ to 75 million	$95,000	$242,100 – $329,600	$50,000	$10,000
75+ to 100 million	$95,000	$329,600 – $417,100	$50,000	$10,000
100+ to 125 million	$95,000	$417,100 – $500,000[a]	$50,000	$10,000
More than 125 million	$95,000	$500,000[a]	$50,000	$10,000

Fees include one-time initial listing charges of $5,000 for the Nasdaq National Market®, $36,800 for NYSE, $5,000 for Amex®, and $5,000 for The Nasdaq SmallCap Market.

The original fees for the Nasdaq National Market and The Nasdaq SmallCap Market are based on total shares outstanding. The original listing fees for NYSE and Amex are based on the total number of shares outstanding plus any shares reserved for a specific future issuance.

[a] The initial fee component of the original listing fee for common shares is capped at $500,000 including the $36,800 special charge.

Source: The American Stock Exchange, New York Stock Exchange, The Nasdaq Stock Market (March 2000).

The risks of an IPO are demonstrated by the experience of Orbital Science Corporation, a space technologies firm. Orbital Science Corporation specializes in launching satellites into orbit from underneath the wing of a large plane. The firm and underwriter originally scheduled an IPO of stock to occur a month before the first rocket launch. Then an article appeared in the *Wall Street Journal* describing how this first launch could make or break the company. Obviously, there was a risk that the launch would fail and the stock's value would diminish. To reduce the price risk, Orbital Science and the underwriter delayed the issue until the outcome of the launch was known. On 5 April 1990, at 12:10 Pacific Daylight Time, Orbital Science successfully launched its first rocket. On 24 April 1990, Orbital Science sold about 2.4 million shares of stock at $14 per share during its initial public offering.[3] Clearly, an unsuccessful launch would have greatly influenced the issuing price.

If the IPO had not been deployed and the launch had failed, the underwriter could have suffered a very big loss. To reduce this risk exposure, underwriters form syndicates (purchase groups), groups of investment bankers that agree to participate in the risk related to the sale of an IPO. Participation includes accepting part of the risk, as well as part of the potential revenues. The syndicate also forms a selling group that includes the investment bankers in the syndicate, as well as others whose sole focus is distribution of the shares in the IPO. The selling group typically does not take any risk. Exhibit 3.4(a) shows an announcement of an IPO. The syndicate (purchase group) is Bear, Stearns & Co., Inc., Hambrecht & Quist and Wit Capital Corporation (the lead investment bankers). The remaining firms listed make up the selling group. Such an announcement is called a *tombstone*. The IPO is for selling 10,781,250 common shares of drkoop.com, at a price of $9.00 per share. On 2 August 1999, the price of drkoop.com (symbol: 'Koop'), was $21 per share, a rise of 133% from its IPO date.

Exhibit 3.4(b) shows two companies which had gone public in 1999 at the Nasdaq. The exhibit describes all the relevant data of the two stocks, IVGN and BIGI. It is very interesting to look at the price of the stocks in May 2001. The IPO price of IVGN was $15 and the price in May 2001 is $75. But for BIGI the story is not the same. The price of the IPO was $14 but in May 2001, the price of the stock is only $6.

Exhibit 3.4(c) lists some of the IPO filings in the US market in May 2001. The investment banking industry also underwrites issues that are not IPOs, namely stocks of firms that have outstanding shares. In this case, the market price is known. Generally, when additional shares are issued, the price of identical shares outstanding is temporarily depressed, and the underwriter must take this into account. The firm is trying to sell a large number of shares at one time, and there may not be willing buyers. Price pressure from the new supply of shares can result in a significant stock price reduction. For example, when General Motors announced its plans to issue $2.9 billion in new stock, the stock price sank $2.7 per share, to $39.625 (a decline of more than 6%).

In response to this type of problem, in 1982 the Securities and Exchange Commission (SEC) allowed for *shelf registration* under Rule 415 for certain types of securities. This rule allows large firms to register security issues and sell the issues in pieces during the two years following the initial registration (possibly on short notice). Thus, firms can reduce the losses due to price pressure by issuing the shares when the market is strong.

---

[3] Based on several articles appearing in the *Wall Street Journal*, 13 February, 23 March, 26 March, 6 April, and 25 April 1990.

PRACTICE BOX

Problem

Suppose Kidder Peabody was the underwriter of a 3 million common stock issue under a firm commitment. The IPO was issued at \$10 per share, and the firm commitment for \$9.875 per share. What was Kidder Peabody's gross spread? What was the gross spread as a percentage of the firm's proceeds?

Solution

The gross spread is the difference between the issue price and the firm commitment price (see Equation 3.1), or $\$10 - \$9.875 = \$0.125$ per share, or $\$0.125 \times 3$ million $= \$375{,}000$. The firm's proceeds are $\$9.875 \times 3$ million $= \$29.625$ million. Hence, the percentage gross spread is $\$375{,}000/\$29{,}625{,}000 = 0.01266$, or 1.266%.

Exhibit 3.4(a)

This announcement is neither an offer to sell nor a solicitation of an offer to buy any of these securities.
The offering is made only by the Prospectus.

New Issue

10,781,250 Shares

drkoop .com

Common Stock
Price \$9.00 Per Share

Copies of the Prospectus may be obtained in any State in which this announcement is circulated from only such of the Underwriters, including the undersigned, as may lawfully offer these securities in such State.

Bear, Stearns & Co. Inc. | **Hambrecht & Quist** | **Wit Capital Corporation** *as e-Manager™*

Banc of America Securities LLC
Goldman, Sachs & Co.
Warburg Dillon Read LLC
Access Financial Group, Inc.
Chatsworth Securities LLC
Kenny Securities Corp.
Vector Securities International, Inc.

BancBoston Robertson Stephens
ING Baring Furman Selz LLC
Thomas Weisel Partners
William Blair & Company
Friedman, Billings, Ramsey & Co., Inc.
Leerink Swann & Company
Volpe Brown Whelan & Company

Deutsche Banc Alex. Brown
Merrill Lynch & Co.
SG Cowen, B.C. Ziegler and Company
Cantor, Weiss & Friedner, Inc.
Josephthal & Co. Inc.
Southwest Securities
Wunderlich Securities, Inc.

Source: *Wall Street Journal*, 24 June 1999, p. C2. Wall Street Journal (Online) by *Wall Street Journal*. © 1999 by Dow Jones & Co., Inc. Reproduced with permission of Dow Jones & Co., Inc. in the format *Fundamentals of Investments* via Copyright Clearance Center.

Exhibit 3.4(b) Two US listings from the 1999 Nasdaq IPO case studies

Invitrogen Corporation IVGN
Carlsbad, CA

Develops, manufactures, and sells products designed to facilitate molecular biology research.

SIC 2836	Biological Products
CEO	Mr. Lyle C. Turner
CFO	Mr. James R. Glynn
Lead Manager	Donaldson, Lufkin & Jenrette
Co-Managers	Warburg Dillon Read
	U.S. Bancorp Piper Jaffray Inc.
IPO Price	$15.000
IPO Shares	3,500,000
Closing price on first day of trading (26/02/99)	$15.375
Closing price on 31/12/99	$60.000*
Price appreciation from first day traded to year end	290%
Market Makers	8
IPO Market Value	$189,363,150
Market value at end of first day of trading	$194,097,229
Market value as of 31/12/99	$970,920,000

Pinnacle Holdings, Inc. BIGI
Sarasota, FL

Provides wireless communications tower space, primarily in the Southeastern United States.

SIC 4899	Communication Services
CEO	Mr. Robert Wolsey
CFO	Mr. Steven Day
Lead Manager	Deutsche Banc Alex. Brown
Co-Managers	Salomon Smith Barney Inc.
	Banc of America Securities
	Raymond James & Associates, Inc.
IPO Price	$14.0000
IPO Shares	20,000,000
Closing price on first day of trading (19/02/99)	$14.0625
Closing price on 31/12/99	$42.3750†
Price appreciation from first day traded to year end	201%
Market Makers	13
IPO Market Value	$419,999,314
Market value at end of first day of trading	$421,874,311
Market value as of 31/12/99	$1,741,400,625

* The price in May 2001 was $75.
† The price in May 2001 was $6.

Source: Website at http://www.finance.yahoo.com. Nasdaq data © 2002, The Nasdaq Stock Market, Inc. Reprinted with the permission of The Nasdaq Stock Market, Inc.

Exhibit 3.4(c) Some IPO filings in May 2001

Company Name	Symbol	Market	IPO Date	Price	Shares	Received	Form Type
QUANTUM BRIDGE...	QBCI	Nasdaq National Market	–	–	–	5/25/2001	RW
GPC CAPITAL COR ...	GPA	New York Stock Exchange	–	–	–	5/24/2001	RW
ECHAPMAN COM IN...	ECMN	Nasdaq National Market	6/20/2000	13.00	1,260,000	5/23/2001	424B3
SMITH & WOLLENS...	SWRG	Nasdaq National Market	5/23/2001	8.50	5,295,972	5/23/2001	424B4
SMITH & WOLLENS...	SWRG	Nasdaq National Market	5/23/2001	8.50	5,295,972	5/23/2001	S-1MEF
PEABODY ENERGY ...	BTU	New York Stock Exchange	5/22/2001	28.00	15,000,000	5/22/2001	424B1
NATUS MEDICAL I...	BABY	Nasdaq National Market	–	$10.00–$12.00	4,500,000	5/22/2001	S-1/A
PEABODY ENERGY ...	BTU	New York Stock Exchange	5/22/2001	28.00	15,000,000	5/22/2001	424B1
FMC TECHNOLOGIE...	FTI	New York Stock Exchange	–	$19.00–$21.00	8,840,000	5/21/2001	S-1/A
GLOBAL POWER EQ...	GEG	New York Stock Exchange	5/18/2001	20.00	7,350,000	5/21/2001	424B4
PRINCETON REVIE...	REVU	Nasdaq National Market	–	$11.00–$13.00	5,400,000	5/21/2001	S-1/A
KRAFT FOODS INC	KFT	New York Stock Exchange	–	$27.00–$30.00	280,000,000	5/21/2001	S-1/A
MULTILINK TECHN...	MLTC	Nasdaq National Market	–	$10.00	8,000,000	5/18/2001	S-1/A
CHARTER FINANCI...	–	Nasdaq National Market	–	$10.00	5,157,750	5/18/2001	S-1/A
INSTINET GROUP...	INET	Nasdaq National Market	5/18/2001	14.50	32,000,000	5/18/2001	424B1
PEABODY ENERGY ...	BTU	New York Stock Exchange	5/22/2001	28.00	15,000,000	5/17/2001	S-1/A
TELLIUM INC	TELM	Nasdaq National Market	5/17/2001	15.00	9,000,000	5/17/2001	424B4
BIRCH TELECOM I...	–	Nasdaq National Market	–	0	1	5/17/2001	RW
TELLIUM INC	TELM	Nasdaq National Market	5/17/2001	15.00	9,000,000	5/17/2001	S-1MEF
WEBGAIN INC	WEBG	Nasdaq National Market	–	$10.00–$12.00	6,000,000	5/17/2001	S-1/A
KRAFT FOODS INC	KFT	New York Stock Exchange	–	$27.00–$30.00	280,000,000	5/17/2001	S-1/A
INSTINET GROUP ...	INET	Nasdaq National Market	5/18/2001	14.50	32,000,000	5/17/2001	S-1MEF
GLOBAL POWER EQ...	GEG	New York Stock Exchange	5/18/2001	20.00	7,350,000	5/16/2001	S-1/A
INSTINET GROUP...	INET	Nasdaq National Market	5/18/2001	14.50	32,000,000	5/16/2001	S-1/A
SMTC CORP	SMTX	Nasdaq National Market	7/21/2000	16.00	11,000,000	5/16/2001	424B3

Source: Website at http://www.nasdaq.com/reference/IPOs.stm, 27 May 2001. Nasdaq data © 2001, The Nasdaq Stock Market, Inc. Reprinted with the permission of The Nasdaq Stock Market, Inc.

3.2.2 IPOs versus private placement

An alternative way to raise capital in the primary market is through a private placement. A private placement is an offering of a security directly to one investor or group of investors.

For example, on 21 January 1998 the Macerich Company (MAC) raised $100 million from a private placement with Security Capital Group Incorporated (SCZ). A private placement bypasses the public marketplace and is therefore generally less costly than IPOs. Why do firms sometimes select private placements rather than public issues? In the United States, private placements do not require a prospectus. However, a private placement memorandum, which provides information regarding the new issue, is required. A private placement memorandum is less exhaustive than a prospectus. Prior to April 1990, private placements could not be resold for two years. This restriction greatly hampered the private placement market by effectively eliminating any liquidity. In April 1990, however, the SEC adopted Rule 144A, which allows 'large' institutions to trade private placements with other 'large' institutions without having to wait two years or register the placement with the SEC.

Initial public offerings in the United States require prior review by the SEC, as well as compliance with a large number of costly regulations. Section (2) of the Securities Act of 1933 exempts 'nonpublic' or private offerings. Regulation D adopted by the SEC in 1982 gave specific guidelines for what is exempt under Section 4(2) of the 1933 act. These guidelines require no general advertising for private issues. However, the sale must be to 'sophisticated' investors who can evaluate the risk and return and who have substantial economic resources.[4]

Exhibit 3.5(a) shows the instructions for joining the London Stock Exchange. Exhibit 3.5(b) shows the list of rules and regulatory guidance of the London Stock Exchange, and Exhibit 3.5(c) shows the new issues list as of 27 May 2001.

3.2.3 Underpricing IPOs and price discovery

If IBM were to consider issuing stocks when its stock is already traded in the market at $80, the underwriters as well as potential investors would know that the issuing price could not be much further away from $80. IPOs, on the other hand, have no pre-existing market price. Thus, the underwriter has to evaluate and estimate the 'fair' price for the stock. Pricing IPOs is very complicated and requires tools that are covered in the remainder of this book. Setting aside the issue of determining the appropriate value of a security, let us examine why underwriters tend to underprice IPOs relative to their 'fair' value.

Underwriters face a dilemma in pricing IPOs. If they overprice the issue, then the investors who buy the IPOs will lose both money and trust in the investment bankers. If they underprice the issue, then the issuing firm will lose both capital and trust in the investment bankers. On average, underwriters historically have underpriced IPOs.[5] For example, during the week 14–18 June 1999, 10 IPOs came to the market, raising $1.2 billion. Because of the underpricing, these 10 IPOs averaged a 35% gain on the first day of trade, with 'PHONE.COM' picking up 150.8% on the first day of trade!

Several explanations are often given for IPO underpricing:

1 *Information asymmetry.* Differences in the information available to the firm, investment banker and potential investors is known as information asymmetry. For example, the firm and the investment banker may have better information than investors. If this is the case, the investors who are less informed will have greater

[4] For more details, see Frank J. Fabozzi and Franco Modigliani, *Capital Markets Institutions and Instruments* (Englewood Cliffs, NJ: Prentice-Hall, 1992).

[5] See Clifford W. Smith, 'Investment banking and the capital acquisition process', *Journal of Financial Economics*, 15 (January–February 1986): 3–29.

Exhibit 3.5(a) **Instructions for joining the London Stock Exchange**

HOW TO JOIN OUR MARKETS

We provide a range of markets for UK and international companies of all sizes to facilitate capital raising and trading in their shares. This section gives companies an overview of the markets and information on how to join them.

The London Stock Exchange plays a vital role in maintaining London's position as one of the world's leading financial centres. As the national stock exchange for the UK and the world's main marketplace for listing UK and international equities, the Exchange provides an environment where the trading of securities can flourish.

The Exchange provides a choice of markets – allowing companies large and small to raise capital and to have their shares traded publicly. Companies can join either the main market or the **Alternative Investment Market (AIM)**. Technology companies joining the main market may also be eligible to join **techMARK**, the Exchange's new market for innovative technology companies. The companies on the Exchange's markets represent over 60 countries from around the world. By listing in London, these companies have been able to reach a substantial and diverse investor base and to raise funds in the world's most heavily traded international market.

The Exchange regulates capital raising, assessing the applications of companies, monitoring listed and AIM companies' ongoing compliance with the rules, and dealing with any rule breaches. In the secondary market, in its role as a Recognised Investment Exchange (RIE), the Exchange is responsible for maintaining orderly markets and protecting against market abuse.

A two-stage admission process applies to companies that list in London. A company's securities need to be admitted to the Official List by the UK Listing Authority (UKLA), a division of the Financial Services Authority, and also admitted to trading by the Exchange. Once both processes are complete, the securities are officially listed on the Exchange. In parallel to the UKLA's listing process, the Exchange has its own set of Admission and Disclosure Standards which are designed to sit alongside the UKLA's Listing Rules to make access to the Exchange as straightforward as possible.

The Standards, which can be downloaded **here** contain admission requirements and ongoing disclosure requirements to be observed by companies seeking admission, or already admitted, to trading on our markets for listed securities. They do not apply to companies seeking to be admitted to AIM, our market for unlisted securities.

For further information about the admission process, please contact the Company Services Help Line on 020-7797-1600.

The Exchange has revised its 'Admission and Disclosure Standards'. The revised standards, which detail the Exchange's role in the admission of securities to trading, will come into effect on 1 June 2001. The Exchange has made a number of changes including:

- the techMARK eligibility and admission criteria have been incorporated into the Standards and revised to enable the inclusion of listed international equity securities and retail depositary receipts;
- a requirement that techMARK securities must be eligible for electronic settlement and admitted to trading on the London Stock Exchange's Domestic Equity Market ("DEM"); a requirement that all applications for admission to techMARK must be supported by a written submission;
- an obligation to submit information for the New Issues List with consequent inclusion of the New Issues Form in the Standards; and
- the removal of the requirement for the Block Admission Six Monthly Return (Schedule 2) to be submitted.

The changes to the techMARK eligibility criteria are supported by an extension of the arrangements for the admission of international companies to the DEM announced in January 2001. From 1 June 2001 international companies will be eligible for admission to the DEM where:

- they are either joining techMARK or are constituents of the Eurotop 300 or S&P 500 indices;
- they are admitted to the UK Listing Authority's Official List (either primary or secondary listing);
- there are adequate arrangements for electronic settlement by UK investors; and
- the issuer pays fees at the UK rate.

All trading and reporting obligations, as set out in the Rules of the London Stock Exchange, will apply to any security admitted to the DEM. The platform (SETS, SEAQ etc) used to trade the securities will depend on the same measures, including liquidity, as for securities issued by companies incorporated in the UK.

As a domestic company with equity lines of stock listed on the London Stock Exchange, you will be provided with free access to our new Company Report Service. This is a secure website that provides high quality interactive reports of your company's market performance, covering share price, trading and market value movements over the previous month and in the last 12 months. It allows you to select up to 5 key competitors/peers to benchmark your company's performance against. For more details of this service, select the 'Your Company Report', button.

For more information on the markets, please see the **Regulatory Guides** section and the **Stock Exchange Notices** section. Notices are issued periodically throughout the year and contain information of a regulatory nature and amendments to rules and/or guidance.

Source: Website at http://www.londonstockexchange.com/join/default.asp, 27 May 2001. © London Stock Exchange 2001. Reprinted with permission.

Exhibit 3.5(b) Rules and regulatory guidance for the London Stock Exchange

RULES & REGULATORY GUIDANCE

This section provides details about the regulatory role of the London Stock Exchange as well as Stock Exchange Notices, Regulatory Guides and Making a complaint.

Overview of the Exchange's regulatory role.

Regulatory Forms contains a number of standard forms in PDF format, which are used by member firms for regulatory purposes. Each form can be downloaded, printed, completed and returned to the relevant Exchange department.

Market Rules contains all chapters of "Rules of the London Stock Exchange" and rule update pages issued this year – Intended audience – member firms.

Stock Exchange Notices provides a search engine for new and historic Notices together with a **registration facility**. Intended audience – member firms and market professionals.

Regulatory Guides provide rules and guidance for the markets of the London Stock Exchange. Intended audience – member firms and market professionals.

Global lending agreement contains the prescribed agreement for on-exchange stock borrowing and lending transactions – intended audience member firms and market participants.

Making a complaint explains what to do if you have a complaint and how to make it. Intended audience – private investors.

List of Member Firms provides both an alphabetical and a regional list of member firms of the London Stock Exchange. Intended audience – member firms, market professionals and private investors.

Source: Website at http://www.londonstockexchange.com/regulation/default.asp, 27 May 2001. © London Stock Exchange 2001. Reprinted with permission.

Exhibit 3.5(c) London Stock Exchange new issues list on 27 May 2001

NEW ISSUES

The New Issues List is a list of all new companies which are either seeking admission to one of our markets or have been admitted to trading within the last seven days. This list provides basic information on the company, terms of the offer and its sponsors.

Company name ▼▲	Market ▼▲	Expected first day of trading ▼▲	Expected offer price (p)	Method of issue
Pursuit Dynamics plc	AIM	23/05/2001	N/A	N/A
Imprint Search and Selection plc	**AIM**	**23/05/2001**	**80p**	**Placing**
Transware plc	techMARK	21/06/2001	N/A	Introduction
Friends Provident Group Plc	**Main**	**09/07/2001**	**N/A**	**N/A**
Atlantic Global Plc	AIM	May 2001	25p	Placing
Cytomyx Holdings plc	**AIM**	**TBC**	**TBC**	**TBC**
Digital Broadcasting Corporation Plc	AIM	TBC	TBC	TBC
Picardy Media Group Plc	**AIM**	**TBC**	**N/A**	**N/A**

Source: Website at http://www.londonstockexchange.com/newissues/brokers/brokers.asp, 27 May 2001. © London Stock Exchange 2001. Reprinted with permission.

uncertainty about the issue and therefore will not buy it unless they are offered a lower price. Higher potential returns must be offered to attract investors to participate in the IPO market. These higher returns translate into underpricing.

2 *Scalping.* Higher returns have to be offered, because investment bankers and their affiliates tend to buy the really 'good' issues and leave the 'scraps' to the investing public. This skimming of quality issues is called scalping. To compensate the public for buying the 'scraps', a higher return should be offered, which again implies underpricing.

3 *Liquidity.* One benefit provided by the secondary market is liquidity. Investors will not buy IPOs that subsequently are hard to sell. One argument for why IPOs are underpriced is that underpricing is compensation for the relatively low liquidity. Also, there is uncertainty regarding the degree of liquidity that a security will subsequently command. Will there be any active trading in the future? This lack of liquidity is paid for by the firm by underpricing its IPO.

4 *Appraisal costs.* Assessing the fair value of an IPO has a cost. This cost has to be compensated. The prospectus must be studied, market data have to be collected and evaluated, and industry analysis is usually performed. If only one investor had to incur this cost, perhaps it would be negligible. Unfortunately, stock exchanges require a wide ownership of shares to facilitate trading and limit corporate control. Thus, every IPO must be evaluated by many investors. The more investors there are, the higher the total appraisal cost will be.

For example, if one investor buys the entire $100 million IPO and has $1,000 appraisal costs, the IPO should be underpriced by 0.001% ($1,000/$100,000,000). However, if 1,000 investors each buy $100,000 of the IPO, each investor's cost will be 1% ($1,000/$100,000), so the IPO likewise must be underpriced by 1%. In this case, the total appraisal cost is $1,000,000, or 1,000 × $1,000. Thus, private placements are less costly because they are evaluated by only one investor.

Obviously, when an IPO is substantially underpriced, the issuing firm suffers a loss because it could issue the stocks at a higher price and obtain more cash inflow per share. The underwriter has an interest in underwriting the issue to protect itself from potential loss. Recently, firms have broken the tradition and go through OpenIPO. Exhibit 3.6 provides the details of some companies who completed the process of an OpenIPO. By opening an account, every individual can bid for the IPO through the Internet. The first main feature of this OpenIPO is that it is sold at an auction in a price range of $10.50−$13.50 per share. Thus, if the stock is relatively highly evaluated by the investor, it will be sold close to the upper bound and the loss to the issuing firm is minimized. If the investor thinks that the stock is not worth much, it will end up closer to the lower bound. The second feature is that large institutional investors and individual investors have an equal chance to bid for the IPO.

3.3 THE SECONDARY SECURITY MARKET

In the secondary market, previously issued securities are traded between investors. The proceeds of selling a security go to the current owner of the security, not to the original issuing company. The secondary market provides liquidity to individuals who acquire securities in the primary market. The secondary market consists of major stock exchanges and over-the-counter markets. The most well-known and active stock exchanges are the New York Stock Exchange (NYSE), the American Stock

Exhibit 3.6

Completed OpenIPOs

$16,000,000 Briazz, Inc. (BRZZ) OpenIPO Lead Manager Offering Price: $8 Date: 5/02/01	**$26,400,000** Peet's Coffee & Tea (PEET) OpenIPO Lead Manager Offering Price: $8 Date: 1/25/01	**$42,000,000** **NOGA**TECH Nogatech, Inc. (NGTC) OpenIPO Lead Manager Offering Price: $12 Date: 5/17/00	**$82,800,000** Andover.net (ANDN) OpenIPO Lead Manager Offering Price: $18 Date: 12/8/99
$27,300,000 **salon.com** Salon.com (SALN) OpenIPO Lead Manager Offering Price: $10.50 Date: 6/22/99	**$11,550,000** RAVENSWOOD Ravenswood (RVWD) OpenIPO Lead Manager Offering Price: $10.50 Date: 4/9/99		

Source: Website at http://www.wrhambrecht.com/ind/auctions/openipo/completed.html, 10 February 2002. Reprinted with permission.
OpenIPO levels the playing field in initial public offerings, allowing individuals and institutional investors to bid online for shares in an IPO. All investors end up paying the same price – a price determined by the auction. WR Hambrecht & Co, for example, founded in 1998 by William R. Hambrecht, is a financial services firm committed to using the Internet and auction process to level the playing field for investors and issuers. The firm's impartial Internet-based auctions, which allow the market to determine pricing and allocation, are dramatically changing the financial services landscape.

Exchange (AMEX) and the Tokyo Stock Exchange (TSE). In over-the-counter (OTC) markets, transactions are conducted by the National Association of Securities Dealers' Automated Quotations (Nasdaq) system, interbank markets, and major commodity and derivative exchanges. The Chicago Board of Trade (CBOT) and the Chicago Mercantile Exchange (CME) are exchanges where commodity and derivative securities such as stock options are traded.

The New York Stock Exchange is the oldest (established in 1792) and the largest stock exchange in the United States. Stocks were auctioned alongside bonds and lottery tickets whenever wealthy investors needed some cash. They signed the Buttonwood Agreement, named after a buttonwood tree in Wall Street under which securities traders met. The pact obligated them to 'give preference' to one another in stock trading and collect a minimum fixed commission on stock sales. Buttonwood's effect became clear when winter came. The 24 brokers moved their business to a cosy back room of Wall Street's Tontine Coffee House, leaving other auctioneers and brokers shivering in the cold. The NYSE is also called the Big Board or simply The Exchange. The NYSE is a corporation governed by a board of directors composed of 27 individuals representing the public and the exchange membership. The chairman and presidents are appointed and the remaining board of members are elected by the members of the exchange. The total number of voting members is fixed at 1,366 'seats', which are owned by individuals, usually officers of security firms. When members die or retire, the seats are usually auctioned to bidders approved for membership by the NYSE. The price of the seats varies from as low as $35,000 in 1977 to more than $2.6 million in 2002. In comparison, a seat on the AMEX sold for $260,000 on 13 February 2002 – considerably less than for a seat on the NYSE.[6] The higher the potential income of the member because of the ownership of a seat, the higher the price of the seat (for example, in January 2002 the daily average volume of stock traded on the NYSE was 1,426 billion compared with about 51 million on AMEX).

About 28,000 corporations are listed on the NYSE,[7] with nearly $16 trillion in global market capitalization. The stocks, bonds, options, rights and warrants of these corporations are traded in 20 trading posts, each representing the market for all securities located on the *floor*.

A large range of trading activities is conducted in the secondary market. Transactions in this market are categorized as follows.

First market transactions are trades of securities that are actually made on the floor of the exchange on which the security is listed. For example, AT&T is a stock that is traded on the NYSE. When AT&T is traded on the NYSE, it is said to be traded in the first market. Similarly, when Carmel (less well known than AT&T) is traded on the AMEX, it is said to be traded on the first market. Exhibit 3.7 shows a post of a specialist (left corner) as well as the various people involved with the trade and the various screens with current information on the traded stocks. As we can see, nowadays the scene of trading is more like a beehive than a quiet buttonwood tree.

Exhibit 3.7 Part of the NYSE trading floor

Source: Used with permission of the New York Stock Exchange.

---

[6] See 'AMEX STATS' at http://www.AMEX.com.
[7] We recommend that you visit the NYSE website at www.nyse.com for the most recent information.

Second market transactions are over-the-counter (OTC) trades that are made in the over-the-counter market. The OTC is not a formal exchange. There are no membership requirements, and thousands of brokers register with the SEC as dealers on the market. The NASD (National Association of Securities Dealers) is a nonprofit organization formed under the joint sponsorship of the Investment Bankers' Conference and the Securities and Exchange Commission. NASD members include virtually all investment houses and firms dealing with the OTC market. The NASD establishes and enforces fair and equitable rules for security trading on the OTC. The NASD owns the Nasdaq, which is a computerized system that provides brokers and dealers with price quotations for securities traded on OTC markets as well as for many NYSE-linked securities. A security traded on OTC must, however, be listed on the computer-linked network called Nasdaq. Thus, the over-the-counter market is a telephone- and computer-linked network for trading securities. Securities listed on the OTC market are not listed on an exchange. Generally, securities of small firms which do not meet the requirements of the NYSE or AMEX (earlier) listings are traded on the OTC market (the OTC market will be discussed in more detail later in the chapter).

Third market transactions are trades in *exchange-listed* issues that take place off the exchange floor with the aid of brokers. An example would be an AT&T trade that is conducted through an OTC market. (Recall that AT&T is listed on the NYSE.)

Fourth market transactions are trades in exchange-listed issues that are arranged by the buyers and sellers off the exchange floor, without the aid of brokers. An example would be trading AT&T with your uncle.[8]

Upstairs market transactions are trades that are arranged from a network of trading desks that negotiate large block transactions.

Securities can be listed on more than one exchange. This is known as dual listing. Dual listing enhances the level of competition and is thought to lower the cost of trading.[9] Dual listing in international markets, as well as on the east and west coasts in the United States, expands the hours when trading can occur. There are various regulations restricting dual listings. For example, securities listed on the NYSE cannot also be listed on the AMEX.

The NYSE is the most important US exchange, and it celebrated its 200th birthday in 1992. Institutional investors play a major role in trading on the NYSE. (The ownership of shares by households and non-profit organizations fell from 91.3% in 1950 to 47.7%

Exhibit 3.8(a) Listing requirements for the NYSE, AMEX and Nasdaq

Characteristic	NYSE	AMEX	Nasdaq
Minimum shares publicly held	1.1 million	0.5 million	1.0 million
Minimum number of shareholders	2,000	800	300
Minimum pre-tax income last year	$2.5 million	$0.75 million	–
Minimum market capitalization	$10 million	$3 million	$50 million

---

[8] The back of a stock certificate, like a title to an automobile, contains the appropriate forms for transferring ownership. The stock certificate is then mailed to the corporate registrar, who will issue a new certificate.

[9] Some argue that dual listing actually increases the cost of trading, because multiple dealers all have to cover the same fixed expenses with lower volume.

Exhibit 3.8(b) New York Stock Exchange listing requirements

Minimum Distribution Criteria		Requirements
Shareholders[A]		
Round-lot holders (holders of a unit of trading – generally 100 shares)		2,000
or		
Total shareholders together with		2,200
Average monthly trading volume (for the most recent six months)		100,000 shares
or		
Total shareholders together with		500
Average monthly trading volume (for most recent twelve months)		1,000,000 shares
Public shares[B]		1,100,000 outstanding
Market value of public shares[B,C]		$60,000,000 (IPOs, spin-offs & carve-outs)
		$100,000,000 (public companies)
Minimum Quantitative standards		
Earnings		
Aggregate for the last three years achieved as	Pre-tax earnings[D]	$6,500,000
Most recent year	Pre-tax earnings[D]	$2,500,000
Each of the two preceeding years	Pre-tax earnings[D]	$2,000,000
or		
Most recent year (all three years must be profitable)	Pre-tax earnings[D]	$4,500,000
or		
Operating cash flow		
For companies with not less than $500 million in global market capitalization and $100 million in revenues in the last 12 months:		
Aggregate for the last three years[E] (each year must be a positive amount)	Adjusted cash flow	$25,000,000
or		
Global market capitalization		
Revenues for last fiscal year		$100,000,000
and average global market capitalization[F].		$1,000,000,000

[A] The number of beneficial holders of stock held in "street name" will be considered in addition to the holders of record. The exchange will make any necessary check of such holdings that are in the name of exchange member organizations.

[B] In connection with initial public offerings (including spin-offs and carve-outs), the NYSE requires a letter of undertaking from the company's underwriter or representations from a financial advisor in the case of a spin-off to ensure that the offering or distribution will meet or exceed NYSE standards.

[C] Shares held by directors, officers or their immediate families and other concentrated holdings of 10% or more are excluded in calculating the number of publicly held shares. If a company either has a significant concentration of stock, or if changing market forces have adversely impacted the public market value of a company which otherwise would qualify for listing on the exchange, such that its public market value is no more than 10 per cent below $60,000,000 or $100,000,000 as applicable, the exchange will generally consider $60,000,000 or $100,000,000, as applicable, in stockholders' equity as an alternate measure of size and therefore as an alternate basis on which to list the company.

[D] Pre-tax earnings is adjusted for various items as defined in the NYSE Listed Company Manual.

[E] Represents net cash provided by operating activities excluding the changes in working capital or in operating assets and liabilities, as adjusted for various items defined in the NYSE Listed Company Manual.

[F] Average global market capitalization for already existing public companies is represented by the most recent six months of trading history. For IPOs, spin-offs, and carve-outs it is represented by the valuation of the company as demonstrated in the case of a spin-off, by the distribution ratio as priced or, in the case of an IPO/carve-out, the as priced offering in relation to the company's total valuation.

Source: Website at http://www.nyse.com/pdfs/04_LISTEDCOMPANIES.pdf, 12 March 2002. Used with permission of the NYSE.

Exhibit 3.8(c)
AMEX listing guidelines for international companies

Regular financial guidelines	
Pre-tax income	$750,000 latest fiscal year or in 2 of most recent 3 fiscal years
Market value of public float	$3,000,000
Price	$3
Operating history	–
Stockholders' equity	$4,000,000

Alternative financial guidelines	
Pre-tax income	–
Market value of public float	$15,000,000
Price	$3
Operating history	2 years
Stockholders' equity	$4,000,000

Distribution guidelines
(applicable to regular and
alternative guidelines)

Alternative 1	
Public float	500,000
Public stockholders	800
Average daily volume	–

Alternative 2	
Public float	1,000,000
Public stockholders	400
Average daily volume	–

Alternative 3	
Public float	500,000
Public stockholders	400
Average daily volume	2,000

Alternative 4	
Public float	1,000,000 worldwide
Public stockholders	800 worldwide
Average daily volume	–

Source: Website at http://www.amex.com/about/amex_listonu.stm, 27 May 2001. Reprinted with permission.

in the third quarter of 1996).[10] Shares are owned primarily by institutional investors, including mutual funds. As will be discussed later, the stock exchanges responded to this changing composition by catering more to institutional investors (although not neglecting the needs of individual investors).

In order for stocks to trade on exchanges, minimum requirements have to be met. Exhibit 3.8(a) presents the minimum listing requirements for the NYSE, AMEX and Nasdaq. Exhibit 3.8(b) shows the full listing requirements at the NYSE, Exhibit 3.8(c) shows the listing requirements for international companies, and Exhibit 3.8(d) is a short list of some of the international companies that joined the AMEX in 1999.

---

[10] See 'Mutual funds: navigating the future', *Fortune*, 24 November 1997, p. S4.

Exhibit 3.8(d) Some of the international companies that joined the AMEX in 1999

Issuer	Country	Market[1]	Offer Price	Global Offering Value[2]	Market Value	Offer Date	Lead Managers	Co-Managers	Issuer Legal Counsel
Ebookers.com	United Kingdom	NNM	18.000	70,380,000		11/10/1999	J.P. Morgan Securities	Commerzbank AG / Salomon Smith Barney Inc. / SG Cowen Securities Corporation	Brobeck Hale and Dorr International
QXL.com	United Kingdom	NNM	16.150	90,440,000	367,489,729	10/07/1999	Credit Suisse First Boston	Robertson Stephens / SG Cowen Securities Corporation / Warburg Dillon Read	
i-Cable Communications Ltd	China	NNM	27.000	522,450,000	2,160,000,000	11/18/1999	Merrill Lynch & Co.	Lehman Brothers / Morgan Stanley Dean Witter	Rogers & Wells
MIH Limited	Virgin Islands	NNM	18.000	187,830,000	898,051,950	04/13/1999	Merrill Lynch & Co.	Donaldson, Lufkin & Jenrette	Harney, Westwood & Riegels / Cravath Swaine & Moore
PrimaCom AG	Germany	NNM	16.250	163,569,000	641,177,940	02/19/1999	Morgan Stanley Dean Witter / Dresdner Kleinwort Benson North America	LB Rheinland Pfalz / Lehman Brothers / Paribas Corporation	Baker & McKenzie
United Pan Europe Communications NV	Netherlands	NNM	32.780	1,461,988,000	4,085,899,912	02/12/1999	Goldman, Sachs & Co. / Morgan Stanley Dean Witter	Donaldson, Lufkin & Jenrette	Holme Roberts & Owen LLP
ECtel Ltd	Israel	NNM	12.000	42,000,000	186,750,000	10/26/1999	Chase H & Q	Salomon Smith Barney Inc. / CIBC World Markets	Fulbright & Jaworski L.L.P.
Qiao Xing Universal Telephone, Inc.	China	NNM	5.500	8,800,000	52,800,000	02/17/1999	Barron Chase Securities, Inc.		
Optibase Ltd.	Israel	NNM	7.000	30,450,000	57,001,000	04/07/1999	C.E. Unterberg, Towbin Co.	Needham & Company, Inc. / Nomura Securities International, Inc. / Oddo Et Enterprise	
China.com	China	NNM	20.000	96,600,000	422,138,400	07/12/1999	Lehman Brothers	Bear, Stearns & Co.	Rogers & Wells
El Sitio Inc	Argentina	NNM	16.000	150,880,000	617,191,360	12/09/1999	Credit Suisse First Boston / Lehman Brothers	Merrill Lynch & Co. / Salomon Smith Barney Inc. / WIT Capital Corporation	Conyers, Dill & Pearman / Paul, Hastings, Janofsky & Walker
Freeserve	United Kingdom	NNM	23.670	362,254,000		07/25/1999	Credit Suisse First Boston	Robertson Stephens / Cazenove Incorporated / Donaldson, Lufkin & Jenrette / Merrill Lynch & Co. / Warburg Dillon Read	Shearman & Sterling
Korea Thrunet Co., Ltd	Korea	NNM	18.000	209,070,000	1,186,508,592	11/16/1999	Lehman Brothers	Bear, Stearns & Co. / CIBC World Markets	Shearman & Sterling
Satyam Infoway Ltd	India	NNM	18.000	86,423,000	380,808,000	10/18/1999	Merrill Lynch & Co.	Salomon Smith Barney Inc.	Latham & Watkins
Infosys Technologies Limited	India	NNM	34.000	70,380,000	1,119,769,600	03/11/1999	Banc of America Securities	Robertson Stephens / Deutsche Banc Alex. Brown / Thomas Weisel Partners L.L.C.	Wilson Sonsini Goodrich & Rosat
Radware Ltd	Israel	NNM	18.000	81,900,000	262,875,762	09/29/1999	Salomon Smith Barney Inc.	CIBC World Markets / U.S. Bancorp Piper Jaffray Inc.	
E-Cruiter.com	Canada	SCM	6.000	14,700,000	44,283,666	12/07/1999	Whale Securities Co., L.P.		Weil Gotshal & Manges

Source. Website at http://www.amex.com

The NYSE and the AMEX are national exchanges; they trade securities that command a national, and sometimes international, investor following. There are other stock exchanges in the United States besides the NYSE and the AMEX that cater to securities that have only regional interests. The trading volume on these exchanges is much lower. Regional stock exchanges include the Midwest Stock Exchange, the Pacific Stock Exchange, the Boston Stock Exchange and the Philadelphia Stock Exchange.

An alternative to trading on a stock exchange is the OTC market. As mentioned above, the OTC market is traditionally for securities of smaller companies. However, there are exceptions, such as Intel, Microsoft, Netscape and Apple Computer, which are large firms whose stocks trade on the OTC market. The decision of where to list a security is primarily made by the company issuing stock to the public.

Stocks are traded on the OTC market in several ways. First, the OTC traded stocks are generally less active issues that are usually traded in regional brokerage offices. For example, a small Alabama firm's stock may trade only within the Southeast. This firm could opt for a regional stock exchange. Second, the OTC market trades less active issues that have national trading activity. For these issues, quotations are reported daily on 'pink sheets' that are mailed to national brokers by the National Quotations Bureau. Third, the OTC market trades issues that are listed on the Nasdaq. Trade on the Nasdaq system, however, is not limited to only the OTC stocks. Actually, the Nasdaq is an electronic trading system and stocks linked on NYSE and AMEX can also be traded on this system.

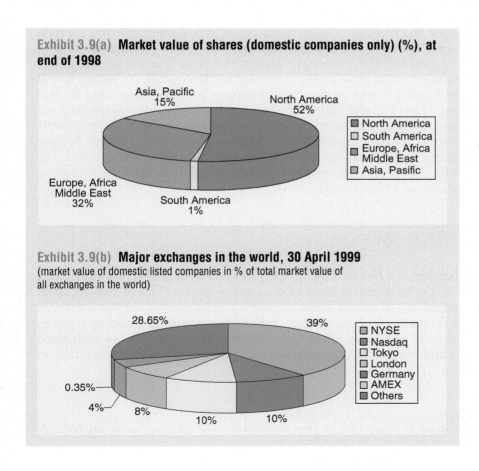

Exhibit 3.9(a) **Market value of shares (domestic companies only) (%), at end of 1998**

Asia, Pacific 15%
North America 52%
Europe, Africa Middle East 32%
South America 1%

Legend:
- North America
- South America
- Europe, Africa Middle East
- Asia, Pasific

Exhibit 3.9(b) **Major exchanges in the world, 30 April 1999**
(market value of domestic listed companies in % of total market value of all exchanges in the world)

28.65%
39%
0.35%
4%
8%
10%
10%

Legend:
- NYSE
- Nasdaq
- Tokyo
- London
- Germany
- AMEX
- Others

The Nasdaq lists over 5,540 domestic and foreign companies. In 1996, the share volume was 138.1 billion shares, with a dollar volume of $3.3 trillion, surpassing the other markets.[11] Finally, the OTC market's most actively traded issues are listed on the Nasdaq's more sophisticated system, called the National Market System (NMS).

Exhibit 3.9(a) shows the market value of various regions in the world as a percentage of the total value in the world. The exchanges in North America have 52% of the total world value, while Europe, Africa and the Middle East have 32%. However, Europe's total value is growing faster than the North American value. The value of Europe's exchange rose by 27.4% in 1998, while in North America the total market value rose by 19.2%. Exhibit 3.9(b) shows the market capitalization distribution of the major exchanges. Once again, the NYSE dominates the market for equity, with 39% of the total equity.

In 1998 a possible merger between Nasdaq and AMEX was discussed. If approved by the membership of both exchanges, as well as the SEC, the make-up of the financial markets will change. Among the benefits cited are better quality trades and lower costs. In April 1998 the merger was approved by both the Nasdaq and AMEX boards of directors.

The secondary market must be sensitive to investor needs. Providing a secondary market is a competitive business, with the market shares going to those exchanges that best serve the investors at the lowest cost. An exchange is constantly trying to attract firms that will allow it to trade their shares. Exchanges have distinguished themselves in many different ways. For example, the NYSE and the AMEX cater to larger firms, whereas the OTC market primarily caters to smaller firms. To understand the importance of the various exchanges, note that when we measure size by the volume of shares traded, then the Nasdaq is larger than the NYSE, AMEX and the regional exchanges together. However, when size is measured by volume in dollars, its proportion declines (since dollar values are almost the same size for all the above exchanges), because relatively small stocks are traded on the Nasdaq. No matter how it is measured, the Nasdaq is one of the most important trading systems and its role continues to grow. The NYSE and other exchanges are moving quickly towards 24-hour trading to increase trading activity and respond to investor demand. Some markets already offer investors the opportunity to trade 24 hours a day. The idea that 24-hour trading will increase trading activity has been validated in many circumstances. For example, US dollar index futures contracts experienced a 35% increase in trading during the first month of 24-hour trading.[12]

3.4   TRADING MECHANICS

The actual mechanisms in a financial market that facilitate trading are known as market microstructure, or the institutional setup of a securities market. This section identifies some typical setups and discusses some underlying principles of market design. It reviews some of the goals of trading systems, various participants in securities markets, and the establishment of market prices. Also included is an overview of automated trading systems and various issues important to investors when they are trying to execute a trade.

---

[11] See the Nasdaq website at http://www.NASDAQ.com.
[12] Based on a letter dated 31 March 1992 by Peter Burton, director of Financial Instruments Exchange (FINEX), a division of then New York Cotton Exchange.

3.4.1 **Securities trading systems**

The trading of securities is conducted by members of the exchange or by an official of the exchange. However, trades are not conducted in the same manner in all stock exchanges around the world (or even in the United States). The three main trading systems are the call market, continuous market and mixed market.

In the call market, trading and prices are determined at a specified time during the day by a designated person collecting all of the buy and sell orders and then determining the equilibrium price (that is, the price where supply and demand are equal). For example, suppose that by 2:00 p.m. the total accumulated buy orders by all investors in Sabra stock is as follows:

- Buy 60 shares at $13 per share or less
- Buy 70 shares at $12 per share or less
- Buy 80 shares at $11 per share or less
- Buy 100 shares at $10 per share or less.

Note that the higher price is associated with a smaller number of shares demanded. Similarly, the following might be the aggregate supply of orders:

- Sell 10 shares at $11 per share or more
- Sell 40 shares at $12 per share or more
- Sell 70 shares at $13 per share or more
- Sell 150 shares at $14 per share or more.

Note that the higher the price, the more shares are made available to sell. From the aggregate supply and demand information, we see that the equilibrium price is $13 per share and 60 shares traded. Those investors wanting to sell securities at a higher price than $13 will be unable to find a buyer, and those wishing to buy securities at a price less than $13 will be unable to find a seller. Also note that in our example a total of 70 shares were offered for sale at a price of $13; however, the investors were willing to purchase only 60 shares at this price, leaving 10 sell orders not executed. In practice, demand is always equal to supply at a given price. If the investors wish to sell these 10 shares, they must decrease the price to, say, $12^1/_2$ in order to create new demand and supply functions until equilibrium is reached. When trade in one security is finished, trade in the second security takes place, and so on until all securities are traded. All unfulfilled orders can be resubmitted the following day or the next time the security is traded. Call market trading usually occurs once a day, but in some countries it can occur two to three times a day.

Call market trading is common in Hong Kong, Austria and Norway. In most large exchanges (for example, in the United States, Canada and the United Kingdom), where the volume of trading and the number of listed securities is large, the continuous market system of trading is employed. As the name indicates, trades in each security occur at any time when the stock exchange is open. If there are a seller and a buyer of IBM shares at an agreed price, for example at 10:00 a.m., the transaction is conducted in a matter of minutes. Five minutes later, another transaction in the same stock may be executed at a different price. For example, on some of the business television news networks in the United States, you can view the NYSE and Nasdaq transactions occurring throughout the day by watching the information scrolling across the television screen. This information includes, for example, the ticker symbol of the stock, volume traded, last price, and change in price from the previous one.

In some countries (for example, Switzerland and France), a mixed market exists. In this system, a group of stocks is traded continuously for, say, half an hour, and then another group of stocks is traded continuously for half an hour, and so forth throughout the day.

Exhibit 3.10 summarizes the impact of automation on the regulated exchanges around the world. Several of the exchanges have adopted automated systems modelled after the Nasdaq (developed in 1971). For example, the Easdaq (Nasdaq Europe), which is a subsidiary of the Nasdaq stock market, was developed in 1996 (see www.easdaq.be). Others (for example, German exchanges) combine a number of different trading structures. Below, we elaborate on the Nasdaq trading system.

3.4.2 The Nasdaq trading system

As will be explained below, trade on the NYSE and AMEX is done by market makers who organize all the trade in a given stock in one post. On the Nasdaq the trade is done in a different way: by the use of computers. There is no one physical place where all trades are conducted. Dealers can trade with the public by posting bid and ask quotes. An investor who wishes to buy or sell shares calls a broker who tries to locate a dealer on the Nasdaq with the best deal. The dealer trades on his or her account and makes a profit due to the spread.

Exhibit 3.10 **Trading characteristics of stock exchanges**

Exchange site	Exchange characteristics
United States	Largest single marketplace is the NYSE, which is principally a floor-based system; the OTC market introduced an automated system in 1971 (Nasdaq), which is an interdealer quotation system; real-time trade reporting was established in 1982; National Market System (NMS) legislation was enacted in 1975.
Japan	Among the eight stock exchanges, 80% of the trading volume occurs on the Tokyo Stock Exchange (TSE), which is principally a floor-based system; equities may trade through the Jasdaq, which was modelled after Nasdaq; the bulk of bond trading occurs on the OTC market.
Europe	Quote-driven dealer market; screen-based trading system (EASDAQ, a subsidiary of Nasdaq) allows dealers to disseminate price quotes; in September 1995, Tradepoint, a new trading system, went into effect in the United Kingdom at the London Stock Exchange (LSE), and permits investors and broker-dealers to trade directly and anonymously with one another.
Paris	Continuous order-driven screen-based trading system replaced the periodic call auctions with open outcry in 1986; a new exchange was established in Paris in 1996 for young, innovative, high-risk companies to trade; similar markets have opened in Germany, Belgium and the Netherlands.
Germany	Combines three different trading structures: (1) floor trading (still used in eight regional exchanges, Frankfurt being the most important); (2) electronic trading system; and (3) off-exchange telephone market; an interesting feature is that many companies are listed on several exchanges, and prices often vary across exchanges.

Source: Financial Market Trends, No. 65, November 1996. © OECD, 1996. Reprinted with permission.

Exhibit 3.11 illustrates the bid–ask spread (which is the difference between the bid and asked price of the stocks, see Section 3.9.1). provided by various dealers, as well as the best bid–ask offer for Microsoft, as quoted by Bloomberg on 15 June 1999. The best quotes are at the top of the table. Five dealers are ready to sell at $84^3/_4$ (see SLKC for example), and one dealer (see MASH) is ready to buy at $84^{13}/_{16}$. The rest of the quotes made by various dealers are worse, as the bids are at a lower price than $84^3/_4$ and all ask quotes are for higher prices than $84^{13}/_{16}$.

Note also that some dealers who are obligated to suggest bid–ask quotes are not really trading in the market, hence suggesting residual quotes: e.g. AXCS has a bid–ask quote of $10−$300. Obviously, the best quotes (at the top of the table) may change continuously, when a trade takes place or a dealer suggests new quotes.

In 1994 the Justice Department announced an investigation of the Nasdaq stock market. It was found that Nasdaq stock traded at a bid–ask spread of odd eighths, that is $^1/_8$, $^3/_8$, $^5/_8$ and $^7/_8$, very rarely. Thus, the spreads are commonly $^1/_4$, $^1/_2$, etc., which implies a relatively large profit to the dealers. It raises the suspicion that there is collusion among dealers who decided to maintain these large spreads, which is a violation of the anti-trust laws. In 1996 the Justice Department and the SEC settled with the dealers. The dealers agreed not to refrain from making transactions with dealers who suggest cutting the spread and to make sure that no collusion occurs.

Exhibit 3.11 **Bid–ask spreads and best offer for Microsoft, 15 June 1999**

HELP for explanation, MENU for similar functions. P183 **Equity CQ**
MSFT US $ Market Q 84 $^3/_4$ 84 $^7/_8$ Q 10×10 Vol 19, 700 Prev 84$^{15}/_{16}$
Competing Quotes Monitor

MSFT   **US**   MICROSOFT CORP

Prev 84$^3/_4$–84$^{13}/_{16}$

Vol: 0

5 SLKC MLCO GSCO FBCO NFSC	84$^3/_4$		−84$^{13}/_{16}$	MASH			1
				LEHMp	84$^1/_2$	−84$^7/_8$	PIPRp 84$^1/_4$ −85$^1/_4$
AANAp	84$^1/_4$	−86	DLJPp 84$^5/_{16}$ −84$^7/_8$	MADFp	84$^9/_{16}$	−84$^7/_8$	PRUSp 84$^1/_4$ −84$^7/_8$
AGISp	83$^7/_3$	−84$^7/_3$	EVRNp 83$^3/_4$ −86	MASHp	84$^{11}/_{16}$	−84$^{13}/_{16}$	PUREp 51$^7/_8$ −140
ALLNp	83$^7/_8$	−95$^3/_8$	FBCOp 84$^3/_4$ −85$^1/_4$	MDSNp	82	−88$^3/_{16}$	PWJCp 84$^1/_4$ −85
ALWCp	40	−120	FCAPp 83 −90$^1/_2$	MHILp	82	−92	RAGNp 83 −85$^1/_2$
AXCSp	10	−300	FEDEp 50 −200	MHMYp	83$^1/_2$	−85$^1/_2$	RAJAp 84 −87
BARDp	83$^1/_4$	−85$^9/_{16}$	GKMCp 84$^1/_4$ −85$^3/_8$	MLCOp	84$^3/_4$	−85	RAMSp 84$^1/_4$ −90
BESTp	84$^1/_{16}$	−85$^1/_{16}$	GSCOp 84$^3/_4$ −85$^1/_{16}$	MONTp	84$^1/_4$	−85$^1/_4$	RSSFp 84$^1/_8$ −90$^3/_{10}$
BUCKp	84$^1/_4$	−88$^5/_8$	GVRCp 83$^1/_2$ −87$^1/_2$	MSCOp	84$^7/_{16}$	−84$^{15}/_{16}$	SBSHp 84$^1/_3$ −85
CANTp	84$^1/_4$	−86$^1/_4$	HRCOp 1 −300	MWSE	84$^1/_2$	−85$^3/_4$	SELZp 84$^1/_4$ −85$^1/_2$
CIBCp	84	−85$^1/_4$	HRZGp 84$^1/_4$ −84$^7/_8$	NEEDp	83$^{13}/_{16}$	−87$^1/_2$	SHWDp 84$^1/_4$ −85
COSTp	84	−85	ISLD −	NFSCp	84$^3/_4$	−85$^3/_4$	SLKCp 84$^3/_4$ −85$^3/_4$
COWNp	83$^1/_8$	−85$^1/_8$	JBOCp 75 −95	NITEp	84$^1/_4$	−84$^{15}/_{16}$	SNDSp 83$^3/_4$ −85$^1/_4$
CWCOp	84$^7/_{16}$	−85$^5/_8$	JEFFp 84$^1/_4$ −86$^1/_4$	NTRD	80	−91	SNDVp 84$^1/_{16}$ −86$^1/_{16}$
DBKSp	83$^3/_4$	−85$^1/_8$	JOSEp 82$^3/_4$ −85$^3/_4$	OLDEp	84$^1/_4$	−85$^1/_8$	STAFp 75 −105
DEANp	84$^1/_4$	−86$^1/_4$	JPMSp 84$^9/_{16}$ −84$^{15}/_{16}$	PERTp	83$^7/_8$	−85$^5/_8$	SWSTp 83$^3/_4$ −85$^1/_2$
DKNYp	84$^1/_2$	−84$^{15}/_{16}$	KCMOp 84$^1/_4$ −85$^1/_4$	PFSlp	83$^1/_2$	−85$^1/_2$	TWPTp 84 −87

▪ Trading firms

On 9 August 1999 the *Wall Street Journal of Europe* reported that British funds intended to form a trading firm. The top managers could trade between themselves, a move akin to steps being taken in the US by securities brokerage firms to expand the role of electronic trading systems. The new company, called E-crossnet Ltd, will save traders about 80% of the transaction costs. Apart from cost savings, the new trade between funds will eliminate to some degree the effect that large stock market transactions can have on share prices. E-crossnet will still need, however, the London Stock Exchange to quote prices. However, when one fund's manager wants to sell stocks and another manager wants to buy them, this can be done anonymously and without affecting the stock market. Such a move puts more pressure on the big exchanges, because like electronic trading it is challenging the Nasdaq, the NYSE and other major exchanges for business.

3.4.3 Goals of trading systems

Markets facilitate trading, and investors will trade on the market that provides the best service at the most competitive price. When a new market is being developed, several questions need to be addressed by the market designers. There is no clear-cut answer to all these issues, and not all exchanges around the world adopt the same policy. The important questions are:[13]

1 *Should all information be made public?* For example, how can information known only to insiders, such as corporate executives, be used? Exchanges in the USA do not permit insider trading, because it is illegal.
2 *If all information is not made public, then should at least the trading record be public information?* For example, should you be able to know who is doing the trading? On the NYSE, investors may trade without revealing who they are. Thus, the NYSE has decided that it is in the best interest of investors to be able to trade in secret. Although corporate executives must report their trading activities to the appropriate regulatory agencies, they do not have to reveal their trading activities until *after* the trade has been executed.
3 *Are prices allowed to gyrate wildly, or are there constraints on how much prices can move?* Are there daily price limits? The NYSE has adopted a circuit breaker system in response to the stock market crash of 1987. By Rule 80B, when the Dow Jones Industrial Average (DJIA) falls by 350 points from the previous day's close, trading is stopped for half an hour. If the DJIA continues to fall to 550 points below the previous day's close, trading is stopped for one hour.[14] The idea is that these trading halts will give potential buyers an opportunity to assess the market and be willing to place orders to buy.
4 *Will the market attract a large number of traders who will provide the necessary liquidity?*
5 *Will this market require an individual to specialize in providing liquidity for a particular security?* For example, the NYSE has such a person, whereas the OTC market does not.

Several of these issues are conflicting. For example, how can there be an informationally efficient market (Question 1) and, at the same time, a market that disallows large

---

[13] Based on Joel Hasbrouck, 'Security markets, information and liquidity', *Financial Practice and Education* 1 (Fall–Winter 1991): 7–16.
[14] *NYSE Fact Book for the Year 1996* (New York: New York Stock Exchange, Inc., 1996), pp. 22–23.

price swings (Question 3)? This is impossible, because information can arrive in a dramatic fashion. Consider the possible effect on a market of the news of an earthquake, a major accident or a political event.

3.4.4 Participants in securities markets

All participants in security markets are referred to generically as *traders*. The most important traders are the market makers, or the individuals determining the bid and asked price quotes. The bid price is the price at which the public can sell securities and the market maker must buy securities. The asked price is the price at which the public can buy securities and the market maker must sell securities. Clearly, for the market maker to make a living, the bid price must be less than the asked price. Exhibit 3.12, taken from the Internet, shows the bid and ask prices of IBM's shares in June 1999 as quoted by Charles Schwab. We see that the dealer is ready to buy some shares of IBM at $119^5/_8$ and to sell some shares at $119^3/_4$ Thus, the spread in this case is $\$^3/_4 - \$^5/_8 = \$^1/_8$ per share. That is, the market maker must be buying at the bid price for less than what he or she is selling at the asked price. Brokers who know at which post of the floor a given stock is traded sometimes meet and enact a transaction between themselves 'inside the quotes'. For example, if the bid quote of Xerox is $113 and the asking price is $113^1/_4$, they can conduct the transaction at $113^1/_8$. Such a transaction is called an 'inside the quotes' transaction.

The members of the exchange are involved in transactions in the listed securities. They have various functions, and hence various sources of income. The main players

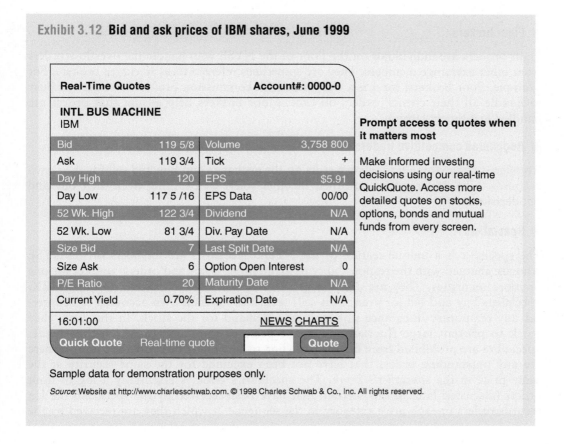

Exhibit 3.12 Bid and ask prices of IBM shares, June 1999

Real-Time Quotes		Account#: 0000-0	
INTL BUS MACHINE			
IBM			
Bid	119 5/8	Volume	3,758 800
Ask	119 3/4	Tick	+
Day High	120	EPS	$5.91
Day Low	117 5 /16	EPS Data	00/00
52 Wk. High	122 3/4	Dividend	N/A
52 Wk. Low	81 3/4	Div. Pay Date	N/A
Size Bid	7	Last Split Date	N/A
Size Ask	6	Option Open Interest	0
P/E Ratio	20	Maturity Date	N/A
Current Yield	0.70%	Expiration Date	N/A
16:01:00		NEWS CHARTS	
Quick Quote	Real-time quote		Quote

Prompt access to quotes when it matters most

Make informed investing decisions using our real-time QuickQuote. Access more detailed quotes on stocks, options, bonds and mutual funds from every screen.

Sample data for demonstration purposes only.

on the floor of most exchanges, such as the NYSE, include commission brokers, dealers, floor brokers, registered competitive traders and specialists. Some exchange members buy or sell for their own account. Some function as brokers (now also called *registered representatives*). Generally, brokers are persons who act as intermediaries between a buyer and a seller, a service for which they charge a commission. Brokers must register with the exchange where the stocks are traded (hence the name *registered representative*).

■ Commission brokers

Commission brokers buy and sell securities for clients of brokerage houses. They are connected to the brokerage houses (for example, Merrill Lynch) by either telephones or computer terminals, and they receive requests to buy or sell securities, execute the trade, and then send back a confirmation message to the brokerage firm. For this service, they charge a commission fee. Of course, commission brokers also trade for their own accounts and thus also act as dealers (discussed next).

■ Dealers

Dealers maintain their own inventory of securities and buy and sell securities from this inventory; thus, dealers are market makers. In this capacity, they do not serve as intermediaries but rather take the risk of holding the securities in their own account. Because most brokerage firms operate both as commission brokers and as dealers, the term *broker-dealer* is often used. Dealers earn their incomes from selling securities they own at a higher price than they initially paid for them.

■ Floor brokers

Floor brokers are individuals on the floor of the NYSE who handle the overflow orders from other exchange members. They are sometimes referred to as freelance brokers. For example, floor brokers, for a fee, will work with commission brokers who get too busy to handle all their clients' orders on time. Floor brokers help ensure that orders are handled in a timely fashion.

■ Registered competitive traders

Registered competitive traders own seats on the exchange and buy and sell for their own accounts. Like dealers, they earn their incomes solely by profiting from their buy and sell decisions.

■ Specialists

The specialist is a unique feature of the NYSE. Specialists are members of the NYSE who are charged with the responsibility of maintaining a fair and orderly market for one or more securities. They are called registered equity market makers on the AMEX. Specialists buy and sell (or even short-sell) securities for their own accounts to counteract any temporary imbalance in supply and demand for the stock. In this way, they work to prevent large fluctuations in the price of the stock in which they trade. Specialists are prohibited from buying or selling securities for their own accounts if there are any outstanding orders that have not been executed for the same security at the same price in the *specialist's book*. The specialist's book is essentially a log of limit orders (discussed later in this section) that have been received by the specialist; the log records orders in each price category in the sequence in which they are received by the specialist. Each stock is traded only by one specialist who has a post on the floor of the exchange. However, one specialist can handle the trade of several stocks. The specialist who maintains an inventory of stocks publishes quotes of bid and ask spreads and is obligated to execute (even from his or her portfolio) at least a limited number of market orders at these quotes. Then, the specialist may decide to have another bid–ask quote to which once again they are obligated. The specialist has to use the highest outstanding purchase price and the lowest outstanding offered selling price when he or she makes a trade. Thus, it is an auction market, because all buy–sell orders are concentrated in one place and the best offers are executed, i.e. win in the auction. When a transaction is executed, the specialist reports it and it appears on the screen (see the bottom of your TV set when you watch the CNN news).

The specialist has an important role in making the market a continuous one. To illustrate, suppose that the highest limit order to buy IBM stock is \$120, whereas the lowest limit order to sell is \$122. As market buy and sell orders come to the floor, the market price of IBM stock fluctuates from \$120 to \$122. The specialist is expected, and has agreed, to reduce this relatively large fluctuation by stepping in and buying and selling IBM stock for his or her own account at bid and ask prices between these two prices, such that the range would be only between $\frac{1}{4}$ and $\frac{1}{2}$. In this way, the specialist provides continuity.

Specialists earn income in two ways. First, as brokers, they receive commission fees for executing orders. Second, as dealers, they receive income by selling securities held in their own inventory at prices greater than the original purchase price.

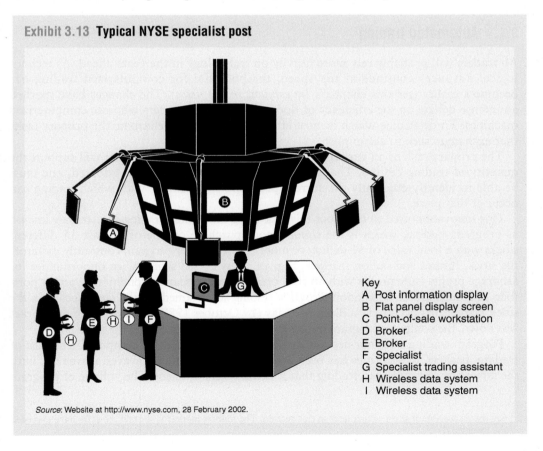

Exhibit 3.13 Typical NYSE specialist post

Key
A Post information display
B Flat panel display screen
C Point-of-sale workstation
D Broker
E Broker
F Specialist
G Specialist trading assistant
H Wireless data system
I Wireless data system

Source: Website at http://www.nyse.com, 28 February 2002.

Exhibit 3.13 illustrates a typical post of a specialist of the NYSE, with the data screens available to customers and with the trading assistant who helps the specialist, as well as other people with whom he or she conducts business.

3.4.5 Establishing market prices

The difference between the asked price and the bid price – what determines the market maker's income – is known as the bid–ask spread. For example, Microsoft stock may be quoted at 83 bid and $83^{1}/_{8}$ asked. Thus, the bid–ask spread is $^{1}/_{8}$ of a dollar, or $0.125 per share.

The bid–ask spread set by the market maker is determined by several factors:

1 Fixed operating costs (such as leasing an office and computer terminals) and anticipated volume of activity.
2 Nonfinancing variable cost per transaction (labour and supplies).
3 Cost of financing the inventory of securities.
4 Risk of price depreciation if inventory is held, and risk of price appreciation if sales have exceeded inventory.[15]
5 Likelihood of trading with those who have superior information (insiders). Because the first three factors are relatively stable, many investors monitor the size of the bid–ask spread for clues regarding how the market maker views the volatility of a stock. Larger bid–ask spreads signal larger uncertainty.

3.4.6 Automated trading

All traders will probably rely more heavily on technology in the years ahead. As technological advances continue at top speed, the potential for computerized trading has become a reality (see this chapter's *Investment in the news*). The changes have sparked an intense debate on the efficiency of floor traders versus traders who use computerized machines. To determine which is most efficient, we need to determine the primary tasks that exchanges seek to accomplish.

The primary task of an exchange is determining the current price that will support the quantity of trading desired. That is, whatever trading framework is adopted, one must be able to identify efficiently the current price and the quantity with which trading can occur at that price.

One innovation used to carry out this task using automated trading is a strategy known as program trading, which is the simultaneous purchase or sale of at least 15 different stocks with a total value of $1 million or more. The computer program constantly monitors the stock, futures and option markets. It gives a buy or sell signal when opportunities for arbitrage profits (sure profits with no risk) occur, or when market conditions warrant portfolio accumulation or liquidation. Program trading was blamed for the large decline in the stock market that occurred on Black Monday (19 October 1987), because when the market was down, the computer program triggered a sale order that enhanced the price fall.

Program trading does not necessarily have to be transacted via computer. The idea of trading 'baskets' of securities has been around for a long time; however, it was not until the advent of computerized trading that it became very efficient. The volume of program

---

[15] See the discussion of short selling later in this section. The market marker is short if the sales have exceeded the inventory.

trading is enormous. For example, program trading on the NYSE averaged 16.8% of the average daily trading volume for 10–14 November 1997.[16]

The GLOBEX trading system, which was developed by a joint venture between the Chicago Mercantile Exchange and Reuters (a British information distribution company), promises to be the security exchange of the future. GLOBEX is a global OTC market where many different types of securities trade. Reuters has more than 200,000 terminals in more than 120 countries. Hence, GLOBEX has a phenomenal degree of direct access to trading.

3.4.7 **Types of orders**

Investors can use different types of orders to buy and sell securities. The most common is a market order, which is an order to buy or sell a specified quantity of a specified security *at the best price currently available*. In contrast, a limit order is an order to buy or sell a specified quantity of a specified security *at a specified price or better*. The trade will occur only when the specified price is available.

For example, suppose the current bid and asked prices for Microsoft stock are $89^7/$_8$ bid and $90^1/$_8$ asked. A market order to buy Microsoft stock would be executed with the market maker at $90^1/$_8$. A market order to sell Microsoft stock would be executed at $89^7/$_8$. Rather than issue a market order, the investor could issue a limit order to buy, say, 100 shares (one round lot) of Microsoft common stock at $89. This order would not be executed until the asked price dropped to $89 or lower. If the price did fall – say, to $89 – then the market maker would sell 100 shares of Microsoft at $89 to the investor. In the same fashion, a limit order to sell Microsoft stock could be placed at $91. This sell order would not be executed until the bid price rose to $91 or higher.

All orders are day orders unless otherwise specified. That is, all limit orders expire at the end of the trading day if not executed. Market orders are day orders by definition, because they are executed very quickly. An alternative to a day order is the good-till-cancelled (GTC) order, a limit order that remains in effect until it is executed or cancelled.

Other specialized orders include the not-held order and the stop order. A not-held (NH) order, given to a floor broker, allows the broker to try and obtain a better price, but the broker is not held responsible if he or she is unsuccessful. For example, on a NH order to sell, the broker is not liable if the price falls sharply and the broker does not successfully sell an order at the higher price. A stop order is an order to sell if the price falls below a specified price or to buy if the price rises above a specified price. Stop orders are used to limit losses or protect accumulated gains. If you purchased Microsoft when it was trading at $50, and it rose to $200, you could limit your risk of losing this gain with a stop order to sell if the price falls below $190. Thus, you protect your accumulated gain by a sell stop order.

Similarly, if the stock price of, say IBM, rises about $120 you can give a buy order to stockholders. Such an order is usually given by investors who are in short position (see Section 3.4.9) in IBM stocks, hence they lose money when the stock price rises. By buying the stock if it goes above $120, they put a limit on the losses in the short position. Exhibit 3.14 lists other unusual types of orders that currently exist.

---

[16] See 'NYSE program trading averages 16.8 percent of volume', at
http://www.f2.yahoo.com/finance/finance/971120/NYSEprogram_trading_1.html.

Exhibit 3.14 Specialized orders for securities

Type of order	Definition
All-or-none order	Partial execution of an order is prohibited. For example, assume you have a seller wishing to sell 1,000 shares of IBM stock at $80 per share, and the buy limit order is for 2,000 shares at $80. Because the order would be only partially filled, it would not be executed.
Minimum-fill order	Execution of the order will take place at a prespecified minimum volume of trading.
Market opening/closing order	Order is executed only at the opening or closing of the market.
Last-sale-price order	Order must be executed at a price equal to or better than the last sale price.
Mid-market order	Execution of this order must be at the middle of the most recent bid–offer spread only.
Basket trade	Purchase (or sale) of a given security may be executed only in conjunction with the sale (or purchase) of another security.
Index-related trade	The execution price is related to the value of a specified market index (could be considered a type of limit order).
Spot/future trade	Execution of a cash position is permitted only if a prespecified and simultaneous execution occurs in a futures market.

Finally, although most orders are for round lots (increments of 100 shares), trading can be in odd lots, which is any number of shares not in increments of 100. For example, a 50-share trade would be an odd-lot trade. Odd-lot trades, however, incur substantially higher fees; thus, it is more economical to trade round lots. In 1996, 104.6 *billion* shares in round lots traded on the NYSE, whereas only 381,932 *million* odd-lot shares were purchased.[17]

3.4.8 Placing an order: call your broker or trade via the Internet

Investors can place buy or sell orders in one of three ways. The standard method is a phone call to a broker, who executes the trades. Investors can also trade from their personal computers. Trading through a personal computer is typically done with a modem and dial-in capabilities with a broker. Trades can also be initiated with a call on a touch-tone phone to a broker's computer.

Nowadays, electronic trading via the Internet plays a very large role in securities trading. Exhibit 3.15 shows how you can fill an order. After having your account with the broker, you fill in the type of order you submit, concerning shares you want to buy and at what price.

Although there are different ways to initiate a trade, the path the trade takes after the order is given is typically the same (Exhibit 3.16). The client contacts the broker with an order (1). The broker keys the order into the firm's computer (2). The computer is programmed to locate the exchange with the best available price to make the trade (3). Depending on the type of order, the trade will be executed either electronically (4) or by

---

[17] *NYSE Fact Book for the Year 1996* (New York: New York Stock Exchange, Inc., May 1997), p. 11.

Exhibit 3.15 Placing trade orders

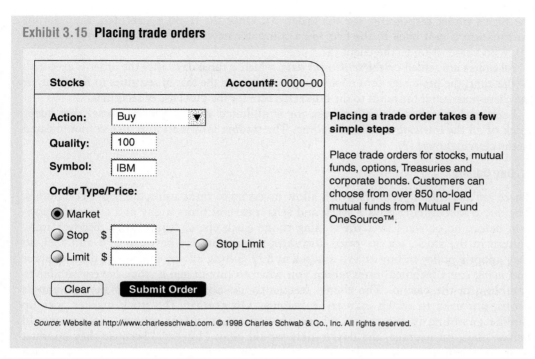

Exhibit 3.16 The path of a stock trade

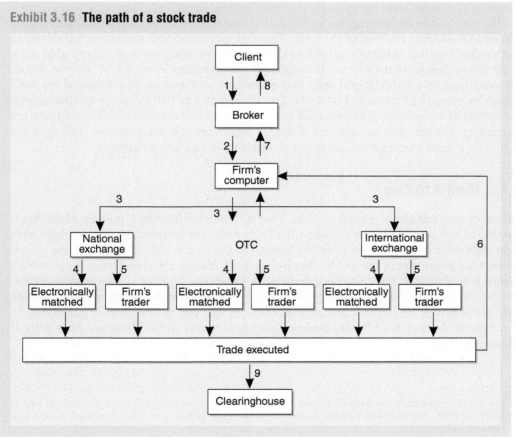

the firm's trader responsible for the order (5). Once the trade is executed, the relevant information is sent back to the firm via a computer network (6) and given to the broker (7), who passes it on to the client (8).

All orders are settled on the *settlement date*, which is three days after the order is executed. At this time, the brokerage firm remits the proceeds from the sale of securities to the client, or the client must remit the funds to the brokerage firm for the purchase of securities.

Each exchange has a clearinghouse (or is affiliated with a clearinghouse) that keeps track of all the intricate details of trading. The trading information is also communicated to the clearinghouse (9).

▇ Day traders

There are day trading brokers which allow investors to trade using the firm's computers. The day trader usually buys a stock and sells it several times a day and closes the position before he or she leaves the trading room. Such clients 'think' they discover some pattern in the stock, e.g. its price fluctuates within the day between $98 and $99, so they adopt a policy to buy at $98 and sell at $99. Sitting all day in front of the computer and using some technical rates telling you when to buy or sell a stock is very similar to gambling in the casino. The clients frequently do not know what is the company's profit, nor even to which industry it belongs. On average, the stock market goes up (unlike gambling in the casino where, on average, you lose money), so one would believe that, on average, the day traders would gain. However, because they conduct many transactions within a day, they pay the day trading company transaction costs; hence, it is claimed that, on average, they lose money.

The day traders are not regular investors who invest for the long run presumably, based on some economic analysis of the firm. They are gamblers, and sometimes gamblers, as with other possibly addictive behaviours, do not know when to stop. Many also leave their job to devote all their time (day and night) to gambling in stocks. When you devote all your time to gambling, you may lose everything and end up in tragedy of the kind which happened in Atlanta in July 1999. Day trading and its bad influence on clients, with its emphasis on gambling rather than investment, is now a topic which regulators are discussing. No one will be surprised if the US regulators will disallow day trading in the future or at least constrain its operations to investors in one way or another.

3.4.9 Margin trading

Investors may engage in margin trading. That is, they may borrow a portion of the funds needed to buy stock from their brokers. By borrowing, the investor can take a larger position than otherwise would be possible; hence, the investor is able to 'leverage' the investment. One advantage of margin trading is that if the stock price appreciates, the investor's return is enhanced. If the stock price declines, however, the investor's losses are magnified.

The interest rate charged by the broker on the borrowed funds is known as the call loan rate or the broker loan rate. The maximum amount that can be borrowed is established by the Federal Reserve Board's Regulation T and is currently 50% of the purchase price.[18] However, brokers may require investors to put up more than 50% of the purchase price.

---

[18] The margin requirement has been 50% since 3 January 1974. The margin requirement had been as high as 100% (in 1946) and as low as 40% (in the late 1930s and early 1940s). (See *NYSE Fact Book for the Year 1996*, p. 79.)

As stock prices fall, the percentage of borrowed money in relation to security value will rise. If this percentage rises above the allowable limit, the investor must supply more funds to reduce the amount borrowed. When a broker calls for more money, it is a margin call. One factor to consider before buying on margin is at what price level a margin call will go out.

The initial margin (IM) is the percentage of the dollar amount originally required by the lender to be put up by the borrower:

$$IM = \frac{\text{total amount put up by investor}}{\text{total value of the shares}}$$

which can be expressed in symbols as

$$IM = \frac{\text{total purchase} - \text{borrowing}}{\text{total purchase}}$$

For example, if you purchased 200 shares of AT&T at $60 per share, then the total cost is $12,000. An initial margin of 50% would require that you borrow no more than 50% of $12,000, namely, $6,000:

$$IM = \frac{(\$60 \times 200) - \$6,000}{\$200 \times \$60} = 0.5, \text{ or } 50\%$$

The percentage of the total current market value that an investor originally put up is known as the actual margin. As prices fall, the actual margin will also fall. For example, if the AT&T stock price falls to $55, then the investor's actual margin (AM) is

$$AM = \frac{\text{value of stock} - \text{borrowing}}{\text{value of stock}} = \frac{(200 \times \$55) - \$6,000}{200 \times \$55} = 0.45, \text{ or } 45\%$$

To minimize the risk of default by the investor, the broker has a minimum margin requirement, known as the maintenance margin, which is the percentage of the dollar amount of the securities market value that must always be set aside as margin. If the margin falls below the maintenance margin, the investor pays the broker cash to reduce the amount of borrowing. The maintenance margin is always less than the initial margin. The maintenance margin (MM) can be written as

$$MM = \frac{(N \times P') - B}{N \times P'} \tag{3.2}$$

where P' is the price at which a margin call will be issued. Solving for P', we find

$$P' = \frac{B}{N(1 - MM)} \tag{3.2'}$$

Suppose you purchased 100 shares ($N = 100$) of Microsoft common stock for $90 by borrowing $4,500 and providing $4,500 of your own funds (because of the initial margin of 50%). Now suppose the maintenance margin is 40% (MM = 0.4). The price below which you will receive a margin call is

$$P' = \frac{4{,}500}{100(1 - 0.4)} = \frac{4{,}500}{60} = \$75$$

Hence, you will not receive a margin call as long as the price remains above \$75. If the price suddenly falls to \$60, how much will you have to add in cash to hold this position? To reduce the amount of money borrowed, you will have to add the amount of cash that will bring the maintenance margin back to 40%, or from Equation 3.2:

$$MM = 0.40 = \frac{(100 \times 60) - \$4{,}500 + cash}{100 \times \$60}$$

$$cash = (0.40 \times 100 \times \$60) - (100 \times \$60) + \$4{,}500 = \$900$$

where \$4,500 is the borrowing and \$60 is the new market price of the stock.

Indeed, the amount borrowed decreases to \$4,500 − \$900 = \$3,600, and the maintenance margin (MM) is:

$$\frac{(100 \times 60) - \$3{,}600}{(100 \times 60)} = \frac{6{,}000 - 3{,}600}{6{,}000} = \frac{2{,}400}{6{,}000} = 0.40, \text{ or } 40\%$$

as required.

Most investors buy securities with the expectation that they will appreciate in value. Margin trading is one method to enhance the return when a security's price rises.

PRACTICE BOX

Problem

Suppose you purchased 1,000 shares of GE common stock for \$65 by borrowing \$30,000. Thus, the initial margin is \$35,000 [(\$65 × 1,000) − \$30,000], or 53.85% (\$35,000/\$65,000). Now suppose the maintenance margin is 25%. What is the price below which you would receive a margin call?

Solution

Given the information above, $N = 1{,}000$, $B = \$30{,}000$ and MM = 0.25. Therefore, from Equation 3.2', you have:

$$P' = \frac{\$30{,}000}{1{,}000(1 - 0.25)} = \$40$$

If the stock price fell below \$40, you would receive a margin call.

3.4.10 Short selling

How can you profit when stock prices are falling? Is selling your own stocks the best that you can do? Short selling is a method that allows you to profit when a stock's price falls by selling securities that you borrow. Actually, your broker borrows these securities from the inventory of other clients. If the price falls, the short seller can buy the securities back at a lower price. By selling high and buying low, the short seller can make a profit. Thus, the short seller is hoping prices will fall.

To demonstrate how a short sale works, assume you borrow from your broker 100 shares of GM stock, and you sell them for $40. Assume further that the price falls to $38. Now you buy the stock back and return it to the broker. From this transaction, you make a profit of $2 per share. However, if the price goes up to $42, you have to pay $42 to buy it, and you lose $2 per share.

The short seller must pay any dividends due to the original owner of the shorted securities. Also, the proceeds from the short sale are held by the broker as collateral for the borrowed securities and the short seller receives interest on the held proceeds. The short seller must provide additional money to insure against default. If 100 shares of GM are sold short at $40, and GM's stock price rises to $50, then the brokerage firm will lose $1,000, or 100($50 − $40), if the short seller defaults. The current minimum initial margin requirement for short selling set by the Federal Reserve is 50%.[19]

Stocks can be sold short only if prior to the short sale they have traded on an uptick or zero-plus tick. Trading on an uptick refers to a security's last trade price exceeding the previous trade price (for example, $101\frac{1}{8}$, then $101\frac{1}{4}$). Trading on a zero-plus tick refers to a security's last trade price being the same as the previous trade price, but the previous trade price exceeding the one before it (for example, $101\frac{1}{8}$, then $101\frac{1}{4}$, then $101\frac{1}{4}$).

Short selling is a high-risk position, because the securities may continue to rise. For example, if an investor had sold short 100 shares of Microsoft when it was trading at $50 per share in the late 1980s, the investor would be required to cover this short position by buying Microsoft. Microsoft common stock is currently trading for about $250 (adjusting for splits). In this case, the investor is facing a $200 loss per share. The investor could wait, but then the price might go even higher.

When investors buy stock (a long position), the most they can lose is the investment itself (when or if the stock price falls to zero). However, when investors sell short (a short position), their loss has no bounds because there is no upper limit to the stock price. The higher the price, the larger the loss.

3.4.11 Brokers

There are two basic types of brokers: full-service brokers and discount-service brokers. Full-service brokers earn commissions based on the volume of trading they transact. At a full-service brokerage firm, an investor is assigned to a broker, and that broker notifies the investor about prospects on various securities. The broker also shares advice from the firm's research group as to the anticipated direction of security prices. Full-service brokers typically have analyses of most major corporations. The commission can be as high as 2% of the value of the transaction.

Discount-service brokers are paid a set salary. Investors do not receive any investment advice from discount-service brokers. However, the cost of trading is from 50% to 70% less than the prices charged by full-service brokers.

---

[19] See *Federal Reserve Bulletin*, December 1992 (Washington, DC: Board of Governors of the Federal Reserve System), p. A26.

Exhibit 3.17	Equities (stocks and warrants) transaction costs
	• $5 market/$10 limit for equity orders up to 5,000 shares online, touchtone, or PC line.
	• $12 additional for broker-assisted equity orders.
	• Add $0.01 per share for total orders over 5,000 shares retroactive to the first share.
	• For online, touchtone, or PC line option orders: $5 + $1.50/contract for market orders; $10 + $1.50/contract for limit/stop orders, $15 minimum; $25 minimum for broker-assisted orders.
	• See commission and fee schedule for full details.

Note: Brown & Co. does not offer brokerage services to non-US citizens.
Source: Website at http://www.brownco.com, 12 March 2002. Reprinted with permission.

Commission schedule

The typical discount brokerage's equities transaction costs are listed in Exhibit 3.17.[20] For example, purchasing 400 shares of $20 stock (i.e. $8,000 investment) would cost

Exhibit 3.18

Flat Free Trading® Makes The Difference

	200 sh. @$25	300 sh. @$20	500 sh. @$18	1000 sh. @$14
Schwab	89.00	95.60	106.60	123.60
Fidelity	88.50	95.10	106.10	123.10
Quick & Reilly	60.50	65.00	81.50	94.00
NDB	24.95/ 27.95*	24.95/ 27.95*	24.95/ 27.95*	24.95/ 27.95*

BROKER-ASSISTED RATES BASED ON SURVEY DONE 8/28/97.

*DOMESTIC STOCK, MARKET ORDER VS. LIMIT ORDER, LISTED ORDERS IN EXCESS OF 5,000 SHARES WILL INCUR A 1 PERCENT PER SHARE CHARGE ON THE ENTIRE ORDER. OTHER PRODUCTS AND SERVICES ARE AVAILABLE AT OTHER PRICES AND FEES.

National Discount
BROKERS

1-800-4-1-PRICE
www.ndb.com

help@ndb.com • 1-800-888-3999• Member NASD, SIPC, MSRB and Discount Brokers Association.
A National Discount Brokers Group Company • Listed on the NYSE (Symbol:NDB)

N D B
Listed
NYSE

Source: Barron's, 6 October 1997, p. 64. Barron's Online by *Barron's.* © 1997 by Dow Jones & Co., Inc. Reproduced with permission of Dow Jones & Co., Inc. in the format *Fundamentals of Investments* via Copyright Clearance Center.

---

[20] This commission schedule is from Brown & Company. Full-service brokerage fees are usually much more complicated. Typically, they will be at least 100% more than the fee schedule given here.

$83, or $35 + (0.006 × 20 × 400). Most firms have both maximum and minimum fees. Trading odd lots is more expensive.

There are big differences in commission rates among firms, as the advertisement in Exhibit 3.18 reveals. For a 200-share transaction with a price of $25 per share, Schwab charges $89, which implies that the commission as a percentage of the transaction is $89/(200 shares × $25) = $89/$5,000 = 0.0178, or 1.78%. NDB charges just a little more than a quarter of Schwab's commission.

▪ Brokerage services

Discount-service and full-service brokerage firms offer several services. These services vary widely, so investors should compare brokerage firms before choosing one. Most firms offer an 800 (toll-free in the US) telephone number to buy and sell securities. They also provide a toll-free number to receive current stock quotes and provide execution capabilities on all US security markets. Some brokerage firms also handle international trades and provide real-time quotes via the Internet. Several houses offer money market rates for idle cash between investments, as well as checking services. Most firms provide complete safekeeping and record-keeping services (usually monthly). Finally, most brokerage houses offer up to $500,000 in insurance through the Securities Investor Protection Corporation (SIPC). The SIPC insurance covers the risk that the brokerage firm might become insolvent. It does not, however, cover losses from a fall in security prices.[21]

3.4.12 Financial planners

Rather than dealing directly with brokers, individual investors sometimes use financial planners. Financial planners evaluate an investor's situation and formulate a strategic investment plan. The academic field of financial planning is still in its infancy. Although financial planning has gone on for centuries, the label *financial planner* is new. Just about anyone can be a financial planner in the United States simply by paying $150 and registering with the SEC. (Some states require registration with state officials as well.)

Most financial planners generate their revenues from commissions. Hence, investors must exercise care when soliciting their advice. It is now possible to call state securities departments to find out if a particular financial planner has ever been in trouble. The North American Administrators Association and the National Association of Securities Dealers (NASD) have developed a computer database of financial planners that covers all 50 states. The system, known as the Central Registration Depository, lists a financial planner's education, employment, any bankruptcy filings, any legal injunctions against his or her business, and any criminal convictions.[22]

3.5 WORLD SECURITY MARKETS

So far the chapter's description of security markets has covered only the workings of US markets. With today's technology, however, investors can routinely search the entire globe for the securities that best meet their needs. Most major brokerage firms have offices in every continent and can effectively conduct international securities transactions.

---

[21] To gain a greater understanding of the services provided by different brokerage firms, call a few local brokerage houses (see 'Stock Brokers' in the telephone book) and request information.
[22] Based on an article by Ellen E. Schultz, *Wall Street Journal*, 13 September 1990, p. C1.

The history of world security markets is long and varied. Babylonian merchants financed their activities from the savings of the rich around 2000 BC. By 400 BC the Greeks had their equivalent of a modern joint-stock company and markets for handling currencies and interest-bearing securities.[23] With the exception of the Middle Ages and major wars, the move towards more sophisticated security markets has never stopped. Today's world security markets include bond, stock and derivative markets.

3.5.1 World bond markets

The world bond market has increased more than 15-fold in the past 30 years – from $700 billion in 1966 to over $21 trillion at the end of 1994.[24] As Exhibit 3.19 illustrates, the majority of this debt is from governments. Notice that government borrowing makes up approximately 62% of the total bond market.

There have been numerous advances in the international money market. For example, Germany moved into the commercial paper (CP) market in 1991, when 'certain amendments to section 795 of the German Civil Code made it possible to issue short-dated domestic securities'.[25] The market for Deutsche Mark CP developed rapidly and was being widely used by German firms, as well as German subsidiaries of foreign firms.

US Treasury securities constitute one of the largest and most liquid capital markets in the world. Other major governments, however, also have substantial treasury issues. Exhibit 3.20 summarizes the major government bond markets and their sizes. The US

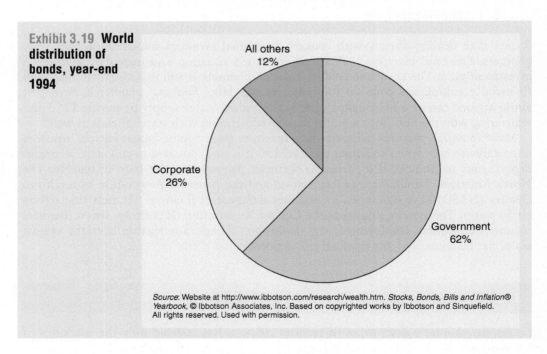

Exhibit 3.19 World distribution of bonds, year-end 1994

All others 12%

Corporate 26%

Government 62%

---

[23] See D.E. Ayling, *The Internationalization of Stock Markets* (Brookfield, VT: Gower Publishing, 1986), p. 44, and http://www.ibbotson.com/research/wealth.htm, Laurence B. Siegel, 'The $40 trillion market: global stock and bond capitalization and returns'.

[24] For perspective, $1 million in tightly bound $1,000 bills makes a stack approximately 4 inches tall. Thus, $20 trillion in tightly bound $1,000 bills makes a stack approximately 1,290 miles high!

[25] See Peter Lee, 'Deutschmark CP gets into gear', *Euromoney*, August 1991, p. 51.

government bond market is the largest, making up 48.5% of the world market. The Japanese market follows, with 26.3%, and then the German market, with 10.9%. Thus, the government bond market is highly concentrated in just a few countries.

Government bonds are traded on the major exchanges and the over-the-counter market, as well as in interbank markets. For example, as of 31 December 1996, there were 640 government issues listed on the NYSE with a total par value of $2.55 billion.[26]

Exhibit 3.20 Major national government bond markets as of year-end 1994

Country	Market value (US $ billion)	Percentage (rounded)
United States	5,489	48.5
Japan	2,977	26.3
Germany	1,236	10.9
France	513	4.5
Canada	335	3.0
United Kingdom	331	2.9
Netherlands	253	2.2
Australia	82	0.7
Denmark	72	0.6
Switzerland	37	0.3
Total	11,325	100

Source: Website at http://www.ibbotson.com/research/wealth.htm. *Stocks, Bonds, Bills and Inflation® Yearbook*, © Ibbotson Associates, Inc. Based on copyrighted works by Ibbotson and Sinquefield. All rights reserved. Used with permission.

Exhibit 3.21 Global distribution of corporate bonds, 1994

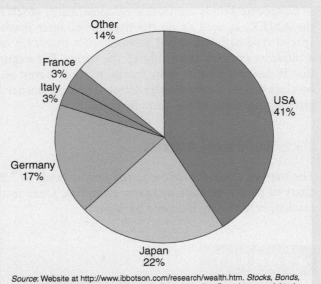

Source: Website at http://www.ibbotson.com/research/wealth.htm. *Stocks, Bonds, Bills and Inflation® Yearbook*, © Ibbotson Associates, Inc. Based on copyrighted works by Ibbotson and Sinquefield. All rights reserved. Used with permission.

---

[26] See *NYSE Fact Book for the Year 1996*, p. 84.

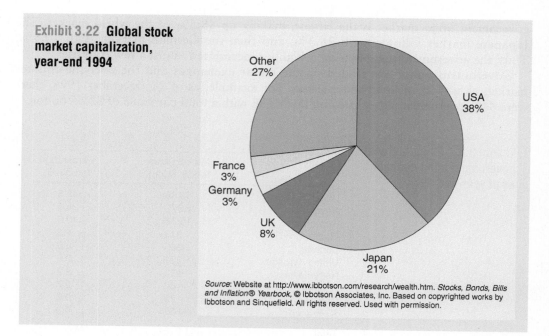

Exhibit 3.22 **Global stock market capitalization, year-end 1994**

The world corporate bond market stands at over $5.4 trillion. Exhibit 3.21 provides a breakdown by major country. Again, the United States dominates, with 41% of the market. Five countries capture all but 14% of the market.

Corporate bonds are an attractive means of raising capital, because the interest expense is tax deductible (whereas dividend payments are not). However, recall that corporate bonds also increase the likelihood that the firm will go bankrupt in hard economic times.

Corporate bonds are traded on most major stock exchanges, such as the NYSE and the AMEX, as well as on the over-the-counter market. The international arena has a special type of bond, called a crossborder bond. Crossborder bonds are bonds issued in a different country from that of the issuer. For example, a bond that a US firm issues that is denominated in Swiss francs, paying interest and principal in Swiss francs, would be classified as a crossborder bond. The crossborder bond has been one of the fastest-growing segments of the bond market.

3.5.2 World stock markets

The market value of world equities now exceeds $17.8 trillion. Exhibit 3.22 shows a pie chart of equity markets by major countries. Once again, the United States is the largest market, here closely followed by Japan.

SUMMARY

■ *Describe the function of security markets.*
A security market that functions effectively provides accurate information, accurate prices and liquidity. Buyers and sellers have access to timely and accurate information. Market prices reflect all known information. When markets are liquid, transactions are completed quickly.

■ *Contrast the primary and secondary markets.*

The primary market is the mechanism through which a firm can raise additional capital by selling stocks, bonds and other securities. The secondary market is where previously issued securities trade among investors. An alternative to raising capital by an initial public offering is with a private placement. The secondary market includes national exchanges such as the New York Stock Exchange (NYSE) and the American Stock Exchange (AMEX), regional exchanges such as the Pacific Stock Exchange and the Boston Stock Exchange, and the over-the-counter (OTC) market.

■ *Describe the basic structure of security markets.*

Security exchanges seek to have a trading mechanism that satisfies competing constraints. For example, determining what information must be made public and what information is to remain private is a difficult task. Market makers are individuals who set the bid and asked price quotes. The bid price is the price at which investors can sell securities, and the asked price is the price at which investors can buy securities.

■ *Survey world security markets.*

The world security markets include bond, stock and derivative markets. The $21 trillion bond market is dominated by the United States. The $17.8 trillion stock market is led in size by the United States, followed closely by Japan. The world security markets also include more than 87 security exchanges that trade derivative securities, such as options and futures.

KEY TERMS

Actual margin (AM)	Gross spread (GS)	Program trading
Asked price	Information asymmetry	Prospectus
Bid–ask spread	Initial margin (IM)	Registered competitive
Bid price	Initial public offering	trader
Breadth	(IPO)	Registered equity market
Broker	Investment banker	maker
Broker loan rate	Limit order	Resiliency
Call loan rate	Maintenance margin	Round lot
Call market	(MM)	Scalping
Commission broker	Margin call	Seasoned new issue
Continuous market	Margin trading	Second market
Crossborder bond	Market	Secondary market
Day order	Market maker	Shallow market
Day trader	Market microstructure	Short selling
Dealer	Market order	Specialist
Depth	Mixed market	Stop order
Discount-service broker	Not-held (NH) order	Syndicate
Dual listing	Odd lot	Thin market
Execution cost	Over-the-counter market	Third market
First market	Price continuity	Underwriter
Floor broker	Primary market	Underwriter's
Fourth market	Primary offering	discount
Full-service broker	Private placement	Upstairs market
Good-till-cancelled (GTC)	Private placement	Uptick
order	memorandum	Zero-plus tick

QUESTIONS

3.1 What are the main explanations given for IPOs being underpriced?

3.2 How are the US secondary market transactions categorized?

3.3 Describe the three major categories of secondary markets.

3.4 Describe the market maker on the NYSE.

3.5 What factors affect the bid–ask spread?

3.6 What is margin trading and why is it considered risky?

3.7 Suppose you purchase 500 shares of Wal-Mart common stock at $75 per share by borrowing funds, and your initial margin is 65%. The maintenance margin is 55%.

  (a) How much of your own money will you have to provide?
  (b) What is the price at which you would begin to receive a margin call?

3.8 Using the commission schedules provided in this chapter, how much would you pay in commission to a discount-service brokerage firm if you bought 700 shares of Ford Motor Company's common stock at $35 per share?

3.9 Suppose IBM stock is trading for $70 a share. You borrow from your broker 100 shares and sell them. Calculate your dollar profit if IBM's stock price drops to $60 per share. Also calculate your dollar loss if IBM's stock price rises to $80 a share. Are your profits limited? Are your losses limited? Explain.

3.10 Suppose you are an underwriter who has a firm commitment to sell a million shares at $100 a share. You have an agreement to give the issuing firm $95 per share. Suppose there is a 50% chance that all shares will be sold at $100 and a 50% chance that the issue will not go well and the market price will end up being only $92 per share. What is, on average, the underwriter spread?

3.11 Suppose you invested $400,000 with your broker, and the broker went bankrupt. Are you insured? Suppose now that the value of your assets went down to $200,000 because of bankruptcies of firms that issued the shares you hold. Are you insured now?

3.12 A specialist at Xerox Corporation has an asked price of 20\frac{1}{8}$ and a bid price of 19\frac{1}{2}$. How can you explain these differences in the bid and asked prices?

3.13 The bid price of Stock A is $1, and the asked price is 1\frac{1}{8}$. The bid and asked prices of Stock B are $100 and 100\frac{1}{8}$, respectively. Which stock do you think is more volatile?

3.14 Suppose an underwriter has a firm commitment on two issues, each issue at $10 per share and for 1 million shares. Suppose the price falls to $9 in both issues. Would the underwriter be better off by having one issue of 2 million shares and having the price of the issue fall from $10 to $9?

3.15 In light of your answer to Question 3.14, why do underwriters form syndicates?

3.16 The stock price is $P = \$100$, and you bought 1,000 shares of this particular stock. The initial margin you use is 20%. How much did you borrow? (Use Equation 3.2′.)

SELECTED REFERENCES

Benos, A., and M. Crouhy. 'Changes in the structure and dynamics of European markets'. *Financial Analysts Journal*, May–June 1995, pp. 37–50.
This article provides a description of changes in European securities markets and the prevailing tracking systems in the various exchanges in Europe.

Eatwell, John, Murray Milgate, and Peter Newman (eds). *New Palgrave Dictionary of Money and Finance*. New York: W.W. Norton, 1989.
This is a detailed dictionary of financial concepts. The terms are defined and discussed by leading academics in finance.

Fabozzi, Frank J., and Franco Modigliani. *Capital Markets Institutions and Instruments*. Englewood Cliffs, NJ: Prentice-Hall, 1992.
This text provides a detailed analysis of world capital markets, with special emphasis on the United States.

Fridson, Martin S., and Gao Yan. 'Primary versus secondary pricing of high-yield bonds'. *Financial Analysts Journal*, May–June 1996, pp. 20–7.
This article analyzes the underpricing of newly floated securities vis-à-vis secondary market price levels.

Griffin, Mark W. 'A global perspective on pension fund asset allocation'. *Financial Analysts Journal*, March–April 1998, pp. 60–8.
This article provides a detailed comparison of pension fund asset allocation around the globe with an emphasis on equities versus bonds.

Hasbrouck, Joel. 'Security markets, information and liquidity'. *Financial Practice and Education*, 1 (2), Fall–Winter 1991, pp. 7–16.
This article is a good summary of market microstructure.

Lederman, Jess, and Keith K. H. Park (eds). *The Global Bond Markets State-of-the-Art Research, Analysis and Investment Strategies*. Chicago: Probus Publishing, 1991.
This book surveys the major world bond markets and addresses some of the more sophisticated global bond investment strategies.

Livingston, Miles. *Money and Capital Markets: Financial Instruments and Their Uses*. Englewood Cliffs, NJ: Prentice-Hall, 1990.
This text provides many useful technical details of capital markets, with an emphasis on pricing.

Mann, Steven V., and Robert W. Seijas. 'Bid-ask spreads, NYSE specialists and NASD dealers'. *Journal of Portfolio Management*, Fall 1991, pp. 54–8.
This article describes the salient differences between the NYSE specialist system and the NASD dealer system of making a market. The authors view these different systems as 'cousins' and not 'twins'.

Robertson, Malcolm J. *Directory of World Futures and Options*. Englewood Cliffs, NJ: Prentice-Hall, 1990.
This is an exhaustive directory of futures and options markets worldwide.

Scarlata, Jodi G. 'Institutional developments in the globalization of securities and futures markets'. *Federal Reserve Bank of St Louis*, January–February 1992, pp. 17–30.
This article provides a good survey of recent developments in globalization. Particularly helpful is the summary of computerized trading systems.

Schwartz, Robert A. *Equity Markets: Structure, Trading, and Performance*. New York: Harper & Row, 1988.
This book provides the institutional detail of US security markets and focuses on market microstructure issues and regulations.

Tucker, Alan L. *Financial Futures, Options, and Swaps*. St Paul, MN: West Publishing, 1991.
This is a detailed introduction to futures, options and swaps.

SUPPLEMENTARY REFERENCES

AMEX Fact Book. Annual. New York: American Stock Exchange.

Bancel, F. and R. Mittoo. 'European managerial perceptions of the net benefits of foreign stock listings'. *European Financial Management*, 2001, Vol. 7, Issue 2.

Bae, Sung C., and Haim Levy. 'The valuation of firm commitment underwriting contracts for seasoned new equity issues: theory and evidence'. *Financial Management,* Summer 1990, pp. 48–59.

DiNoia, C., 'Competition and integration among Stock Exchanges in Europe: Network effects, implicit mergers and remote access'. *European Financial Management*, 2001, Vol. 7.

Glosten, Lawrence R. 'Insider trading, liquidity, and the role of the monopolist specialist'. *Journal of Business*, April 1989, pp. 211–35.

Lazer, R., B. Lev, and J. Livnat. 'Internet traffic and portfolio returns'. *Financial Analysts Journal*, May/June 2001.

NASD Fact Book. Annual. Washington, DC: National Association of Securities Dealers.

NYSE Fact Book. Annual. New York: New York Stock Exchange.

Smith, Clifford W. 'Investment banking and the capital acquisition process'. *Journal of Financial Economics,* 15, January–February 1986, pp. 3–29.

Tokyo Stock Exchange Fact Book. Annual. Tokyo: Tokyo Stock Exchange.

Chapter 4

THE PAST: RETURN, RISK AND RISK PREMIUM – DEFINITIONS, MEASUREMENT AND THE HISTORICAL RECORD

Learning objectives

After studying this chapter you should be able to:

1 Understand how to compute past rates of return.

2 Understand how to incorporate taxes and inflation into the calculation of rates of return.

3 Understand the differences between the arithmetic average and geometric average rates of return.

4 Calculate the volatility of past rates of return by the variance and standard deviation.

5 Understand the past relationship between volatility, average rate of return and risk premium.

INVESTMENT IN THE NEWS

Media, banks, oils prop up FTSE 100

Vince Heaney

A late run on the media sector kept the FTSE 100 in the black on Monday, despite weakness in technology stocks.

The Daily Mail Group led the blue-chip leaderboard at the close, with Granada firming.

Simon Baker, media analyst at SG Securities, said of the Daily Mail: 'There were some encouraging national newspaper circulation figures for December recently and [the markets] could be looking forward to some positive statement at next month's AGM.'

Tech sentiment was dealt a fresh blow after upbeat results from chip designer ARM Holdings were followed by a drop in the share price as analysts focused on the cautious outlook.

Heavyweights

It was left to the market heavyweights in the blue-chip oils and banking sectors to prop up the market, with both sectors benefiting from positive broker comment.

The FTSE 100 closed 0.6 per cent firmer at 5,223.6, while the FTSE Techmark was 1.5 per cent weaker at 1,371.5.

Source: Website at http://www.ftmarketwatch.com, 28 January 2002. (Now www.ftinvestor.com). Reprinted with permission from FT Investor. © Financial Times Limited 2002.

INVESTMENT IN THE NEWS

Exhibit 4.1 London gainers and losers, 28 January 2002

(a) FTSE 100 Gainers   FT

Gainers	Value	% Change
Tea Plantations...	1.25	+66.67
Rts Networks Gr...	1.25	+66.67
Transacsys	4.50	+20.00
Convergent Comm...	8.00	+10.34
Creightons	3.25	+8.33
Widney	102.50	+7.89
Howard Holdings	36.50	+7.35
M.L. Laboratorie...	39.50	+6.76
Pennant Intl Gr...	8.50	+6.25
Cabouchon Colle...	34.50	+6.15
Marlborough Int...	17.50	+6.06
Centamin Egypt	9.00	+5.88
Direct Message	5.00	+5.26
Schroder Asia P...	10.50	+5.00
Macro 4	160.00	+4.92

Source: Website at http://www.ftmarketwatch.com/tools/indices.asp?region=100§ion=101

(b) FTSE 100 Losers

Losers	Value	% Change
Anglesey Mining	1.00	−33.33
Elementis	0.75	−25.00
Smartlogik Group	1.00	−20.00
Invesco Asia Trust	3.50	−17.65
World Travel Hldgs	3.00	−14.29
Chaucer Holdings	6.00	−14.29
Martin Currie Jap	3.00	−14.29
Gartmore Selec Jap	1.50	−14.29
Orchestream Hldgs	11.50	−13.21
Electra Inv Trust	590.00	−12.59
Pacific Horizon It	0.44	−12.50
Gameplay	0.53	−12.50
Cash Converters In	1.75	−12.50
Stockbourne	1.75	−12.50
Synigence	8.50	−10.53

Source: Website at http://www.ftmarketwatch.com/tools/indices.asp?region=100 (now www.ftinvestor.com), 29 January 2002. Reprinted with permission from FT Investor.

Exhibit 4.2 FTSE 100 index, 28 January 2002

© BigCharts.com

Source: Website at http://www.ftmarketwatch.com/tools/indices.asp?region=100 (now www.ftinvestor.com), 29 January 2002. © BigCharts.com. Reproduced by permission of FT Investors and Big Charts.

Investors buy securities for their returns. In most cases there is also a risk attached to each investment. No one can guarantee that Tea Plantations will not be a loser next day or sometime in the near future, despite its performance on 28 January 2002. Being on the 'honour roll' one year or one day does not necessarily mean that the stock will appear on the 'honour roll' the next year. Uncertainty (or risk) therefore exists regarding future returns on an investment in the capital market. The main dilemma of the investor is how to choose from various available assets with different risk–return characteristics.

In this chapter we demonstrate how to calculate past rates of return. We then discuss the various multi-period averages of rates of return, which measure the average past profitability of an asset. We are also interested in knowing how to calculate the dispersion of rates of return around the average, which measures the historical risk or volatility of the investment. We then present the historical record of various assets in order to demonstrate that, in general, the higher the average rate of return on an asset, the higher its risk. Historical data are frequently used to estimate future expected rates of return and risk. These estimates are required for investment decision-making, a process which will be discussed in the next chapter.

4.1   RATES OF RETURN

As discussed below, one important use of rates of return is as a measure of comparison of the profitability of different investments. It is standard practice for investment managers to present the profitability of financial assets in percentages rather than in dollars or pounds. This enables investors to compare the rates of return on alternative assets whatever their price level. In this chapter we first demonstrate how to calculate rates of return on the investments.

Investors and investment analysts have three uses for past rates of return:

1 *Measuring historical performance.* Investors generally compare the rates of return on alternative investments, e.g. of alternative unit trusts. Suppose, for example, that two unit trusts are managed by two professional managers, Abraham and Alita. Fund managers are to be compensated according to performance. The historical or realized rate of return on a fund is an important measure of a manager's performance.

   However, rates of return are not in themselves a sufficient criterion for ranking the two managers. One would also need to know how much risk each manager has taken on.

2 *Estimating future rates of return.* Investors may use historical rates of return to estimate future *expected* rates of return and risk of various securities in order to make portfolio investment decisions.

   In general, future fluctuations in rates of return can be estimated from historical fluctuations. For example, the fluctuations in the technology stocks rate of return are higher than those of the big stocks (such as the Gas Corporation or the Electricity Corporation). These *ex-post* fluctuations can be used to estimate future (or *ex-ante*) fluctuations which, in turn, can be used in constructing an investment portfolio.

3 *Estimating cost of capital.* Finally, past rates of return can be used to estimate a firm's cost of equity, a term which is probably familiar to students who have studied corporate finance. Financial managers use the cost of equity (or cost of capital) in

capital budgeting decisions. One method of estimating the appropriate discount rate (for use in net-present-value calculations) utilizes the average historical rate of return on equity.

Similarily, investors and investment analysts who are considering buying a stock may use the *ex-post* average rate of return in order to discount the expected future dividends of the stock.

Historical rates of return, therefore, fulfil several functions for investors, analysts and financial managers.

4.2   RATE-OF-RETURN CALCULATIONS

Rates of return can be calculated in more than one way. Different methods yield different results, and money managers, who are rated on their performance, have an incentive to use those methods that make them look the best. Bearing this problem in mind, in 1992 the Committee for Performance Presentation Standards (CPPS) of the Association for Investment Management and Research (AIMR) established strict guidelines for its members to follow in presenting historical performance measures. The AIMR is the largest association of financial analysts in the world and you will most likely have to adhere to their standards if you become involved in the money management industry. This section reviews the techniques used in complying with the AIMR standards.[1]

4.2.1 Simple rate of return

Investors hold a security for a given period. The rate of return measured for this period is called the *holding period return* (HPR). There are several ways to measure security rates of return. This discussion begins with the *simple* rate of return.

The simple rate of return measures how much the value of a given investment increases or decreases over a given period of time. The simple rate of return (R) is given by

$$R = \frac{\text{EMV} - \text{BMV} + I}{\text{BMV}} \tag{4.1}$$

where EMV is the end-of-period market value, BMV is the beginning-of-period market value, and I is the income (generally in the form of interest and dividends) received from the investment during the period. This is the simplest and most common way of calculating the rate of return. Equation 4.1 gives rates of return in decimal form. To arrive at percentages, simply multiply by 100.

To demonstrate the simple rate-of-return calculation, assume you purchased one share of stock at the beginning of the year for £100 per share. You receive an

---

[1] Adapted with permission from the *Report of the Performance Presentation Standards Implementation Committee.* © 1991, Association for Investment Management and Research, Charlottesville, VA. All rights reserved.

£8 cash dividend per share. The stock is trading at the end of the year at £110 per share. Because EMV = £110, BMV = £100 and I = £8, the simple rate of return in this case is:

$$R = \frac{£110 - £100 + £8}{£100} = \frac{£18}{£100} = 0.18 \text{ or } 18\%$$

Note that the rate of return is the percentage change in the value of the investment; it does not matter whether you buy 200, 100 or one share of stock.

Equation 4.1 can also be written as

$$R = \frac{EMV + I}{BMV} - \frac{BMV}{BMV} = \frac{EMV + I}{BMV} - 1$$

and hence,

$$1 + R = \frac{EMV + I}{BMV}$$

which, in the earlier example, would be

$$1 + R = \frac{£110 + £8}{£100} = 1.18$$

which tells us that the value of £1 at the end of the period is £1.18. That is, £1 invested one period earlier would be worth £1.18 at the end of the period.

Determining a stock's or portfolio's performance using the simple rate of return calculation is appropriate when income is received at the end of the period. If dividends are paid during the period the simple rate of return has certain limitations.

In the next section, we calculate the adjusted rate of return. We use the simple rates of return in the calculation of the adjusted rate of return, which correctly takes into account the timing of the dividend and interest income.

4.2.2 Adjusted rate of return

The simple rate of return is easy to calculate and gives us an idea of the asset's rate of return. However, as mentioned above, it is not accurate, since it does not take into account the timing of dividends. To illustrate, consider two stocks, priced at £100 at the beginning of the year and £110 at the end of the year. The cash dividend is £10 for each stock. However, on one stock, the £10 is paid in January, while on the other it is paid in December. The simple rate of return shows a 20% rate of return on both stocks, regardless of the timing of cash dividends. However, investors are not indifferent to the timing of cash dividends. The earlier the dividends are obtained, the better off the investors are (this is the idea of 'time value of money' studied in corporate finance). The adjusted rate of return takes into account the timing of cash dividends and interest payments. Since the adjusted rate of return takes into account the timing of the cash flows, it is also called the time-weighted rate of return. This more correct measure of rate of return is used in the rest of the chapter and will be termed *the rate of return* to distinguish it from the *simple rate of return*. The rate of return assumes that all interim cash flows (in the form of dividends, interest and other cash benefits) are reinvested in the security under consideration. For example, if an investor wants to measure the rate of return on Marks & Spencer stock for the year

2001, and $10 dividends are paid in January 2001, then the method of calculation presented below implicitly assumes that the $10 is used to purchase more Marks & Spencer stock immediately upon being received. The AIMR explains the philosophy of this adjustment as follows:

> If cash flows occur during the period, they must theoretically be used, in effect, 'to buy additional units' of the portfolio at the market price on the day that they are received. Thus, the most accurate approach is to calculate the market value of the portfolio on the date of each flow, calculate an interim rate of return for the sub-period, and then link the sub-period returns to get the return for the month or quarter.[2]

Therefore, we must correctly incorporate the timing of cash flows to the investor or make adjustments to allow for the fact that dividends are in general not paid at the end of the year. The method for computing the rate of return is called the linking method. According to this method, we first calculate the simple rate of return for each sub-period where the cash dividend date determines the end of each sub-period, and then calculate the rate of return from these simple rates of return. The following numerical example illustrates this method.

Assume you are investing in shares of EMI Group. Exhibit 4.3(a) provides the necessary data for your calculations. Assume that EMI Group paid quarterly cash dividends and its stock price fluctuated considerably during the year.[3] Specifically, notice that the price fell early in the year, rose during the latter part of the year, and fell again to its original level by year's end.

Using the linking method, the simple rate of return (r_t) is calculated for each sub-period (t). The rate of return (R) for the entire period is then obtained by Rule 1, as follows.

Rule 1: To obtain the adjusted rate of return, first calculate the simple rate of return corresponding to each period, add 1 to it, multiply these terms and finally subtract 1:

$$R = [(1 + r_1)(1 + r_2) \ldots (1 + r_m)] - 1 \qquad (4.2)$$

where m is the number of sub-periods. By this method the value of the investment at the end of the first sub-period $(1 + r_1)$, including the obtained dividend, is reinvested for the second period, and so on up to the last period. This is equivalent to using dividends to purchase additional stock immediately upon receiving them.

Exhibit 4.3(b) illustrates the linking method for computing returns. The simple rate of return for Period 1 (January 1 through February 15) is $[(£80 − £100 + £2)/£100] = −0.18$, and for Period 2 (February 15 through May 15) is $[(£95 − £80 + £2)/£80] = 0.2125$. Thus, the rate of return over the period January 1 through May 15 is calculated by $([1 + (− 0.18)][1 + 0.2125] − 1) = −0.0057$. Continuing this procedure, the rate of return for the whole year is found to be 0.0842, or 8.42% (see the last entry in the last column of Exhibit 4.3(b)). Note that the simple rate of return is calculated such that the final date of each period is determined by the dividend payment date (e.g. February 15). Thus, it is equal to the rate of return for this sub-period and hence is an accurate measure of profitability for the given sub-period.

---

[2] AIMR, p. 28 (see footnote 1).
[3] Dividends are typically declared about a month after the end of a fiscal quarter and paid two weeks later. Hence, most firms pay dividends in February, May, August and November.

Exhibit 4.3 Calculating a rate of return for EMI Group

(a) Table of input information

Date	Dividend per share (£)	Stock price when dividend is received (£)
January 1		100
February 15	2	80
May 15	2	95
August 15	2	105
November 15	2	120
December 31		100

(b) Calculating a rate of return by the linking method

Date	Interim period	Interim simple rate of return	Cumulative rate of return
January 1			
February 15	1	−0.18	−0.18
May 15	2	0.2125	−0.0057
August 15	3	0.1263	0.1198
November 15	4	0.1619	0.3011
December 31	5	−0.1667	0.0842

To sum up, the 8% simple rate of return method (using the simple rate of return equation given by Equation 4.1) assumes that when the dividends are received they are either left idle or spent, whereas the rate of return (8.42%) calculated using Equation 4.2 assumes reinvestment of the cash dividends. The rate of return is superior to the simple rate of return because it appropriately addresses the timing of cash flows. Investors prefer to receive money earlier rather than later, a fact that is ignored by the simple rate of return. The rate of return method guarantees that profitability on various assets is compared for the same level of pound investment. Investors want to know how well different securities have performed over time. It must, therefore, be assumed that interim cash flows are invested in the security itself. For example, suppose you want to compare the historical rates of return on two firms, A and B. You invest £100 in Firm A and £100 in Firm B. Firm A pays you £50 in dividends after one day. Firm B does not pay dividends at all. Using the simple method to calculate rates of return does not make sense, because your investment in Firm A is reduced by £50 after one day (hence the firm has less resources to invest, creating less returns). Thus, by the simple method, you actually compare the return on an investment of £100 in Firm B to £50 in Firm A. Therefore, the reinvestment of the obtained cash flow assumption is incorporated in order to reach an accurate measure of performance for a particular security, independent of its dividend policy and the size of the investment.[4]

---

[4] Appendix 4A at the end of the chapter provides a rate of return measure where the investment level changes over time. For example, suppose that an investor increases his or her investment in a given stock every month by allocating some percentage of the monthly salary to such an investment. This is a rate of return that measures the investor's percentage profit but not the rate of return on the security itself. It is affected by the rate of return on the asset in various periods as well as the amount of money invested by the investor in each period.

PRACTICE BOX

Problem

Suppose you purchased 100 shares of Misys on 1 January at £50 per share. Misys pays £2.30 annual dividend per share on 15 March, when the stock is trading at £55. Misys declares a 3-for-2 stock split effective on 30 May, when the stock is trading at £60. (A 3-for-2 stock split implies three new shares are substituted for two old shares held.) If Misys closed on 31 December at £35 per share, what would your rate of return be using the linking method?

Solution

The following table summarizes the basic data regarding Misys which is relevant for the rate of return calculation:

Date	Dividend	Split	Adjusted price Market price of stock
January 1			£50
March 15	£2.30		£55
May 30		3-for-2 shares	£40
December 31			£35

The simple rate of return for the period 1 January through 15 March is:

$$\frac{£55 + £2.30 - £50}{£50} = \frac{£7.3}{£50} = 0.1466 \text{ or } 14.6\%$$

The simple rate of return for the period 15 March through 30 May is:

$$\frac{1.5 \times £40 - £55}{£55} = \frac{£60 - £55}{£55} = \frac{£5}{£55} \cong 0.0909 \text{ or } 9.09\%$$

Note that we multiply the end of the period price of £40 by 1.5 because a 3-for-2 split implies a 50% increase in the number of shares holding. As we assume in the calculation that one share was bought at the beginning of the period, 1.5 shares are held at the end of the period due to the split. Finally, the rate of return for the last period is:

$$\frac{£35 - £40}{£40} = \frac{-£5}{£40} \cong -0.125 \text{ or } -12.5\%$$

Using the linking method (Equation 4.2), the rate of return for the year is given by

$$R = [(1 + 0.1466)(1 + 0.0909)(1 - 0.125)] - 1 \cong 0.09447 \text{ or about } 9.447\%$$

Nonetheless, in many cases cash dividends are relatively small; hence, the simple and adjusted rates of return are not that different. This explains why the simple and quick method is sometimes employed despite its lack of precision.

Notice that the various methods of calculation do not attempt to identify the best strategy for the investor but rather endeavour to measure the correct rate of return. For example, sometimes reinvesting dividends reduces the rate of return (as, for example, when the stock price falls). However, only the rate of return method gives the true historical rate of return on a given asset.

Thus far, we have demonstrated how to adjust the rate of return for cash dividends. If the firm makes other distributions to stockholders apart from cash dividends, they must obviously be incorporated into the rate of return calculation. For example, if the firm pays stock dividends of say 10%, the stock price generally drops. This reflects the fact that there are more outstanding shares, although the investor holds only 1.1 shares for each share bought at the beginning of the period (i.e. a 10% increase in the number of shares held). This fact should be incorporated into the rate of return calculation. Similarly, if the firm splits its stocks, adjustments should be made, since the investor holds more shares, albeit at a lower price. The company may also issue rights offerings, i.e. rights issued to stockholders to purchase new shares at a relatively low price (called the subscription price). These rights have a market value that also needs to be incorporated in the rate of return calculation.

Stock split

On 23 February 2001, Misys Company split its stock in a 2-for-1 ratio. This means that an investor holding 100 shares of Misys before the split holds 200 shares after the split. The investor returns the 100 old shares to the firm and gets 200 new shares instead with no additional investment. Thus, no cash flows are involved. How does such a split affect the rate of return calculation? The practice box above demonstrates how to incorporate stock split and cash dividends into the rate of return calculations.

Stock dividends

Stock dividends are incorporated into the calculation exactly as is the split. This is because the stock dividend increases the number of shares held with no cash flow involved. To illustrate, suppose that 10% stock dividends are paid, the stock price being £38 at the beginning of the period and £40 at the end. Then, for each share bought at the beginning of the period, the investor would hold 1.1 shares (due to the 10% stock dividends); hence we should multiply £40 by 1.1 to obtain the value of the investor's holding at the end of the period. The rate of return for our example at the end of the period would be

$$\frac{1.1 \times £40 - £38}{£38} = \frac{£44 - £38}{£38} = \frac{£6}{£38} \cong 0.1579 \text{ or } 15.79\%$$

Rights

Firms may raise equity by rights offerings, whereby existing stockholders have the right to buy new shares at a price lower than the market price. Rights offerings affect the end of a period stock price, and thus affect the rate of return on the stock.

Rights offerings are incorporated into the simple rate of return like cash dividends. To illustrate, suppose that for every two shares held, the investor earned the right to buy one share at a lower than market price. One right is linked to each old stock (i.e., in our specific example, for every stock the investor has a right to buy half a new share). The right has economic value and therefore we have to add the market value of the right to the end-of-period value of the investment. These rights are traded separately from the stocks and have market value. Because existing stockholders receive a right to buy new shares at a price lower than the market price of the stock, the stock price generally drops when the rights are traded separately from the stock. Suppose that the stock price at the beginning of the period on 1 January is £100 and on 10 March the rights were traded for £5 a right (thus, the value of the right attached to each share is £5). On 10 March, after the right was traded separately from the stock for the first time, the stock price was £107. Assuming no other distributions, the rate of return for this period is given by

$$\frac{£107 + £5 - £100}{£100} = \frac{£12}{£100} = 0.12 \text{ or } 12\%$$

It is assumed that investors obtain the £5 and this is treated the same as cash dividends. It is, therefore, assumed that investors will sell the stock and the right at the end of the sub-period and receive £107 plus £5.

We would like to emphasize that the price of rights as published in the media (e.g. *The Wall Street Journal*) is the value attached to each old stock regardless of the allocation ratio. Thus if, for example, the right allocation ratio is one right for each two old stocks and an investor wishes to exercise the right (i.e. buy more shares at the relatively low price), he or she needs two rights (or a value of £10) to buy one new share.

Indeed, investors who do not hold firm stocks can buy two rights for £10 and add the subscription price, say £97, to purchase one share of the firm. What is important for the rate of return calculation is that the value of the right is added to the end-of-period value exactly as cash dividends are added, regardless of whether the investor exercises the rights or simply sells them in the market.

Rate of return on derivatives

Call and put options are financial assets which are traded in the market. The call option holder of, say, Hilton is entitled to buy one share of Hilton at a given price for a given period. This predetermined price is called the *strike price*, and the option is intact up to a given date in the future, called the *expiration date*. A put option holder has the right to sell the stock at a predetermined price. If the stock price in the market goes up, we expect the call price to rise and the put price to decline. Call and put options pay no dividends and interest; hence, the rate of return calculation on these two assets is very simple, solely reflecting the capital gain or capital loss.

The following practice box illustrates such a calculation for options on Hilton share.

4.2.3 Bond returns on an accrual basis

Calculating the rate of return on bonds raises an additional issue regarding the timing of cash flows because of the way bond prices are quoted. Whereas the cash dividends on stocks are paid on a periodic (most often quarterly) basis, bond coupon interest accrues daily. *The bond prices quoted by the financial media and market makers do not include accrued interest in most cases.* However, the actual price paid for the bonds includes accrued interest. Thus, the equation for calculating bond returns must incorporate that accrued interest. When calculating the rates of return of bonds, the investor must, therefore, incorporate accrued interest. The CPPS of the AIMR describes the underlying philosophy of rate of return calculations for bonds:

> The Standards clearly state that an accrual basis, rather than a cash basis, should be used for calculating interest income. The guiding premise, again, should be to include that income to

PRACTICE BOX

Problem

The following data, taken from the *Financial Times*, provides the Hilton stock price, the call option price and the option price for two days, 31 and 30 December 2000. The strike price of each option is £200. Calculate the one-day rate of return on Hilton share as well as the put and the call option.

	31 December	30 December
Hilton stock	£209	£212
Hilton Feb call option	£9	£10
Hilton Feb put option	£18½	£17½

Solution

Let us calculate the daily rate of return on the stocks, on the call option and on the put option.

The rate of return on Hilton share (no dividends were paid on the day) for the one day was

$$R = \frac{£209 - £212}{£212} \cong -0.0142 \text{ or } -1.42\%$$

The rate of return on the call option was

$$R = \frac{£9 - £10}{£9} \cong -0.11 \text{ or } -11.11\%$$

and the rate of return on the put option was

$$R = \frac{£18½ - £17½}{£17½} \cong 0.0571 \text{ or } 5.71\%$$

which the portfolio was truly entitled if the security were sold at the end of the performance interval. Stock dividends do not become payable unless the stock is owned on the ex-dividend date. Dividends should therefore be accrued as income of their ex-date. Interest on most fixed-income securities becomes payable pro rata as long as the security is held. Interest should therefore be accrued according to whatever method is appropriate for the specific issue.[5]

Using the quoted bond prices to calculate the rates of return for bonds on a cash basis ignores the accrued interest (which the buyer has to pay and seller receives), and thus is not accurate. To account for accrued interest, simply add the values for accrued interest at the beginning and end of the period to the respective beginning and ending prices in Equation 4.1. Formally, the simple rate of return (R_t) can be expressed as

$$R_t = \frac{P_t + C_t - (P_{t-1} + AI_{t-1})}{P_{t-1} + AI_{t-1}} \tag{4.3}$$

---

[5] Adapted with permission from the *Report of the Performance Presentation Standards Implementation Committee*, December 1991, pp. 31–32. © 1991, Association for Investment Management and Research, Charlottesville, VA. All rights reserved.

where the date on which a coupon C_t is paid is determined by the end of the sub-period corresponding to the simple rate of return calculation. P_t is the price of the bond at the end of Period t, P_{t-1} is the price of the bond at the end of Period $(t-1)$, AI_{t-1} is the accrued interest as of the end of Period $(t-1)$ (investors must pay it when they buy the bonds), and C_t is the coupon paid at the end of sub-period t. If the rate of return is calculated from one coupon payout date to another, then there is no accrued interest. Similarly, if one chooses a different date for the end of the period than that of the accrued interest rate, AI_t rather than C_t should be added to P_t.

In general, for any selected period the rate of return on bonds is calculated by Rule 2.

Rule 2: Take the price of the bond at the end of the period and add to it the received or accrued interest. Subtract from it the price of the bond at the beginning of the period and the payment for the accrued period up to the bond's purchasing date. Divide this difference by the investment which is the bond price at the beginning of the period and the accrued interest.

Let us illustrate how to calculate the rate of return for bonds on an accrual basis. Consider a coupon bond that pays 8% on a semiannual basis. Assume that £40 in interest is paid on 15 November and 15 January. Exhibit 4.4 illustrates how to calculate the rate of return by the linking method. The exhibit lists the coupon payments, market prices and accrued interest for each date. Recall from Equation 4.3 that the rate of return requires calculating the beginning and ending market values. The accrual basis incorporates accrued interest in these values. For example, consider the rate of return during the period 1 January through 15 May, where the beginning market value is £1,000 (£990 + £10, where £10 is accrued interest). The accrued interest can be estimated as the fraction of the period since the last payment times the payment amount. In this case, it is (1.5 months/6 months) × £40 = £10. The 1.5 months is 15 November to 1 January. The ending market value is £1,030. The income paid in this period is the coupon payment of £40. Thus, the rate of return for the first time interval is

$$R_1 = \frac{£1,030 + £40 - (£990 + £10)}{£990 + £10} = \frac{£70}{£1,000} = 0.07 \text{ or } 7\%$$

In a similar way the simple rate of return is calculated for the other time interval. Note that for the last time interval, the investor received £10 accrued interest. The adjusted rate of return for the whole year is 9.03%.

Exhibit 4.4 **Calculating the rate of return for an 8% semiannual coupon-bearing bond**

Computing the rate of return by the linking method

Date (t)	Interim period	Coupon	Market price	Accrued interest	Accrued rate of return	Rate of return to date t
Jan. 1			£990	£10[a]		
May 15	1	£40	£1,030	£0	0.07	0.07
Nov. 15	2	£40	£1,020	£0	0.0291	0.1011[b]
Dec. 31	3		£1,000	£10[a]	−0.0098	0.0903[c]

[a] (1,000) (0.08) (1.5/12) = £10 (interest is paid on 15 May and 15 November).
[b] (1 + 0.07) × (1 + 0.0291) − 1 = 0.1011.
[c] (1 + 0.1011) × (1 − 0.0098) − 1 = 0.0903.

Note that the accrued interest at the end of period t will be zero if there is a coupon payment. That is, all interest that has been accrued was paid via the coupon payment. From Exhibit 4.4 we find that the rate of return on this bond over this year was 9.03%.

4.3   AFTER-TAX RATES OF RETURN

Taxes generally change the rate of return an investor receives. Although many pension funds and other portfolios are tax exempt, the security holdings of many investors are taxable. The procedure for calculating after-tax rates of return is conceptually similar to the simple rate of return calculations in Section 4.2. The only difference is the reduction of rates of return resulting from taxes.

To illustrate, suppose that your marginal income tax is 30%, and that you pay 20% capital gains tax.[6] You hold the stock for one year and you receive the dividend of £10 at the end of the year. The stock's price at the beginning of the year is £100 and at the end of the year £140.

The *pre-tax* rate of return is:

$$\frac{£140 + £10 - £100}{£100} = 0.50 \text{ or } 50\%$$

The *after-tax* rate of return is:

$$\frac{£140 + £10 - £100 - (£140 - £100) \times 0.2 - (£10 \times 0.30)}{£100}$$

$$= \frac{£50 - £8 - £3}{£100} = \frac{£39}{£100} = 0.39 \text{ or } 39\%$$

The investor, therefore, pays £8 capital gains tax and £3 income tax on dividends; hence the after-tax rate of return is, in this example, only 39% as opposed to 50% on a pre-tax basis.

4.4   INFLATION-ADJUSTED RATES OF RETURN

Thus far we have calculated rates of return in nominal terms, ignoring the effect of inflation.[7] Inflation causes investors to lose purchasing power when they sell their financial assets in the future and wish to buy goods with the proceeds. Investors would probably prefer that there was no inflation. The consumer price index (denoted CPI in the UK financial press) measures the inflation rate. The CPI provides the percentage change in the price of a specified basket of consumer goods.

Inflation reduces the purchasing power of an investment. That is, a person may invest £1,000 with the expectation of receiving £1,100 back within a year and using this sum

---

[6] By the current tax laws in the UK you have to pay capital gains tax of 10% (if you're earning up to £1,880), 20% (if you're earning up to £29,400) or 40% (if you're earning over £29,400). For all related tax issues, we recommend you to visit www.inlandrevenue.gov.uk.

[7] *Inflation* is the increase over time in the cost of goods and services. *Deflation* refers to the decrease over time in the cost of goods and services. In most years inflation rather than deflation has prevailed in the Western world.

to purchase goods and services. But, if the overall cost of goods and services rises more than 10% over the year the investment will not have been worthwhile.

The real rate of return is the nominal rate of return adjusted for inflation. The real rate of return (R_{real}) is calculated as

$$R_{real} = \frac{1 + R_{nom}}{1 + h} - 1 \tag{4.4}$$

where R_{nom} is the nominal rate of return and h is the inflation rate.[8] For example, if the nominal rate of return is 10% and inflation is 15%, the real rate of return is

$$R_{real} = \frac{1 + 0.1}{1 + 0.15} - 1 \cong -0.0435 \text{ or } -4.35\%$$

Note two properties of real rates of return:

1 In the case of no inflation ($h = 0$), the real rate of return is equal to the nominal rate of return.
2 If the nominal rate of return is equal to the inflation rate ($R_{nom} = h$), then in real terms, the rate of return is zero.

Let us turn to our previous example where the rate of return on the stock was 50% before tax and 39% after tax. Assuming an additional 5% annual inflation, the after-tax *real* rate of return would be:

$$\frac{1 + 0.39}{1 + 0.05} - 1 \cong 0.324 \text{ or approximately } 32.4\%$$

Thus, in our example, both inflation and taxes reduce the nominal rate of return from 50% to about 32.4%.

4.4.1 Calculating the rate of return values – an example

Let us now employ actual data to demonstrate the various rates of return on the stock of 'Hi Tech Dream' (HD) corresponding to the year 2001.

Exhibit 4.5 provides the basic data regarding HD. The table provides the stock prices at the beginning of the year, at the end of the year, and at each date where a dividend was paid. These prices are necessary for calculating the simple rate of return for each sub-period. The dividend paid in 2001 was four times £0.5, i.e. £2 for the year.

The simple rate of return for the year is:

$$\frac{(£71.5625 - £60.625) + £2}{£60.625} \cong 0.2134 \text{ or } 21.34\%$$

Note that the price of £71.5625 is quoted as £71$^9/_{16}$. We thus transfer the prices here to decimals. To calculate the rate of return, we first need to calculate the rate of return

---

[8] Equation 4.4 can be approximated by $R_{real} = R_{nom} - h$, where R_{real} is the real rate of return, R_{nom} is the nominal rate of return and h is the inflation rate. This is known as the *Fisher relationship*, which was originally proposed by I. Fisher, in *The Theory of Interest* (New York: Macmillan, 1930).

for each sub-period ending at the date when a dividend was paid. For example, for the first period, covering 2 January 2001 through 17 February 2001, the simple rate of return is:

$$\frac{(£64.875 - £60.625) + £0.5}{£60.625} \cong 0.0783 \text{ or } 7.83\%$$

Using the data in Exhibit 4.5, the simple rate of return corresponding to the other sub-periods was calculated in a similar way. Having the simple rates of return, we can employ the linking method to obtain the before-taxes rate of return for the year as follows:

$$[(1.0783)(1.1349)(0.9504)(0.9638)(1.0843)] - 1 \cong 0.2155 \text{ or } 21.55\%$$

The before-taxes real rate of return for 2001 is given by:

$$\frac{1.2155}{1.016} - 1 \cong 0.1964 \text{ or } 19.64\%$$

where $h = 1.6\%$ is the annual inflation corresponding to the year 2001.

We employ the same method to calculate the simple after-tax rate of return and the after-tax rate of return in nominal and real terms, yielding a nominal rate of return of 16.81% and after-tax real rate of return of 14.97%. To calculate the after-tax rate of return, it is assumed that a 30% tax rate is paid on the cash dividends and 20% on capital gains. Of course, any other tax rates corresponding to the individual taxpayer rates can be used in the after-tax calculation. However, since it is assumed in this example that the holding period of the stock is one year (any other arbitrary holding period is possible), the capital gains tax is paid only at the end of the year when the stock is sold. For example, for the first sub-period (see Exhibit 4.5) the after-tax rate of return is given by:

$$\frac{(£64.875 - £60.625) + £0.5 - 0.3 \times £0.5}{£60.625} \cong 0.0759 \text{ or } 7.59\%$$

where $-0.3 \times £0.5 = -£0.15$ is the tax paid on the first £0.5 of dividends. Note that no capital gains tax is paid because it is assumed that the stock is not sold at the end of the first time interval.

The calculation of the after-tax rate of return of the last period corresponding to Exhibit 4.5 is a little more complicated because capital gains tax is paid on the difference between the price at the end of the year (when the stock is assumed to be sold) and the price at the beginning of the year (when the stock is assumed to be bought). We thus have the following after-tax rate of return for this period:

$$\frac{(£71.5625 - £66) - 0.2 \times (71.5625 - £60.625)}{£66} =$$

$$\frac{(£71.5625 - £66) - £2.1875}{£66} \cong 0.0511 \text{ or } 5.11\%$$

where £2.1875 is the capital gains tax paid on the difference between the prices at the end and the beginning of the year.

4.5 AVERAGE RATE OF RETURN: THE MEASURE OF PROFITABILITY

The past average rate of return measures the average profitability of an investment. To see why such an average is needed, suppose that you observe the following rates of return on stock A and B over the past two years:

Year	Stock A	Stock B
1	−10%	+1%
2	+60%	+45%

Which stock has a better historical record? For year 1, stock B is better, because its rate of return is 1%, while stock A suffers a loss of 10%. The opposite holds for year 2. Thus, to answer the question 'which stock has a better historical record?' we need to calculate some average rate of return which takes the two years (as in our example) into account. This average reflects the average rate of return per period; i.e. per year in our specific example.

There are two main methods for calculating the average rate of return, yielding the arithmetic average and the geometric average. Because the two methods yield different results, it is important to study them and to be able to understand the interpretation of both these averages.

This section discusses historical averages, called *ex-post* averages, to distinguish them from expected values or means, which relate to future values (*ex-ante* values). The arithmetic method of determining the average rate of return adds the realized rates of return over different periods[9] identified by subscript t (R_t) and divides by the number of observations (m). This is summarized by Rule 3 below.

Rule 3: To obtain the arithmetic historical mean, sum all the historical returns and divide by the number of observations. That is,

$$\overline{R}_A = \frac{\sum_{t=1}^{m} R_t}{m} \tag{4.5}$$

---

[9] At this point, the length of the period (t) does not matter. It can be a year, a quarter or even a day.

where $\overline{R}_A$ is the *arithmetic* average rate of return. Note that we distinguish between the forward-looking, or *ex-ante*, expected returns (denoted as $E(R)$) and historical, or *ex-post*, returns (denoted as $\overline{R}$). The expected rate of return will be discussed in the next chapter.

The geometric method is an averaging method that compounds rates of return. That is, if £1 is invested in Period 1, then it will be worth $£(1 + R_1)$ at the end of Period 1. The geometric method assumes that the amount $£(1 + R_1)$ is invested for Period 2. At the end of Period 2, the investment will be worth the amount invested at the beginning of Period 2 times 1 + the rate of return in Period 2. That is, the investment at the end of Period 2 is worth $£(1 + R_1)(1 + R_2)$. Continuing this procedure over all *ex-post* periods would give us the value at the end of m periods of a £1 investment at the beginning of the period. This total return is averaged by taking the mth root. The geometric average can, therefore, be expressed as Rule 4.

Rule 4: To obtain the historical geometric mean, add 1 to the rate of return of each period, multiply all these terms, take the mth root and subtract 1. That is,

$$\overline{R}_G = [(1 + R_1)(1 + R_2)...(1 + R_m)]^{1/m} - 1 \qquad (4.6)$$

where $\overline{R}_G$ is the geometric average rate of return.

Using our previous example we have:

Stock	Arithmetic average	Geometric average
A	$\dfrac{-0.1 + 0.60}{2} = 0.25$ or 25%	$[(0.9)\,(1.60)]^{1/2} - 1 = 0.2$ or 20%
B	$\dfrac{0.01 + 0.45}{2} = 0.23$ or 23%	$[(1.01)\,(1.45)]^{1/2} - 1 \cong 0.2102$ or 21.02%

Thus, by the arithmetic average, stock A has a better historical record, while the opposite holds when the historical record is measured by the geometric mean.

Let us look at a more dramatic case to illustrate the different results obtained from these two methods. Suppose a unit trust paid no dividends and began with a market value of £100 per share. At the end of the first year, the unit trust was worth £50 per share, and at the end of the second year, the fund was once again worth £100 per share. The rate of return in the first year was $[(£50 - £100)/£100] = -0.50$, or a loss of 50%. The rate of return in the second year was $[(£100 - £50)/£50] = 1.0$, or a profit of 100%. The arithmetic average is $(-0.5 + 1.0)/2 = 0.25$, or 25%. The geometric average, however, is $[(1 - 0.5)(1 + 1)]^{1/2} - 1 = 0\%$.

Because the geometric and the arithmetic averages may drastically differ from each other, it is important to guide the reader under what circumstances each average is more meaningful. When one holds the asset for several periods (years) the geometric average is more meaningful. To see this, suppose you invest for two years in the fund. Which averaging method is correct – the 0% geometric average rate of return or the 25% arithmetic average rate of return?

In this case, you originally invested £100 and after two years ended up with £100. Clearly, from an investor's viewpoint, there was no profit, or the investor obtained a 0% rate of return. The geometric average, therefore, is the correct average because it shows a zero rate of return that reflects the change in the value to the investor over the two years. Indeed, the geometric average can be interpreted as being the actual growth rate of the asset, and the arithmetic average is meaningless in this case.

In three situations, however, the arithmetic average should be used:

1 The arithmetic method is correct when estimating the average performance across different securities for one period of time. For example, you would use the arithmetic average when calculating the average rate of return for securities within a specific industry. If you wanted to assess the performance of the automobile industry over the last year, you would take the arithmetic average of rates of return of automobile stocks (in this calculation, m is the number of stocks rather than the number of periods). That is, you would not be measuring growth over time but rather the average performance during one period of time.

2 Suppose that investors hold the stock for one year only. About half of the investors invest for year 1 and about half for year 2. Hence, we are not interested in the growth in the portfolio over time. In this case, the arithmetic average measures more meaningfully the average profitability of the various investors who invested in the stock.

3 Probably the most important case for using the arithmetic average is when one uses historical rates of return to estimate the future average return, which is needed for investment decision-making. The arithmetic average is an *unbiased* estimate of future expected rates of return.[10] To illustrate, suppose we want to invest in Microsoft for just one year. By taking the arithmetic average of the last 10 years, we get the best

PRACTICE BOX

Problem

Calculate the arithmetic and geometric annual average rates of return for the Abbott and Costello unit trusts. Explain the differences between the two results.

Year	Abbott Trust	Costello Trust
1	10%	8%
2	5%	12%
3	−15%	11%
4	40%	9%

Solution

Writing the rates of return in decimal figures, the arithmetic averages are

$$\overline{R}_{A,Abbott} = \frac{0.1 + 0.05 - 0.15 + 0.4}{4} = 0.10$$

$$\overline{R}_{A,Costello} = \frac{0.08 + 0.12 + 0.11 + 0.09}{4} = 0.10$$

The geometric averages are

$$\overline{R}_{G,Abbott} = [(1 + 0.1)(1 + 0.05)(1 - 0.15)(1 + 0.4)]^{1/4} - 1 \cong 0.083$$

$$\overline{R}_{G,Costello} = [(1 + 0.08)(1 + 0.12)(1 + 0.11)(1 + 0.09)]^{1/4} - 1 \cong 0.0999$$

The difference between the geometric and arithmetic averages is larger for the Abbott Trust because it has greater volatility (−15% to 40%: see Section 4.6). The more volatile the returns, the greater the difference between the geometric average and the arithmetic average.

---

[10] Unbiased estimate has the property that if a sample of periods is taken many times, on average, we obtain exactly the expected value. This assumes, of course, that the probability distribution is stable. That is, the distribution from which historical observations were made is the same as the distribution from which future observations will be made. The mathematical proof of this assertion can be found in most basic statistics books.

estimate of next year's rate of return. To see this, recall the unit trust example. Looking at past performance, we know that in one year the rate of return was −50%, and in the second year it was +100%. Suppose further that these are the only two possible outcomes for the future. Because we do not know which outcome will occur next year, our best estimate is that on average, we will make 25%, a case where the arithmetic average is relevant. Note once again that we are not addressing the issue of the long-run performance of the fund but only what we expect to earn over the next year. For portfolio investment decisions discussed in Chapter 6, we use the arithmetic average as an estimate of the expected rate of return on individual assets and on portfolios.

The arithmetic average will exceed the geometric average as long as rates of return are not constant. The difference between these two averages is greater when the volatility of returns is larger. If there is zero volatility across time, then the arithmetic average is equal to the geometric average. The arithmetic average is more often used in this textbook; hence, in the rest of the book, when we state 'average' we mean arithmetic average. When we refer to the geometric average, we will explicitly state it.

4.6 THE STANDARD DEVIATION: THE MEASURE OF RISK

4.6.1 Returns, average return and risk

The rates of return on some assets, e.g. government bonds, are quite stable, while the rates of return on other assets, e.g. stocks of hi-tech firms, are relatively volatile. The dispersion of the rates of return around the average rate of return is frequently used to measure the risk of the investment. If the rate of return deviates far from the average, we say that the dispersion is large and there is relatively large volatility (or risk) with such an investment.[11] Generally, the volatility of past rates of return also provides an indication for the future risk involved with the investment under consideration. The following simple example demonstrates why dispersion spells risk and how to measure the dispersion of historical rates of return. To illustrate the risk due to the volatility of returns, suppose we have the following three years' rates of return:

Year	Rates of return (%)	
	Stock A	Stock B
1	−10	4
2	0	6
3	+40	5
Average	10	5

The average rate of return on Stock A is 10% and the average rate of return on Stock B is 5%. Thus, Stock A, on average, is more profitable than Stock B. In practice, investors do not receive the average rate of return; rather they buy the stock for a given

---

[11] For simplicity, we assume here that the investor holds only the asset under consideration. In Chapter 6 we will discuss the effect of correlation between rates of return of various assets on the portfolio risk, i.e. the volatility of the portfolio's returns.

period, say a year. Therefore what is relevant for them is the rate of return realized in this particular year, not the average return across several years. Thus, it is clear that not all investors were better off in the past by buying Stock A rather than Stock B. For example, an investor who invests in year 1 lost 10% on Stock A and gained 4% on Stock B. Also, an investor who invested in year 2 was better off with Stock B rather than Stock A. Thus, because of its dispersion, Stock A was not necessarily better than Stock B. To see the negative effect of the dispersion on stockholders, suppose that there was no volatility in Stock A, i.e. the rate of return was 10% in each of the three years. In this case, there is a clear dominance of Stock A over Stock B because in each of the three years it would provide a higher rate of return. Thus, the actual dispersion of the rates of return of Stock A casts doubt on its superiority over Stock B, because with no volatility Stock A would be superior to Stock B (with a higher return in each of the three years) and with the actual dispersion such a superiority is no longer obvious. From this example, we can conclude that holding all other factors, including the mean rate of return, constant, investors dislike dispersion because the larger the dispersion (or volatility) the larger the risk involved with the investment. Therefore, in the rest of the book we use the terms volatility and risk interchangeably.

The dispersion of the past rates of return around the mean measures the historical volatility attached to the corresponding investment. It is common to measure the dispersion of rates of return by the standard deviation or by the variance of the rates of return. The standard deviation is denoted by the Greek letter σ and the variance is its squared value, denoted by σ^2. The past (or sample) variance is given by Rule 5.

Rule 5: The historical variance is calculated by the sum of the squared deviations (of the returns from the mean) divided by the number of observations minus 1. That is,

$$\sigma^2 = \frac{\sum_{t=1}^{m} (R_t - \overline{R})^2}{m - 1} \tag{4.7}$$

The standard deviation is the square root of the variance, given by $\sigma = (\sigma^2)^{1/2}$. R_t is the rate of return corresponding to period t (year t in our example), $\overline{R}$ is the arithmetic average and m is the number of years (periods) included in this calculation.[12]

Using our previous example with $m = 3$, we have the following variances for Stocks A and B, respectively:

Variance of Stock A: $[(-10 - 10)^2 + (0 - 10)^2 + (40 - 10)^2]/(3 - 1) = 700$

Variance of Stock B: $[(4 - 5)^2 + (6 - 5)^2 + (5 - 5)^2]/(3 - 1) = 1$

The dimension of σ^2 is 'percentage squared', which is meaningless. Therefore, we take the square root of these figures to calculate the standard deviations denoted by σ, which is given in percentage terms. However, note that to obtain the standard deviation we need to first calculate the variance.

---

[12] Dividing by $m - 1$ rather than by m provides an unbiased estimate of the variance which is needed for future investment decision-making. For the notion of an unbiased estimate, see footnote 10.

To sum up this example, the variance and the standard deviation of the above two stocks is calculated as follows:

Stock	Variance, σ^2	Standard deviation, σ
A	700	$\sqrt{700} \cong 26.46\%$
B	1	$\sqrt{1} = 1\%$

Thus, Stock A, with higher fluctuations than Stock B, indeed has a higher standard deviation (26.46% versus 1%), reflecting its historical volatility, which is much greater than the volatility of Stock B. Thus, historically, Stock A has a higher profitability than Stock B but also a higher risk.

4.6.2 Historical risk premium

From the above example, it is clear that volatility hurts investors. The relatively large volatility of Stock A makes it less attractive relative to the hypothetical case of no volatility but with the same average rate of return of 10%. Investors generally dislike volatility, and hence will require a relatively high average rate of return from assets with a relatively high volatility. Otherwise, they will not purchase them. Thus, generally, the higher the volatility, the higher the risk, and investors require risk premium to compensate them for risk. Though the concept of required risk premium has to do with the future rates of return and will be discussed in the next chapter, one can examine if in the past, with realized returns, indeed a positive risk premium prevailed. The historical risk premium is defined as:

$$\text{Historical risk premium} = \text{historical average rate of return} - \text{historical riskless interest rate}$$

This relationship can also be rewritten as:

$$\text{Historical average rate of return} = \text{historical riskless interest rate} + \text{historical risk premium}$$

Suppose that the average rate of return on Stock B and Stock A is 5% and 10%, respectively, and the risk-free interest is 5%. Then the historical risk premium for Stocks B and A discussed above is given by:

$$\text{Risk premium of Stock B} = 5\% - 4\% = 1\%$$

$$\text{Risk premium of Stock A} = 10\% - 4\% = 6\%$$

Thus, the greater the risk, the greater the required risk premium. The relationship between volatility and risk premium is, of course, an empirical question. In the next section we show that indeed such a strong relationship prevailed in the past.

4.7   THE HISTORICAL RECORD

Exhibit 4.6 provides the historical record on several classes of assets: large company stocks, small company stocks, bonds with long maturity (20 years), bonds with intermediate maturity (5 years) and US Treasury bills with 30 days maturity. Generally,

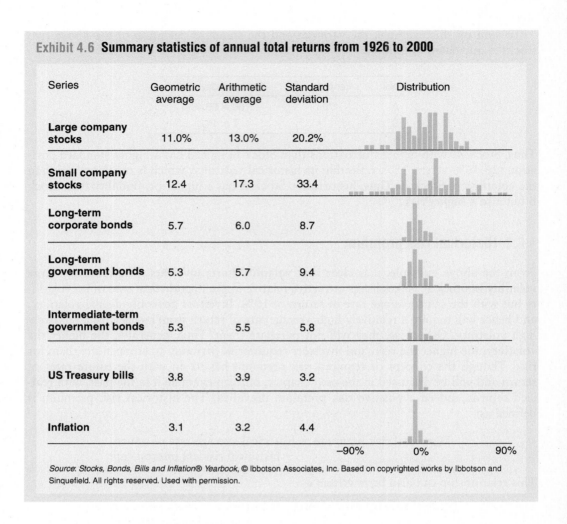

Exhibit 4.6 **Summary statistics of annual total returns from 1926 to 2000**

Series	Geometric average	Arithmetic average	Standard deviation	Distribution
Large company stocks	11.0%	13.0%	20.2%	
Small company stocks	12.4	17.3	33.4	
Long-term corporate bonds	5.7	6.0	8.7	
Long-term government bonds	5.3	5.7	9.4	
Intermediate-term government bonds	5.3	5.5	5.8	
US Treasury bills	3.8	3.9	3.2	
Inflation	3.1	3.2	4.4	

stocks of small firms are considered to be very risky, and therefore yield a relatively high average rate of return. Also, long-term bonds are considered to be riskier than short-term bonds, and corporate bonds are riskier than government bonds. Finally, US Treasury bills are the assets with the smallest risk, hence with the smallest average rate of return.

Exhibit 4.7 and Appendix 4B reveal the historical record regarding these assets. Focusing on the arithmetic average, the small company stocks (i.e. the average rate of return of stocks falling in this category) yielded in the period 1926−2000 the highest average rate of return: 17.3% per year. However, if an investor invested in one year selected at random from these years, he or she would also be exposed to the highest risk. This can be seen from the standard deviation corresponding to small company stocks (33.4%), as well as from the histogram given on the right-hand side of Exhibit 4.7. Years with very large negative and positive rates of return characterized small company stocks while much less dispersion is observed with the other assets. Assuming that the rate of return on Treasury bills is a good proxy to the riskless interest rate, the risk premium on small company stocks is given by 17.3% − 3.9% = 13.4% while it is only 5.7% − 3.9% = 1.8% for long-term government bonds. Exhibit 4.7 shows what happened to an investment of $1 in 1926 in

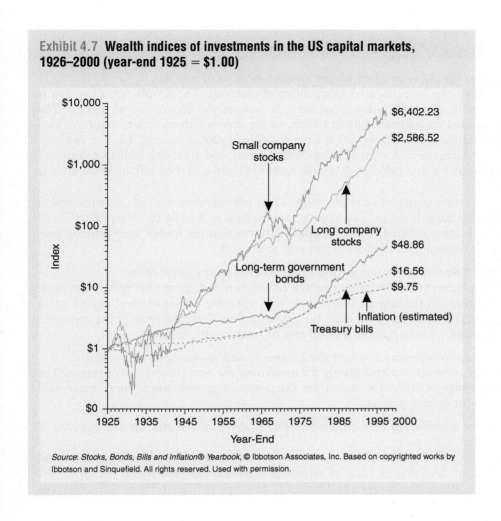

Exhibit 4.7 Wealth indices of investments in the US capital markets, 1926–2000 (year-end 1925 = $1.00)

each of these assets: for example a $1 investment in small company stocks in 1926 will yield about $6,402 in the year 2000.

The main conclusion from Exhibits 4.6 and 4.7 is that historically, the higher the volatility (standard deviation), the higher the risk, and therefore the higher the average rate of return, reflecting a higher required premium by the investors. As we shall see, this is consistent with the concept of risk aversion – investors dislike volatility or risk, and the larger the volatility, the larger the required risk premium. Based on this past observation, in the next chapter we analyze risk aversion and volatility when probabilities and future possible rates of return rather than past annual rates of return are employed. However, we keep in mind in the next chapter's analysis that history teaches us that investors dislike volatility and require compensation for the risk of fluctuation in the rates of return. Based on this historical observation, one can construct a theory regarding risk aversion and investors' preferences.

Appendix 4C shows the historical returns of some of the European indexes, relating to the Dow Jones, during 1991–2001. These charts can teach you about the level of risk and the rate of return of each European index relative to this level in the US, as described by the Dow Jones index.

SUMMARY

■ *Understand the different methods for computing rates of return.*

Rates of return can be calculated using different methods. The simple rate of return is the dollar profit divided by the investment. It ignores the time value of money. The method that uses the adjusted rate of return, or the time-weighted rate of return (which we call rate of return to distinguish it from the simple rate of return), has the endorsement of the Association for Investment Management and Research (AIMR). Rates of return are found by first calculating simple rates of return and then linking these returns together.

The idea of time-weighted rates of return is that any interim cash flow is reinvested in the asset under consideration. The appropriate method to handle the rates of return of bonds is the accrual method, which basically assumes that the bonds were actually purchased at the beginning of the period and sold at the end.

■ *Analyze the impact of taxes and inflation on rate of return calculations.*

Taxes and inflation affect the rate of return calculation and, generally, reduce the overall rate of return. In the case of taxes, there is a reduction of income and capital gains (tax payment), which reduces the after-tax rate of return. Inflation reduces the investor's purchasing power, which reduces the real rate of return to the investor.

■ *Understand the difference between the arithmetic and geometric average return.*

The arithmetic average is useful mainly for estimating the next period rate of return. The geometric average is useful for measuring the portfolio growth when the investor held the portfolio for several periods.

■ *Analyze the relationship between volatility of rates of return and the average rate of return.*

The higher the volatility the higher the risk of losing money. The volatility is measured by the standard deviation of rates of return. It is shown that, generally, the larger the standard deviation, the larger the historical average rate of return, reflecting the required risk premium by investors as compensation for the risk involved.

■ *Compare the historical risk–return trade-off for stocks and bonds.*

Historically, common stocks have been more volatile than bonds. Also, common stocks have offered a higher average rate of return than bonds. There appears to be a positive relationship between volatility and average rate of return.

KEY TERMS

Adjusted rate of return	Geometric average (or	Simple rate of return
Arithmetic average (or	mean)	Standard deviation
mean)	Geometric method	Time-weighted rate of
Arithmetic method	Linking method	return
Dollar-weighted average	Rate of return	Variance
rate of return (see	Real rate of return	Volatility
Appendix 4A)	Realized rate of return	
Ex-post rate of return	Risk premium	

QUESTIONS

4.1 A stock that was purchased in January for £50 paid a £3 dividend in December, when its price was £55.

(a) Calculate the pound *return* on this investment if 100 shares were purchased.
(b) Calculate the *rate of return* on this investment if 100 shares were purchased.
(c) How would your answers to (a) and (b) change if 200 shares were purchased?
(d) How would your answers to (a) and (b) change if the stock split 3-for-1 before the end of the year? (Hence, the £55 is the price after the stock split was taken.)

4.2 A zero-coupon bond was purchased in January for £875 per £1,000 par. In December the bond was trading for £950.

(a) Calculate the return and rate of return on this bond.
(b) If the tax rate were 30%, what was the after-tax rate of return?
(c) If deflation of 3% occurred during the year (that is, −3% inflation), what was the real, after-tax rate of return?

4.3 Suppose a United Kingdom bond was purchased by an American investor in January for £500 when the exchange rate was $2.0/pound. Assume no coupon payments; also, the bond was sold for £475 in December, when the exchange rate was $2.2/pound.

(a) What was the rate of return on the bond in British pounds?
(b) What was the rate of return to the American investor on the exchange rate only?
(c) What was the rate of return in US dollars?

4.4 Use the data in Question 4.3, and assume that the inflation rate was 5% in the United States and 10% in the United Kingdom.

(a) What was the real rate of return in British pounds?
(b) What was the real rate of return in US dollars?

4.5 The following table gives the NYSE composite index over a 15-year period:

End of year	NYSE composite	End of year	NYSE composite
2000	71.11	2008	195.04
2001	81.03	2009	180.49
2002	95.18	2010	229.44
2003	96.38	2011	240.21
2004	121.58	2012	259.08
2005	138.58	2013	250.94
2006	138.23	2014	329.51
2007	156.26	2015	392.30

(a) Ignoring dividends, calculate the simple annual rates of return.
(b) Calculate the arithmetic average of the annual rates of return.
(c) Calculate the geometric average of the annual rate of return.
(d) Compare your answers to (b) and (c). How do you account for the difference between these averages?

4.6 The following table gives the Consumer Price Index (CPI) over a recent 10-year period:

End of year	CPI	End of year	CPI
2000	109.6	2006	140.3
2001	113.6	2007	144.5
2002	118.3	2008	148.2
2003	124.0	2009	152.4
2004	130.7	2010	156.9
2005	136.2		

(a) Compute the inflation rates for each year over this 10-year period.
(b) Compute the geometric-average inflation rate over this 10-year period.
(c) Calculate the real rate of return on the NYSE composite (using the data in Question 4.5) for each year.

4.7   Suppose we have the following information on Xerox, Inc.:

Dividends paid ($)	Date	Stock price ($)	Date
0.75	2 February	$61\frac{1}{4}$	4 January
0.75	4 May	$52\frac{3}{8}$	2 February
0.75	30 July	$64\frac{7}{8}$	4 May
0.75	25 October	$70\frac{1}{2}$	30 July
		$75\frac{3}{4}$	25 October
		71	30 December

(a) Calculate the simple rate of return for the period 4 January through 30 December.
(b) Calculate the rate of return for the period 4 January through 30 December using the linking method.
(c) Calculate the rate of return for the period 4 January through 30 December using the index method.
(d) Explain any differences in rates of return.

4.8   Rework Question 4.7(b), assuming that the income tax rate on dividends is 25% and the capital gains tax rate is 15%.

4.9   Using the data in Question 4.7, suppose Xerox, Inc., also had a rights issue of one share for each existing share. In a rights issue, the firm gives its existing shareholders the right to buy additional shares of common stock at a specified price. For each share owned, a shareholder receives one right. Rights were traded in the secondary market. In this case, Xerox began trading the rights on 25 October at $1 per right. Rework Question 4.7(c), incorporating the effects of this rights offering.

4.10   Suppose you purchased 1,000 shares of Hardin Bread Company on 1 January at £60 per share. Hardin pays £1.50 annual dividend on 22 April, when the stock is trading at £42. Hardin declares a 5-for-1 stock split effective 28 August, when the stock is trading at £54.

(a) If Hardin closed on 29 December at £15 per share, what was your rate of return by the index method?
(b) If the inflation rate was 7.8%, what was your real rate of return?

4.11   We are given the following information on Goodyear on 15 October 2001, 7.35% coupon-bearing bonds:

Date	Coupon	Price (in % of £1,000 par)	Accrued interest
January 3		$101\frac{3}{4}$	£15.3
April 15	£36.75	$93\frac{1}{8}$	
October 15	£36.75	$97\frac{3}{4}$	
December 27		$99\frac{3}{4}$	£15.2

(a) Calculate the annual rate of return based on the index method.
(b) How does your answer to (a) compare with the simple-rate-of-return calculation? Explain.

SELECTED REFERENCES

Association for Investment Management and Research. *Report of the Performance Presentation Standards Implementation Committee*. Charlottesville, VA: AIMR, December 1991.
This 47-page monograph explains the recently adopted standards for reporting rates of returns by the AIMR, a leading financial analysts' association.

Eiteman, David K., Arthur I. Stonehill, and Michael H. Moffett. *Multinational Business Finance*, 6th edn. Reading, MA: Addison-Wesley, 1992, p. 25.

Fisher, I. *The Theory of Interest*. New York: Macmillan, 1930.

Jakobsen, J., and O. Sorensen. 'Decomposing and testing long-term returns: an application of Danish IPO'. *European Financial Management*, 7(2), 2001.

Larsen, Glen A. Jr., and B.G. Rasnick. 'Parameter estimation techniques, optimization frequency and portfolio return enhancement'. *Journal of Portfolio Management*, 27(4), Summer 2001.

Levy, Haim, and Marshall Sarnat. *Portfolio and Investment Selection: Theory and Practice*. Englewood Cliffs, NJ: Prentice-Hall International, 1984.

Reilly, Frank K., G. Wenchi Kao, and David J. Wright. 'Alternative bond market indexes'. *Financial Analysts Journal*, May–June 1992, pp. 44–58.
This article is a detailed analysis of the major alternative bond market indexes.

Siegel, Jeremy J. 'The equity premium: stock and bond returns since 1802'. *Financial Analysts Journal*, January–February 1992, pp. 28–46.

Appendix 4A   DOLLAR-WEIGHTED AVERAGE RATE OF RETURN

This chapter discussed arithmetic and geometric rates of return. Both measure the average rate of return per $1 invested. These two averages are not affected by the dollar amount invested. However, in some cases the dollar amount invested across time changes. The dollar-weighted average rate of return takes this factor into account.

To illustrate, consider the following example. Suppose a stock's price at the beginning of the first year is $100, and at the end of the first year it is $110. At the end of the second year, the share price is $132. For simplicity, assume that no dividend is paid and that an investor buys one share at the beginning of the first year and buys one more share at the beginning of the second year. Then, at the end of the second year, the two shares are sold. The rate of return for the first year is 10%, or ($110/$100) −1, and for the second year it is 20%, or ($132/$110) −1. In this case, the arithmetic average is

$$\overline{R}_A = \frac{10\% + 20\%}{2} = 15\%$$

and the geometric average is

$$\overline{R}_G = [(1 + 0.1)(1 + 0.2)]^{1/2} - 1 \cong 0.1489 \text{ or } 14.89\%$$

These two averages are not affected by the dollar amount invested in each year. They will be the same if the investor buys, say, five shares rather than one share at the beginning of the first year.

The dollar-weighted average rate of return is the internal rate of return (IRR; see Appendix A) that solves the following equation:

$$100 = -\frac{1 \times \$110}{1 + \text{IRR}} + \frac{2 \times \$132}{(1 + \text{IRR})^2}$$

where $110 is the dollar amount invested in purchasing one more share. Using a hand calculator, we find that IRR = 16.54%.

Note that one share was bought for $100 at the beginning of the first year and another share was bought at the beginning of the second year. Then, at the end of the second year, two shares are sold for $132 each. Thus, the IRR is the rate of return on the investment, taking into account that $100 is invested at the beginning of the first year and that an additional $110 is invested in the second year. If the investor buys, say, an additional five shares rather than one share at the end of the first year, the IRR is the value that solves the following equation:

$$100 = -\frac{5 \times \$110}{(1 + \text{IRR})} + \frac{6 \times \$132}{(1 + \text{IRR})^2}$$

Hence, IRR = 18.48%.

Thus, the IRR is affected by the amount invested in each period of time – hence the term dollar-weighted average rate of return. In our example, investing more monies in the second year increases the rate of return. This result is not surprising, however, because in this case the rate of return in the first year is 10% and in the second year 20%. The concept of the dollar-weighted average rate of return is important because dividends are often reinvested (for example, in mutual funds) and additional shares of stock are purchased.

Appendix 4B   ANNUAL RATES OF RETURN, 1926–2000

Year	Large company stocks	Small company stocks	Long-term corporate bonds	Long-term government bonds	Intermediate-term government bonds	US Treasury bills	Inflation
1926	11.62	0.28	7.37	7.77	5.38	3.27	−1.49
1927	37.49	22.10	7.44	8.93	4.52	3.12	−2.08
1928	43.61	39.69	2.84	0.10	0.92	3.56	−0.97
1929	−8.42	−51.36	3.27	3.42	6.01	4.75	0.20
1930	−24.90	−38.15	7.98	4.66	6.72	2.41	−6.03
1931	−43.34	−49.75	−1.85	−5.31	−2.32	1.07	−9.52
1932	−8.19	−5.39	10.82	16.84	8.81	0.96	−10.30
1933	53.99	142.87	10.38	−0.07	1.83	0.30	0.51
1934	−1.44	24.22	13.84	10.03	9.00	0.16	2.03
1935	47.67	40.19	9.61	4.98	7.01	0.17	2.99
1936	33.92	64.80	6.74	7.52	3.06	0.18	1.21
1937	−35.03	−58.01	2.75	0.23	1.56	0.31	3.10
1938	31.12	32.80	6.13	5.53	6.23	−0.02	−2.78
1939	−0.41	0.35	3.97	5.94	4.52	0.02	−0.48
1940	−9.78	−5.16	3.39	6.09	2.96	0.00	0.96
1941	−11.59	−9.00	2.73	0.93	0.50	0.06	9.72
1942	20.34	44.51	2.60	3.22	1.94	0.27	9.29
1943	25.90	88.37	2.83	2.08	2.81	0.35	3.16
1944	19.75	53.72	4.73	2.81	1.80	0.33	2.11
1945	36.44	73.61	4.08	10.73	2.22	0.33	2.25
1946	−8.07	−11.63	1.72	−0.10	1.00	0.35	18.16
1947	5.71	0.92	−2.34	−2.62	0.91	0.50	9.01
1948	5.50	−2.11	4.14	3.40	1.85	0.81	2.71
1949	18.79	19.75	3.31	6.45	2.32	1.10	−1.80
1950	31.71	38.75	2.12	0.06	0.70	1.20	5.79
1951	24.02	7.80	−2.69	−3.93	0.36	1.49	5.87
1952	18.37	3.03	3.52	1.16	1.63	1.66	0.88
1953	−0.99	−6.49	3.41	3.64	3.23	1.82	0.62
1954	52.62	60.58	5.39	7.19	2.68	0.86	−0.50
1955	31.56	20.44	0.48	−1.29	−0.65	1.57	0.37
1956	6.56	4.28	−6.81	−5.59	−0.42	2.46	2.86
1957	−10.78	−14.57	8.71	7.46	7.84	3.14	3.02
1958	43.36	64.89	−2.22	−6.09	−1.29	1.54	1.76
1959	11.96	16.40	−0.97	−2.26	−0.39	2.95	1.50
1960	0.47	−3.29	9.07	13.78	11.76	2.66	1.48
1961	26.89	32.09	4.82	0.97	1.85	2.13	0.67
1962	−8.73	−11.90	7.95	6.89	5.56	2.73	1.22
1963	22.80	23.57	2.19	1.21	1.64	3.12	1.65
1964	16.48	23.52	4.77	3.51	4.04	3.54	1.19
1965	12.45	41.75	−0.46	0.71	1.02	3.93	1.92
1966	−10.06	−7.01	0.20	3.65	4.69	4.76	3.35
1967	23.98	83.57	−4.95	−9.18	1.01	4.21	3.04
1968	11.06	35.97	2.57	−0.26	4.54	5.21	4.72
1969	−8.50	−25.05	−8.09	−5.07	−0.74	6.58	6.11
1970	4.01	−17.43	18.37	12.11	16.86	6.52	5.49

▶

Year	Large company stocks	Small company stocks	Long-term corporate bonds	Long-term government bonds	Intermediate-term government bonds	US Treasury bills	Inflation
1971	14.31	16.50	11.01	13.23	8.72	4.39	3.36
1972	18.98	4.43	7.26	5.69	5.16	3.84	3.41
1973	−14.66	−30.90	1.14	−1.11	4.61	6.93	8.80
1974	−26.47	−19.95	−3.06	4.35	5.69	8.00	12.20
1975	37.20	52.82	14.64	9.20	7.83	5.80	7.01
1976	23.84	57.38	18.65	16.75	12.87	5.08	4.81
1977	−7.18	25.38	1.71	−0.69	1.41	5.12	6.77
1978	6.56	23.46	−0.07	−1.18	3.49	7.18	9.03
1979	18.44	43.46	−4.18	−1.23	4.09	10.38	13.31
1980	32.42	39.88	−2.76	−3.95	3.91	11.24	12.40
1981	−4.91	13.88	−1.24	1.86	9.45	14.71	8.94
1982	21.41	28.01	42.56	40.36	29.10	10.54	3.87
1983	22.51	39.67	6.26	0.65	7.41	8.80	3.80
1984	6.27	−6.67	16.86	15.48	14.02	9.85	3.95
1985	32.16	24.66	30.09	30.97	20.33	7.72	3.77
1986	18.47	6.85	19.85	24.53	15.14	6.16	1.13
1987	5.23	−9.30	−0.27	−2.71	2.90	5.47	4.41
1988	16.81	22.87	10.70	9.67	6.10	6.35	4.42
1989	31.49	10.18	16.23	18.11	13.29	8.37	4.65
1990	−3.17	−21.56	6.78	6.18	9.73	7.81	6.11
1991	30.55	44.63	19.89	19.30	15.46	5.60	3.06
1992	7.67	23.35	9.39	8.05	7.19	3.51	2.90
1993	9.99	20.98	13.19	18.24	11.24	2.90	2.75
1994	1.31	3.11	−5.76	−7.77	−5.14	3.90	2.67
1995	37.43	34.46	27.20	31.67	16.80	5.60	2.54
1996	23.07	17.62	1.40	−0.93	2.10	5.21	3.32
1997	33.36	22.78	12.95	15.85	8.38	5.26	1.70
1998	28.58	−7.31	10.76	13.06	10.21	4.86	1.61
1999	21.04	29.79	−7.45	−8.96	−1.77	4.68	2.68
2000	−9.11	−3.59	12.87	21.48	12.59	5.89	3.39

Appendix 4C	RATES OF RETURN OF SOME EUROPEAN INDEXES, 1991–2001

Exhibit 4C.1 London: the FTSE 100 index, 25 March 2001

Sunday, March 25 2001 1:27am ET – U.S. Markets Closed.

FTSE 100 INDEX (FSI:^FTSE)-More Info: News – Trade NEW!: N/A					
Last Trade	Change		Prev Cls	Volume	Div Date
Mar 23 · **5402.3**	+87.5 (+1.65%)		5314.8	N/A	N/A
Day's Range	Bid	Ask	Open	Avg Vol	Ex-Div
5314.8 – 5438.0	N/A	N/A	5314.8	N/A	N/A
YTD Range	Earn/Shr	P/E	Mkt Cap	Div/Shr	Yield
5279.6 – 6360.3	N/A	N/A	N/A	N/A	N/A

FTSE 100 Index as of 23–Mar–2001

Source: Website at http://www.finance.yahoo.com, 25 March 2001.

Exhibit 4C.2 France: the CAC 40 index, 25 March 2001

Sunday, March 25 2001 1:22am ET – U.S. Markets Closed.

CAC 40 INDEX (PAR:^FCHI)-More Info: News – Trade NEW!: N/A					
Last Trade	Change		Prev Cls	Volume	Div Date
Mar 23 · **4951.13**	+126.31 (+2.62%)		4824.82	N/A	N/A
Day's Range	Bid	Ask	Open	Avg Vol	Ex-Div
4911.54 – 4968.52	N/A	N/A	4922.39	N/A	N/A
YTD Range	Earn/Shr	P/E	Mkt Cap	Div/Shr	Yield
4804.40 – 5999.18	N/A	N/A	N/A	N/A	N/A

France CAC–40 Index as of 23–Mar–2001

Source: Website at http://finance.yahoo.com, 25 March 2001. CAC 40 is a registered trademark of Euronext Paris SA, which designates the index it calculates and publishes. Euronext Paris SA makes no warranty as to the figure at which the said index stands at any particular time. Reprinted with permission.

Exhibit 4C.3 Germany: the DAX index, 25 March 2001

Sunday, March 25 2001 1:25am ET - U.S. Markets Closed.

XETRA DAX INDEX (GER:^GDAXI)-More Info: News - Trade NEW!: N/A					
Last Trade Mar 23 . **5544.67**	Change +156.65 (+2.91%)		Prev Cls 5388.02	Volume N/A	Div Date N/A
Day's Range 5396.63 - 5574.99	Bid N/A	Ask N/A	Open 5396.63	Avg Vol N/A	Ex-Div N/A
52 week Range 5351.48 - 6795.14	Earn/Shr N/A	P/E N/A	Mkt Cap N/A	Div/Shr N/A	Yield N/A

FTSE 100 Index as of 23–Mar–2001

Source: Website at http://www.finance.yahoo.com, 25 March 2001.

Exhibit 4C.4 Sweden: the Stockholm General index, 25 March 2001

Sunday, March 25 2001 1:26am ET – U.S. Markets Closed.

STOCKHOLM GENERAL (STO:^SFOG)-More Info: N/A – Trade NEW!: N/A					
Last Trade Mar 23 · **3898.70**	Change +73.74 (+1.93%)		Prev Cls 3824.96	Volume N/A	Div Date N/A
Day's Range 3824.96 – 3931.62	Bid N/A	Ask N/A	Open 3824.96	Avg Vol N/A	Ex-Div N/A
YTD Range 3766.28 – 5036.13	Earn/Shr N/A	P/E N/A	Mkt Cap N/A	Div/Shr N/A	Yield N/A

Sweden Stockholm General Index as of 23–Mar–2001

Source: Website at http://www.finance.yahoo.com, 25 March 2001.

Chapter 5

THE FUTURE: RETURN, RISK, RISK AVERSION, RISK PREMIUM AND ASSET PRICES

Learning objectives

After studying this chapter you should be able to:

1 Compare the maximum return and maximum expected return criteria as investment selection methods.

2 Explain what a risk averter is.

3 Calculate the required risk premium.

4 Apply the mean–variance criterion in asset selection.

INVESTMENT IN THE NEWS

Why risk matters

How important is a fund's risk profile? This important: It can tell you more – and sometimes a lot more – than past performance. This year, beginning in our annual summer Retirement Guide and continuing in this year-end investment issue, we've introduced into our list of best mutual funds a statistical measure called 'standard deviation'. Even if you are only a casual follower of mutual funds, chances are you've heard of it, since standard deviation, which in this case gauges a fund's volatility, has become an increasingly popular yardstick of risk. Simply put, standard deviation tells you how much a fund's short-term results vary from its long-term average; the higher the standard deviation, the more the fund's results jump around. If investing is like a roller-coaster ride – and that's as good as any analogy – then standard deviation tells you what to expect in the way of dips and rolls. It tells you how scared you'll be.... The fact is, standard deviation can be an important tool for investors – one that can offer some insight not only into how risky a fund is but even into how it might perform in a given market environment in the future....

Source: David Whitford, 'Why risk matters', *Fortune*, 29 December 1997, pp. 147–152. Reprinted from the 29 December 1997 issue of *Fortune* by special permission. © 1997, Time, Inc.

The goal of investors is to maximize their wealth. There is a chance that this goal will not be achieved, however, because most investments are risky. This chapter's *Investment in the news* highlights not only the importance of risk but also the practical use of one measure of risk – standard deviation. Although the article focuses on the standard deviation (the square root of variance) of mutual funds, this statistical measure is also commonly used to examine the volatility of an individual stock or bond.

As the article asserts, one needs the standard deviation of *future* rates of return ('standard deviation can be an important tool for investors'). This chapter examines volatility of future rates of return, defines a quantitative measure of risk, and shows that the larger the volatility, the worse off investors are because their risk increases. The chapter formally introduces the concepts of risk, risk aversion, risk premium, and variance of rates of return. For simplicity in introducing these concepts, it is assumed that investors hold a portfolio of only one asset or one mutual fund. In Chapter 6 we will discuss the case where several assets are held.

In the previous chapter we introduced these concepts based on past data, using the realized rates of return to calculate the average and the standard deviation. In this chapter we employ probabilities which are related to future returns rather than past returns. We address the meaning of an asset's risk, its measurement, and how the market compensates investors for bearing this risk. In particular, the higher the risk of an asset, the higher is its required expected return. This future risk–return relationship hypothesis is confirmed with the past risk–return relationships discussed in the previous chapter.

To gain a clear perspective on how asset prices change when risk prevails, this chapter first examines how current asset prices change in the unrealistic case where future prices are known with certainty. Then, we discuss the risk–return relationship in the case of uncertainty of future returns.

5.1   THE CASE OF CERTAINTY

We saw in Chapter 4 that different assets can yield different average rates of return. We introduce in this chapter the concept of uncertainty and risk premium. The higher the uncertainty, the higher the average return which compensates the investor for risk; hence the higher the risk premium. However, if future value of the various investments is certain, we would expect the same rate of return on all assets and zero risk premium, simply because there is no risk. If this is not the case, investors would sell the asset with the lowest rate of return and switch their investment to the asset with the highest rate of return. Because we are now assuming that the future is known with certainty, all investors will hold the asset offering the highest rate of return. In contrast to the certainty case, we will see that when the future is uncertain, the higher the volatility the higher the expected rate of return. Therefore, with uncertainty, not all investors will invest only in the asset with the highest expected rate of return.

We start with two investments and demonstrate how current prices are established on these two assets when future prices are known with certainty. Similar trading and price changes take place with uncertain rates of return. Suppose two assets exist, A and B, each with a market price of £100. We know with certainty that Asset A's price one year hence will be £110 and Asset B's price one year hence will be £120; no dividend or interest is paid on these assets. Is the market in equilibrium? No, it is not. Because Assets A and B have the same current price of £100, and Asset B provides a higher certain future return, an investor currently holding Asset A should sell it and buy Asset B. The investor would be sure of earning £10, or £120−£110, in the future, with no additional investment. This type of trading strategy, in which profits are made with no risk and no additional investment, is known as arbitrage. (Remember, this is a world of certainty.) This arbitrage trading will cause the price of Asset A to fall (because there will be a glut of Asset A on the market) and the price of Asset B to rise (because it will be in great demand) until the two assets yield the same certain rate of return. To illustrate this idea, suppose that the price of Asset A falls to £95. What should the equilibrium price of Asset B be?

To answer this question we turn to the definition of *rate of return* given in Chapter 4. Recall that by assumption there are no dividends; hence the rate of return on an investment over Period 1 is (see Equation 4.1)

$$R_1 = \frac{P_1 - P_0}{P_0} = \frac{P_1}{P_0} - 1$$

where P_1 represents the price at the end of the period and P_0 represents the price at the beginning of the period. Because the rates of return for Assets A and B must be identical in equilibrium, the following should hold:

$$(£110/£95) - 1 = (£120/P_{B,0}) - 1$$

where $P_{B,0}$ is the equilibrium market price of Asset B today. Solving for $P_{B,0}$, we find that $P_{B,0} = £103.64$. For this market price, the return on Asset A is

$$(£110/£95) - 1 \cong 0.158 \text{ or } 15.8\%$$

and the rate of return on Asset B is

$$(£120/£103.64) - 1 \cong 0.158 \text{ or } 15.8\%$$

Once the certain returns on the two assets are identical, there are no more arbitrage opportunities, and the market is said to be in equilibrium for these two specific assets.

PRACTICE BOX

Problem
Suppose there are two stocks worth with certainty £110 and £200, respectively, one year from now. The current price of the first stock is £100. What is the equilibrium price of the second stock?

Solution
In equilibrium, the rate of return on both securities must be identical and be equal to 10%, because $(£110/£100) - 1 = 0.10$, or 10%. Therefore, $£110/£100 = £200/P_2$, or $P_2 = (£200 × £100)/£110 \cong £181.82$. Notice that with this price, the rate of return on this asset is also 10%.

Rates of return on various assets actually observed in the markets, as shown in Chapter 4, are in fact different, however, which clearly indicates that future returns are uncertain. Outside the realm of textbooks, uncertainty regarding future rates of return prevails. Moreover, even average rates of return on various assets are not identical over the years. The different average returns reflect the market compensation for the differential uncertainty or risk characterizing various assets. However, average rates of return on various assets are not arbitrarily determined, and as we shall see in the next chapter as well as in Chapter 14, investors will shift from one portfolio of assets to another in a similar way to the certainty case to guarantee that each asset will have the average return such that the investor will be compensated for the risk involved. If the expected rate of return on a given asset is 'too high', investors will buy it, and the stock price will go up exactly as in the certainty case described above until equilibrium is reached.

There is one asset, however, whose rate of return is *almost* certain. US or UK short-term Treasury bills (T-bills) yield almost a certain return. Ignoring inflation and the chance of a revolution in the United States or the United Kingdom, Treasury bills will pay with certainty the stated yield. Also, because they are a short-term asset, changes in interest rates do not significantly affect the price. Therefore, it is common to refer to the yield on T-bills as the *riskless interest rate*. It is true that over time, the yield on T-bills changes. However, when you purchase a given T-bill on a given date, the rate of return you earn is fixed if you hold it to maturity. Nevertheless, we would like to emphasize that the rate of return on T-bills is almost certain but not absolutely certain, because inflation in practice cannot be ignored. For example, in January 1999 the inflation rate in the US was 0.7% and in August 1999 fears of inflation arose again. The same fears were renewed in the UK in March 2001 as you can see in the following boxed article. As we can see from this article, interest rates, stock prices and inflation are all related factors, which will be analyzed in this book. Moreover, the US, UK and other stock markets are closely related and affect each other. Yet, it is common to refer to T-bills as the riskless asset. Understanding that the rates of return on most assets are uncertain, we are now prepared to introduce risk into the investment analysis.

British investors eye CPI, fear plunge after Wall St havoc

By Peter Nielsen

LONDON (Reuters) – The nerves of British investors will be tested on Monday following Friday's bloodbath on Wall Street, renewed inflation fears and dire newspaper warnings about a plunge in share prices when the London market reopens after the weekend.

Reassuring words from Group of Seven (G7) financial leaders in Washington about solid economic fundamentals in the United States and Europe are unlikely to soothe investors rattled by newspaper headlines such as the Sunday Telegraph's 'Europe Poised for Massive Sell-off' or the Observer's 'City Set for Big Bust'.

Worries over further interest rate rises in Britain will become a focus for markets with the release of consumer prices on Tuesday, Wednesday's policy meeting notes from the Bank of England and retail sales on Thursday.

Inflation fears were stoked late Friday when Mervyn King, deputy governor of the Bank of England, spelt out the dangers of allowing domestic demand to grow significantly above its sustainable level for too long, as it has done in recent years.

King's statement is likely to spook share markets by stirring speculation the central bank will raise rates again in coming months, after pushing up the cost of borrowing four times in the past eight months to the current level of six percent.

'We could get a real bloodbath on Monday', said one share analyst, quoted by The Sunday Times.

European exchanges had closed on Friday before U.S. inflation data caused major losses on Wall Street and havoc in the technology-weighted Nasdaq index.

Stoking Friday's sell-off on Wall Street was news that U.S. inflation in March raced at its highest speed in more than five years. The fear of further U.S. interest rate rises hit the Dow Jones industrial average, which tumbled nearly six percent, following a dive of nearly 10 percent on the tech-weighted Nasdaq composite index, putting the two indices 12 percent and 34 percent respectively off their year highs.

Source: Website at http://uk.news.yahoo.com/000416/5/a35rq.html, 16 April 2001.

5.2 THE NATURE OF RISK

Suppose you invest for one year in a government bond with a zero-coupon rate and £100 face value. The price of the bond is £90. The bond matures exactly one year from today. What rate of return will you earn on this bond if you hold it to maturity? You are sure that you wish to invest for one year; hence, the bond is riskless.[1]

A simple calculation reveals that the rate of return is

$$(£100/£90) - 1 \cong 0.111 \text{ or } 11.1\%$$

Because the £100 is received with *certainty* when the bond matures one year from now, the 11.1% represents a certain rate of return. Also, because the government cannot realistically go bankrupt, there is no default risk on this investment.

Now suppose instead that you purchase a share of British Airways which was traded on 16 March 2001 for £319. Obviously, unlike the government bond that matures one year from now, the value of the stock one year from now is uncertain. Suppose no dividends are paid, and the stock price at the end of the year is either £380 with a probability (chance) of $^1/_2$ or £300 with a probability (chance) of $^1/_2$. Given that the stock price today is £319, the rate of return will also be uncertain with the following values: either $(£380/£319) - 1 \cong 0.191$ or 19.1% with a probability of $^1/_2$, or $(£300/£319) - 1 = -0.0596$ or -5.96% with a probability of $^1/_2$.

In such a case we say that the investment in the stock is risky, which means that a rate of return obtained in the future is not known with certainty. Namely, the distribution of possible rates of return is known, but which of the outcomes will occur is unknown.

These two investment examples indicate that an investor can distinguish between two alternative situations: certainty, the situation in which the future value of the asset (or the rate of return) is known with a probability of 1, and uncertainty or risk, the situation in which there is more than one possible future value of the asset (or more than one possible rate of return). In this case, the asset's future value is not known with certainty. In such a case we say that the future value is a *random variable*. If investors know the probability of each random outcome, they face *risk*. If the probability of each outcome is unknown to investors, they face *uncertainty*. Note that in both uncertainty and risk, more than one future value is possible. Most assets traded in the market fall in this category. In Section 5.5 we suggest to measure the risk by the variance (or standard deviation) of returns as asserted in the *Investment in the news* article.

Actual probabilities that are known (as in a coin-flipping experiment) are called objective probabilities. In actual decision-making by investors and, in particular, in decisions made by people in business, the true probabilities are rarely known. Normally, the investor can collect some rates of return taken from the past few years on the same stock (see Chapter 4) and, based on these data, estimate the probabilities of possible future rates of return. These probability estimates are called subjective probabilities. Thus, even if the objective probabilities are unknown, an investor can attach subjective probabilities to each possible future value of an asset. By doing so, the investor faces a situation defined as risk rather than uncertainty. Because an investor can always assign

---

[1] For simplicity, assume no inflation. Otherwise, the bond is risky in real terms. If there is inflation, then the rate of return on bonds whose principal and interest are linked to the cost of living index is riskless. Such bonds are issued by the US government and are called inflation-indexed Treasury securities.

subjective probabilities to the various possible outcomes, the rest of this book uses the words *uncertainty* and *risk* interchangeably.

Note that although some assets in the market yield an almost certain rate of return (short-term government T-bills), most assets (stocks, long-term debt, options, investments in real estate, and so forth) yield uncertain rates of return. Therefore, an investor must develop systematic rules to use in choosing among assets characterized by uncertain returns and, in particular, to find the best diversification strategy among such assets.

Different assets have different expected rates of return, as well as different degrees of risk, so investors need criteria for selecting the best asset. The historical record given in Chapter 4 (see Exhibit 4.6 and Appendix 4B), shows that, on average, assets with higher risk also offer higher average rates of return. This property generally characterizes future returns as well, which are relevant for investment decision-making. How does an investor go about selecting the best asset for a particular investor? We present below several investment decision criteria when both certain and uncertain returns prevail.

5.3 THE CALCULATED EXPECTED RATE OF RETURN

In the rest of this chapter and in Chapter 6 we focus on the mean–variance investment criterion. The mean–variance criterion (MVC), which was developed by Harry Markowitz,[2] for which he won the 1990 Nobel Prize in economics, is the foundation of modern portfolio theory. According to this investment rule, the mean measures the profitability of the investment and the variance measures the risk involved. In this section we explain how to calculate the expected rate of return.

5.3.1 Calculating the expected return

Consider the four securities illustrated in Exhibit 5.1. All four investments require the same initial outlay of, say, £10,000. If only investments A and B are considered, the choice is simple: investment in Security A clearly is better than investment in Security B, because 6% is greater than 5%. Deciding between Securities A and C, however, is not so straightforward. If we look at the − 10% return from Security C and compare it with Security A's return, then Security A is superior by this rule. However, if we take

Exhibit 5.1 Possible rates of return on four securities with a £10,000 investment

Security A		Security B		Security C		Security D	
Rate of return (%)	Probability	Rate of return (%)	Probability	Rate of return (%)	Probability	Rate of return (%)	Probability
6	1	5	1	−10	$1/4$	−20	$1/4$
				0	$1/4$	10	$1/2$
				20	$1/2$	40	$1/4$

---

[2] See Harry Markowitz, 'Portfolio selection', *Journal of Finance*, 7, no. 1 (1952): 77–91.

the +20% return from Security C and compare it with Security A's return, then Security C turns out to be better.

Thus, when we compare certain and uncertain choices or two uncertain choices, the selection is not simple as in the case of the trivial comparison of two certain choices. In uncertain cases, we have to identify for each asset the average profitability and the risk involved. Let us first focus on profitability as measured by the expected return.

Rule 1: To calculate the expected rate of return, multiply each possible return by the probability to obtain it and sum all these terms. That is,

$$E(R) = \sum_{i=1}^{m} P_i R_i \tag{5.1}$$

where R_i is the rate of return on an asset in a given state (the ith return), P_i is the probability corresponding to R_i, m is the number of possible rates of return (or possible values of R), and E stands for the 'expected' return.

The expected rate of return is the average of all possible rates of return. The expected return is also known as the *mean return* or simply as the mean. Expected returns have two components: probabilities and rates of return on an asset. The probabilities and rates of return are multiplied and then summed across *states*. States refer to each estimate of probability and rate of return. To avoid confusion from now on, when past returns are employed to calculate the average return, we call it the average rate of return; when probabilities are employed (the future), we call it the expected rate of return, or the mean rate of return.

Applying this formula to the examples in Exhibit 5.1, we have:

Security	Expected return, $E(R)$
A	$E(R_A) = 1 \times 6\% = 6\%$
B	$E(R_B) = 1 \times 5\% = 5\%$
C	$E(R_C) = (^1/_4) \times (-10\%) + ^1/_4 \times 0 + ^1/_2 \times 20\% = 7.5\%$
D	$E(R_D) = (^1/_4) \times (-20\%) + ^1/_2 \times 10 + ^1/_4 \times 40 = 10\%$

Based solely on expected return, we see that Security D is the best, because it yields the largest expected rate of return (10%).

When each rate of return is equally probable – that is, $P_i = 1/m$ for each i – then for Equation 5.1 we have:

$$E(R) = \sum_{i=1}^{m} \frac{1}{m} R_i = \frac{1}{m} \sum_{i=1}^{m} R_i$$

(We can move the $1/m$ term outside the summation, because it is a constant (see also the next Practice Box).)

Finally, where we have a continuous distribution function, e.g. a normal distribution (see, for example, Exhibit 5.4), then the expected rate of return is

$$E(R) = \int_{-\infty}^{\infty} R f(R) \, dR$$

where $f(R)$ is the density function of the return R.

Will you choose the investment with the highest expected return? Not necessarily, because it may also be the most risky. To see this, compare Securities C and D given in the previous example. Although Security D provides the highest expected return, it also exposes the investor to the maximum possible loss, −20%. To understand the risk involved with investment D, suppose that Bobby Jones, a student at the London School

PRACTICE BOX

Problem

Calculate the expected rate of return on Boston Celtics and Boston Edison common stock, given the following historical rates of return. Suppose that the investor selects the investment by the expected rate of return. Which is better?

Boston Celtics		Boston Edison	
Rate of return (%)	Probability	Rate of return (%)	Probability
7	$1/4$	8	$1/4$
−5	$1/4$	4	$1/4$
12	$1/4$	9	$1/4$
6	$1/4$	7	$1/4$

Solution

From Equation 5.1, we have:

$$E(R_{\text{Celtics}}) = 1/4\,(0.07) - 1/4\,(0.05) + 1/4(0.12) + 1/4(0.06)$$

$$= \frac{0.07 - 0.05 + 0.12 + 0.06}{4} = 0.05 \text{ or } 5\%$$

and

$$E(R_{\text{Edison}}) = 1/4\,(0.08) + 1/4(0.04) + 1/4(0.09) + 1/4(0.07)$$

$$= \frac{0.08 + 0.04 + 0.09 + 0.07}{4} = 0.07 \text{ or } 7\%$$

Thus, Boston Edison would be selected by the expected rate of return maximization.

of Business (LSB), has an initial wealth of £10,000. To pay for tuition and living expenses next year, he needs a minimum of £9,000. If he invests in Security C for one year and the lowest return occurs, he will still have £9,000 at year-end:

$$£10,000 \times [1 + (-0.1)] = £10,000 \times 0.9 = £9,000$$

where −0.10 is the lowest possible rate of return. If Jones invests in Security D and the worst outcome occurs, he will end up with

$$£10,000 \times [1 + (-0.2)] = £10,000 \times 0.8 = £8,000$$

and he will not have the minimum funds he needs for school next year. Jones is an ambitious student; hence, he would see it as a disaster if he had to drop out of school because of a lack of money. Therefore, he will avoid investment in Security D, because it puts his college career at risk.

However, for other investors who need a minimum of, say, only £5,000 next year, Security D may be preferable. (Again, assume a £10,000 starting amount.) In a nutshell, Security D has the advantage of having the largest mean rate of return, but it also has the disadvantage of having the lowest possible rate of return, −20%. Therefore, it is also the most risky. Thus, the choice between Securities A, C and D is difficult and may vary from one investor to another, depending on the investor's future financial needs or obligations. An investor with a strong distaste for risk may prefer Security C, whereas an investor who is more willing to take risk (in pursuit of higher returns) may prefer Security D. The next section links investor preference with asset risk.

5.4 RISK AVERSION

In the example illustrated in Exhibit 5.1, a tough decision had to be made. In contrast, Exhibit 5.2 presents an easier case where the mean return on the two assets is identical. Both Security A and Security B have the expected return of £120 on a £100 investment. The return on Security A is certain (£120 with a probability of 100%), whereas the return on Security B is uncertain, because it yields £110 with a probability of 50% and £130 with a probability of 50%.

Looking at Exhibit 5.2, which investment would you prefer? Empirical evidence and data taken from the stock market reveal that most investors would prefer Security A.

5.4.1 Definition of risk averters

The investors who prefer Security A over Security B are called risk averters. Risk averters, other things being equal, are investors who dislike volatility or risk. They always prefer a certain investment over an uncertain investment (namely, they prefer Security A over Security B) *as long as* the expected returns on the two investments are identical. Thus, for risk averters to be convinced to buy Security B, they would have to be compensated by a higher expected return. The difference between the expected rate of return on a risky asset and the riskless interest rate is known as the risk premium. In Chapter 4 we discussed the concept of past or historical risk premium. This past data is the base for the hypothesis that most investors are risk averters, and as such, risk premium prevails also with future return.

To provide an intuitive explanation of why most investors are risk averters, consider Leslie Chin, a junior in the business school at the London School of Business, who gets £120 per week for food from her parents. The £120 is exactly enough for food and one movie a week (no soda or popcorn). If we offer Chin £110 with a probability of $\frac{1}{2}$ and £130 with a probability of $\frac{1}{2}$ rather than the option of getting £120 for sure, she would probably refuse the offer. The reason is that on the one hand, with £110, she would have to cut out the movie. On the other hand, with £130, she could go to two movies a week. However, because the *satisfaction* or *utility* she would derive from having a second movie per week is less than the loss of satisfaction induced by giving up one movie per week, Chin would prefer £120 with certainty. Leslie Chin is called a risk averter, because when she is faced with two alternative investments with identical expected returns, she chooses the safer one.

5.4.2 Required risk premium

In this section, we discuss the required risk premium on future investments given the future returns and probabilities, in contrast to the observed risk premiums discussed in Chapter 4. Let us return to the example in Exhibit 5.2, where investments in Securities A and B have the same expected rate of return, +20%. Suppose all investors in the market are risk averters. Then all will buy Security A and none will buy Security B. Is this possible? Of course not; someone must hold Security B. Assets in the financial markets are at times like the infamous hot potato. If you don't want it, you have to sell

Exhibit 5.2   Dispersion of returns: returns on securities A and B with a £100 investment

	Security A		Security B	
	Return (£)	Probability	Return (£)	Probability
	120	1	110	$\frac{1}{2}$
			130	$\frac{1}{2}$
Mean return (£)	120		120	
Mean return (%)	20		20	

it. To induce someone to buy an undesirable asset, you have to lower its price to make it more attractive to the buyer.

Thus, the market mechanism is similar to the one described in the certainty case (see Section 5.1): the price of Security B will fall (because it has no demand), say, to £95. At this price, some investors may find it an attractive investment. Assume that at this price, the market is in equilibrium; no one wants to sell or buy stocks. The rate of return on Security B with a current purchase price of £95 is

$$(£110/£95) - 1 \cong 15.79\% \text{ with a probability of } \frac{1}{2}$$

and

$$(£130/£95) - 1 \cong 36.84\% \text{ with a probability of } \frac{1}{2}$$

The mean rate of return on Security B is therefore

$$\frac{1}{2}(15.79\%) + \frac{1}{2}(36.84\%) \cong 26.31\%$$

whereas the mean return on Security A remains 20% (or £120 per £100 invested). Suppose the market is in equilibrium. That is, at these prices there is neither excess demand nor excess supply, and all available assets are bought by investors. Because the rate of return on Security A is certain, the difference in the mean return on these two assets when the market is in equilibrium is called the *required risk premium* or simply *risk premium*. Namely,

$$\text{Required risk premium} = 26.31\% - 20\% = 6.31\%$$

This is the premium on Security B required by the market to compensate investors for the risk involved with this asset.

Thus, we can say that the mean rate of return on risky assets is composed of the following two elements.

Rule 2: The expected rate of return is equal to the riskless interest rate plus the required risk premium. Namely,

$$\begin{array}{ccc} \text{Mean rate of return} & = & \text{rate of return} \\ \text{on risky asset} & & \text{on riskless asset} \end{array} + \begin{array}{c} \text{required risk} \\ \text{premium} \end{array} \qquad (5.2)$$

The more risk averse investors are (for example, avoiding the dissatisfaction of not finishing college, the danger of going bankrupt, and so forth), the lower the equilibrium price of Security B and, hence, the larger the required risk premium. In Chapter 4 we introduced the past observed historical risk premium on various assets. The past risk premium can be negative if the sample of years covers periods with large negative rates of return in the stock

---

PRACTICE BOX

Problem

Investment A yields a 10% rate of return with certainty. Investment B yields −10% with a probability of $^1/_2$, and 40% with a probability of $^1/_2$, and the market is in equilibrium. Calculate the risk premium.

Solution

From Equation 5.2, we know that the risk premium is equal to the mean rate of return on the risky asset minus the rate of return on the riskless asset (Investment A). In this case, the mean return on the risky asset is

$$E(R_B) = {^1/_2}(-10\%) + {^1/_2}(40\%) = 15\%$$

Thus, the risk premium is 15% − 10% = 5%.

---

market. Here, in contrast, we discussed the future required, or risk, premium. Therefore, it is common to add 'required' risk premium, emphasizing that it is related to future investment. If risk aversion prevails, the required risk premium is always positive.

In Exhibit 5.2, Security B has only two possible outcomes (£110 and £130). It is clear that the larger the deviation of these outcomes from the £120 mean (for example, £100 and £140), the greater the risk. When there are more than two outcomes, however, an investor needs to find a quantitative measure for the risk. One common measure of the risk is the variability (measured by the variance or standard deviation: see *Investment in the news*) of the rates of return.

5.5   CALCULATING VARIANCE

The variance of returns is a measure of the dispersion around the mean and is used as a measure of risk.[3] The variance of the possible returns for an asset is denoted by σ^2 (σ is the Greek letter sigma) and is calculated as follows.

Rule 3: The variance is the sum of the probability times the squared deviations from the mean:

$$\sigma^2 = \sum_{i=1}^{m} P_i[R_i - E(R)]^2 \tag{5.3}$$

where P_i is the probability of outcome i, R_i is the rate of return on the asset in State i, $E(R)$ is the expected return on R (see Equation 5.1), and m is the number of possible states.

For example, consider an investment that has two states. In State 1 the investment offers 0% with probability of $\frac{1}{3}$, and in State 2 it offers 30% with probability of $\frac{2}{3}$ over the next year. The expected rate of return one year from now is $\frac{1}{3} \times 0.0\% + \frac{2}{3} \times 0.3\% = 0.2$ or 20%, and the variance is

$$\sigma^2 = \tfrac{1}{3}(0.0 - 0.2)^2 + \tfrac{2}{3}(0.3 - 0.2)^2 = 0.02$$

---

[3] Variance is the measure of risk of a portfolio held. The risk of an individual asset held in the portfolio is beta, which is discussed in Chapter 14.

If the probability of each return is equal, simply substitute $1/m$ for P_i, where m is the number of possible returns to obtain:[4]

$$\sigma^2 = \sum_{i=1}^{m} \frac{1}{m}[R_i - E(R)]^2 \tag{5.4}$$

For example, if the rates of return for British Airways common stock are 37%, −17% and 17% with an equal probability of $\frac{1}{3}$ then the expected return is

$$E(R_{\text{British Airways}}) = (0.37 - 0.17 + 0.17)/3 \cong 0.123 \text{ or } 12.3\%$$

and the variance is

$$\sigma^2_{\text{British Airways}} = \tfrac{1}{3}(0.37 - 0.123)^2 + \tfrac{1}{3}(-0.17 - 0.123)^2 + \tfrac{1}{3}(0.17 - 0.123)^2 \cong 0.0497$$

Note that if the rates of return are expressed in percentage figures, then the unit of variance is *per cent squared*. If the rates of return are in dollar figures, then the unit of variance is *dollars squared*. These terms are difficult to interpret. Therefore, it is common to take the square root of the variance, which is called the standard deviation. The standard deviation, denoted by σ, is stated as a percentage or in dollars and is expressed as

$$\sigma = \left\{ \sum_{i=1}^{m} P_i[R_i - E(R)]^2 \right\}^{1/2} \tag{5.5}$$

In the preceding example, we found the variance to be 0.0497. Therefore, the standard deviation is

$$\sigma_{\text{British Airways}} = (0.0497)^{1/2} \cong 0.223 \text{ or } 22.3\%$$

Note that if R_i is measured in percent then σ is also given in percent. If R_i is measured in dollar return than σ is given in dollars. Thus, R_i and σ (as well as the mean) have the same dimension.

Once again, when we have a continuous random variable, R (e.g. see Exhibit 5.4), the variance is given by

$$\sigma^2 = \int_{-\infty}^{\infty} [R - E(R)]^2 \times f(R)\mathrm{d}R$$

where R is the density function of the return R. A short-cut formula for the variance is

$$\sigma^2 = ER^2 - (ER)^2$$

where

$$ER^2 = \sum_{i=1}^{m} P_i R_i^2$$

and ER is the expected return as discussed above. Using this equation to calculate the variance of British Airways we get:

$$ER^2 = \frac{0.37^2 + 0.17^2 + 0.17^2}{3} = 0.0649$$

---

[4] Note that when historical rates of return are employed to estimate the variance of future rates of return, and there are m observations, we divide the sum of the squared deviations by $m - 1$ (see Chapter 4). The reason is that by dividing by $m - 1$ we obtain the best (unbiased) estimate of σ^2. But here we do not need to estimate σ^2; we calculate it where $1/m$ is the probability of each state.

$$(ER)^2 = 0.123^2 = 0.01513$$

$$\text{and } \sigma^2 = ER^2 - (ER)^2 = 0.0649 - 0.01513 = 0.0497$$

as before.

5.6   THE MEAN–VARIANCE CRITERION

Now that we know that most investors are risk averse, we can refine our investment selection criteria. To include this risk aversion characteristic in the decision of security selection, we turn to the mean–variance criterion (MVC). We see from the variance formula that the greater the uncertainty of future returns, the higher the variance. Therefore, the MVC is used to select those assets (or portfolios of assets) with (1) the lowest variance for the same (or higher) expected return, or (2) the highest expected return for the same (or lower) variance.[5]

Suppose that asset A has a greater (or equal) mean than asset B (otherwise we change the roles of A and B). In a comparison of two assets, A and B, there are then six possibilities:

1 $E(R_A) > E(R_B)$ and $\sigma_A^2 < \sigma_B^2$

2 $E(R_A) > E(R_B)$ and $\sigma_A^2 = \sigma_B^2$

3 $E(R_A) > E(R_B)$ and $\sigma_A^2 > \sigma_B^2$

4 $E(R_A) = E(R_B)$ and $\sigma_A^2 < \sigma_B^2$

5 $E(R_A) = E(R_B)$ and $\sigma_A^2 = \sigma_B^2$

6 $E(R_A) = E(R_B)$ and $\sigma_A^2 > \sigma_B^2$

Thus, we can say that by the MVC, asset A is preferred to asset B in cases 1, 2 and 4 above. In case 5, the investor is indifferent between the two assets, while in case 3 one cannot tell which asset is better because A has a higher expected return as well as a higher variance. Finally, in case 6 asset B is preferred because it has the same mean as asset A with a lower variance. We need to know the investor's preference to decide between A and B in case 5 (see Section 5.8).

Suppose that each investor holds only one asset (either A or B), or alternatively that A and B are portfolios rather than individual assets. We claim that in equilibrium, only cases 3 and 5 above prevail, i.e. no one portfolio is better than the other by the MVC. We illustrate this issue with Exhibit 5.3. Exhibit 5.3 shows that the variance can be increased with no change in the mean return. Security A yields £130 with certainty, Security B yields £120 and £140 with equal probability, and Security C yields £110 and £150 with equal probability. As we move from A to B to C, £10 is added and subtracted with equal probability, creating a larger dispersion (variance) without changing the mean return. This movement, which increases the variance but does not change the mean return, causes the risk averter to be worse off, according to the MVC.

---

[5] So far, it is assumed that only one asset or one portfolio is selected. When we discuss the risk of an asset when a portfolio is constructed, we will also incorporate correlations as important factors determining the portfolio variability (or risk) (see Chapter 6).

Exhibit 5.3 Expected return and variance: returns on Securities A, B and C with a £100 investment

Security A		Security B		Security C	
Return (£)	Probability	Return (£)	Probability	Return (£)	Probability
130	1	120	$\frac{1}{2}$	110	$\frac{1}{2}$
		140	$\frac{1}{2}$	150	$\frac{1}{2}$
Mean (£)	130	130[a]		130[b]	
Variance	0	100[c]		400[d]	
Standard deviation (£)	0	10		20	

[a] $\frac{1}{2}(120) + \frac{1}{2}(140) = 130$.
[b] $\frac{1}{2}(110) + \frac{1}{2}(150) = 130$.
[c] $\frac{1}{2}(120 - 130)^2 + \frac{1}{2}(140 - 130)^2 = 100$.
[d] $\frac{1}{2}(110 - 130)^2 + \frac{1}{2}(150 - 130)^2 = 400$.

The reason risk averters would not like this movement is that the joy or satisfaction they get from the increase of £10 is smaller for them than the sorrow or damage caused by a loss of £10 in the case where the lower income is realized. Thus, for risk averters, Security A is preferred to Security B, and Security B is preferred to Security C. Risk averters prefer to avoid the honey (higher return) not because they do not like honey but because they know there is a probability that they could get stung!

Thus, by case 2 above, asset A is preferred to asset B and asset B is preferred to asset C. Is is possible to hold in equilibrium? Absolutely not! Assuming that all or most investors are risk averters, the stock price of Security B must drop, and the stock price of Security C must drop even further relative to Security A, otherwise no one will buy them. Once all available assets have been purchased and the market is cleared, we will find that, in fact, there is a risk premium on Securities B and C and that the risk premium on Security C is larger than the risk premium on Security B.

For example, if the price of Security A is £100, the price of Security B may drop to £98, and the price of Security C may drop to £95. Suppose that at these prices, the market is in equilibrium; hence, there is neither an excess demand nor an excess supply of securities. In this case, the mean rate of return would be:

$$\text{Security A: } (£130/£100) - 1 = 0.3 \text{ or } 30\%$$

$$\text{Security B: } [\frac{1}{2}(£120/£98) + \frac{1}{2}(£140/£98)] - 1$$
$$\cong [(\frac{1}{2} \times 1.22) + (\frac{1}{2} \times 1.43)] - 1 = 0.325 \text{ or } 32.5\%$$

$$\text{Security C: } [(\frac{1}{2}(£110/£95) + \frac{1}{2}(£150/£95)] - 1$$
$$\cong [(\frac{1}{2} \times 1.16) + (\frac{1}{2} \times 1.58)] - 1 = 0.37 \text{ or } 37\%$$

After the prices dropped, case 3 above holds and one asset is not preferred over another by the MVC. Thus, we may be in equilibrium. Therefore, for these assumed equilibrium prices, the required risk premiums on Securities A, B and C are as follows:

$$\text{Security A: Certainty, hence zero risk premium}$$

$$\text{Security B: Risk premium} = 32.5\% - 30\% = 2.5\%$$

$$\text{Security C: Risk premium} = 37\% - 30\% = 7\%$$

As you can see, the larger the variance, the lower the price and the larger the required risk premium.

Finally, note that we do not claim that the market is always in equilibrium. If the investor identifies portfolios like those described in cases 1, 2 and 3 above, portfolio A should be preferred. However, when the market realizes the existence of A over B, the stock price of A will go up, and the investors who first identify this disequilibrium will have a capital gain.

Exhibit 5.4(a) illustrates two bell-shaped normal distributions with the same variance but with different expected returns corresponding to the rates of return on two stocks, A and B. In this case both stocks have the same risk but stock B is more profitable because it has a higher expected rate of return. Exhibit 5.4(b) illustrates two distributions with the same expected return but different variance. In this case stock B is worse because it has the same profitably as stock A but a higher risk. To see why a lower variance or a lower standard deviation means a greater certainty (and hence smaller risk) consider the case where both stocks have the same mean of 10%, and standard deviations $\sigma_A = 5\%$ and $\sigma_B = 20\%$, respectively. With normal distributions, there is about a 64% chance that the actual returns will deviate from the expected value by one standard deviation or less, and about a 95% chance that the deviation will be by two standard deviations or less.

Thus, we can say that in our case there is a 64% chance that the realized return on stock A will be 10% ± 5% and for stock B it will be 10% ± 20%. Thus we see that the range of return on stock A is from 5% to 15% and for stock B from 10% to 30%. From this example we see that the returns on stock A with a lower σ are less dispersed. The same phenomenon holds for two standard deviations, and in fact any number of

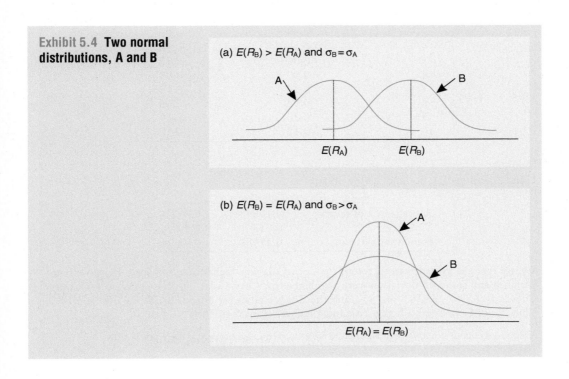

Exhibit 5.4 Two normal distributions, A and B

(a) $E(R_B) > E(R_A)$ and $\sigma_B = \sigma_A$

$E(R_A)$ $E(R_B)$

(b) $E(R_B) = E(R_A)$ and $\sigma_B > \sigma_A$

$E(R_A) = E(R_B)$

standard deviations one selects. When the number of standard deviations increases, we can say that the return will fall in a certain range with a greater chance or greater probability. However, the smaller the σ, the smaller will be the range of possible returns. Because the return on the stock with the lower deviation is more certain, we can conclude that the higher the standard deviation, the higher the uncertainty of future return, hence σ measures the risk involved. Finally, we demonstrate calculation for normal distribution, but similar results hold for other distributions of returns.

5.7   OTHER ATTITUDES TOWARDS RISK

Investors who are risk neutral completely ignore an asset's variance and make investment decisions based only on the asset's expected rate of return. In the example given in Exhibit 5.3, the risk-neutral investor will be indifferent between Securities A, B and C. If

PRACTICE BOX

Problem

The following are 10 states and the corresponding rates of return on Coca-Cola and Ford stocks. Assume that each state has an equal probability of $1/m = 1/10$. It is given that the riskless interest rate is 6.1%. Calculate the mean, variance, standard deviation and risk premium.

State	Coca-Cola Rate of return (%)	Ford Rate of return (%)
1	0.15%	0.08%
2	0.135	0.09
3	−0.04	0.05
4	0.16	0.10
5	0.08	0.12
6	−0.10	0.03
7	0.24	0.15
8	0.02	0.06
9	0.30	0.14
10	0.12	0.10

Solution

Using Equations 5.1, 5.4 and 5.5 we obtain:*

Average rate of return	0.1065%	0.092%
Variance	0.013	0.001
Standard deviation	0.114%	0.032%

We see that the average rate of return for Coca-Cola was higher than for Ford. However, the variance and standard deviation were also higher for Coca-Cola. The risk premium for Coca-Cola is 10.65% − 6.1% = 4.55%, and the risk premium for Ford is 9.2% − 6.1% = 3.1%. Thus, Coca-Cola offers a higher risk and a higher return than Ford.

* The average rate of return, variance and standard deviation are calculated using $P_i = 1/m$ where $m = 10$.

all investors were risk neutral, no risk premium would be required, and Securities A, B and C would have the same market price.

Investors are defined as risk seekers if they like risk or variance. These investors will be ready to pay a higher price for an asset whose variance increases. In Exhibit 5.3, risk seekers will prefer Security C over Security B and Security B over Security A. There is ample evidence that some people are risk seekers, at least during some periods of time and for small dollar amounts. For example, most gambling activities, such as state lotteries, have expected payoffs less than the cost to play, yet many people still buy lottery tickets.

If all investors were either risk neutral or risk seeking, there would be no positive risk premium. One way to assess whether financial markets are dominated by risk seekers or risk averters is to examine historical rates of return as was done in Chapter 4. If riskier securities earn, on average, higher returns, then we can infer that on the whole, the market participants are risk averse. It has been shown in Chapter 4 that the historical risk premium was positive. Moreover, the larger the standard deviation of rates of return, the larger the average return, implying that, at least historically, risk premium is related to the size of the standard deviation of rates of return.[6] Because positive risk premiums are found in the market, we can conclude that risk aversion is the dominating preference in the marketplace. Therefore, in the rest of the book, we assume that investors are risk averse.[7]

5.8 DEGREE OF RISK AND THE INVESTMENT CHOICE

Given the positive historical risk premium (see Chapter 4) we can safely assert that most investors are risk averters, and therefore they dislike variance. For a given expected future value of an asset, the higher the variance the less money investors will be willing to pay to purchase the asset, hence the higher the mean rate of return and the higher the required risk premium. Thus, in equilibrium we expect that case 3 in Section 5.6 holds: the mean of A and the variance of A are greater than the corresponding values of B. How would one select an investment in such a case? We need to introduce the investors' preference to make a selection in such a case. Let us illustrate. Suppose that the expected price at the end of the year of the two assets A and B is £110. The current price of asset A is £100; hence the expected rate of return is 10%. Asset B has a much higher variance than Asset A; hence, investors are willing to pay only £90 for it. Thus, the expected rate of return on asset B is £110/£90 − 1 ≅ 22.22%, reflecting the relatively high risk of this asset. Of course, each investor has his or her degree of risk aversion. For a given increase in variance, some investors will increase the required rate of return from the asset by only a little and some investors may increase it by a much larger amount, meaning that the increase in variance hurts them very much and they require substantial compensation for their loss. Investors can assign a utility score to the various investments, reflecting their satisfaction from the investment. The one common utility score which takes the expected return $E(R)$ and the variance σ_R^2 into account is given by

$$U = E(R) - a\sigma_R^2 \tag{5.6}$$

---

[6] See Ibbotson Associates, *Stocks, Bonds, Bills and Inflation* (Chicago: Ibbotson Associates, 1999 Yearbook).
[7] See also Jeremy J. Siegel, 'The equity premium: stock and bond returns since 1802', *Financial Analysts Journal*, January–February 1992, pp. 28–38.

U is the utility score from the investment and a is a positive number reflecting the investor's attitude towards risk. When a selection between investments is done, the one with the highest utility score U is selected. The choice depends on the value of a in Equation 5.6. The larger the value of a, the more risk averse the investor is, as a given variance drastically reduces his or her utility score.

To see the meaning of the utility score, let us go back to the previous practice box, comparing Coca-Cola and Ford stocks.[8] Investors with $a = 0$ completely ignore the variance; they are not hurt by the variance, hence they will choose the asset only by the mean rate of return. These investors are risk neutral. They will choose Coca-Cola stock with the higher mean return.

Now assume that $a = 1$; i.e. the investor dislikes variance because utility (or satisfaction from the investment) will be reduced as the variance increases. For $a = 1$ we will get the utility score as follows:

Coca-Cola stock: $\qquad U = 0.1065 - 1 \times 0.013 = 0.0935$

Ford stock: $\qquad U = 0.092 - 1 \times 0.001 = 0.091$

We see that even for $a = 1$, Coca-Cola stock is still a better choice than Ford stock because it provides a higher level of satisfaction or utility score to the investor than Ford stock. For more risk-averse investors with, say, $a = 2$ we have:

Coca-Cola stock: $\qquad U = 0.1065 - 2 \times 0.013 = 0.1065 - 0.026 = 0.0805$

Ford stock: $\qquad U = 0.092 - 2 \times 0.001 = 0.092 - 0.002 = 0.090$

Ford stock is a better choice.

Thus, the utility score reflects the degree of satisfaction from the investment. Some investors badly dislike variance (relatively large a) and some are not much hurt by the variance (relatively low value of a). Thus, if a choice between Coca-Cola and Ford stocks (with no other assets involved) needs to be made, some investors will choose Ford stock and some will choose Coca-Cola stock. Generally speaking, the more risk averse the investor is, the less risky the selected assets will be.

Finally, the choice is simple in a case where the mean of asset 1 is larger than the mean of asset 2, and asset 1 also has a smaller variance. In such a case, any risk averter, regardless of the magnitude of a (which is non-negative for risk averters), will choose

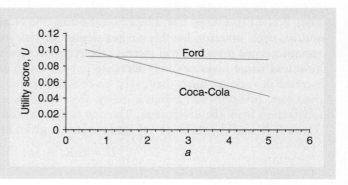

Exhibit 5.5 Rank of Coca-Cola and Ford stocks for various levels of risk coefficient, a

---

[8] We assume that the investor decides to invest either in Ford stock or in Coca-Cola stock. In practice, investors can increase the utility score by diversifying between the two stocks, or by constructing a portfolio of these two stocks. This will be covered in Chapter 6.

asset 1 because always $U(1) > U(2)$, where $U(1)$ and $U(2)$ stand for the utility of assets 1 and 2, respectively.

Exhibit 5.5 demonstrates the utility of Coca-Cola and Ford stocks for various levels of risk coefficient a. As we can see, for relatively low levels of a, Coca-Cola stock is preferred, and for higher values of a Ford stock is preferred. Thus, less risk-averse investors would prefer Coca-Cola, but more risk-averse investors will penalize Coca-Cola for the large uncertainty and would prefer to invest in Ford.

SUMMARY

■ *This chapter first discussed asset pricing under the assumption of certainty.*
Under certainty, in equilibrium all assets will yield the same rate of return. However, we live in a world of uncertainty, where different assets have different expected returns.

■ *Explain how to calculate the expected rate of return and the variance.*
The expected rate of return measures predictability and the variance measures risk.

■ *Explain what a risk averter is.*
A risk averter, other things being equal, dislikes volatility. Such an investor will always prefer a certain investment over an uncertain investment as long as the expected returns on the two investments are identical. To be induced to take risk, risk averters must be offered a risk premium.

■ *Calculate the required risk premium.*
Assuming that the investors hold only one asset, we show that the larger the deviations of the returns from the mean, the more risky the asset and the larger the required risk premium.

■ *Apply the mean–variance criterion in asset selection.*
Risk averters like a high expected return and dislike high variance. The mean–variance criterion (MVC) provides a simple method to assess choices between risky assets. However, in equilibrium, the mean and the variance of one asset are greater than the corresponding figures for another asset and the MVC cannot distinguish between the two assets.

■ *Compare the utility score.*
When two investments exist such that investment 1 has a higher mean and higher variance than investment 2, the choice depends on the degree of risk aversion of the individual investor. Investors with a high degree of risk aversion will tend to invest in asset 2, while the opposite holds for less risk-averse investors. The choice depends on

KEY TERMS

Arbitrage	Objective probability	Standard deviation
Certainty	Risk	Subjective
Expected rate of return	Risk averter	probability
Mean	Risk neutral	Uncertainty
Mean–variance criterion	Risk premium	Utility score
(MVC)	Risk seeker	Variance

the utility score which may vary from one investor to another.

5.1   What is the difference between risk and uncertainty? How are these differences resolved?

5.2   What is an arbitrage transaction?

5.3   Suppose the market is in equilibrium, and there are no mispriced assets. What do different average rates of return in the market reflect?

5.4   When is the MRC the proper investment rule to use?

5.5   What is the relationship between an investor's level of risk aversion and the required risk premium?

5.6   You prefer to get £100 with a probability of $\frac{1}{2}$ and £200 with a probability of $\frac{1}{2}$ over getting £150 with certainty. Are you a risk averter or a risk seeker?

5.7   A firm requires at least a 12% rate of return on a project, the cost of capital is 12% and the interest rate is 5%. What can we learn about the average stockholder's risk preferences? What is the risk premium?

5.8   Consider the following rates of return on stock mutual funds:

Year	Fund A (%)	Fund B (%)
1	−10	−15
2	+20	+23
3	+10	+8
4	+12	+15

Examine whether one fund dominates the MVC.

5.9   What is the annual rate of return on a riskless two-year zero-coupon bond with a face value of £200 that cost you £70?

5.10 Suppose there are two assets, X and Y, and the current price of Asset X is £100. If it is known with certainty that in one year Asset X will be worth £120 and Asset Y will be worth £144, what is the equilibrium price of Asset Y today?

5.11 Suppose a stock that has a current price of £80 has a 50% chance of rising to £120 and a 50% chance of falling to £60 in one year. What is the expected price of the stock? What is the expected pound profit? What is the expected rate of return?

5.12 Consider the following data related to Assets A, B, C and D (given in percentages):

Asset A

Rate of return (%)	Probability
5	1

Asset C

Rate of return (%)	Probability
−20	1/3
15	1/3
30	1/3

Asset B

Rate of return (%)	Probability

−10	1/4
10	3/4

Asset D

Rate of return (%)	Probability
−20	1/4
10	1/2
40	1/4

Which asset is preferable if you decide to choose the investment with the maximum expected return? Explain.

5.13 From Question 5.12, which asset is preferable by the mean–variance criterion (MVC)? Discuss.

5.14 During a recent 10-year period, the following rates of return were earned on General Electric (GE) and Duke Power Company (DP). Assume that these are the population distributions and that each year has a probability of $1/m$, where m is the number of years.

Year	GE	DP	Year	GE	DP
1	0.11	0.10	6	−0.04	−0.01
2	0.13	0.12	7	0.34	0.12
3	−0.06	0.09	8	0.05	0.06
4	0.12	0.17	9	0.26	0.02
5	0.03	0.05	10	0.16	0.08

(a) Calculate the expected rate of return, variance and standard deviation of each stock.
(b) Assume that the riskless interest rate is 4%. What is the risk premium on these two assets? Explain your results.

5.15 Next year a security will yield £90 with a probability of $\frac{1}{2}$ and £110 with a probability of $\frac{1}{2}$. An investor is willing to pay $80 for this asset today. The risk-free interest rate is 15%.

(a) Is this investor a risk seeker or a risk averter?
(b) What is the risk premium?

5.16 Answer Question 5.15 assuming that the investor is ready to pay £95 for this asset.

5.17 Investment A costs £1,000 today, and the return next year is either £900 or £1,300, with an equal probability. Investment B costs £100 today, and the return next year is either £90 or £130, with an equal probability.

(a) Calculate the means and variances of future returns (in pounds) on these two assets.

(b) Calculate the means and variances of future *rates* of return on these two assets.
(c) Suppose Investments A and B are two stocks that exist in the market, and you can buy as much as you wish from these two stocks, but you can buy only one (A or B). Which investment would you prefer?

5.18 Suppose both Stock A and Stock B cost £100. The future returns on these two stocks are as follows:

Stock A

Probability	Return (£)
1/2	90

1/2	150
Stock B	

Probability	Return (£)
1/3	90
2/3	150

(a) Calculate the expected rates of return and the variances of the rates of return on these two assets.

(b) Which investment is better, according to the MVC?

(c) Given that the riskless interest rate is 5%, calculate the risk premium on each of these two assets.

5.19 Repeat Question 5.18 when the return on Stock B is £90 with a probability of $\frac{2}{3}$ and £150 with a probability of $\frac{1}{3}$. The information on Stock A is unchanged.

5.20 'The variance is always a larger number than the standard deviation'. Is this assertion true? Give an example to demonstrate your answer.

SELECTED REFERENCES

Arnott, Robert D., and Ronald J. Ryan. 'The death of the risk premium'. *Journal of Portfolio Management*, Spring 2001.

Arrow, K.J. 'Alternative approaches to the theory of choice in risk-taking situations'. *Econometrica*, October 1951.

Arrow, K.J. 'The role of securities in the optimal allocation of risk-bearing'. *Review of Economic Studies*, April 1964.

Good, Walter R. 'Yes, Virginia, there is a risk premium, but....'. *Financial Analysts Journal*, January/February 1994.

Hirshleifer, J.H. 'On the theory of optimal investment decision'. *Journal of Political Economy*, August 1958.

Levy, H., and A. Cohen. 'On the risks of stocks in the long run: revisited'. *Journal of Portfolio Selection*, Spring 1998.

Markowitz, H. 'Portfolio selection'. *Journal of Finance*, 7(1), March 1952, pp. 77–91.

Markowitz, H.M. *Portfolio Selection*. New York: Wiley, 1959.

Markowitz, H.M. *Mean–Variance Analysis in Portfolio Choice and Capital Markets*. New York: Basil Blackwell, 1987.

Rowe, D. 'The relevance of risk and uncertainty'. *Risk*, December 1999.

Rowe, D. 'Science and sentience'. *Risk*, December 2000.

Sharpe, W.F. 'Risk aversion in the stock market: some empirical evidence'. *Journal of Finance*, June 1976.

Suominen, Matti. 'Trading volume and information revelation in stock markets'. *JFQA*, forthcoming.

Wright, Paul. 'The FSA and a broader view on risk'. *Risk*, October 2001.

Chapter 6

RISK REDUCTION BY DIVERSIFICATION

Learning objectives

After studying this chapter you should be able to:

1 Discuss the rate of return, expected rate of return and variance of a portfolio.

2 Explain the effect of an individual asset's risk on a portfolio's risk.

3 Define and explain covariances and correlation coefficients between pairs of assets.

4 Explain the role of correlation within a portfolio.

INVESTMENT IN THE NEWS

Blue-chip stocks for gold-plated clients

How Todd Morgan manages the rest of Barbra Streisand's millions: very conservatively

Jeanne Lee

The rich are different when they are investors; they're more conservative. As Todd Morgan, chairman of Bell Air Investment Advisors, explains, 'Our clients are already rich. Our goal is not to make them rich but to keep them rich.'....

Accordingly, Morgan's approach is solidly conservative – typically 65% in equities (heavy on the blue chips) and 35% in muni bonds. In particular, he favors premium large-cap growth stocks in financial services, consumer products, health care, and technology, such as Citicorp, Gillette, Kimberly-Clark, and Abbott Laboratories. Even when he gets into tech, it's gold-plated names like Microsoft, Intel, and IBM. 'People are talking about the Internet all the time, but these big-cap names are going to be around longer than any of us,' says Morgan....

Source: Website at http://cgi.pathfinder.com/fortune/investor/1999/06/21/stx3.htm

In Chapters 4 and 5 we defined and discussed the expected rate of return and variance of rates of return of an individual asset. We also explained that the variance is a risk measure. In the above *Investment in the news* article we see that more than one asset is held in the portfolio of Barbra Streisand; it is composed of 65% in equities and 35% in municipal bonds (Muni Bonds). Moreover, the equity itself is composed of various stocks taken from various industries. Like Barbra Streisand, most other investors hold more than one asset in their portfolios. From this we conclude that diversification of the investment among various assets is probably beneficial to the investors.

In this chapter we first define what a portfolio of assets is. We then show:

(a) how to calculate the expected rate of return on a portfolio;
(b) how to calculate the variance of the rate of return on a portfolio;
(c) that when a portfolio composed of several assets is held, the variance of an asset included in the portfolio is not the only indication of its risk. Rather one should also consider the co-movement of the asset's rates of return with other assets' rates of return included in the portfolios.

Thus, the risk and return of a *portfolio* of assets is the subject of this chapter.

6.1   A PORTFOLIO OF ASSETS

A portfolio is a combination of assets. However, at times, we use also the term *portfolio* also to refer to a holding of only one asset. In general, an investor has a portfolio that diversifies wealth in a number of assets, which can be combined in a variety of proportions, or weights. Because the weights are nothing but the proportion of wealth invested in each available asset, the sum of the weights must be equal to 1 (or 100%). For example, a proportion of $\frac{1}{2}$ invested in IBM stock, $\frac{1}{4}$ invested in AT&T stock and $\frac{1}{4}$ invested in T-bills constitutes a portfolio. If, for each dollar invested from the investor's own wealth, $\$\frac{1}{4}$ is *short* in AT&T, it means that the investor sells short the stock of AT&T and receives the cash flow from this sell. Hence, altogether $\$1\frac{1}{4}$ (or 125% of wealth) is to be invested in the other asset, say, IBM. Thus, a portfolio of $-\frac{1}{4}$ short in AT&T and $1\frac{1}{4}$ invested in IBM is also a portfolio with $-\frac{1}{4} + 1\frac{1}{4} = 1$ (or 100%). Any other combination of investment proportions, with negative as well as positive proportions, such that the sum of these proportions is equal to 1, defines a portfolio.

6.2   AN ASSET'S RISK WHEN HELD WITH OTHER ASSETS IN A PORTFOLIO

As Chapters 4 and 5 described, the higher the variance (or standard deviation) of the return on an asset, the higher the risk and therefore the higher the required risk premium. Hence, the variance of the returns on an asset appears to measure the risk of that asset. Although this is true if an investor holds only one asset, the variance is not the sole measure of risk if the investor holds more than one risky asset in his or her portfolio. In a portfolio, the risk of an individual asset is a function not only of its own variance but also of its degree of dependency with the other assets in the portfolio. Let us demonstrate the role that dependency of returns plays in determining the portfolio's risk.

Exhibit 6.1　Return on Assets A and B

	Return on Asset A		Return on Asset B	
	Return	Probability	Return	Probability
	+20%	$\frac{1}{2}$	+20%	$\frac{1}{2}$
	−10%	$\frac{1}{2}$	−10%	$\frac{1}{2}$
Mean	5%		5%	
Variance	225		225	
Standard deviation	15%		15%	

The degree of dependency measures how the returns on two assets move together. If both go up or down together, we say they have *positive dependency*. If one asset goes up when the other goes down or vice versa, we say they have *negative dependency*. In general, the more negative the degree of dependency between assets in a portfolio, the lower the risk of the portfolio, and hence the lower the required risk premium for each specific asset. The precise measure of risk of each asset in a portfolio context is discussed in Chapter 14. This section demonstrates that a risk-averse investor will require a risk premium on the risky portfolio held that decreases as the degree of dependency between the risky assets in the portfolio decreases.

Let us explain this dependency concept with a numerical example. Suppose there are two assets, A and B, whose returns in dollars are given in Exhibit 6.1. Each asset yields +20% and −10% with an equal probability of $\frac{1}{2}$. The expected rate of return on each asset is

$$\tfrac{1}{2}(20\%) + \tfrac{1}{2}(-10\%) = 5\%$$

and the variance is

$$\tfrac{1}{2}(20 - 5)^2 + \tfrac{1}{2}(-10 - 5)^2 = 225$$

Hence, the standard deviation is $\overline{225} = 15\%$.

Exhibit 6.2 lists the distributions of the returns from these two assets together, when a portfolio composed of $\frac{1}{2}$ of the assets are invested in stock A and $\frac{1}{2}$ in stock B, such that the total investment for weights is $\frac{1}{2} + \frac{1}{2} = 1$.

We make different assumptions regarding the dependency between the two assets' distributions. First, let us explain how the portfolio's rate of return is obtained. Suppose that you construct a portfolio such that $\frac{1}{2}$ of it is invested in asset A and $\frac{1}{2}$ of it in asset B. Therefore, if you earn, say, 20% on asset A, the contribution of this asset to the portfolio's rate of return is only 10% because $\frac{1}{2} \times 20\% = 10\%$. Thus, the contribution of each asset to the portfolio rate of return is calculated by the product of the investment proportion in the asset times the return on the asset.

The left column of Exhibit 6.2 assumes an extreme positive dependency between the returns on the two assets.[1] Namely, if +20% is realized on asset A, this return of 20% is also sure to be realized on asset B. Hence, 20% is obtained on each asset with a probability of $\frac{1}{2}$. Because we invest $\frac{1}{2}$ in B, the return on the portfolio in such a

---

[1] This will be measured later by *correlation*, i.e. we have here a correlation of +1 (see Section 6.4).

**Exhibit 6.2 Return on portfolio composed of Asset A and Asset B
(The investment in the portfolio is $100)**

	Positive dependency		No dependency		Negative dependency	
	Return	Probability	Return	Probability	Return	Probability
	20%	$\frac{1}{2}$	20%	$\frac{1}{4}$	5%	1
	−10%	$\frac{1}{2}$	5%	$\frac{1}{2}$		
			−10%	$\frac{1}{4}$		
Mean	5%		5%		5%	
Variance	225[a]		112.5[b]		0	

[a] Variance $= \frac{1}{2}(20\% - 5\%)^2 + \frac{1}{2}(-10\% - 5\%)^2 = 900$.
[b] Variance $= \frac{1}{4}(20\% - 5\%)^2 + \frac{1}{2}(5\% - 5\%)^2 + \frac{1}{4}(-10\% - 5\%)^2 = 112.5$.

case is $\frac{1}{2} \times 20\% + \frac{1}{2} \times 20\% = 20\%$ with a probability of $\frac{1}{2}$. Similarly, if an event occurs with a negative return on asset A (−10%), the same event also causes a loss on asset B of −10%. Thus, with a probability of $\frac{1}{2}$, we get −10% on each asset, or $\frac{1}{2} \times (-10\%) + \frac{1}{2} \times (-10\%) = -10\%$ is obtained on the portfolio composed of these two assets.

The right column in Exhibit 6.2 represents the distribution corresponding to an extreme negative dependency between the two assets.[2] Namely, if asset A has a return of +20%, asset B has a return of −10%, with a total rate of return of $\frac{1}{2} \times (20\%) + \frac{1}{2} \times (-10\%) = 5\%$ on the portfolio of the two assets. Similarly, if the low return is realized on asset A (−10%), a high rate of return is received on asset B (+20%), and once again we end up with a +5% rate of return on the portfolio. Hence, no matter what eventually occurs, the total rate of return obtained on the portfolio is +5%, so we get +5% with a probability of 1 (meaning certainty); therefore, in the extreme negative dependency of the right-hand column, the portfolio's variance is equal to zero.

Finally, the middle column of Exhibit 6.2 reports an intermediate case where the returns have no dependency; there is no association, either positive or negative, between the returns on these two assets. Thus, we get +20% on asset A with a probability of $\frac{1}{2}$ and +20% on asset B with a probability of $\frac{1}{2}$, ending up with 20% (i.e. $\frac{1}{2} \times 20\% + \frac{1}{2} \times 20\% = 20\%$) with a probability of $\frac{1}{2} \times \frac{1}{2} = \frac{1}{4}$. Similarly, we get 10% with a probability of $\frac{1}{4}$. Note, however, that +5% is obtained with a probability of $\frac{1}{2}$, because it encompasses two events: +20% on asset A and −10% on asset B, and −10% on asset A and + 20% on asset B. Because each event has a probability of $\frac{1}{4}$, we end up with 5% with a probability of $\frac{1}{2}$.

The bottom part of Exhibit 6.2 clearly indicates that although the mean return on the two assets combined is 5%, no matter what the assumed degree of dependency between the two assets, the variance of the portfolio returns is a function of their dependency: the lower the dependency, the lower the variance. In the case of an extreme negative dependency, the portfolio's variance is reduced to zero.

Let us return to the relationship between risk premium and variance, taking the case of the extreme negative dependency given in Exhibit 6.2 (right column). At the end of the

---

[2] We shall see in Section 6.4 that this extreme negative dependency corresponds to a correlation of −1.

investment period of, say, one year, an investor receives with certainty a rate of return of 5%. For an investment of, say, $100 ($50 in Stock A and $50 in B), the end-of-period wealth on the portfolio is $105 with certainty, because a 5% rate of return is earned with certainty. Suppose that the riskless interest rate is 5% and that the investor is offered a certain sum of money for selling his portfolio composed of assets A and B when this sum is paid at the end of the period. What should this sum be in order to make the investor indifferent between the two choices? The answer is clearly $105. If you offer the investor $106 at the end of the period for the portfolio he holds, you are 'bribing' him, and he will sell the portfolio to you, because he obtains $105 with certainty on the portfolio. Moreover, the investor can borrow $100 at 5% interest rate, buy these two stocks, sell them to you and make a $1 gain with certainty, because he or she will pay the bank $105 at the end of the period but receive $106 from you. If you offer him $104 he will not agree to sell the portfolio to you because he can sell the stock for $100, deposit it at the bank and receive $105 at the end of the period. Thus, $105 is exactly the point where he is indifferent between selling or not selling his portfolio to you. Because the return on the portfolio is 5% and the interest rate is 5%, it implies that the investor requires no risk premium at all. This makes sense: no risk is involved in holding a portfolio of these two assets, because the return on them is 5% with certainty. Of course, for a $100 investment there is $1 profit which seems negligible. But the same argument holds for a $100 million investment (or even more) which yields a $1 million profit.

The important conclusion from this example is that although each of the two assets, when held *separately*, is risky, the two assets are considered to be riskless when included in a portfolio. The extreme negative dependency between the returns on these two assets completely eliminates the uncertainty involved in the returns. Hence, an asset's own variance should be the measure of risk only when the asset is held separately. When the asset is held in a portfolio with other assets, however, the degree of dependency should be incorporated into the measurement of risk, and hence into the risk premium. Thus, in this case, the *portfolio's variance* is the measure of risk, not the individual asset's variance.

Indeed, the portfolio's variance in the extreme negative dependency of Exhibit 6.2 is equal to zero, which reflects the certainty of the future return. Exhibit 6.2 shows that as negative dependency shifts to no dependency and then to positive dependency, the portfolio variance becomes larger.

In general, the higher the degree of dependency of a particular asset with other risky assets included in a portfolio, the higher this asset's contribution to the portfolio's risk will be and the higher the risk premium required for the asset will be. Therefore, the required risk premium is a function not only of the asset's variance but also of its dependency with other assets.

The discussion so far can be summarized by the following rules:

Rule 1: If an investor holds only one risky asset, the variance is the measure of risk. The higher the variance, the higher the required risk premium from the individual assets in the portfolio.

Rule 2: If an investor holds more than one risky asset in a portfolio, the risk of each asset is a function of both the asset's own variance and its degree of dependency with the other assets held in the portfolio.

Rule 3: The larger the portfolio's variance, the higher the required risk premium on the portfolio and therefore, on average, the larger the required risk premium on each asset.

Thus, the portfolio's variance, rather than the individual asset's variance, is the key factor in determining the required risk premium. In order to further understand the concept, let us first define the portfolio's expected rate of return and portfolio variance and then turn to how the portfolio's risk can be reduced by diversifying among different assets.

6.3 THE EXPECTED RATE OF RETURN ON A PORTFOLIO

When you invest in many assets, the portfolio expected return, denoted by $E(R_p)$, is the weighted average of the expected returns of all the assets held in your portfolio, where the weights are the investment proportions (w_i). This is summarized by Rule 4.

Rule 4: The portfolio expected value of return is the sum of the products of the investment weighted in the individual asset by its expected rate of return:

$$E(R_p) = \sum_{i=1}^{n} w_i E(R_i) \tag{6.1}$$

where n is the number of assets in the portfolio, $E(R_i)$ is the expected rate of return on the ith asset, and w_i is the weight invested in the ith asset. (Note that the weights must sum to 1; that is $\sum_{i=1}^{n} w_i = 1$.)

For example, if there are only two assets in the portfolio ($n = 2$) with expected rates of return of 5% on the first asset and 20% on the second asset, and if $w_1 = \frac{1}{2}$ and $w_2 = \frac{1}{2}$, we have

$$E(R_p) = \tfrac{1}{2}(0.05) + \tfrac{1}{2}(0.20) = 0.125 \text{ or } 12.5\%$$

Of course, when the investment proportions change, the expected rate of return on the portfolio also changes. For example, if $w_1 = \frac{1}{4}$ and $w_2 = \frac{3}{4}$, then

$$E(R_p) = \tfrac{1}{4}(0.05) + \tfrac{3}{4}(0.20) = 0.1625 \text{ or } 16.25\%$$

To show how to calculate the expected return on a portfolio, let us turn first to Exhibit 6.3 where three assets A, B and C are considered and there are three possible scenarios of the economy: the economy may grow, the economy may remain stable, or the economy may go into a recession (see Exhibit 6.3). Note that Asset B provides a higher return in a recession; for example, it may be a firm that produces an inexpensive, low-quality product that is in great demand in a recessionary period. For simplicity we assume that each scenario has a probability of $\frac{1}{3}$. For example, we have a $\frac{1}{3}$ probability that the economy will grow with a 5% rate of return on Asset A, 10% on Asset B and 30% on Asset C. We construct two portfolios: $\frac{1}{2}$B and $\frac{1}{2}$C, and alternatively $\frac{1}{2}$A + $\frac{1}{4}$B + $\frac{1}{4}$C. Of course, the return on each portfolio in each scenario is the corresponding returns on the stock times the investment proportions in these assets. For example, if the economy grows, we get on portfolio $\frac{1}{2}$B + $\frac{1}{2}$C, the return of $\frac{1}{2} \times 0.1 + \frac{1}{2} \times 0.3 = 0.2$ or 20%. In a similar way all returns in Exhibit 6.3 are calculated.

Each scenario (stable, growth or recession) has a probability of $\frac{1}{3}$. Therefore, as in the single asset case, the expected rate of return on portfolio I ($\frac{1}{2}$B + $\frac{1}{2}$C) can be calculated as:

$$E(R_p) = \tfrac{1}{3}(0.20) + \tfrac{1}{3}(0.10) + \tfrac{1}{3}(0.15) = 0.15 \text{ or } 15\%$$

Exhibit 6.3 Rates of return on three assets and two portfolios

1	2	3	4	5	6	7
Scenario	Probability	Asset A	Asset B	Asset C	Portfolio I: $\frac{1}{2}B + \frac{1}{2}C$	Portfolio II: $\frac{1}{2}A + \frac{1}{4}C + \frac{1}{4}C$
Growth	$\frac{1}{3}$	0.05	0.10	0.30	0.20[a]	0.125
Stable	$\frac{1}{3}$	0.05	0.05	0.15	0.10	0.075
Recession	$\frac{1}{3}$	0.05	0.15	0.15	0.15	0.10
Portfolio expected rate of return		0.05	0.10	0.20[b]	0.15[c]	0.10

Demonstration of some of the calculations:
[a] $\frac{1}{2}(0.10) + \frac{1}{2}(0.30) = 0.20$
[b] $\frac{1}{3}(0.30) + \frac{1}{3}(0.15) + \frac{1}{3}(0.15) = 0.20$
[c] $\frac{1}{3}(0.20) + \frac{1}{3}(0.10) + \frac{1}{3}(0.15) = 0.15$

Similarly, the expected rate of return on portfolio II ($\frac{1}{2}A + \frac{1}{2}B + \frac{1}{4}C$) is

$$E(R_p) = \tfrac{1}{3}(0.125) + \tfrac{1}{3}(0.075) + \tfrac{1}{3}(0.10) = 0.10 \text{ or } 10\%$$

In the calculation above we first construct the portfolio's rates of return and then calculate the expected return as we did for a single asset in Chapter 5. When a portfolio of assets is involved, we can apply Equation 6.1 to obtain the portfolio expected rate of return.

Let us verify that Equation 6.1 yields the same result, as obtained with direct calculation shown above. For portfolio I given in Exhibit 6.3 we obtain

$$E(R_p) = \tfrac{1}{2}(0.10) + \tfrac{1}{2}(0.20) = 0.15 \text{ or } 15\%$$

and for portfolio II:

$$E(R_p) = \tfrac{1}{2}(0.05) + \tfrac{1}{4}(0.10) + \tfrac{1}{4}(0.20) = 0.10 \text{ or } 10\%$$

Thus, we obtain the same result as before with the direct calculation of expected return on these two portfolios.

In summary, the expected rate of return on a portfolio can be calculated in two ways:

1 First calculate all possible returns on the portfolio, and then calculate its expected rate of return.
2 Calculate the portfolio expected rate of return using Equation 6.1.

Both methods produce the same results. Actually, one method serves as a verification of the other. The expected rate of return on a portfolio, then, is simply the sum of the expected returns of the various individual assets multiplied by the weights of each asset in the portfolio. Obviously, the higher the proportion of wealth (w_i) invested in the ith security, the higher its individual effect on the portfolio's expected return (or mean). In the extreme, when all the wealth (100%) is invested in only one security, the portfolio's mean rate of return is simply the mean rate of return on a selected security.

PRACTICE BOX

Problem

Assume the following historical rates of return for General Motors (GM) and British Petroleum (BP). Calculate the expected rate of return on a portfolio that has one-third of your wealth invested in GM and two-thirds of your wealth invested in BP. First compute the portfolio rates of return (assume that each year is equally probable), and then employ Equation 6.1 to calculate the portfolio's expected rate of return.

Year	GM	BP
1	10%	15%
2	−5%	10%
3	8%	0%
4	15%	−1%

Solution

To answer this problem, first note that the probability of each outcome is $\frac{1}{4}$, because each year is equally probable, and there are four years. Thus, construct the following table:

Year	Rates of return			Portfolio:
	Probability	GM	BP	$\frac{1}{3}$ GM and $\frac{2}{3}$ BP
1	$\frac{1}{4}$	0.10	0.15	0.1333[a]
2	$\frac{1}{4}$	−0.05	0.10	0.05
3	$\frac{1}{4}$	0.08	0.0	0.0267
4	$\frac{1}{4}$	0.15	−0.01	0.0433
Expected rate of return		0.07[b]	0.06[c]	0.0633[d]

[a] $\frac{1}{3}(0.10) + \frac{2}{3}(0.15) = 0.1333$

[b] $\frac{1}{4}(0.10) + \frac{1}{4}(-0.05) + \frac{1}{4}(0.08) + \frac{1}{4}(0.15) = 0.07$

[c] $\frac{1}{4}(0.15) + \frac{1}{4}(0.10) + \frac{1}{4}(0.0) + \frac{1}{4}(-0.01) = 0.06$

[d] $\frac{1}{4}(0.1333) + \frac{1}{4}(0.05) + \frac{1}{4}(0.0267) + \frac{1}{4}(0.0433) = 0.0633$

Using Equation 6.1 and the results in the table, we have

$$E(R_\mathrm{p}) = \tfrac{1}{3}(0.07) + \tfrac{2}{3}(0.06) \cong 0.0633$$

which is equal to the expected rate of return obtained in the table (see the right column and footnote d).

6.4   COVARIANCES AND CORRELATIONS

We showed above how to calculate the expected rate of return on a portfolio. We turn now to calculate the variance of a portfolio. The portfolio's variance depends on the variances of each asset included in the portfolio and, as we have illustrated in Exhibit 6.2, on the degree of dependence between the assets. In Exhibit 6.2 we illustrated three cases: an extreme negative dependence, an extreme positive dependence and independence. Of course, we may have dependence which is not so extreme and we need to know how to measure it. In this section we define a correlation as an index of the degree of dependence

Exhibit 6.4   Rates of return for two stocks over a four-year period

Year	Stock A	Stock B
1	0.05	0.10
2	0.15	0.20
3	−0.05	−0.10
4	0.25	0.60

between the rates of return on two assets. However, to understand the correlation we first need to define a related measure of dependence called covariance.

Whereas the variance measures the variability of the rates of return on a given asset or portfolio, the covariance measures the 'co-movements', or degree of dependency, of the rates of return of two assets. If the rates of return of two assets tend to go up and down together, they have a positive covariance. If one asset's rate of return is relatively high and the other asset's return tends to be relatively low, the covariance is negative.

Exhibit 6.4 gives the rates of return for two stocks over a four-year period. This exhibit shows a positive co-movement or positive covariance between the two stocks. When one stock is doing relatively well, the other is also doing relatively well, and vice versa.

It is easiest to see positive co-movement in a graph. Exhibit 6.5 shows the rates of return for both stocks plotted in a single graph. Each point represents the pair of returns for both stocks in a given year. For example, in year 2, stock A's rate of return was 15% and stock B's rate of return was 20%. When stock A's rate of return is down, so is stock B's rate of return. When stock A's rate of return is up, so is stock B's rate of return. Notice that the pattern moves upward as you look from left to right (see Exhibit 6.5). This upward pattern characterizes a positive covariance which implies a positive dependence. If there is a downward pattern of the points there is a negative dependency (see next Practice Box), and if there is neither an upward nor a downward pattern, the returns on the two stocks are independent.

Exhibit 6.6 demonstrates how to calculate the covariance between the returns of asset A and asset B. To calculate the covariance of R_A and R_B, denoted by $Cov(R_A, R_B)$, we calculate first the deviation of each observation R_A from its mean $E(R_A)$ (see column 4 in Exhibit 6.6), then the deviation of each observed R_B from its mean $E(R_B)$ (see column 5 in Exhibit 6.6). For example, for year 1 the rate of return on stock A is 0.05 and the mean is 0.10; hence the deviation is $0.05 - 0.10 = -0.05$. We then multiply these deviations (see

Exhibit 6.5 A positive dependancy of returns

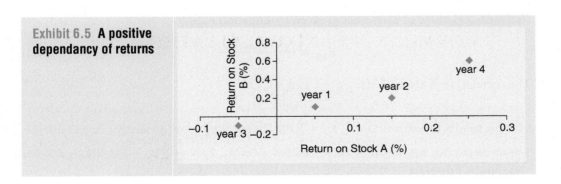

Exhibit 6.6 The covariance calculation

1	2	3	4	5	6
	Rates of return		Deviations from the expected value		
Year	Stock A	Stock B	Stock A	Stock B	(4) × (5)
1	0.05	0.10	−0.05	−0.10	0.005
2	0.15	0.20	0.05	0.00	0.000
3	−0.05	−0.10	−0.15	−0.30	0.045
4	0.25	0.60	0.15	0.40	0.060
Expected value	0.10[a]	0.20[b]			0.0275[c]

[a] (0.05 + 0.15 − 0.05 + 0.25)/4 = 0.10
[b] (0.10 + 0.20 − 0.10 + 0.60)/4 = 0.20
[c] (0.005 + 0.000 + 0.045 + 0.060)/4 = 0.0275

column 6), sum these products and divide by $n = 4$ to obtain $\text{Cov}(R_A, R_B) = 0.0275$. The covariance calculation is summarized in Rule 5.

Rule 5: The covariance of the returns on two stocks A and B, denoted by $\text{Cov}(R_A, R_B)$, is the sum of the products of the deviation of R_A from its mean $E(R_A)$ and the deviation of R_B from its mean $E(R_B)$, multiplied by the probability of obtaining the pair R_A and R_B. Using historical data with an equal probability for say, each year, or in the case where each pair (R_A, R_B) has an equal probability, the covariance is the sum of the product of the deviations divided by n, where n is the number of years (e.g. $n = 4$ in Exhibit 6.6).[3]

Positive and negative covariances tell an investor that the stocks in a portfolio either move together or move in opposite directions, but they do not tell the investor much about the strength of this association. The co-movement of two variables depends, in part, on how volatile the returns are on each asset alone. For example, suppose we find a covariance of 0.003. Is this covariance very large? Is it modestly large? Is it twice as strong as a covariance of 0.0015? If the two variables are not very volatile, then 0.003 may indicate a strong dependency. However, if the two variables are highly volatile, then a covariance of 0.003 may indicate a weak dependency.

By dividing the covariance by the product of the standard deviations of each asset, we can determine the strength of their dependency, or their correlation. The number we obtain is called the *correlation coefficient*, or ρ (Greek letter 'rho'); this is summarized in Rule 6.

Rule 6: The correlation is obtained by dividing the covariance by the product of the standard deviations of each asset as given by Equation 6.2:

$$\rho_{A,B} = \frac{\text{Cov}(R_A, R_B)}{\sigma_A \sigma_B} \tag{6.2}$$

The correlation is always between −1 and +1.

---

[3] Cov can formally be written as $\text{Cov}(R_A, R_B) = \sum_{i=1}^{n} P_i[R_{A_i} - E(R_A)][R_{B_i} - E(R_B)]$ where P_i is the probability to obtain the pair (R_{A_i}, R_{B_i}). When $P_i = 1/n$, it is reduced to $\text{Cov}(R_A, R_B) = \frac{1}{n}\sum_{i=1}^{n}[R_{A_i} - E(R_A)][R_{B_i} - E(R_B)]$ as calculated in Exhibit 6.6.

PRACTICE BOX

Problem

Suppose you are given the following historical data of the returns of stocks A and B. Draw a diagram like Exhibit 6.5 and calculate the covariance between the returns of stocks A and B.

	Rates of return	
Year	Stock A	Stock B
1	0.05	0.20
2	0.15	0.10
3	0.25	−0.10
4	−0.05	0.30

Solution

The figure below shows a tendency for a negative relationship between the returns on the two assets.

When the return on one asset is high, it is relatively low on the other asset. Thus, there is a tendency for the point to decline from left to right, which indicates a negative dependency between the returns on the two stocks.

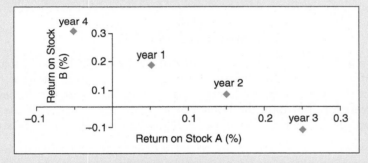

Let us turn to the covariance calculation. Following the procedures illustrated in Exhibit 6.6, construct the following table:

1	2	3	4	5	6
			Deviation from the mean		
Year		Stock A	Stock B	Stock A	Stock B	(4) × (5)
1		0.05	0.20	−0.05	0.075	−0.00375
2		0.15	0.10	0.05	−0.025	−0.00125
3		0.25	−0.10	0.15	−0.225	−0.03375
4		−0.05	0.30	−0.15	−0.175	−0.02625
Expected value		0.10[a]	0.125[b]			

[a] (0.05 + 0.15 + 0.25 − 0.05)/4 = 0.1
[b] (0.2 + 0.1 + (−0.1) + 0.3)/4 = 0.125

Therefore, $\text{Cov}(R_A, R_B) = [(-0.00375) + (-0.00125) + (-0.03375) + (-0.02625)]/4 \cong -0.01625$.

Both covariance and correlation measure the association between the rates of return on two assets. When the covariance is positive, the correlation also will be positive, and vice versa. The advantage of correlation, though, is that it is an absolute number ranging between -1 and $+1$, and it is not in units, such as dollars or percentages. Thus, correlations are directly comparable. For example, if the correlation between rates of return of stocks A and B is 0.8 and the correlation between rates of return of stocks C and D is 0.6, we can state with confidence that stocks A and B have a stronger positive dependency. If there is a *perfect positive association* between rates of return, then the correlation is $+1$. If there is a *perfect negative association*, the correlation is (-1). If the rates of return are unrelated (that is, uncorrelated), the correlation is zero.

Let us calculate the correlation coefficient for the data given in Exhibit 6.6. The standard deviations are as follows:

$$\sigma_A = \left[\frac{(-0.05)^2 + (0.05)^2 + (-0.15)^2 + (0.15)^2}{4} \right]^{\frac{1}{2}} = 0.0125^{\frac{1}{2}} \cong 0.1118$$

$$\sigma_B = \left[\frac{(-0.10)^2 + (0.00)^2 + (-0.30)^2 + (0.40)^2}{4} \right]^{\frac{1}{2}} = 0.065^{\frac{1}{2}} \cong 0.255$$

Thus, the correlation coefficient for stocks A and B, recalling that the covariance was previously found to be $\text{Cov}(R_A, R_B) = 0.0275$ (see Exhibit 6.6), is

$$\rho_{A,B} = \frac{0.0275}{0.1118 \times 0.255} \cong 0.965$$

Thus, we can conclude that the rates of return of stocks A and B have a strong positive dependency of almost $+1$. The correlation is close to a perfect positive one (of $+1$) despite the fact that the covariance is very small. Thus, the covariance is needed to calculate the correlation, but only the latter can measure the intensity of the association between the rates of return on the two assets. (Now look at the Practice Box on p. 181.)

6.5   THE PORTFOLIO VARIANCE

As in the expected return of a portfolio, the variance of a portfolio can also be calculated in two ways. With the first method, the rates of return on the portfolio are calculated for each period (year), and then the variance formula, as in the single asset case, is employed on the portfolio rates of return. Alternatively, one can employ a specific portfolio's variance formula, which will be discussed below, to calculate the portfolio's variance. Both methods are useful. The first method is easy to compute, whereas employing a formula for the portfolio variance calculation has the advantage of demonstrating the relationship between the portfolio variance and individual asset variances as well as the correlation between assets. Using a formula to calculate the portfolio's variance also has an advantage if one wishes to calculate the variance of various portfolios with various diversification strategies (weights). The variance of a portfolio can be calculated *directly* from the portfolio's rates of return, as shown in Exhibit 6.7 on p. 182. To calculate the portfolio's variance directly, one has to first compute the rates of return on the portfolio for each year. For example, in year 1 for portfolio 1, the rate of return is

$$R_p = \tfrac{1}{2}(0.05) + \tfrac{1}{2}(0.10) = 0.075 (\text{Year 1})$$

PRACTICE BOX

Problem

Suppose you are given the following information about stocks A and B. Calculate the correlation coefficient.

State of the economy	Probability	Rates of return	
		R_A	R_B
Growth	$\frac{1}{2}$	0.15	0.30
Stable	$\frac{1}{4}$	0.10	0.05
Recession	$\frac{1}{4}$	0.05	0.10

Solution

Following the procedures outlined in Exhibit 6.6, based on Rule 5 and Equation 6.2, construct the following table:

State of the economy	Probability	R_A	R_B	$R_A - E(R_A)$	$R_B - E(R_B)$	$(R_A - ER_A)$ $(R_B - ER_B)$
Growth	$\frac{1}{2}$	0.15	0.30	0.0375	0.1125	0.00422
Stable	$\frac{1}{4}$	0.10	0.05	−0.0125	−0.1375	0.00172
Recession	$\frac{1}{4}$	0.05	0.10	−0.0625	−0.0875	0.00546
Expected value		0.1125	0.1875			

From Rule 5, the covariance is

$$\text{Cov}(R_A, R_B) = 0.25 \times 0.00422 + 0.25 \times 0.00172 + 0.25 \times 0.00546 = 0.00391$$

And the variances are as follows:

$$\sigma_A^2 = 0.5(0.15 - 0.1125)^2 + 0.25(0.1 - 0.1125)^2 + 0.25(0.05 - 0.1125)^2 = 0.00172$$

$$\sigma_B^2 = 0.5(0.3 - 0.1875)^2 + 0.25(0.05 - 0.1875)^2 + 0.25(0.1 - 0.1875)^2 \cong 0.0130$$

Therefore, the standard deviations are

$$\sigma_A = 0.00172^{\frac{1}{2}} \cong 0.04147$$

$$\sigma_B = 0.0130^{\frac{1}{2}} \cong 0.1140$$

Thus, the correlation coefficient (see Equation 6.2) is

$$\rho_{A,B} = \frac{0.00391}{0.04147 \times 0.1140} \cong 0.827$$

We see that stocks A and B are highly positively correlated. This is not surprising, because when growth occurs, which is likely (a 50% chance), both stocks are up, and when a stable economy or a recession occurs, both stocks are below their means. The relationship is not perfect, hence the correlation is less than +1.

Exhibit 6.7 Rates of return on Assets A and B and on various portfolios

		Individual asset		Portfolios		
				1	2	3
Year	Probability	A	B	$\frac{1}{2}A + \frac{1}{2}B$	$\frac{1}{5}A + \frac{4}{5}B$	$\frac{4}{5}A + \frac{1}{5}B$
1	$\frac{1}{3}$	0.05	0.10	0.075	0.09	0.06
2	$\frac{1}{3}$	0.10	0.05	0.075	0.06	0.09
3	$\frac{1}{3}$	0.15	0.30	0.225	0.27	0.18
Expected rate of return		0.1	0.15	0.125	0.14	0.11
Variance		0.00167[a]	0.01167	0.005[b]	0.0086	0.0026

Demonstrations of some of the calculations:

[a] $\frac{1}{3}(0.05 - 0.10)^2 + \frac{1}{3}(0.10 - 0.10)^2 + \frac{1}{3}(0.15 - 0.10)^2 = 0.00167$

[b] $\frac{1}{3}(0.075 - 0.125)^2 + \frac{1}{3}(0.075 - 0.125)^2 + \frac{1}{3}(0.225 - 0.125)^2 = 0.005$

Similarly, the rates of return of portfolio 1 for years 2 and 3 are found to be

$$R_p = \tfrac{1}{2}(0.10) + \tfrac{1}{2}(0.05) = 0.075 (\text{Year 2})$$

$$R_p = \tfrac{1}{2}(0.15) + \tfrac{1}{2}(0.30) = 0.225 (\text{Year 3})$$

Now the variance of portfolio 1 can be calculated using the single asset formula given in Chapter 5:

$$\sigma_p^2 = \tfrac{1}{3}(0.075 - 0.125)^2 + \tfrac{1}{3}(0.075 - 0.125)^2 + \tfrac{1}{3}(0.225 - 0.125)^2 = 0.005$$

Calculating the portfolio variance by this direct method is straightforward, because the portfolio is treated like any other single asset. Once a series of returns on the portfolio and the corresponding probabilities have been determined, the variance can be easily calculated. (See portfolios 2 and 3 in Exhibit 6.7.)

Calculating first the returns on the portfolio and then the variance of the portfolio as shown in Exhibit 6.7 is very simple. However, for each possible diversification strategy (or weighting of assets A and B), one has first to calculate the portfolio's returns and only then the variance of the portfolio. Moreover, the role of the correlation in determining the portfolio's variance is not transparent. Therefore, we also employ a formula to calculate the portfolio's variance which yields exactly the same result obtained above in Exhibit 6.7, but the role of the correlation in determining the portfolio's variance is explicitly shown.

This formula is given in Equation 6.3 below.

Rule 7: The two-asset portfolio's variance is given by:

$$\sigma_p^2 = w_A^2\,\sigma_A^2 + w_B^2\,\sigma_B^2 + 2w_A w_B \rho_{A,B}\,\sigma_A \sigma_B \qquad (6.3)$$

where w_A and w_B are the weights of these two assets in the portfolio. Because $\rho_{A,B}\,\sigma_A\,\sigma_B$ = Cov(R_A, R_B) (see Equation 6.2), one can use Cov(R_A, R_B) rather than $\rho_{A,B}\,\sigma_A\sigma_B$ in the calculation.

To employ Equation 6.3 on the data of Exhibit 6.7, let us first calculate the covariance of R_A and R_B. The covariance is given by

$$\text{Cov}(R_A, R_B) = [(0.05 - 0.10)(0.10 - 0.15) + (0.10 - 0.10)(0.05 - 0.15)$$
$$+ (0.15 - 0.10)(0.30 - 0.15)]/3 \cong 0.00333$$

Exhibit 6.8 The portfolio variance of the three portfolios in Exhibit 6.7

Portfolio	Allocations (strategy)	$w_A^2 \sigma_A^2$	$w_B^2 \sigma_B^2$	$2w_B w_B Cov(R_A, R_B)$	$= \sigma_p^2$
1	$\frac{1}{2}A + \frac{1}{2}B$	$(\frac{1}{2})^2 \, 0.00167+$	$(\frac{1}{2})^2 \, 0.01167+$	$2(\frac{1}{2})(\frac{1}{2}) \, 0.00333$	$= 0.005$
2	$\frac{1}{5}A + \frac{4}{5}B$	$(\frac{1}{5})^2 \, 0.00167+$	$(\frac{4}{5})^2 \, 0.01167+$	$2(\frac{1}{5})(\frac{4}{5}) \, 0.00333$	$= 0.0086$
3	$\frac{4}{5}A + \frac{1}{5}B$	$(\frac{4}{5})^2 \, 0.00167+$	$(\frac{1}{5})^2 \, 0.01167+$	$2(\frac{4}{5})(\frac{1}{5}) \, 0.00333$	$= 0.0026$

Because $Cov(R_A, R_B) = \rho_{A,B} \, \sigma_A \, \sigma_B$ (see Equation 6.2), we can employ $Cov(R_A, R_B)$ in the portfolio variance as demonstrated in Exhibit 6.8.

Exhibit 6.8 first shows numerically that Equation 6.3 indeed yields the same variance as the direct calculation given in Exhibit 6.7. To be more specific, Exhibit 6.8 demonstrates that this equation is indeed the correct equation for the three portfolios under consideration, as given in Exhibit 6.7. Namely, when we calculate the variance directly from the portfolio's return, as is done in Exhibit 6.7, or by applying Equation 6.3 (see Exhibit 6.8), we get the same results.

In the rest of the book we calculate the portfolio's variance either as demonstrated in Exhibit 6.7 or by employing Equation 6.3. (Now look at the Practice Box on p. 184.)

6.6 THE GAINS FROM DIVERSIFICATION

6.6.1 The gain with two risky assets

Suppose that you have two stocks with the following expected return and standard deviations:

	Stock A	Stock B
Expected return	10%	30%
Standard deviation	20%	40%

The correlation between the return on these two stocks is $\rho_{A,B} = -\frac{1}{2}$. Employing Equation 6.3, the portfolio's variance is given by:

$$\sigma_p^2 = \left[w_A^2(20)^2 + w_B^2(40)^2 + 2w_A w_B(-\tfrac{1}{2}) \times 20 \times 40 \right]^{1/2}$$

One can change the investment proportions w_A and w_B to obtain various possible portfolios with various expected returns and standard deviations. Exhibit 6.9(b) reveals these calculations (see column corresponding to a correlation of $-\frac{1}{2}$) and Exhibit 6.9(c) shows all these portfolios in the mean standard deviation space (see curve 4).

All portfolios located on curve AMB are possible, i.e. there are diversification strategies (w_A, w_B) which yield all the portfolios located on AMB. However, as we can see, only the segment MB is *efficient*, while the segment AM is *inefficient*, and for every inefficient portfolio located on segment AM there is at least one portfolio on segment MB with the same standard deviation and a higher expected rate of return (for example, portfolio C is superior to portfolio C'). Thus, investors will choose either to buy stock B or to diversify between A and B, but not to invest solely in A which is located on the

PRACTICE BOX

Problem

Recalculate the variance of the portfolio $\frac{1}{2}B + \frac{1}{2}C$ (portfolio 1) given in Exhibit 6.3, with the following change: the probability of growth is $\frac{1}{2}$ and the probabilities of a stable economy or a recession are $\frac{1}{4}$ each. Carry out a direct calculation as in Exhibit 6.7, and then apply Equation 6.3. Do you get the same result?

Solution

The calculation by the direct method results in the following (note the change in the expected rate of return):

$$\sigma_p^2 = \tfrac{1}{4}(0.20 - 0.1625)^2 + \tfrac{1}{4}(0.10 - 0.1625)^2 + \tfrac{1}{4}(0.15 - 0.1625)^2 \cong 0.0017$$

where the rates of return on the portfolio

$$E \text{ growth} = 0.20 = \tfrac{1}{2}(0.10) + \tfrac{1}{2}(0.30)$$

$$E \text{ stable} = 0.10 = \tfrac{1}{2}(0.05) + \tfrac{1}{2}(0.15)$$

$$E \text{ recession} = 0.15 = \tfrac{1}{2}(0.15) + \tfrac{1}{2}(0.15)$$

and portfolio 1's expected rate of return is $\frac{1}{2}(0.20) + \frac{1}{4}(0.10) + \frac{1}{4}(0.15) = 0.1625$.

Using Equation 6.3, we first have to find the variances and covariances with the new probabilities. We find:

$$\sigma_B^2 = \tfrac{1}{2}(0.10 - 0.10)^2 + \tfrac{1}{4}(0.05 - 0.10)^2 + \tfrac{1}{4}(0.15 - 0.10)^2 = 0.00125$$
$$\sigma_C^2 = \tfrac{1}{2}(0.30 - 0.225)^2 + \tfrac{1}{4}(0.15 - 0.225)^2 \cong 0.00563$$
$$\text{Cov}(R_B, R_C) = \tfrac{1}{2}[(0.10 - 0.10)(0.30 - 0.20)] + \tfrac{1}{4}[(0.05 - 0.10)(0.15 - 0.20)]$$
$$+ \tfrac{1}{4}[(0.15 - 0.10)(0.15 - 0.20)] = 0$$

hence $\rho_{A,B}$

$= 0$ (see Equation 6.2).

Substituting these results into Equation 6.3, we have

$$\sigma_p^2 = (\tfrac{1}{2})^2 0.00125 + (\tfrac{1}{2})^2 0.00563 + 2 \times \tfrac{1}{2} \times \tfrac{1}{2} \times 0$$
$$= 0.0003 + 0.0014 = 0.0017$$

inefficient frontier. In Exhibit 6.9(b) we add a few columns where the portfolio standard deviation is calculated under various assertions regarding $\rho_{A,B} = -1, \frac{1}{2}, 0$ or 1.

As we can see from Exhibit 6.9(c) all efficient frontiers form a parabola, apart from the case of a perfect negative and perfect positive correlation. In all cases M denotes the portfolio with the minimum possible standard deviation, called the *minimum variance portfolio* or MVP.[4] We can conclude the following from Exhibits 6.9(b) and (c):

1 As expected, the lower the correlation the more to the left is the location of the efficient frontier. This implies that the lower the correlation, the greater the gain from diversification.

2 If $\rho_{A,B} = -1$, we can reduce the portfolio risk to zero if the appropriate investment proportions are selected.

---

[4] The MVP is obtained by $w_A = \dfrac{\sigma_A^2 - \sigma_A \sigma_B \rho_{A,B}}{\sigma_A^2 + \sigma_B^2 - 2\sigma_A \sigma_B \rho_{A,B}}$

Exhibit 6.9 The efficient frontier and the efficient curve for various correlations

(a) The data

	Mean	Standard deviation
Stock A	0.1	0.2
Stock B	0.3	0.4

(b) The means and standard deviations of various portfolios

W_A	W_B	Portfolio mean	Portfolio standard deviation				
			Correlation				
			−1	−0.5	0	0.5	1
0	1	0.30	0.400	0.400	0.400	0.400	0.400
0.1	0.9	0.28	0.340	0.350	0.361	0.370	0.380
0.2	0.8	0.26	0.280	0.302	0.322	0.342	0.360
0.3	0.7	0.24	0.220	0.255	0.286	0.314	0.340
0.4	0.6	0.22	0.160	0.212	0.253	0.288	0.320
0.5	0.5	0.20	0.100	0.173	0.224	0.265	0.300
0.6	0.4	0.18	0.040	0.144	0.200	0.243	0.280
0.7	0.3	0.16	0.020	0.131	0.184	0.225	0.260
0.8	0.2	0.14	0.080	0.139	0.179	0.212	0.240
0.9	0.1	0.12	0.140	0.164	0.184	0.203	0.220
1	0	0.10	0.200	0.200	0.200	0.200	0.200

(c) The efficient frontier for various correlations

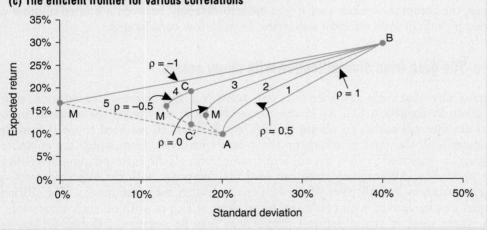

To see the latter point, recall that the portfolio variance in the case of $\rho_{A,B} = -1$ is reduced to (see Equation 6.3):

$$\sigma_p^2 = w_A^2\sigma_A^2 + w_B^2\sigma_B^2 - 2w_Aw_B\sigma_A\sigma_B$$

which can be rewritten as

$$\sigma_p^2 = (w_A\sigma_A - w_B\sigma_B)^2, \text{ or } \sigma_p = w_A\sigma_A - w_B\sigma_B$$

To have $\sigma_p = 0$ we must have

$$w_A\sigma_A = w_B\sigma_B, \text{ or } \frac{w_A}{w_B} = \frac{\sigma_B}{\sigma_A}$$

In our specific example,

$$\sigma_B = 40\% \text{ and } \sigma_A = 20\%, \text{ hence } \frac{w_A}{w_B} = \frac{40\%}{20\%} = 2$$

Because $w_B + w_A = 1$ we have

$$\frac{w_A}{1 - w_A} = 2, \text{ or } w_A = 2 - 2w_A, \text{ or } 3w_A = 2; \text{ hence } w_A = \tfrac{2}{3} \text{ and } w_B = \tfrac{1}{3}.$$

Indeed, for this investment proportion we obtain:[5]

$$\sigma_p^2 = (\tfrac{2}{3})^2 \times 20^2 + (\tfrac{1}{3})^2 \times 40^2 - 2(\tfrac{2}{3})(\tfrac{1}{3})(-1) \times 20 \times 40$$

$$= \frac{4}{9} \times 400 + \frac{1}{9} \times 1600 + \left(-\frac{4}{9}\right) \times 20 \times 40$$

$$= \frac{1600}{9} + \frac{1600}{9} - \frac{3200}{9} = 0$$

Exhibit 6.10 presents the efficient frontier of two pairs: General Motors (GM) and Ford (F), and alternatively GM and Philip Morris (MO). As can be expected, the correlation between GM and Ford is positive and high ($\rho = 0.73$) while it is negative (-0.27) between GM and MO. Indeed, the gain from diversification is much larger when one diversifies between stocks of unrelated industries (GM and MO). We see that for almost any portfolio combination of Ford and GM there is a better portfolio (with the same mean and a lower risk) combined of MO and GM (compare portfolios C and C'). Hence, the common wisdom that if you have to diversify between a limited number of stocks, pick them from different industries, i.e. with low correlations.

6.6.2 The gain from diversification with many assets

Suppose now that there are more than two assets (e.g. five assets whose rates of return are given in Exhibit 6.11). As in the two-assets case, we obtain the efficient set of portfolio diversification. To obtain the efficient frontier, all we need to do is feed the computer with the rates of return on the n assets involved, from which the computer program is employed to yield the efficient frontier with all the corresponding diversification portfolios. Alternatively, one can feed the computer with the expected rates of return, variances and all pairs of correlations to obtain the same results. The efficient frontier can be derived with constraint of no short selling or with no such constraint, a case where some of the investment proportions may be negative. Exhibits 6.11(a)–(e) below show the rates of return on five stocks for the years 1989–98 (the input to the efficient frontier calculation) as well as the computer output: the investment proportions of five points on the frontier (one can add any number of points) and the resulting efficient frontier curve, with and without short sales.

---

[5] If the correlation is $+1$, one can also achieve zero portfolio variance with the proportions $\frac{w_A}{w_B} = -\frac{\sigma_B}{\sigma_A}$ (in this case, one's assets must be sold short to obtain a zero variance portfolio).

Exhibit 6.10 Two efficient frontiers and two-stocks portfolio

(a) The data

	GM	Ford	Philip Morris
Expected return	0.156	0.24	0.249
Standard deviation	0.3	0.37	0.263

	Correlation
$R_{(GM,F)}$	0.73
$R_{(GM,MO)}$	−0.27

(b) The efficient frontiers

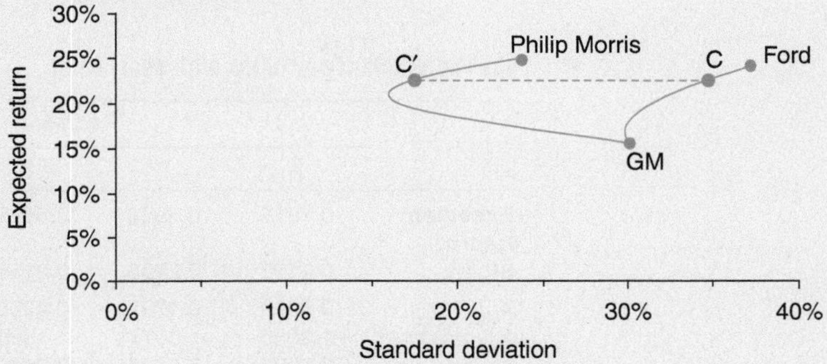

6.6.3 The gain from diversification due to the riskless asset

Suppose that you can diversify between asset A and the riskless asset whose rate of return is r. Thus, the expected rate of return on such a portfolio is

$$E(R_p) = w_A E(A) + w_r r$$

where $w_A + w_r = 1$. Because r is constant, it has a zero variance and zero correlation with R_A; hence by Equation 6.3 the portfolio variance $\sigma^2_{R_p}$ is reduced to:

$$\sigma^2_{R_p} = w^2_A \sigma^2_A$$

Therefore, the standard deviation is $\sigma_{R_p} = w_A \sigma_A$.

By changing the investment proportion w_A, many portfolios with $E(R_p)$ and σ_{R_p} are obtained. Are these portfolios located on a curve as in Exhibit 6.11(e)? No! Because r is constant, all these portfolios are located on a straight line. To see this, employ the portfolio standard deviation formula to isolate $w_A = \sigma_{R_p}/\sigma_A$ and substitute it in the expected return formula to obtain

$$E(R_p) = \left[\frac{\sigma_{R_p}}{\sigma_A}\right] \times E(A) + \left(1 - \frac{\sigma_{R_p}}{\sigma_A}\right) \times r$$

(recall that $w_r = 1 - w_A = 1 - \dfrac{\sigma_{R_p}}{\sigma_A}$), which can be rewritten as:

$$E(R_p) = r + \frac{E(A) - r}{\sigma_A} \sigma_{R_p}$$

Exhibit 6.11

The efficient frontiers with and without short sales

(a) Rates of return

Year	UK	AMR	GE	MO	GM
1989	−0.195	−0.105	0.328	0.439	−0.024
1990	−0.094	0.023	0.062	0.521	−0.063
1991	0.282	0.292	0.266	0.412	−0.078
1992	0.923	−0.110	0.102	0.008	0.212
1993	0.562	0.139	0.316	−0.154	0.653
1994	0.027	−0.218	−0.015	0.064	−0.355
1995	0.690	0.354	0.532	0.604	0.388
1996	0.096	0.059	0.378	0.338	0.155
1997	−0.018	0.571	0.523	0.086	0.076
1998	−0.080	−0.071	0.373	0.174	0.595
Mean	0.219	0.094	0.286	0.249	0.156
SD	0.361	0.234	0.176	0.236	0.300

(b) The efficient portfolios with short sales

	Portfolio				
	1	2	3	4	5
Expected return	0.7815	0.6822	0.5629	0.4238	0.2648
Sigma	0.3198	0.2706	0.2155	0.1622	0.1342
X_{UK}	0.5309	0.4797	0.4028	0.3131	0.2106
X_{AMR}	−1.9085	−1.6077	−1.1565	−0.6301	−0.0284
X_{GE}	3.5580	3.0627	2.3198	1.4530	0.4625
X_{MO}	−0.0849	−0.0181	0.0822	0.1992	0.3329
X_{GM}	−1.0955	−0.9166	−0.6483	−0.3352	0.0225
Total	1	1	1	1	1

(c) The efficient frontier with short sales

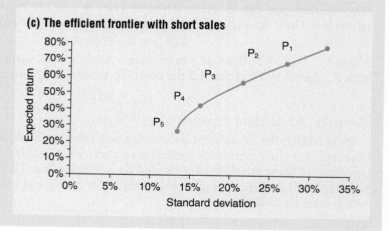

This is a straight-line formula with an intercept r with the vertical axis and a slope $[(E(A) − r]/\sigma_A$. All portfolios located on such a line with (R_p, σ_{R_p}) can be achieved by changing w_A. Exhibit 6.12 demonstrates such a line connecting asset A and the riskless asset r.

Exhibit 6.11 (continued)

(d) The efficient portfolios without short sales

	Portfolio					
	1	2	3	4	5	6
Expected return	0.2669	0.2676	0.2696	0.2739	0.2759	0.2864
Sigma	0.1366	0.1372	0.1393	0.1456	0.1491	0.1763
X_{UK}	0.1415	0.1355	0.1176	0.0797	0.0629	0.0000
X_{AMR}	0.0000	0.0000	0.0000	0.0000	0.0000	0.0000
X_{GE}	0.5904	0.6041	0.6444	0.7298	0.7675	1.0000
X_{MO}	0.2681	0.2604	0.2380	0.1905	0.1696	0.0000
X_{GM}	0.0000	0.0000	0.0000	0.0000	0.0000	0.0000
Total	1	1	1	1	1	1

(e) The efficient frontier without short sales

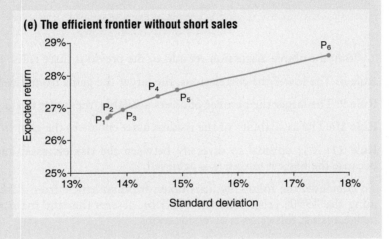

Suppose now that there is another asset B which can be mixed with the riskless asset. It is easy to see that a diversification between B and r is better than a diversification of A and r because a line with a higher slope is achieved. Thus, for any portfolio located on line rA there is a better portfolio on line rB (compare portfolios C′ and C).

By the same logic the investor's goal is to find a line with the maximum slope. Therefore, the best strategy is to diversify between portfolio m and r because by such a diversification the line with the highest possible slope is obtained. With portfolio m we obtain the line:

$$E(R_p) = r + \frac{E(m) - r}{\sigma_m} \sigma_p. \tag{6.4}$$

This line is called the *capital market line* (CML), and portfolio m, the tangency portfolio of the efficient frontier and the straight line rising from point r, is called the *market portfolio*. As we can see, for any portfolio located on the efficient frontier OMF (see Exhibit 6.12) there is a better portfolio on line $rr′$ (e.g. portfolio D′ dominates portfolio D). Hence, by adding the riskless asset, the investor's welfare is enhanced.

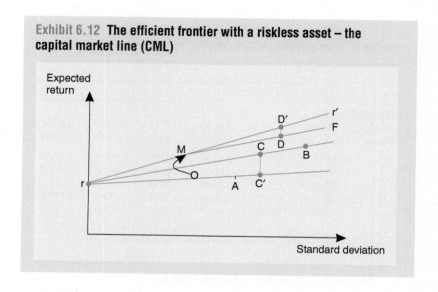

Exhibit 6.12 The efficient frontier with a riskless asset – the capital market line (CML)

From the above discussion we add to the previous three rules, the following rules:

Rule 8: The lower the correlations, the larger the gains from diversification.

Rule 9: The larger the number of assets available, the larger the gain from diversification.

Rule 10: The availability of the riskless asset enhances the gain from diversification.

Rule 11: It is optimal to diversify between the riskless asset and the market portfolio because the highest tangency is achieved.

To conclude, the following lines taken from an article from *Risk Analysis*, while examining the 1990s crisis (Russia, Mexico), asserts that the main tool to use in order to hedge against this crisis is diversification:

'....we must realize that some crises will occur without even a reasonable basis to antici-pate their possibility. In such cases, the surest source of protection is diversification. While history indicates that periodic crises are inevitable, it also indicates that they don't strike all markets and all regions at the same time. The key is to be sure that no one crisis event, no matter how unlikely, can do irreparable damage to one's institution. But be aware that correlations generally behave differently in a crisis than in day-to-day market fluctuations. Psychological contagion is a product of crisis and its behaviour is not well represented by data from more normal times. As a result, a critical eye is needed to assure that apparent diversification will hold up when markets experience extreme stress.'

Source: Risk Analysis, December 1999, p. 57.

SUMMARY

■ *Explain the difference between asset risk when held alone and asset risk when held in a portfolio.*

When an asset is held with other assets in a portfolio, that asset's risk depends not only on the asset's variance but also on the degree of dependency with other assets. When two assets are perfectly negatively correlated, each asset could be very risky in isolation, but when placed together with the correct weights, a riskless portfolio can be created. The dependency among assets plays an important role in determining the portfolio's risk and hence in determining the risk premium.

■ *Discuss the expected rate of return and variance of a portfolio.*
The expected rate of return of a portfolio is the sum of the weights (proportions) invested in an asset times the expected return on that asset, where we sum for all assets. The formula for the variance of a portfolio is much more complicated: the variance of a portfolio is a function of the proportions invested in each asset, the variance of each asset, and the covariances (or correlations) among assets.

■ *Explain covariances and correlation coefficients between assets.*
Covariances (or correlation coefficients) measure the degree of dependency between two assets. The correlation coefficient, ρ, is a number such that $-1 \le \rho \le 1$: the higher the ρ, the higher the degree of dependency between the assets. The covariance (or correlation) plays a major role in determining a portfolio's variance.

■ *Explain the role of correlation within a portfolio.*
When everything else is held constant, the lower the correlation of each pair of assets included in a portfolio, the lower the portfolio's variance will be. Low variance is an attractive feature to risk-averse investors.

■ *Explain the effect of the number of assets on the gain from diversification.*
The larger the number of assets in the portfolio, the larger the gain from diversification.

■ *Explain the importance of the riskless asset in deriving the CML.*
Diversification between the riskless asset and a risky asset creates a straight line from which each investor could select the portfolio. The line with the highest slope is called the capital market line (CML).

KEY TERMS

Correlation	Market portfolio	Portfolio
Covariance	Minimum variance	Portfolio expected return
Efficient frontier	portfolio (MVP)	Variance

QUESTIONS

6.1   Suppose you are given the following information regarding the rates of return on three assets:

		Asset		
State of the economy	Scenario probability	A	B	C
1	$\frac{1}{3}$	5%	10%	30%
2	$\frac{1}{3}$	5	5	15
3	$\frac{1}{3}$	5	15	15

Calculate the expected return, variance and standard deviation for each asset, as well as the covariances and correlation coefficients.

The following are daily price data for four stocks, which will be used for Questions 2 through 5.

Day	A	B	C	D
1	616.4000	23.0000	74.6250	59.0000
2	617.4600	22.5000	74.0000	58.1250
3	621.3200	22.8750	74.8750	59.8750
4	614.1600	22.6250	75.0000	58.7500
5	625.6200	22.1250	74.0000	57.3750

6.2   Calculate the daily rates of return for Stocks A, B, C and D.

6.3   Calculate the average rate of return, variance and standard deviation for Stocks A, B and C.

6.4   Calculate the covariance and correlation coefficient for Stocks B and C.

6.5   Suppose you had \$100,000 to invest in B and C. Calculate the expected rate of return and standard deviation of a portfolio in which an equal dollar amount is invested in each security.

6.6   Suppose you invested 30% in Asset A, which returned 40%; invested 25% in Asset B, which returned -10%; and invested 45% in Asset C, which returned 15%. What was the rate of return on the portfolio?

6.7   Repeat Question 6.6, except assume that instead of rates of return, the returns given are *expected* rates of return. Thus, calculate the expected rate of return on this portfolio.

6.8   'Correlation does not really reduce the risk of a portfolio, because the underlying securities remain risky.' Evaluate this statement, and defend your answer using a portfolio of two securities with identical standard deviations of 30% and in which 50% is invested in each security.

6.9   Prove that the covariance of Asset X with $\frac{1}{2}X$ is equal to one-half the variance of Asset X.

6.10   Calculate the variance of a portfolio that is equally divided among four uncorrelated assets with standard deviation of 10%, 20%, 30% and 40%.

6.11   The following are the rates of return on Assets A and B:

Year	R_A	R_B
1	-10%	$+10\%$
2	20	17
3	-2	0
4	4	8
5	12	19

(a) What is the rate of return on the portfolio if Year 4 occurs and when $w_A = \frac{1}{5}$ and $w_B = \frac{4}{5}$? How would you change your answer if the investment weights were $w_A = \frac{1}{2}$ and $w_B = \frac{1}{2}$?

(b) If each year has a probability of $\frac{1}{5}$, calculate the portfolio mean and variance when $w_A = \frac{1}{2}$ and $w_B = \frac{1}{2}$. First do the calculations by constructing the portfolio rates of return and calculating the mean and variance of these rates of return. Then do the calculations by employing Equation 6.3 in the text. Which method is easier?

6.12   You have two stocks, A and B, with $\sigma_A = 10\%$ and $\sigma_B = 20\%$. The investment proportions in a portfolio are $w_A = w_B = \frac{1}{2}$. It is known that the portfolio standard deviation is $\sigma_p = 5\%$. What is the covariance, or $Cov(R_A, R_B)$?

6.13 You have two stocks with the following rates of return:

Year	R_A	R_B
1	+10%	+10%
2	−5	−5
3	15	15

The probability of each year is $\frac{1}{3}$.

(a) Calculate the correlation between Stock A and Stock B.
(b) Calculate the variance of a portfolio composed of $w_A = \frac{1}{2}$ and $w_B = \frac{1}{2}$. Calculate the variance of a portfolio composed of $w_A = \frac{1}{5}$ and $w_B = \frac{4}{5}$. Explain your results.

SELECTED REFERENCES

See Chapter 5.

Chapter 7

INTEREST RATES AND BOND VALUATION

Learning objectives

After studying this chapter you should be able to:

1 Construct and interpret a yield curve.

2 Use the bond pricing equation to find bond prices and bond yields.

3 Summarize the theories that explain the shape and level of yield curves.

4 Describe the behaviour of the spread over Treasuries.

5 Describe the impact of the call feature and the convertible feature on bond prices.

INVESTMENT IN THE NEWS

Dark day for shares boosts bonds

Government bonds rose in the US and Europe yesterday as investors continued to pull money out of equity markets and shift it to the safety of government debt.

In midday trading on Wall Street, the 10-year **US** Treasury was up $\frac{19}{32}$ to $102\frac{11}{32}$, pushing its yield down to 4.69 per cent. The 30-year bond rose $\frac{27}{32}$ to $102\frac{7}{32}$, yielding 5.22 per cent, while the two-year note gained $\frac{5}{32}$ to $100\frac{29}{32}$, yielding 4.12 per cent.

The buying was triggered by another dark day for equity markets. The Dow Jones Industrial Average was down 305 points at mid-day, falling into 'bear market' territory, while the Nasdaq lost 29 points.

The losses piled up as disappointment lingered over the Federal Reserve's cutting short-term interest rates by only 50 basis points on Tuesday. Many investors had predicted the Fed would cut rates by 75bp amid the turmoil in equity markets.

Bond prices were also boosted by the Treasury's buy-back of $1.75bn in long-term securities as part of its plan to reduce the national debt.

Euro-zone government bond prices also surged yesterday, pushing yields to their lowest in two years.

Bond investors benefited from a combination of weak equity prices and the expectation of an interest rate cut from the European Central Bank.

Following the release of weak German Ifo index data on Wednesday, French economic growth was revised downwards.

There were also signs of weakening consumer confidence in the Netherlands. Some analysts expect a rate cut from the European Central Bank within weeks, following comments by its president, Wim Duisenberg, about the impact of the US slowdown.

The 10-year **German bund** future rose 52 to 110.40 in heavy trading volumes. In the crash market the two-year **schatz** yield fell 10.8bp to 4.059 per cent, while the 10-year bund yield fell 5.9bp to 4.60 per cent. These are the lowest yields since late 1999.

▶

In the UK, **gilt** prices also rose as the FTSE 100 index followed US stock markets and fell to a 29-month low.

Investors are expecting an interest rate cut from the Bank of England after the Confederation of British Industry said that the slow-down of the US economy could have a more serious impact on the UK than previously thought.

In contrast, Japanese government bond prices fell yesterday on weak demand at a auction of 10-year **JGBs** with a record low coupon.

The government sold ¥1,005bn of 10-year JGBs with a 1.1 per cent coupon, resulting in 1.96 bids per value, down from 2.38 registered at last month's auction of 10-year debt with a 1.4 per cent coupon. The lowest price at Thursday's auction was 110.65.

The leading June JGB futures contract fell to 140.15 after the auction results were released. It closed at 140.42, down 0.18 from Wednesday. The yield on the benchmark 10-year cash JGB rose 0.020 to 1.065 per cent.

Source: Financial Times, 23 March 2001, p. 28.

The *Investment in the news* article illustrates the important relationship between various variables: equity markets, changes in interest rate, gains or losses to investors in bonds, the length of the maturity of bonds and the relative performance of corporate and government bonds. In this chapter, we will discuss the relationship between these variables. In particular, we focus on the relationship between interest rates, a bond's yield (called yield to maturity) and the fluctuations of the bond's price as the yield to maturity changes. We will show that the longer the maturity, the larger the risk involved in the investment in bonds.

7.1   THE YIELD CURVE

7.1.1 The yield

A bond represents borrowing by the bond's issuer and saving by the bond's purchaser. The interest earned on a bond if held to its maturity is called the yield to maturity. The demand and supply for bonds with given coupons and par values determine their market prices. A bond's market price, in turn, determines the yield to maturity, which is the percentage profit for the bond buyer and the percentage cost to the bond seller.

Yield to maturity is the annualized discount rate that makes the present value of future cash flows just equal to the current price of the bond. Mathematically, it is calculated from the value of y (that is, the internal rate of return of the bond) in the following equation:

$$P = \sum_{t=1}^{n} \frac{C}{(1 + y)^t} + \frac{\text{Par}}{(1 + y)^n} \tag{7.1}$$

where C is the coupon payment each period, n is the number of periods to maturity, Par is the face value of the bond (payment at maturity), and P is the current market price of the bond.

The yield to maturity is found by applying Rule 1.

Rule 1: Write the cash flow of the bond and calculate the internal rate of return (IRR) of this cash flow (see Appendix A at the end of the book for IRR calculation). The IRR of this cash flow is the bond's yield to maturity. For zero coupon bonds, $C = 0$, hence Equation 7.1 is reduced to:

$$P = \frac{\text{Par}}{(1 + y)^n} \qquad (7.1)'$$

and for a perpetuity bond the par is never paid back and Equation (7.1) is reduced[1] to:

$$P = \sum_{t=1}^{\infty} \frac{C}{(1 + y)^t} = \frac{C}{y} \qquad (7.1)''$$

If coupons are paid annually, then y is the yield to maturity. If coupons are paid semiannually, then the yield to maturity is $(1 + y)^2 - 1$. Thus, the yield to maturity is given on an annual basis. In order to compare profitability on bonds, it is common to state the yield on an annualized basis. Unless stated otherwise, all yields we refer to in the rest of the chapter as well as in the next chapter are annual yields. Because y is the internal rate of return of the bonds, it measures the profit, in percent, to the bondholder provided that the bond is held to maturity. However, if the bond is not held to maturity, the realized rate of return to the bondholder can be very different from the other yield. From Equation 7.1, it seems that lenders, i.e. bond buyers, should choose to lend for time to maturity n with the highest yield to maturity y, because by such a lending policy they obtain the highest annual interest rate (that is, the highest internal rate of return on their investment). For example, the *Financial Times* on 25 January 2002 reported a yield of 4.60% on December 2003 maturity Treasury bonds and a 4.64% yield on 30-year maturity Treasury bonds. So, should all invest in the high-yield bond? Although this is a tempting conclusion, it is generally wrong, because the lending and borrowing decisions are functions not only of the yield but also of the risk of such borrowing – lending activities. The following discussion will elaborate on this point.

The yield curve generally refers to the yield on government bonds, which are default-free. Even in the absence of a risk of bankruptcy, as the time to maturity (n) changes, the yield to maturity (y) that solves Equation 7.1 may change. The yield curve is the relationship between the yield to maturity and the time to maturity. That is, ideally C and Par are held constant, and P and y change as n changes.

Exhibit 7.1 illustrates some recent yield curves for US Treasury securities. Exhibit 7.1(a) shows the yield curve for US Treasury securities on 5 August 1997, when it was sloping upwards. The horizontal axis is time to maturity (n), and the vertical axis is yield to maturity (y). Exhibit 7.1(b) shows a flat yield curve as observed on 29 December 1989, and Exhibit 7.1(c) shows an *inverted* yield curve as observed on 31 December 1980, where the yield decreases as the maturity increases. These graphs show that the yield curve can have a wide variety of shapes.

Analysts seek to determine why bonds of different maturities have different yields to maturity (or why equilibrium interest rates are different for different maturities) and in particular the risk involved with each maturity. That is, they try to determine what factors influence the shape of the yield curve. The next section explains these factors.

---

[1] The present value of a perpetuity C is C/y.

Exhibit 7.1 Examples of actual yield curves
(These curves are based only on the most actively traded issues. Market yields on coupon issues due in less than three months are excluded)

(a) Upward-sloping yield curve – yields of Treasury securities, 5 August 1997 (based on closing quotations)

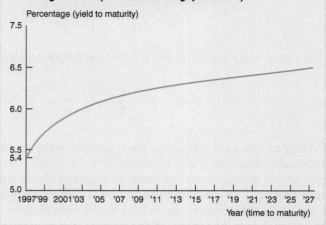

(b) Flat yield curve – yields of Treasury securities, 29 December 1989 (based on closing bid quotations)

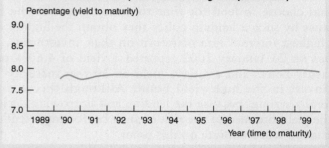

(c) Inverted yield curve – yields of Treasury securities, 31 December 1980 (based on closing bid quotations)

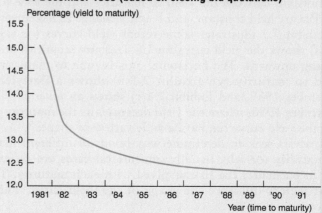

Source: US Treasury Bulletin (Washington, DC: Department of the Treasury, various issues).

7.1.2 **The risk**

Investing in the bond market is not without risks. These risks are a function of the time to maturity of the bond relative to the investor's time horizon. The lender must choose between investing in short-term bonds or long-term bonds. Consider the choices facing young parents who want to invest or lend their money to ensure that their children will have funds to attend college in 15 years' time. Should the parents invest in short-term or long-term bonds? Changing interest rates complicate this decision. If the parents invest over a short period, then they may have to reinvest the money in the near future at a different interest rate, which may be lower. This risk of declining interest rates is known as reinvestment risk – the risk to bondholders that in the future they will not be able to reinvest the cash flows they receive from their investment at the same rate they receive today. Of course if one invests in zero-coupon bonds, and no interest is paid, there is no reinvestment risk.

If long-term lenders expect an increase in interest rates in the future, they should lend for the short term only and reinvest later at a higher interest rate. By purchasing long-term bonds, they might miss out on the higher rates should interest rates go up. Long-term bonds would be a poor investment choice when interest rates rose, because the bond's price would decline as a result of an increase in the interest rate. The longer the length to maturity of a bond, the greater the risk exposure to large price declines. To see this, return to Equation 7.1. As y increases, then the larger is n, the larger is the decline in P, thus the larger is the loss to the investor who holds these bonds. This exposure to price declines is known as price risk. Bond investors experience price risk because increases in interest rates decrease a bond's price. The opposite effect occurs if the investor expects interest rates to fall. In this case, the lender could benefit by investing in long-term bonds and locking in the current higher interest rate.

To summarize, price risk is the negative effect of a possible increase in interest rates on a bond's value; that is, when rates rise, bond prices fall. Reinvestment risk is the negative effect of a decline in interest rates on the cash flows received when those cash flows must be reinvested at a lower interest rate; that is, when interest rates fall, the interest rate available for future investment of cash flows is lower.

Let's turn to the borrower's viewpoint. Assume that a borrower – maybe a corporation – needs money for long-term investment in profitable capital projects. The corporation faces the choice of borrowing for either a short-term or a long-term period. If a corporation chooses a short-term bond, it may have to refinance the bond at higher interest rates. Note that this is exactly opposite to the problem faced by lenders. If the corporation chooses the long-term bond and interest rates fall, the corporation is paying a higher borrowing rate than would have been required if the financing had been short term.

So far, we have assumed that the lender wanted to invest for a long-term period and the borrower needed the money for a long-term period. In reality, lenders and borrowers want to lend and borrow for varying lengths of time. In addition, the needs of borrowers and lenders change over time. These varied needs within the economy create the demand and supply for bonds of varying maturities. The demand and supply for bonds with different maturities determine the yield curve. For example, if pension funds wish to invest in 30-year maturities, and there is a little supply of this bond, the bond price will go up and the yield will go down (see Equation 7.1). Also, individual long-term borrowers and lenders have different preferences regarding risk and different expectations regarding changes in future interest rates. These are the factors that influence the shape of the yield curve. The next section discusses the various hypotheses regarding the role these factors have in determining the shape of the yield curve.

7.2   EXPLAINING THE SHAPE OF THE YIELD CURVE

The behavior of the yield curve, which is also known as the term structure of interest rates, has certain well-known patterns. First, short-term yields are generally more variable than long-term yields. Second, the yield curve is usually upward sloping. Third, inverted or declining yield curves typically occur when the overall level of interest rates is relatively high.

Several hypotheses have been developed in an attempt to explain different yield curve shapes. This section reviews each hypothesis and briefly highlights its strengths and weaknesses. However, first it is necessary to define and explain several concepts related to bonds that are used in the explanation of the shape of the yield curve.

7.2.1   Spot rates, forward rates, forward contracts and holding period rates

The spot rate is the yield to maturity of a zero-coupon bond that has a stated maturity, where zero-coupon bonds are sold at a discount from their par value and pay no coupons. For example, if a one-year bond is trading at $90.9 with $100 par value, we say the spot rate is about 10%, or [($100 − $90.9)/$90.9] × 100.

The forward rate is the yield to maturity of a zero-coupon bond that an investor agrees to purchase at some future specified date. For example, an investor agrees today to purchase *in one year* at $89.286 a bond that has one year to maturity with a par value of $100. In this case there is no cash flow today, and in one year the investor will pay $89.286 for the bond (regardless of its current market price in a year) and will receive $100 two years from today (or one year from the bond purchase date). The forward rate is about 12%, or [($100 − $89.286)/$89.286] × 100. The forward rates can be used in interpreting the information contained in the yield curve, as will be shown later.

A concept related to the forward rate is the forward contract, which is an agreement between a buyer and a seller to trade something in the future at a price negotiated today. A forward contract is obligatory to both the buyer and the seller. For example, a forward contract to buy $1 million of par value of Treasury bills at a 6% discount rate (which determines the bond's price) in six months obligates the buyer to purchase the T-bills at a 6% discount rate; it also obligates the seller to sell the T-bills at the same price. Suppose T-bills are selling for a 7% discount rate in six months when the forward contract matures and the buyer delivers the bills. This means that the T-bills have a lower market price. Recall that when interest rates are up, bond prices are down (that is, there is an inverse relationship between bond prices and yields, see Equation 7.1: when y goes up, p becomes lower). The seller will profit from this transaction, and the buyer will lose, because the buyer is obligated to purchase the T-bills at 6% despite the fact that a 7% rate is available in the market. At a 7% rate, the buyer could purchase the T-bills at the lower market price, but the buyer must buy them at the 6% rate (a higher price) to comply with the forward contract. A range of actively traded forward contracts are available in interest rates, currencies and energy products (such as crude oil or natural gas): see Chapter 12.

Exhibit 7.2 Spot and forward rates for annually compounded, zero-coupon bonds

Maturity (in years, n)	Spot rate (R_n)	Forward rate (f_n) (a contract which starts at year $n-1$ and matures at year n)[a]
1	5%	–
2	5.8	6.606%
3	6.3	7.307
4	6.4	6.701
5	6.45	6.650

[a] $f_2 = [(1 + R_2)^2/(1 + R_1)] - 1 = (1 + 0.058)^2/(1 + 0.05) - 1 \cong 0.06606$
$f_3 = [(1 + R_3)^3/(1 + R_2)^2] - 1 = (1 + 0.063)^3/(1 + 0.058)^2 - 1 \cong 0.07307$
$f_4 = [(1 + R_4)^4/(1 + R_3)^3] - 1 = (1 + 0.064)^4/(1 + 0.063)^3 - 1 \cong 0.06701$
$f_5 = [(1 + R_5)^5/(1 + R_4)^4] - 1 = (1 + 0.0645)^5/(1 + 0.064)^4 - 1 \cong 0.06650$

The forward interest rates can be derived from the spot rates of bonds with various maturities.[2] To see this, consider the numerical example in Exhibit 7.2. The data in the table are spot and forward rates for annually compounded, zero-coupon bonds.[3] The spot and forward rates in this exhibit are equilibrium rates, i.e. the investor is indifferent between various investment strategies, as explained below. A yield curve plotted from these data would slope upwards from 5% for one-year bonds to 6.45% for five-year bonds.

Suppose we wish to invest for two years. Consider the following investment strategies:

- Strategy 1. Invest in a two-year zero-coupon bond and earn 5.8%.
- Strategy 2. Invest in a one-year zero-coupon bond and earn 5%. Also enter into a one-year forward rate agreement (FRA) to invest in one year.

What interest rate on the FRA will make Strategies 1 and 2 equivalent?

It will be the forward rate that results in an overall annual rate of return of 5.8% for two years. To see this, consider investing $1 in each bond, and let R_i denote the spot rate and f_i denote the forward rate for each year, $i = 1, 2$.

- Strategy 1. $\$1(1 + R_2)^2 = \$1(1 + 0.058)^2 = \$1.119364$
- Strategy 2. $\$1(1 + R_1) = \$1(1 + 0.05) = \$1.05$. Then invest $1.05 in the FRA.

The forward rate that makes Strategies 1 and 2 equivalent is $\$1.05(1 + f_2) = \$1.119364$, or $f_2 = 0.06606$, or 6.606%. Thus, in equilibrium we have

$$(1 + R_2)^2 = (1 + R_1)(1 + f_2)$$

Note that if f_2 is higher than 6.606%, all investors will be better off not buying the two-year bond. Its price will fall, and R_2 will go up until the equation $(1 + R_2)^2 = (1 + R_1)(1 + f_2)$ holds. The opposite is true if f_2 is smaller than 6.606%. Similarly, for a three-year period there are three alternative strategies which in equilibrium must yield the same terminal value:

- Strategy 1. Invest in a zero-coupon bond with three years to maturity and earn 6.3%.

---

[2] A market exists for contracts based on forward interest rates. These contracts are known as forward rate agreements, and they are traded in the over-the-counter market primarily between banks.

[3] The following analysis could be conducted with coupon-bearing bonds, but would be slightly more complex.

■ Strategy 2. Invest in a one-year zero-coupon bond, enter into a one-year FRA to invest in one year, and enter again into a one-year FRA to invest in two years.

■ Strategy 3. Invest in a two-year zero-coupon bond and enter into a one-year FRA to invest in two years.

Following the same analysis as before, the return on all of these strategies must be the same. Hence, we arrive at the following equilibrium:

$$(1 + R_3)^3 = (1 + R_1)(1 + f_2)(1 + f_3)$$

However, because in equilibrium, as we have seen before,

$$(1 + R_2)^2 = (1 + R_1)(1 + f_2),$$ this can be rewritten as

$$(1 + R_3)^3 = (1 + R_2)^2(1 + f_3)$$

and for the given spot rates R_2 and R_3, the equilibrium rate f_3 can be determined.

This type of analysis could be conducted for n periods in order to arrive at the following general expression of equilibrium:

$$(1 + R_n)^n = (1 + R_1)(1 + f_2)(1 + f_3)\ldots(1 + f_n) \tag{7.2}$$

or

$$(1 + R_n)^n = (1 + R_{n-1})^{n-1}(1 + f_n) \tag{7.2}'$$

We can use Equation $(7.2)'$ to calculate the equilibrium forward rate. If we know that the four-year spot rate is 6.4% and the five-year spot rate is 6.45%, then we can solve for the forward rate over the fifth year as follows:

$$(1 + 0.0645)^5 = (1 + 0.064)^4(1 + f_5)$$

Solving for f_5, we find the forward rate to be 6.65% (see Exhibit 7.2).

Thus, one can solve for the forward rate (for the nth year) by applying Rule 2.

Rule 2: Observe the yield to maturity on a zero-coupon bond for n years and for $n - 1$ years. Then, the forward rate for the nth year can be solved by employing Equation $(7.2)'$.

From Equation 7.2 we see that spot interest rates for various maturities can be thought of as a portfolio of agreements for forward contracts. If the yield curve is upward sloping, then the implied forward rates are higher than the short-term spot rate. Indeed, in the example, we have an upward-sloping yield curve, and we found $f_5 > R_4$, which confirms this assertion. Similarly, if the yield curve is downward sloping, then the implied forward rates are lower than the short-term spot rate. For a flat yield curve, the forward rates are equal to the spot rate.

The final bond-related concept pertinent to the slope of the yield curve is the holding period rate, the rate of return earned on a bond by holding it for the next period (see Chapter 4). This rate is different from the yield to maturity, because the price of the bond changes over time. Falling bond prices may cause the holding period rate to be negative. The holding period rate is uncertain, whereas the yield to maturity is a fixed number, given the price.

These basic bond and interest rate concepts can help investors understand the various hypotheses that have been developed to explain yield curves. The discussion begins with the expectations hypothesis.

PRACTICE BOX

Problem

Suppose the 10-year spot interest rate was 8%, and the 11-year spot interest rate was 7.9%. What is the equilibrium forward rate for the eleventh period?

Solution

Using Equation 7.2′ and solving for f_n, we have

$$f_n = \frac{(1 + R_n)^n}{(1 + R_{n-1})^{n-1}} - 1$$

Substituting for the spot interest rates, we have

$$f_n = \frac{(1 + R_{11})^{11}}{(1 + R_{10})^{10}} - 1 = \frac{(1 + 0.079)^{11}}{(1 + 0.08)^{10}} - 1$$

$$\cong \frac{2.3080}{2.1589} - 1 \cong 0.069 \text{ or } 6.9\%$$

Once again, notice that the forward rate is less than the 10-year spot rate because the 11-year spot rate is less than the 10-year spot rate.

7.2.2 The expectations hypothesis

The expectations hypothesis, as its name implies, predicts that investors' expectations determine the course of future interest rates. There are two main competing versions of this hypothesis: the local expectations hypothesis and the unbiased expectations hypothesis.

The local expectations hypothesis (LEH) states that all bonds (similar in all respects except for their maturities) will have the same expected holding period rate of return. That is, a one-month bond and a 30-year bond should, on average, provide the same rate of return over the next period (e.g. next month). Thus, by this hypothesis, if you wish to invest for one month, on average, you get the same rate of return if you buy a one-month bond and hold it to maturity or buy a 30-year bond and sell it after one month. The LEH doesn't specify the length of the next period.

Empirical evidence consistently rejects this hypothesis. Specifically, holding period returns on longer-term bonds are, on average, significantly different from holding period returns on shorter-term bonds. On average, the holding period rates of return on longer-term bonds are higher and have higher volatility. Hence, longer-term bonds offer greater rewards, yet have higher risk. The LEH doesn't match our observations that investors are risk averse and require higher returns, on average, to take the higher risk related to long-term bonds. Investor risk aversion implies, in turn, that the yield curve, *on average*, will be upward sloping.

The unbiased expectations hypothesis (UEH) states that the current implied forward rates are unbiased estimators of future spot interest rates. Therefore, if the yield curve is upward sloping, the UEH states that the market expects the spot rates to rise. For example, from Exhibit 7.2 and the UEH, our best estimate in Year 1 of Year 2's spot rate is for it to rise to 6.606% (the implied forward rate). In contrast, if the yield curve is downward sloping, the UEH states that the market expects rates to fall.

The empirical evidence consistently shows that forward rates are biased predictors of future interest rates. Specifically, forward rates generally overestimate future spot rates.[4] This evidence leads to the next hypothesis, the liquidity preference hypothesis.

7.2.3 The liquidity preference hypothesis

The liquidity preference hypothesis (LPH) states that the yield curve should normally be upward sloping, reflecting investors' preferences for the liquidity and lower risk of shorter-term securities. In its purest form, the LPH is not supported by observation of the historical behaviour of the term structure. In fact, on numerous occasions the yield curve has been inverted. However, in real terms the curve may support the LPH. Let us elaborate.

An inverted yield curve does not necessarily contradict the LPH when that hypothesis is combined with the UEH. If nothing is known regarding the future (but interest rates can go up or down with an equal probability), then an upward-sloping yield curve should be expected. Suppose, however, that inflation is so high that it pushes the interest rate to 15% (which in fact occurred in 1980, when interest rates were very high, as shown in Exhibit 7.1(c)). Thus, for short-term bonds, the yield is 15%. However, no one expects this rate of inflation to continue at such a high level for a long period. Hence, for 10-year bonds the yield is only 12.5%, and we observe a decreasing yield curve. Taking these yields and dividing them by the expected inflation rate, the yield curve can be stated in real terms. The resulting real yield curve may be increasing and consistent with the LPH. Thus, the LPH may hold even if there is a decreasing (or inverted) nominal yield curve.

7.2.4 The market segmentations hypothesis

The last hypothesis, the market segmentations hypothesis (MSH), evaluates the yield curve from a slightly different perspective. This hypothesis states that bonds of different maturities trade in separate segmented markets. For example, banks tend to participate exclusively in the short-maturity bond markets, whereas insurance companies or pension funds tend to participate exclusively in the long-maturity markets. The yield curve shape is a function of these different preferences. Thus, the supply and demand preferences of participants within each maturity segment determine the equilibrium yield without regard to the equilibrium interest rate in neighbouring maturities. Under this hypothesis, any shape of yield curve is possible due to the supply demand quantities for bonds with various maturities.

A modified version of the MSH, the preferred habitat hypothesis, states that different participants have preferred locations on the yield curve, but with sufficient incentive they can be induced to move. Thus, segmentation in the bond market affects the term structure, because short-term bonds that are riskless for banks may be risky for insurance firms, which have long-term obligations. If a bank invested in long-term

---

[4] See Eugene F. Fama, 'Forward rates as predictors of future spot interest rates', *Journal of Financial Economics*, October 1976, pp. 361–77; Eugene F. Fama, 'The information in the term structure', *Journal of Financial Economics*, December 1984, pp. 509–28; and Haim Levy and Robert Brooks, 'An empirical analysis of term premiums using stochastic dominance', *Journal of Banking and Finance*, May 1989, pp. 245–60.

bonds, it would be taking considerable price risk. If an insurance company invested in short-term bonds, it would be taking considerable reinvestment risk. Different segments have different risk premiums, but they are ready to take less preferable bonds once the price of the bonds falls below a certain level.

In summary, no theory provides a complete description of what we actually observe. Each hypothesis offers insight into what may drive the current shape of the yield curve. Expectations and risk clearly play a role in determining the shape of the yield curve.

7.3   OTHER MEASURES OF BOND YIELDS

This text uses the term *yield* to mean *yield to maturity*. Among investors and in the financial media, the term *yield* has various meanings. This section introduces five different definitions of *yield*.

The coupon yield or nominal yield is the promised annual coupon rate. For example, if the annual coupon payment is $120 and the par value is $1,000, then the coupon or nominal yield is 12%.

Current yield is found by taking the stated annual coupon payment and dividing it by the current market price of the bond. Current market prices for bonds can be found in any financial newspaper or through a broker. A 12% coupon bond selling at $900, for example, has a current yield of $120/$900 $\cong$ 13.33% (where $120 is 12% of $1,000 par).

The yield to maturity is a more complex yield and represents the internal rate of return of a bond investment, as discussed earlier. That is, it is y that solves the standard bond-pricing equation given by Equation 7.1.

The yield to call is similar to the yield to maturity, except it assumes that the bond will be called at the first possible call date. The call feature allows the bond's issuer to essentially buy back bonds at a specified price. In this case, instead of using the par value at maturity as the final payment, we use the amount to be paid to bondholders when the bond is called. Specifically:

$$P = \sum_{t=1}^{nc} \frac{C}{(1 + y)^t} + \frac{\text{call price}}{(1 + y)^{nc}} \tag{7.3}$$

where nc is the number of coupon payments until the first call date. Note that if C is paid semiannually, then y is the semiannual yield, and the annual yield is $(1 + y)^2 - 1$.

This call price is typically in excess of the par value. For example, the call price may be set at par plus one year's interest. However, the investor is not assured that the bonds will in fact be called on this date. (For more on callable bonds' features, see Section 7.6.1.)

The yield to call is summarized in Rule 3.

Rule 3: The yield to call is the bond's cash flow internal rate of return on the assumption that the bond is called on the first call date.

Finally, the realized yield refers to the holding period rate of return actually generated from an investment in a bond. It is the return found after the bond has matured and all risks have been resolved. The calculation of this rate of return was explained in Chapter 4.

When referring to yield, be careful to specify exactly which yield calculation you mean. The most common yield quoted is the yield to maturity. However, there are no set standards in interest rate quotations, and as the previous discussion shows, the yield calculation does make a difference in the returns.

PRACTICE BOX

Problem

Calculate the five different yields given the following information. The bond is a two-year, 8% annual coupon, and it has $1,000 par. The bond is currently trading for $1,030 and is callable at $1,050 (without interest included) in one year. After one year the bond is trading for $1,010 (without interest).

Solution

The current yield is

$$C/P = \$80/\$1,030 \cong 7.77\%$$

The coupon or nominal yield is

$$C/Par = \$80/\$1,000 = 8.0\%$$

The yield to maturity is found using software or a handheld calculator by solving the following equation:

$$\$1,030 = \sum_{t=1}^{2} \frac{\$80}{(1 + y)^t} + \frac{\$1,000}{(1 + y)^2}$$

Using a financial calculator, we get 6.36%.

The yield to call is found by solving this equation:

$$\$1,030 = \sum_{t=1}^{1} \frac{\$80}{(1 + y)^t} + \frac{\$1,050}{(1 + y)^1} = \frac{\$1,130}{(1 + y)}$$

Thus, the yield to call is 9.71%.

Finally, assuming that the bond has not been called, the realized yield if the bond was actually held for one year is

$$R = [(\$1,010 + \$80)/\$1,030] - 1 \cong 5.83\%$$

Thus, we see that none of the yields are the same.

7.4   PRICING BONDS IN PRACTICE

The price of a bond can be expressed as the present value of its coupon payments plus the present value of the par value, discounted at the yield to maturity (y) as expressed in Equation 7.1. For example, a 10% annual coupon, $1000 par bond with a yield to maturity of 12% and 30 years to maturity is worth

$$P = \sum_{t=1}^{30} \frac{\$100}{(1 + 0.12)^t} + \frac{\$1,000}{(1 + 0.12)^{30}} \cong \$838.90$$

Of course, as the market interest rate changes, the yield to maturity changes, and the bond prices change to adjust to the new yield to maturity. The longer the maturity, the more sensitive the bond price to changes in yield.

Exhibit 7.3 lists the prices of several bonds, all with 10% coupon rates, for various interest rates. At yields of 10%, all the bonds are priced at $1,000.

Exhibit 7.3 **Bond prices and changes in yield to maturity**

(a) Bond prices for 10% coupon bonds, par value of $1,000

Years to maturity	Yield to maturity (y)		
	12%	10%	8%
1	$982.14	$1,000.00	$1,018.52
10	887.00	1,000.00	1,134.20
30	838.90	1,000.00	1,225.16
Infinity	833.33	1,000.00	1,250.00

(b) Percentage changes, mean and standard deviation (assuming 12%, 10% and 8% are equally probable)

Years to maturity	Yield to maturity			Mean	Standard deviation
	12%	10%	8%		
1	−1.79	0.00	1.85	0.02[a]	1.49[b]
10	−11.30	0.00	13.42	0.71[c]	10.10
30	−16.11	0.00	22.52	2.14	15.84
Infinity	−16.67	0.00	25.00	2.78	17.12

[a] $\frac{1}{3}(-1.79\%)\frac{1}{3} + \frac{1}{3}(0\%) + \frac{1}{3}(1.85\%) = 0.02\%$ because we assume each outcome to be equally likely.
[b] $[\frac{1}{3}(-1.79 - 0.02)^2 + \frac{1}{3}(0.00 - 0.02)^2 + \frac{1}{3}(1.85 - 0.02)^2]^{1/2} = 1.49\%$
[c] The mean and standard deviations of the other bonds are calculated in a similar manner.

Note in Exhibit 7.3(a) that longer-term bonds experience greater fluctuations in price than do shorter-term bonds. For example, when yields rise from 10% to 12%, one-year bonds drop $17.86 (or $1,000 − $982.14), whereas bonds with no stated maturity (n approaches infinity) drop $166.67 (or $1,000 − $833.33).

Exhibit 7.3(b) illustrates the percentage change (or rate of return) on a bond if it originally had a 10% yield to maturity and then immediately rose to 12%, stayed the same (at 10%), or dropped to 8% with equal probability. A couple of interesting properties can be observed.[5] First, longer-term bonds have a higher standard deviation of rates of return than do shorter-term bonds. Therefore, the longer the maturity, the larger the risk for short-term holding period investors. Second, for the same absolute change in interest rates, a rate decline produces a larger gain than a rate increase produces losses. For example, the 10-year bond gained 13.42% on a rate decline, whereas it lost only 11.30% on a rate increase. The result is a positive expected rate of return.

Exhibit 7.4 illustrates these observations with the 10-year bond and with the perpetual bond. Notice that the 10-year bond and the perpetual bond have the same price when rates are 10%. The reason is that by assumption, they are 10% coupon-bearing bonds, and when the coupon yield equals the yield to maturity the bonds will trade at par. However, when yields change, the perpetual bond price is more sensitive. Also, when rates fall, prices move up by a greater amount than when rates rise and prices fall. Hence,

---

[5] These properties and others will be more formally developed in Chapter 8.

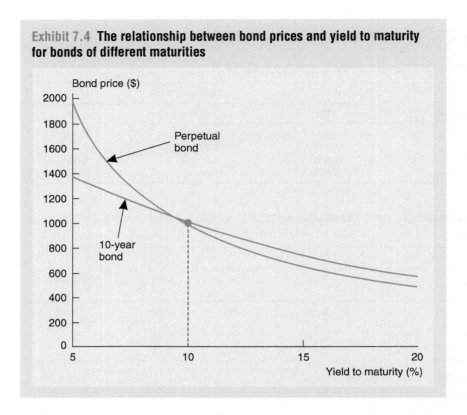

Exhibit 7.4 The relationship between bond prices and yield to maturity for bonds of different maturities

perpetuities are generally considered to be more risky. As you will see in more detail in Chapter 8, longer-maturity bonds are more sensitive to changes in yield than are shorter-maturity bonds.

7.5   SPREADS OVER TREASURIES

So far this chapter has discussed only one type of risk: the risk associated with changes in the interest rate and its effect on the price of a bond. With government bonds this is the only real risk investors face. With corporate bonds, however, there is an additional risk factor: the risk of default. The risk of default applies to both the firm's failure to pay the coupon payments and the par value at maturity. Thus, there is no guarantee that bond issuers will honour their commitments. The uncertainty over whether the lender will make coupon and principal payments is called *default risk*, and it causes the yields to maturity for corporate bonds to exceed those for Treasury bonds. This difference is known as the *spread over Treasuries*, and it is a measure of default risk.

The analyses of bond pricing and yield to maturity in the previous sections were based on the assumption that the bond's coupon and par value would be paid in a timely way. For US or UK Treasury securities, this is a reasonable assumption. However, for corporate bonds, there exists a significant risk of default. If investors believe there is a possibility the bond issuer will default, they will demand a higher yield to maturity on corporate bonds than on Treasury bonds with similar characteristics.

In July 1999 Ford Unit (the finance arm) issued the largest corporate bond offering in US history. They sold $8.6 billion in debt. The bond issue was for 32 years with a spread of 1.4% over US Treasury (140 basis points) and the portion of bonds sold for two years was only 0.17% (17 bonus points) over the three-month LIBOR rate. Thus, we see that the spread is also a function of the time to maturity of the bonds and it makes sense. The chance that Ford Unit will be unable to pay its debt in the short run is very close to zero. However, the chance of default during the next 32 years cannot be ignored, e.g. considering another possible oil crisis.

7.5.1 Bond ratings

At least four independent firms assess the credit risk of a bond issue. The most familiar rating services are Moody's Investors Service, Standard & Poor's, Fitch Investors Services, and Duff and Phelps. Credit risk is the risk that the interest or principal will not be paid as agreed. The firms that assess this risk are known as rating agencies, because they seek to 'rate' bonds on a scale from low credit risk to high credit risk. Corporations issuing bonds pay a rating fee ranging from a few thousand dollars to over $50,000.

Exhibit 7.5 lists the categories the rating agencies use. The highest-rated bonds are known as *prime-rated bonds* (Aaa by Moody's and AAA by the other three firms). These bonds are referred to as triple A and are perceived to have very little credit risk. They are described as being of high credit quality, indicating a low risk of default. The next level down in credit quality is a high-quality rating, or double A (Aa by Moody's and AA by the other three firms). The main difference between double A and triple A is the amount of cushion available to avoid default. Double A bonds have a smaller cushion, but are still very strong and have relatively low credit risk. Double A and triple A bonds are sometimes called high-grade bonds.

Single A bonds are the third level down on the rating scale, indicating slightly higher credit risk than double A. These bonds are referred to as *upper-medium-grade* bonds, and they may suffer under circumstances such as an economic downturn in the firm's industry.

The next rating category is *medium-grade bonds*, which is denoted as Baa by Moody's and BBB by the other three firms. These bonds are more vulnerable to default if the firm encounters hard times.

Triple A through triple B bonds fall under the classification of investment grade. Many professionally managed funds are restricted to investing solely in investment grade securities. For example, the Vanguard Bond Market mutual fund must invest in investment grade bonds.[6] Because of these restrictions, firms strive to keep the ratings on their bonds at or above triple B in order to maintain greater demand for their bonds and hence also maintain a lower required yield to maturity.

Bonds rated below investment grade (below triple B) are referred to as speculative grade bonds or junk bonds. At the upper end of speculative grade bonds are Ba, BB or double B. These bonds are considered to have 'major ongoing uncertainties'. That is, they face considerable risks in an economic downturn. Single B bonds are slightly more risky than double B. Bonds in categories CCC and below are bonds nearing default or in default. Also, triple C and double C sometimes refer to bonds that are subordinated to bonds holding B ratings that are not already in default (the term subordinated bonds

---

[6] See *The Individual Investor's Guide to No-load Mutual Funds*, 10th edition, 1991, p. 433.

Exhibit 7.5 **Bond rating categories by company**

Category	Moody[a]	S&P[b]	Fitch[b]	DP[b]	Description
Prime	Aaa	AAA	AAA	AAA	Best quality, extemely strong
High quality	Aa	AA	AA	AA	Strong capacity to pay
Upper medium	A	A	A	A	Adequate capacity to pay
Medium	Baa	BBB	BBB	BBB	Changing circumstances could affect ability to pay
Speculative	Ba	BB	BB	BB	Has speculative elements
Speculative	B	B	B	B	Lacks quality
Default	Caa	CCC	CCC	CCC	Poor standing
Default	Ca	CC	CC		Highly speculative
Default		C	C		Low quality, may never repay
Default		D	DDD[c] DD D	DD	In default

Moody = Moody's Investors Services, Inc.; S&P = Standard & Poor's, Inc.; Fitch = Fitch Investors Services, Inc.; DP = Duff and Phelps.
[a] Applies numerical modifiers 1, 2 and 3 to indicate relative position within rating category. For example, Baa will be Baa-1, Baa-2 or Baa-3.
[b] Uses + or − to indicate relative position within the rating category. For example, BBB will be either BBB+, BBB or BBB−.
[c] Different degrees of default, with D being worse than DD and DDD.

means bonds that stand behind senior bonds in the credit line in the event of default). Junk bonds are discussed in detail later in the chapter.

To enhance the credit quality of their bonds (to improve the rating and reduce the interest cost), firms agree to abide by certain restrictions and requirements that are spelled out in the bond indenture agreement. The bond indenture is a legal agreement between the bond issuer and the bondholders covering all the terms of the issue. It includes such stipulations as type of bond issued and amount of the issue, sinking fund provisions, restrictions on financial ratios, and call features.

Some bonds are secured with collateral and are thus called secured bonds. Mortgage bonds are an example of secured bonds. In the event of default, the bondholder takes possession of the underlying collateral (which may be in the form of land, buildings or even equipment). Unsecured bonds, known as debentures, are only backed by the 'full faith and credit' of the issuing firm.

A sinking fund is money put into a separate custodial account that is used to reduce the outstanding principal through repurchases. An independent third party manages the sinking fund. The effect of a sinking fund is to reduce the likelihood of default at the time of bond maturity.

Restrictions on financial ratios are established in an effort to ensure that the firm has the ability to meet its interest payments, as well as its sinking fund requirements. For example, there may be a restriction that requires the current ratio (the ratio of current assets divided by current liabilities) to be greater than 2. The purpose of this restriction is to ensure that the issuing firm has the liquidity necessary to make the bond's coupon payment. Indeed, financial analysts examine the financial ratios of some items taken from the firm's financial statements as indicators of the firm's financial strength.

Many firms like to have the option of calling their bonds back and refinancing them if interest rates fall. Typically, this call feature requires paying a bonus above the par value. The size of the bonus varies across bonds and even during the life of a bond, but it is typically about one year's interest. This call feature gives added flexibility to the issuing firm.

There is evidence that bond rating changes follow a pattern. Specifically, a bond that is downgraded once is much more likely to be downgraded a second time. Exhibit 7.6 presents some evidence of this phenomenon. Note that 64.4% of bond rating changes are downgrades. Of the bonds downgraded, a whopping 71.8% are downgraded a second time. For BBB bonds, the probability of a change in either direction is almost even after a first downgrade. After an upgrade, a bond's next ratings change is more likely to be another upgrade, but this is not significant (with the exception of AA bonds). The investment implication is that if a bond experiences a downgrade (except for the original rating of BBB), then you should consider selling the bond, because it is a good candidate for yet another downgrade which will induce a loss to the investors.

In an effort to provide timely information on bond ratings, S&P has developed a tool called CreditWatch.[7] When a firm is placed on CreditWatch, investors know that a potential rating change may be forthcoming. With this information, bond investors may reallocate their holdings of these bonds. For example, if a firm decides to increase its financial leverage, it may not be able to meet future debt obligations. Therefore, the risk of bankruptcy increases, and the firm may be moved to the CreditWatch list.

Rating agencies are used throughout the world. Rating agencies also evaluate the ability of governmental units, such as the Republic of Italy or Mexico, to meet their financial obligations.

Exhibit 7.6 Bond rating change experience, 1970 to 1985

Rating	First rating change		First rating change is down then next rating change is		First rating change is up, then next rating change is	
	Downgrade	Upgrade	Down	Up	Down	Up
AAA	100.0%	0.0%	78.6%	21.4%	N/A	N/A
AA	83.5	16.5	80.8	19.2	91.8%	8.2%
A	57.1	42.9	65.6	34.4	45.9	54.1
BBB	43.8	56.2	54.3	45.7	40.5	59.5
NIG[a]	50.0	50.0	72.0	28.0	42.9	57.1
Total	64.4	35.6	71.8	28.2	49.6	50.4

[a] NIG – not investment grade.

Source: Reprinted with permission from Edward I. Altman and Duen Li Kao, 'The implications of corporate bond ratings drift', *Financial Analysts Journal*, May–June 1992, p. 71. © 1992, Association for Investment Management and Research, Charlottesville, VA. Reproduced and republished from *Financial Analysts Journal* with permission from the Association for Investment Management and Research. All rights reserved.

[7] CreditWatch is a service that alerts subscribers to the S&P bond rating agency that a particular security is being closely examined for a rating change.

7.5.2 Bond ratings and spreads over Treasuries

We have seen that bond ratings influence bond prices and, consequently, bond yields. The spread over Treasuries for similar bonds varies over time. For example, Exhibit 7.7 gives the yield to maturity for 10-year corporate bonds rated Baa by Moody's and for 10-year Treasury bonds from 1986 to 1996. The difference in yield between Baa bonds and Treasuries has changed over time.

For example, in 1989, the economy was strong, with the gross domestic product (GDP) growing at 7.7% per annum.[8] Yields on 10-year Treasury bonds were 8.49% and the spread was 0.79%; by 1995, the economy had slowed and the GDP was only 4.6% per annum. Treasury bond yields were at 6.57% and the spread was 1.97%. The increase in the spread reflects the market's demanding a premium for an increase in the risk of bankruptcy during a recessionary period. Thus, the health of the economy determines the chance of bankruptcy, hence the spread.

Another example corresponds to 1978–82 (not shown in Exhibit 7.7), when the interest rate rose sharply and bondholders incurred relatively large losses. An investment in 10-year Treasury bonds at $1,000 par in 1978 would have fallen to $824 in 1982 because of the increase in interest rates.[9] This is a 17.65% loss. Because the spread also widened, an investment in Baa bonds at a $1,000 par in 1978 would have fallen to $764, a 23.57% loss.[10] Thus, the widening of the spread from 1.08% in 1978 to 3.11% in 1982 resulted in an additional 5.92% loss.

The boxed *Financial Times* article opposite shows that the spreads widened due to the crisis in the equity markets, and the low-graded bonds were hit harder.

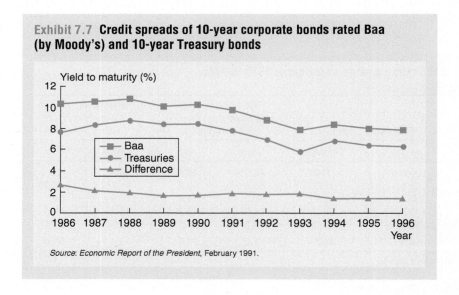

Exhibit 7.7 Credit spreads of 10-year corporate bonds rated Baa (by Moody's) and 10-year Treasury bonds

Source: *Economic Report of the President*, February 1991.

---

[8] The growth rate of the GDP is a measure of economic health. The higher the growth in the GDP, the healthier the economy (see Chapter 11).

[9] The value $824 was calculated using the standard bond pricing equation with the bond now being a six-year bond (four years have elapsed), and the yield to maturity has risen.

[10] These computations are based on semiannual bonds with 10 years to maturity initially (Treasury bonds with 8.41% coupon and Baa bonds with 9.49% coupon) and then six years to maturity left in 1982 to calculate the losses.

Secondary yield spreads widen

Yield spreads in the secondary market widened yesterday, in the first sign that the sharp declines in equity prices were feeding through to corporate bonds. The FTSE 100 index suffered its biggest one-day loss since October 1992 yesterday and the Dow Jones Industrial Average hit bear market territory. Traders said that there were no heavy selling of corporate bonds, but spreads were around 5 basis points wider. Bonds rated lower than Single A were hit harder.

Source: Financial Times, 23 March 2001, p. 28. Reprinted with permission.

PRACTICE BOX

Problem

After conducting extensive analysis, you believe the economy will continue to grow steadily, accompanied by very little change in Treasury yields. How could you profit from this belief (assuming it turns out to be correct)? Specifically, there is a BB bond with 30 years to maturity that is currently trading at par with a yield to maturity of 10%.

Solution

In a strengthening economy, the credit spread tends to decline, reflecting the lower default risk. Hence, you could invest in lower-rated bonds with the expectation that if the bond yields do decline, bond prices will rise. For example, if you invest in the BB bond and the credit spread narrows by 2%, then the price will appreciate by $225.16. (See Exhibit 7.3 for the 30-year bond: at 10% the bond trades at par of $1,000, and at 8% the bond trades for $1,225.16.)

Pre-tax and post-tax yields

The yield to maturity published in the financial media is the pretax yield. Because investors pay income tax on regular interest and capital gains tax on realized profit from the sale of the bonds, the published yields do not reflect the investor's after-tax rate of return. Municipal bonds (bonds issued by a state or local government) are exempt from income tax, whereas all other bonds are taxable. Hence, a comparison of the pretax yields on various types of bonds may be misleading.

Exhibit 7.8 provides the yields on utility bonds, long-term Treasury bonds and municipal bonds. It shows that the yield on municipal bonds is smaller than the yield on Treasury bonds. This phenomenon is quite common. For example, on 2 July 2001, the yield to maturity on Chicago Airport Financing was 5.561%, whereas the yield to maturity on US Treasury bonds (with the same 30 years to maturity) was 5.78%. Does this mean that municipals are less risky than government bonds? The reason municipals offer such low yields is that they are exempt from Federal income tax – not because their risk is lower than that of Treasury bonds.

From Chapter 2 recall that

$$R_{AT} = R_{BT}(1 - T)$$

where R_{AT} is the rate of return after taxes, R_{BT} is the rate of return before taxes, and T is the income tax rate.

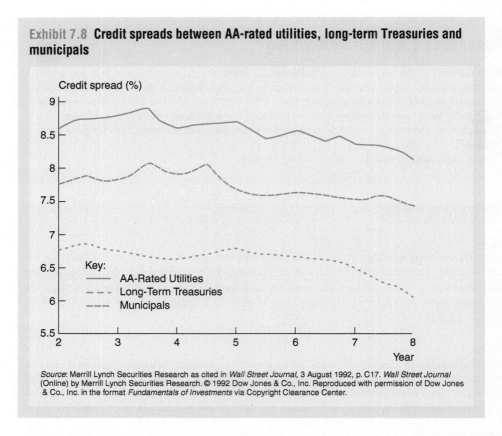

Exhibit 7.8 **Credit spreads between AA-rated utilities, long-term Treasuries and municipals**

Source: Merrill Lynch Securities Research as cited in *Wall Street Journal*, 3 August 1992, p. C17. *Wall Street Journal* (Online) by Merrill Lynch Securities Research. © 1992 Dow Jones & Co., Inc. Reproduced with permission of Dow Jones & Co., Inc. in the format *Fundamentals of Investments* via Copyright Clearance Center.

Thus, the implied before-tax rate of return when $T = 39.6\%$ and $R_{AT} = 6.06\%$ (Year 8 in Exhibit 7.8) is

$$R_{BT} = R_{AT}/(1 - T) = 6.06\%/(1 - 0.396\%) \cong 10.03\%$$

which exceeds both the Treasury bonds with eight years to maturity (at 7.48%) and the AA bonds (at 8.14%). Hence, we see that, as expected, municipals have significantly higher before-tax yields, which reflect the default risk premium.

7.5.3 Junk bonds

On 2 July 2001 the yield to maturity on Polaroid Bond was 40.4%. Did it become a very good investment? Not necessarily so, because it is a *junk bond*, on which the investor may lose the principal as well as the interest. What are junk bonds?

Junk bonds are lower-rated corporate bonds. About 25% of the junk bond market consists of bonds that were once investment grade but have had their credit rating downgraded below BBB (or Baa). These are known as fallen angels. Another 25% of the junk bond market consists of bonds issued by corporations that initially do not carry a high credit rating. Finally, about 50% of the junk bond market is composed of bonds issued in major restructurings, such as leveraged buyouts. This segment of the junk bond market was primarily composed of bonds issued in the period 1986 to 1989.[11]

---

[11] Edward I. Altman, 'Revisiting the high-yield bond market', *Financial Management*, Summer 1992, p. 78.

Exhibit 7.9 Historical default rates for junk bonds

Calendar year	Par value outstanding (billion $)	Par value in default (billion $)	Default rate (%)
1991	209	18.9	9.0
1990	210	18.4	8.7
1989	201	8.1	4.0
1988	159	3.9	2.5
1987	137	1.8	1.3
1986	93	3.2	3.4
1985	59	0.99	1.7
1984	41.7	0.034	0.83
1983	28	0.3	1.1
1982	18.5	0.58	3.1
1981	17.4	0.027	0.16
1980	15.1	0.2	1.48
1979	10.7	0.02	0.19
1978	9.4	0.12	1.27

Sources: Years 1978–88 from Edward I. Altman, *The High-Yield Debt Market: Investment Performance and Economic Impact* (Homewood, IL: Dow Jones-Irwin, 1990), p. 45; years 1989–91 from Edward I. Altman, 'Revising the high-yield bond market', *Financial Management*, Summer 1992, p. 82, Exhibit 4.

Exhibit 7.9 illustrates the growth of the junk bond market, as well as the subsequent growth of default rates. It was not until 1987 that the junk bond market exceeded $100 billion in par value. By 1989, however, it exceeded $200 billion. Notice that the default rates lagged behind this phenomenal growth by a few years. Clearly, the high default rates in the early 1990s were a result of excessive optimism in the late 1980s.

Although junk bonds have a considerable amount of default risk, they have one very attractive feature. Their yields are relatively high, which implies a high realized rate of return if bankruptcy does not occur. For example, the yield to maturity on 2 July 2001, was 6.84% on IBM and as high as 40.4% on Polaroid.[12] Because these bonds are so sensitive to the overall health of the issuing firm, each bond's price moves more with information related to the firm than with changes in overall interest rates. It turns out that a diversified portfolio of junk bonds with a relatively low correlation is many times less volatile than a diversified portfolio of US Treasury securities. Recall from our portfolio analysis that securities that have low correlations can be used to form portfolios with relatively low overall volatility.

7.5.4 Inflation-indexed bonds

Some countries that suffer from relatively high inflation issue bonds whose principal and interest are linked to the cost of living index (indexed bonds). For example, if a bond's face value is $1,000 and there was 10% inflation in the first year after the bond was issued and 20% inflation in the second year, then the bond's face value is adjusted to

$$\$1,000 \times 1.1 \times 1.2 = \$1,320$$

Similarly, the interest coupon payments are adjusted for inflation.

---

[12] See *Barron's*, 2 July 2001, p. MW47.

Recently, the US Treasury issued inflation-adjusted securities. The yield to maturity on such bonds is smaller than the yield to maturity on nonindexed bonds; however, these two yields are not comparable: one is real yield, whereas the other is nominal yield. For example, the yield to maturity in July 2001 was 3.375% on indexed bonds that mature in the year 2007, whereas the yield to maturity was about 5.16% on Treasury bonds with a similar maturity. The difference between these two yields reflects the expected annual inflation. The higher the inflation, the bigger is the expected difference between the nominal and real yields.

7.5.5 International bond markets

Recall from Chapter 3 (Exhibit 3.21) that US bonds account for nearly half of the global corporate bond market. As investors strive to achieve returns in excess of Treasuries, one popular strategy is a global bond portfolio. Although the potential returns are great, however, there are several risks.

The global bond market has its own terminology. For example, yankee bonds are issued by foreign corporations and foreign banks that pay in US dollars. Hence, yankee bonds are an efficient way to diversify default risk. If you allocate a portion of your bond portfolio to yankee bonds, when the United States goes into a severe recession you may not suffer as great a loss if these foreign corporations are not hit as hard.

As the financial markets become increasingly interrelated, corporations seeking the lowest funding costs are issuing bonds in different countries. These bonds, referred to as Eurobonds, are not related in any way to Europe. Eurobonds are sold to investors outside the issuing corporation's country. For example, Samurai bonds are yen-denominated Eurobonds offered by non-Japanese firms.

The primary benefits of international bonds, from the investor's point of view, are enhanced returns and diversification. Because of supply and demand imbalances, many international bonds have yields to maturity higher than comparable domestic securities even after adjusting for exchange risk. Also, international bonds are not perfectly correlated. Thus, it is possible to build an international bond portfolio that has a higher expected return and a lower volatility than a domestic bond portfolio.

The yields of a long-maturity bond in different countries reflect the expectation of a change in the foreign exchange rates of this currency. For example, in the US the yield is about 5.4%, in the UK about 4.25% and in Japan about 2%.

Why not issue bonds in Japan at 2% a year and lend in the United Kingdom at 4.25% a year and make a profit? This tempting transaction does not guarantee an arbitrage profit. The reason is that the difference in the yields represents different expected inflation rates in these two countries, which in turn reflects an expectation that the British pound will depreciate against the Japanese yen. When the investor converts the British pound back to Japanese yen (because the investor needs to pay back the loan), she may find that she loses money on what seems to be an arbitrage transaction.

7.6 THE IMPACT OF EMBEDDED OPTIONS

Issuers often add provisions to bonds to protect themselves from interest rate changes or to make the bonds more attractive to investors. Many features in corporate bond issues are essentially options. Recall from Chapter 2 that an option gives its holder the right, but not the obligation, to do something in the future. Both callable and convertible bonds contain option-like features. The option to call a bond and the option to convert a bond to stock dramatically change the fundamental price behaviour of bonds.

7.6.1 **The call feature**

In Section 7.3 we define the concept of yield to call. Here we elaborate on the features of callable bonds.

Most corporate bonds issued in the United States are callable by the issuing firm. That is, the issuer has the right to buy the bonds back at a stated redemption price. The bondholders face the risk that the bonds will be called at a time when they would prefer to hold them.

For example, in 1979, Duke Power Company issued a $10^{1}/_{8}$ coupon bond at $1,000 par that had a stated maturity of 1 March 2009.[13] The bonds were rated Aa by Moody's and thus contained little credit risk.

Suppose these bonds were purchased with the idea of holding them until 2009. As interest rates fell in the late 1980s and early 1990s, these bonds should have experienced a dramatic rise in price, except they were callable at 105.65% of par, or $1,056.50. Thus, even though yields on comparable bonds reached the mid-8% level, these bonds never rose much above $1,056.50. Thus, the call provision put a ceiling on the possible profit due to a fall in interest rates. No investor would be willing to pay more than $1,056.50 for such a bond knowing that the firm can redeem it at this price. On 23 December 1991, Duke Power Company called the bonds back and paid $1,056.50 (plus accrued interest).

The investor then had the problem of what to do with the $1,056.50 proceeds per bond. Unfortunately, the investor had to replace a $10^{1}/_{8}$ coupon bond with an $8^{1}/_{2}$ bond (the yield available at the time), resulting in an annual coupon loss of $1^{5}/_{8}$, or $16.25 − (0.01625 × $1,000), per bond per year.

Exhibit 7.10 illustrates the impact of the call feature on bond price behaviour with respect to yield to maturity, assuming everything else about the bonds is the same (maturity, coupon and so forth). If the callable and the noncallable bonds were priced the same, which bond would you rather own? You would prefer the noncallable bond, of course, because you could gain more if there were a large increase in price because of falling interest rates. Because every investor would prefer the noncallable bonds under these assumptions, their price must be high as shown in Exhibit 7.10. For example, for the same yield to maturity y_0, bond b (noncallable) is priced higher than bond a (callable). Thus, for similar bonds, a noncallable bond is always worth more. Indeed, Exhibit 7.10 demonstrates this property. The exhibit also shows that as yields to maturity get progressively higher, the difference in prices gradually declines. An investor would not expect too great a threat from a call feature at 105% of par when the bond is trading at, say, 70% of its par value. For example, if the two bonds issued at yield to maturity, y_0, and the yield goes up to y_1, the price of both bonds sharply declines. Thus, the market value of the call feature declines as yields to maturity rise.

Exhibit 7.10 also highlights the divergence in price when interest rates fall. Specifically, the callable bond usually does not trade much above the price at which the firm can call the bonds. Notice the left-hand side of Exhibit 7.10. As rates fall, the noncallable bond's

---

[13] From Moody's, *Corporate Bond Guide* (New York: Moody's Investor Service, 1991), p. 69.

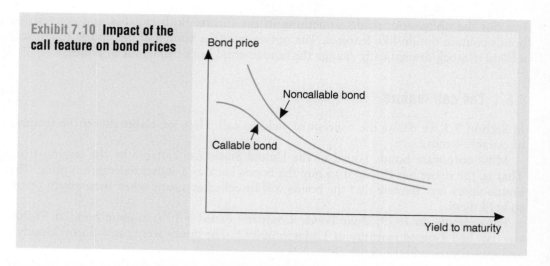

Exhibit 7.10 Impact of the call feature on bond prices

price continues to rise. However, the callable bond levels off at the value of the bond if it were called.

Why, then, do investors buy callable bonds? The reason is that issuing firms offer 'sweeteners' in the form of higher coupon rates in return for the call feature. The issuing firm of callable bonds offers the investor a higher yield to maturity. This means that with the high yield of the callable bond, we may have two bonds such as a and a′, with the same market price, but the callable bond has a higher price. Once again, there is a trade-off between risk (the call feature) and return (the higher initial yield to maturity).

Why, then, do firms issue callable bonds? The call feature allows firms some flexibility in their financing policies. In particular, the firm is not locked into an expensive debt issue. When interest rates fall, the bonds can be refinanced at a lower rate.

7.6.2 The conversion feature

When firms want to reduce their required coupon rate, they sometimes offer to make their bonds convertible to common or preferred stock. One advantage from the issuing firm's viewpoint is that it will issue new common stock at a relatively high price when the conversion takes place in the future. Typically, the conversion price (which equals the par value of the bond divided by the conversion ratio) is set significantly above the current common stock price. If the firm raised capital through a new issue of common stock, it would have to offer the new issue at a price slightly less than the current stock price. Therefore, convertible bonds provide a way to achieve, albeit in the future, an equity issue at a higher price.

Consider the Cray Research Inc. (makers of supercomputers), coupon, semiannual convertible bonds, maturing on 1 February 2011, with a rating of Baa-2 by Moody's. The conversion ratio is 12.82, which means that for every bond converted, the firm will issue 12.82 shares of common stock. Thus, the conversion price is about $78 (par/conversion ratio = $1,000/12.82).

On 24 July 1992, the bonds closed at $73\frac{1}{2}$% of par, and the common stock closed at $29\frac{3}{8}$. These bonds offer a yield to maturity of approximately 9%. At the time, the Cray Research bonds offered a yield to maturity that was indistinguishable from comparable nonconvertible bonds. The conversion feature had very little value. The stock price must rise by 165.53% before the conversion price is reached [($78 − $29\frac{3}{8}$)/$29\frac{3}{8}$].

Exhibit 7.11 **Impact of the conversion feature on bond prices**

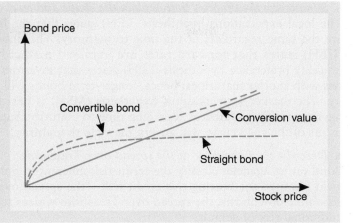

Thus, these bonds offer a strong 9% yield to maturity, and they also contain an 'equity kicker'. If the common stock price goes up considerably, then these bonds will likewise rise.

Convertible bond price behaviour is quite different from the price behaviour of regular bonds. The conversion value is the value of the bond if it is immediately converted into stock. Hence, as the stock price rises, so does the conversion value. Exhibit 7.11 illustrates the price behaviour of these bonds and compares them to the conversion value. Notice that the straight (nonconvertible) bond is almost insensitive to stock price changes except when the firm's stock price gets very low. For a very low stock price, a bankruptcy is possible, a case where the bonds lose value. When the stock price declines, the straight bond value is above the conversion value because it pays (if the firm does not go bankrupt) a fixed interest rate. The straight line represents the value of the bond if it is converted into stock. This value is known as the *conversion value*, which equals the conversion ratio times the current stock price. Clearly, as the stock price rises, so does the conversion value. Notice that the convertible bond price always exceeds the straight bond price, even for low stock prices, because the ability to convert the bonds to stock is always worth something (although it may not be worth very much at low stock prices). At a very high stock price, the convertible bond value converges to the conversion value because its value is very high and its lower value as a bond is irrelevant. Namely, the bond almost surely will be converted into stock. For example, if the stated price of Cray Research jumped to $200, the bond would be worth $200 \times 12.82 = \$2,564$, and the value of a bond of about $1000 is completely irrelevant.

SUMMARY

■ *The yield to maturity is the interest earned on a bond if held to its maturity.*
A yield curve is a relationship between a bond's time to maturity and its yield to maturity. The yield curve provides some clues regarding the future course of interest rates.

■ *Use the bond pricing equation to find bond prices and bond yields.*
When the bond's price is given, and given the coupons and par value, the yield to maturity can be computed. There is an inverse relationship between yield to maturity and bond prices.

■ *Summarize the theories that explain the shape and level of yield curves.*
The local expectations hypothesis (LEH) states that the holding period rates of return are the same regardless of the time to maturity. The unbiased expectations hypothesis (UEH) states that forward rates are unbiased predictors of future spot rates. The liquidity preference hypothesis (LPH) states that investors have a preference for securities with shorter maturities; hence, longer-term bonds will have a higher yield to maturity. The market segmentations hypothesis (MSH) is based on investors and borrowers having specific preferences regarding time to maturity. Supply and demand in these segments of the yield curve will govern the yield to maturity.

■ *Describe the behaviour of the spread over Treasuries.*
Bond rating agencies classify the credit risk inherent in bonds. Over time, the additional yield required for bearing this credit risk – the spread over Treasuries – varies. During economic downturns, the spread over Treasuries widens to compensate investors for the additional risk of default.

■ *Describe the impact of the call feature and the convertible feature on bond prices.*
The call feature causes bond prices not to rise as much as a comparable noncallable bond when interest rates (hence yields) fall. The option to call a bond held by the issuer becomes more valuable to the issuer of the bond when interest rates fall, because the bonds can be refinanced at a lower rate. The conversion feature causes bonds to behave like the underlying stock after the stock price has risen sufficiently.

KEY TERMS

Bond indenture	Investment grade	Reinvestment risk
Callable bond	Junk bond	Secured bonds
Convertible bond	Liquidity preference	Sinking fund
Coupon yield	hypothesis (LPH)	Speculative grade
Credit quality	Liquidity premium	bond
Credit risk	Local expectations	Spot rate
Current yield	hypothesis (LEH)	Subordinated bond
Debenture	Market segmentations	Term structure of interest
Fallen angel	hypothesis (MSH)	rates
Forward contract	Nominal yield	Unbiased expectations
Forward rate	Preferred habitat	hypothesis (UEH)
agreement (FRA)	hypothesis	Wealth effect
High grade	Price risk	Yield curve
Holding period rate	Rating agency	Yield to call
Indexed bond	Realized yield	Yield to maturity

QUESTIONS

7.1   What sparked the changes in bond management in the 1970s?

7.2   What determines the equilibrium level of interest rates?

7.3   If interest rates rise, will individuals save more or less? Explain your answer.

7.4 Describe some historical characteristics of the US Treasury yield curve.

7.5 Identify and discuss the various theories related to the behaviour of the yield curve.

7.6 Assuming a flat yield curve and a bond that is trading at par, why does the yield to call exceed the yield to maturity?

7.7 'The stock market seems risky these days. I am going to put my money in safe, 30-year US Treasury bonds.' Evaluate this statement.

7.8 Because of financial stress, the bonds of Intelo have been downgraded by Moody's from A to BBB. What is the predicted effect on the bonds' price? What is the predicted effect on the bonds' yield to maturity?

7.9 Suppose the only information you had regarding the current health of a country's economy was its credit spread between triple-B bonds and Treasury bonds. Specifically, the spread had recently widened considerably. What would you infer?

7.10 Suppose you are given the following information:

Maturities	Spot rates	Forward rates
1	8%	—[a]
2		7.8%
3	7.2	
4		6.0
5	5.0	

[a] Recall that forward rates involve an interest rate starting at some future point in time. Hence, most practitioners say the forward rate during the first period is just the one-period spot rate, which in this case is 8%.

(a) Complete the table assuming the rates are for annual, zero-coupon bonds.
(b) If the unbiased expectations hypothesis (UEH) is strictly true, what is the market forecast for the one-year spot rate in one year?

7.11 Describe the empirical evidence regarding patterns in bond rating changes. Is this evidence consistent with the efficient market hypothesis?

7.12 The maturity of a bond is one year ($n = 1$), the annual coupon is $C = \$100$, the par value is $1,000, and the market value is $P = \$950$. Calculate the yield to maturity.

7.13 The yield on a one-year municipal bond is 6.4%, and the yield on a one-year Treasury bond is 7.5%. Ignoring default risk, if the tax rate is $T = 31\%$, which bond would you prefer? Why?

7.14 'If the yield to maturity is zero, no matter what the maturity is, the par value of the bond must be equal to its market value.' Evaluate this statement. Is there a specific type of bond for which this is true?

7.15 Suppose you are the chief financial officer of a large life insurance company. Looking at mortality tables, you estimate that you will have to pay the insured families $100 million in each of the next five years and $900 million in Year 6. What kind of bonds would you seek to make these payments? Would it make a difference whether the yield curve is flat or upward sloping?

7.16 Short-term bonds traded in the United States, like Treasury bills, are often referred to as the risk-free asset. In what respect are they risk-free?

7.17 Which asset would you consider to be riskier: three-month Treasury bills or a 30-year Treasury bond that matures in three months?

7.18 Looking at the international financial statistics, we find that the interest paid to US banks on loans to some Latin American countries is about 30% per year. The interest within the United States is only 10%.

(a) How can you explain the difference in interest rates if the loans are made in local currency?

(b) How can you explain the difference in interest rates when the loan in made in US dollars? After all, it is said, the government cannot go bankrupt. Why do US banks receive such a high interest rate on foreign loans?

SELECTED REFERENCES

Altman, Edward I. *The High-Yield Debt Market: Investment Performance and Economic Impact*. Homewood, IL: Dow Jones–Irwin, 1990.
This is an exhaustive book of readings related to the junk bond market.

Altman, Edward I., and Duen Li Kao. 'The implications of corporate bond ratings drift'. *Financial Analysts Journal*, May–June 1992, pp. 64–75.
This article examines in detail the corporate ratings drift.

Cottle, Sidney, Roger F. Murray, and Frank E. Block. *Graham and Dodd's Security Analysis*, 5th edn. New York: McGraw-Hill, 1988.
This reworking of a classic applies the basic principles of security analysis in determining security value.

Geanuracos, John, and Bill Millar. *The Power of Financial Innovation*. New York: Harper Business, 1991.
This book provides interesting insights into the global bond markets and has an emphasis on derivative securities.

Livingston, Miles. *Money and Capital Markets: Financial Instruments and Their Uses*. Englewood Cliffs, NJ: Prentice-Hall, 1990.
This book covers thoroughly many of the technical aspects of bond pricing and theories of term structure.

SUPPLEMENTARY REFERENCES

Altman, Edward I. 'Measuring corporate bond mortality and performance'. *Journal of Finance*, September 1989, pp. 909–22.

Altman, Edward I. 'Setting the record straight on junk bonds'. *Journal of Applied Corporate Finance*, Summer 1990, pp. 82–95.

Altman, Edward I. 'Revisiting the high-yield bond market'. *Financial Management*, Summer 1992, pp. 78–92.

Asquith, Paul, David W. Mullins, Jr., and Eric D. Wolff. 'Original issue high-yield bonds: aging analysis of defaults, exchanges and call'. *Journal of Finance*, September 1989, pp. 923–52.

Balduzzi, P., E.J. Elton, and T. Clifton Green. 'Economic news and bond prices: evidence from the U.S. Treasury market'. *JFQA*, forthcoming (2002).

Best, Peter, Alistair Byrne, and Antli Ilmanen. 'What really happened to U.S. bond yield'. *Financial Analysts Journal*, May–June 1998, pp. 41–9.

Blume, Marshall E., and Donald B. Keim. 'Realized returns and defaults on low-grade bonds: the cohort of 1977 and 1978'. *Financial Analysts Journal*, March–April 1991, pp. 63–72.

Blume, Marshall E., and Donald B. Keim. 'The risk and return of low-grade bonds: an update'. *Financial Analysts Journal*, September–October 1991, pp. 85–9.

Cornell, Bradfors. 'Liquidity and the pricing of low-grade bonds'. *Financial Analysts Journal*, January–February 1991, pp. 63–7, 74.

Fabozzi, Frank J. (ed.). *The New High-Yield Debt Market: A Handbook for Portfolio Managers and Analysts*. New York: HarperCollins, 1990.

Fama, Eugene F. 'Forward rates as predictors of future spot interest rates'. *Journal of Financial Economics*, October 1976, pp. 361–77.

Fama, Eugene F. 'The information in the term structure'. *Journal of Financial Economics*, December 1984, pp. 509–28.

Fons, Jerome S., and Andrew E. Kimball. 'Corporate bond defaults and default rates 1970–1990'. *Journal of Fixed Income*, June 1991, pp. 36–47.

Fridson, Martin S., Michael A. Cherry, Joseph A. Kim, and Stephen W. Weiss. 'What drives the flows of high-yield mutual funds?'. *Journal of Fixed Income*, December 1992, pp. 47–59.

Fridson, Martin S., and Christopher Garman. 'Determinants of spreads on new high yield bonds'. *Financial Analysts Journal*, March–April 1998, pp. 28–39.

Lederman, Jess, and Michael P. Sullivan (eds). *The New High-Yield Bond Market: Investment Opportunities, Strategies and Analysis*. Chicago: Probus Publishing, 1993.

Levy, Haim, and Robert Brooks. 'An empirical analysis of term premiums using stochastic dominance'. *Journal of Banking and Finance*, May 1989, pp. 245–60.

Lobo, B.J. 'Asymmetric effects of interest rate changes on stock prices'. *Financial Review*, 35(3), August 2000.

Ma, Christopher K., Ramesh Rao, and Richard L. Peterson. 'The resiliency of the high-yield bond market: the LTV default'. *Journal of Finance*, September 1989, pp. 1085–97.

Ryan, Patrick J. 'Junk bonds – opportunity knocks?' *Financial Analysts Journal*, May–June 1990, pp. 13–16.

Yan, Hong. 'Dynamic modeling of the term structure'. *Financial Analysts Journal*, July/August 2000.

Chapter 9

COMMON STOCKS: VALUATION

Learning objectives

After studying this chapter you should be able to:

1 Explain how investors use stock valuation models.
2 Describe the assumptions underlying the constant dividend growth model.
3 Value firms that are presently experiencing supergrowth.
4 Explain under what conditions the P/E ratio can be used safely.
5 Discuss the three main financial statements of the firm (Appendix 9A).
6 Warn that earnings can be manipulated.

INVESTMENT IN THE NEWS

Rating Your Broker's Stock Picks

Value investors learn new tricks: How they're adapting to the new economy

For years, two great armies of investors have done battle on Wall Street. In one camp stand the growth investors, willing to pay dearly for companies that they believe can generate big profits for years to come. In the other camp are the value investors. They're leery of the rosy forecasts. They'll buy only into companies with real assets and solid earnings in the here and now – and at bargain prices. . . .

The new value investing relies more on forecasting – long a taboo for value investors. Benjamin Graham and David L. Dodd, who laid down the principles of value investing in the 1930s, frowned on earnings forecasts because they were too speculative. The new value investing looks more to another author of the same era, economist John Burr Williams. Williams' Theory of Investment Value taught that an investment was worth the present value of its future cash flows – which, of course, had to be estimated. 'People have been using static methods to think about a dynamic world', says Michael J. Mauboussin, an investment strategist at Credit Suisse First Boston. 'No wonder value investing hasn't worked well.'. . . .

Source: Jeffrey M. Laderman, *Business Week*, 14 June 1999.

This chapter and Chapter 10 introduce methods investors use to value stocks. Most of the methods described are based on discounting future cash flows. In addition to valuation methods based on discounted cash flows, the price/earnings (P/E) ratio is also discussed. This widely used valuation measure, which is based on past performance, often appears in the financial press. Thus, investors should understand its predictive power and limitations.

Finally, although theoretically only future cash flows are relevant for stock valuation, in practice many other investment criteria are employed. As some of these investment criteria rely also on accounting data, we briefly discuss in Appendix 9A the firm's financial statements and the information contained in these statements.

As will be explained later in the chapter, in calculating the present value of future dividends we must assume some discount rate. The discount rate is the required rate of return by investors, given the riskiness of the stock. If investors hold only one stock in their portfolio, then the variability of future dividends determines the value of the discount rate (k). If investors hold many assets in their portfolios, then the variability of the asset's return, as well as the various correlations, determine the risk – hence determining the discount rate. Thus, the valuation method presented in this chapter does not contradict the portfolio analysis studied in Chapter 6 (see also Chapter 14).

For a given discount rate, valuation models are developed based on the future average cash flow. This chapter assesses whether investors should discount earnings, dividends or the future stock price. Also, it analyzes how retained earnings and the firm's reinvestment policy affect the stock price.

9.1   USES OF STOCK VALUATION MODELS

Why should stock valuation models be studied? Many investors rely on the stock values, obtained from the valuation models described in this chapter, to make investment decisions. This section looks at typical applications of model-generated stock values to demonstrate the use of stock valuation models in practice.

9.1.1 Assessing investment opportunities

The most important use of valuation models is in selecting stocks for investment. How can you tell if a share of British Airways stock traded at £302 is a good investment? Is the stock underpriced? Is it overpriced? The ability to correctly value securities is essential to successful investing. For example, if you value Amoco stock at £100 and the current market price is £85, this valuation suggests you should buy Amoco stock. Of course, you should actually buy the stock only after rigorously testing your model and gaining confidence in its valuation capabilities.

One group of investment theorists believe that changes in stock prices, particularly short-run changes in stock prices, cannot be predicted. They feel that no stock valuation model can locate underpriced or overpriced stock. Other groups of professional investors as well as investment theorists believe that underpriced stocks can be detected. We claim that even though you may not believe stock valuation models can locate mispriced stocks, you must include other people's opinions in your assessment of stock prices. After all, if a group of believers in a particular model of stock valuation predict that prices will move in a given direction, their actions could affect stock prices even though there is no economic foundation for this price change. For example, adherents of the 'Super Bowl indicator' will buy stocks after an NFL win and thus push stock prices higher (statistics reveal that after an NFL win, the stock market tends to rise significantly more than after an NFL loss). You may not agree with these investors, but you could benefit from knowing the direction the market will take based on their actions. If you weren't aware of their valuation model, you might miss a stock market rally. Indeed, the famous economist John Maynard Keynes describes the stock exchange as a place where successful investing is the art of what people think other people think about stock prices.[1]

9.1.2 Valuing a common stock issue: the case of IPO

When a firm goes public, it needs some method to estimate the value of its stock. Suppose you own a successful family firm that needs additional capital to expand internationally. You decide to issue stock to the public. (Recall from Chapter 3 that this is called an initial public offering, or IPO.) When you make this decision, there is no market price for your shares. To determine the selling price of your firm's stock, you need a way to value your equity. Even if you believe the market price of common stock equals the value of the stock, you need to employ a stock valuation model, because at the time of the first public offering there is no market price for the shares. By the same token, an underwriter who insures your issue needs some valuation model in order to decide the firm's economic value to be insured.

9.1.3 Estimating the appropriate discount rate

You studied the concept of a firm's cost of capital or discount rate in your course on the principles of finance. The evaluation of an investment project requires an estimate of the firm's cost of capital. The cost of equity is a major component in the cost of capital. Financial managers can use stock prices and stock valuation models to calculate the cost of equity.

9.1.4 Understanding the financial media

Articles and reports in the financial media use terms from stock valuation models: growth rate, supergrowth firms, price/earnings ratios, and so forth. By studying stock valuation models, you will know what these terms mean and how to apply them.

Many stock valuation models exist. The following sections explain how the different methods should be used and under what situations all these methods yield the same results.

---

[1] See John Maynard Keynes, *The General Theory of Employment and Money* (New York: Harcourt Brace, 1936), p. 156.

9.2 THE DISCOUNTED CASH FLOW PRINCIPLE

9.2.1 Buyers and sellers of a stock

Many stock valuation models have their roots in the discounted cash flow (DCF) principle, which states that the current value of any asset is the present value of all its future cash flows.

A stock is an asset whose future expected cash flows are $CF_1, CF_2, \ldots, CF_n$, where the subscript $i = 1, 2, \ldots, n$ denotes the year in which the cash flow is obtained. The value of the stock is simply the discounted value of all these cash flows. The cash flows to the investor are the received dividends and the cash flow from selling the stock. To illustrate how to value a given stock, suppose you forecast that Ford Motor Company will pay a £4 cash dividend per share at the end of the next year and a £5 cash dividend per share at the end of the second year. Furthermore, you estimate that you will be able to sell the shares of Ford two years from now for £130. Because these are only estimates, they are uncertain; and like any uncertain cash flow stream, you discount the cash flows at a discount rate (k), which is composed of the risk-free interest rate (time value of money) and a risk premium.[2] Suppose the discount rate is $k = 15\%$. The current stock price as published in the *Financial Times* is $P_0 = £100$. Should you buy the Ford stock? Like any other capital budgeting project, your decision is given by Rule 1 (where PV is the present value of the expected cash flows).

Rule 1: The decision is:
If $PV > P_0$, buy the stock (NPV > 0).
If $PV < P_0$, do not buy the stock (NPV < 0).
If $PV = P_0$, you are indifferent whether or not to buy the stock (NPV = 0).

These decision rules can be applied to all valuation models presented in this chapter.

To continue the example, the present value of Ford's £4 dividend paid at the first year is £3.48 (see Exhibit 9.1). At the end of the second year, £5 dividends are paid; however, the stock is also expected to be sold at £130, making the total expected cash flow £135, with a discounted value of £102.08. Therefore, the present value of all

Exhibit 9.1 Present value of £4 dividend in Year 1 and £5 dividend and £130 stock price in Year 2

	Beginning of first year (t_0)	End of first year (t_1)	End of second year (t_2)
Expected dividends		£4	£5
Expected price			£130
Total expected cash flow		£4	£135
Discount factor for each year		$1/1.15$	$1/1.15^2$
Contribution to present value		$£4/1.15 \cong £3.48$	$£135/1.15^2 \cong £102.08$
Present value of the total cash flows		$£3.48 + £102.08 = £105.56$	

---

[2] For simplicity, we ignore the effects of inflation.

expected cash flows is PV = £105.56. Because £105.56 is greater than the current price (P_0 = £100), the net present value (NPV = PV − P_0 = £105.56 − £100 = £5.56) is positive. If you expect these cash flows, you should buy the stock.

Who, then, sells Ford stock? Other investors in the market may have different predictions of the cash flows and hence a different future stock price. Suppose another investor believes, as you do, that the dividends will be £4 next year and £5 in two years, but unlike you, this investor believes that at the end of the second year the Ford stock will be selling only at £120. Even if this investor also uses a 15% discount rate, the present value of these cash flows is £98, as shown in Exhibit 9.2.

Suppose the second investor owns Ford stock. Because the present value is £98, which is less than the current stock price (P_0 = £100), this investor should sell the stock for £100. Indeed, every day investors trade Ford stock and almost all other stocks. Investors who believe a stock is undervalued buy the stock, and investors who believe a stock is overvalued sell their stock. Because investors have differing opinions, the stock of Ford, as well as the stocks of other firms, changes hands. However, note that in both cases, the stock valuation method employed is based on the discounted cash flow principle.

9.2.2 The investment holding period

The stockholder is entitled to an infinite stream of cash dividends. This infinite cash flow determines the stock's value. When the cash flow is cash dividends, stock valuation models based on the discounted cash flow principle are called dividend discount models (DDMs). However, in practice, investors do not hold the stock for an infinite period. How does this fact affect the valuation procedure? How does it affect the stock's price? In the examples in Exhibits 9.1 and 9.2, we assumed that investors hold the stock for two years, get two annual dividends, and then sell the stock. Now we will see that the valuation result does not change whether investors hold the stock for any number of years. We show below that the holding period does not affect the value of the stock.

To see this, suppose an investor invests for, say, one year and receives at the end of the first year a dividend of d_1. Then the investor sells the stock for P_1, where P_1 is the expected stock price at the end of the first year. The market is in equilibrium, namely, PV = P_0. How are P_0, P_1 and d_1 related? Because the current stock price is nothing but

---

Exhibit 9.2 Present value of £4 dividend in Year 1 and £5 dividend and £120 stock price in Year 2

Beginning of first year (t_0)	End of first year (t_1)	End of second year (t_2)
Expected dividends	£4	£5
Expected price		£120
Total expected cash flow	£4	£125
Discount factor for each year	1/1.15	$1/1.15^2$
Contribution to present value	£4/1.15 ≅ £3.48	$£125/1.15^2$ ≅ £94.52
Present value of the total cash flows	£3.48 + £94.52 = £98.00	

the discounted cash flows from future dividends and the stock sale, the stock price (P_0) is given by

$$P_0 = \frac{d_1}{1+k} + \frac{P_1}{1+k} \qquad (9.1)$$

where k is the investor's required rate of return (given the stock's risk). For example, suppose that $d_1 = £5$ and $P_1 = £116$ and the discount rate is $k = 10\%$. Then, the current stock price which represents the PV of future cash flow will be:

$$P_0 = \frac{£5}{1.10} + \frac{£116}{1.10} = \frac{£121}{1.10} = £110$$

However, what if the investor considers holding the stock for two years and then selling it? We demonstrate below that the PV, i.e. the stock price, is not affected by the assumed length of time the investor plans to hold the stock. Let us show this claim. Assume that the investor invests for two years. The investor gets dividend d_1 at the end of the first year and d_2 at the end of the second year, and sells the stock for P_2 at the end of the second year, where P_2 is the expected stock price two years from now.

Suppose that the investor expects to get £5 in dividends in the first year and £6 at the second year. Because $P_1 = £116$ one can first estimate the stock price at the end of year 2. Given that $P_1 = £116$ (see above) is the PV of P_2 and d_2, P_2 should be the value which fulfils the following:

$$P_1 = £116 = \frac{£6}{1.1} + \frac{P_2}{1.1}$$

Therefore, $P_2 = £116 \times 1.1 - £6 = £127.6 - £6 = £121.6$.

If the investor holds the stock for two years rather than one year, the PV of all cash flows is

$$PV = \frac{£5}{1.1} + \frac{£6}{(1.1)^2} + \frac{£121.6}{(1.1)^2} \cong £4.54 + £4.96 + £100.50 = £110$$

Thus, $P_0 = PV = £110$, regardless of whether the stock is held for one year or two years.

One can continue the same logic and show that in general the stock price P_0 is given by

$$P_0 = \frac{d_1}{1+k} + \frac{d_2}{(1+k)^2} + \frac{d_3}{(1+k)^2} + \ldots$$

$$= \sum_{t=1}^{\infty} \frac{d_t}{(1+k)^t} = \sum_{t=1}^{n} \frac{d_t}{(1+k)^t} + \frac{P_n}{(1+k)^n} \qquad (9.2)$$

where d_t is the dividend paid at the end of Year t, and n is the number of future dividend payments. Thus, if we discount all future dividends, or discount the n future dividends plus P_n, we get the same stock price, P_0.

Regardless of the assumed holding period, you will get the same value for the discounted cash flows (P_0). The intuitive explanation of this fact is that in Equation 9.1

PRACTICE BOX

Problem

Suppose you know that Zoom, Inc., is going to pay £5 in dividends at the end of next year and £6 in dividends at the end of Year 2, and you estimate a price of the stock at the end of Year 2 of £110. Suppose the required rate of return (k) is 12%.

1. What is the stock price today (P_0) based on Equation 9.2 when $n = 2$?
2. What is the price at the end of Year 1 (P_1)?
3. What is the price today (P_0) based on Equation 9.1 when the holding period is one year?

Solution

1. Based on Equation 9.2 and the data given in the problem,

$$P_0 = \frac{£5}{1 + 0.12} + \frac{£6 + £110}{(1 + 0.12)^2} \cong £96.94$$

2. The value P_1 is given by

$$P_1 = \frac{£6 + £110}{1 + 0.12} \cong £103.57$$

3. Based on Equation 9.1,

$$P_0 = \frac{£5}{1 + 0.12} + \frac{£103.57}{1 + 0.12} \cong £96.94$$

We see that the price today is independent of whether it is assumed that the investor holds the stock for one year or two years.

we discount the price P_1. However, P_1 is nothing but the discounted dividends paid in Year 2 plus the discounted value of the price, P_2. Continuing this process, we find that the stock price (P_0) is nothing but the discounted value of all future dividends plus the discounted value of the stock price at the end of the nth year, $P_n/(1 + k)^n$. As n approaches infinity, however, the present value of the stock approaches zero, and we can ignore the price of the stock for dividend-paying firms.[3] The discounted cash flow method is summarized in Rule 2.

Rule 2: To find the value of the stock, decide first on the holding period. Then estimate all cash flows, from dividends and from selling the stock. The current value of the stock is the present value of all these cash flows. Changing the planned holding period does not affect the current value of the stock.

Some investors may claim that they definitely will not hold the stock for an infinite number of years. Moreover, they may claim that they intend to hold the stock for a few years, and hence Equation 9.2, which discounts an infinite series of dividends, is irrelevant for them. As has just been demonstrated, if these investors employ an equation that assumes holding the stock for one year and then selling the stock, or

---

[3] Of course, we assume that the firm pays dividends such that the denominator $(1 + k)^n$ grows faster than the stock price. Otherwise, the stock price would be infinite.

holding the stock for two years and then selling it, or for that matter holding the stock for any finite number of years, the same result is obtained if the DCF principle (which relies on an infinite stream of dividends) is used. Thus, a stock valuation formula should be based on all future dividends. However, the same value is also obtained when the investment is assumed to be for n years only. In such a case, the current stock price is the present value of the n years' cash dividends plus the present value of the stock price that is sold after n years. Therefore, Equation 9.2 can safely be employed for stock valuation even if the stock will be held only for a short period. Therefore, from now on this chapter simply assumes that the stock price is nothing but the DCF of all future dividends. It also employs an equation that assumes an infinite holding period or, interchangeably, the DCF of any finite number of dividends plus the discounted value of the stock price when sold.

As will be shown, the DCF principle is the foundation on which several valuation models are built. The next section describes a dividend discount model that incorporates a simple growth rate of dividends into the investor's assessment of a given stock.

9.3 THE CONSTANT DIVIDEND GROWTH MODEL (CDGM)

When stock valuation is based on future dividends, it is called the *dividend discount model* because it discounts cash dividends. When the dividends grow at a constant rate every period, it is called the constant dividend growth model. The constant dividend growth model (CDGM) is the most common valuation model used to determine both stock values and the firm's cost of equity. This model determines the stock price by the first-year dividend (d_1), the discount rate (k) and the growth rate (g).

The model assumes that the firm pays a constant proportion of its earnings as dividends and the rest of the earnings are retained in the firm. It also assumes that the firm's earnings per share, dividends per share, and – as a result – the stock price are expected to grow every year by a constant growth rate denoted by g, where g is expressed as a percentage:[4]

$$P_1 = P_0(1 + g) \tag{9.3}$$

Substituting P_1 from Equation 9.3 into Equation 9.1 yields the following:

$$P_0 = \frac{d_1}{1 + k} + \frac{P_0(1 + g)}{1 + k} \tag{9.4}$$

Multiplying both sides of Equation 9.4 by $(1 + k)$ yields

$$P_0(1 + k) = d_1 + P_0(1 + g)$$

or

$$P_0(1 + k) - P_0(1 + g) = d_1$$

---

[4] Note that $P_0 = \dfrac{d_1}{1 + k} + \dfrac{d_1(1 + g)}{(1 + k)^2} + \dfrac{d_1(1 + g)^2}{(1 + k)^3} + \cdots$

and after a year,

$P_1 = \dfrac{d_1(1 + g)}{1 + k} + \dfrac{d_1(1 + g)^2}{(1 + k)^2} + \cdots$

because the dividend grows annually by g. As, after a year elapses, all terms in the numerators grow by g, the stock price also grows by g, and $P_1 = (1 + g)P_0$.

which can be further simplified as follows:

$$P_0(k - g) = d_1$$

The last equation can be written as the constant dividend growth model:[5]

$$P_0 = \frac{d_1}{k - g} \tag{9.5}$$

The constant dividend growth model given by Equation 9.5 asserts that the value of the stock (P_0) is nothing but the first-year dividend per share (d_1), i.e. the dividend which will be paid one year hence, divided by the discount rate (k) minus the constant growth rate (g). Obviously, the greater the growth rate (g), other things being the same, the larger the discounted future dividends will be, resulting in a greater stock price (P_0). One nice feature of this model is that all future dividends do not have to be estimated directly. We need only estimate g. Rule 3 summarizes the CGDM.

Rule 3: To obtain the value of the stock today by the CDGM, you need to estimate the discount rate k and the growth rate g. The stock value is next year's dividend, d_1, divided by $k - g$.

Note that this formula holds only when the growth rate (g) is smaller than the discount factor (k). If $g > k$, dividends grow faster than the discount rate, and the DCF of an infinite stream of dividends yields an infinite price. Also, $g = k$ is not possible; it results in an infinite price. Because an infinite stock price does not exist in the market, we safely assume that $g < k$, or at least that $g > k$ cannot continue forever. The case where $g > k$ for a limited period of time is discussed later in the chapter.

9.4 SOURCES OF GROWTH

Very few firms fit neatly into the assumptions needed to derive the constant dividend growth model. This section examines the sources of growth and how to apply the constant dividend growth model effectively. It also explains when this basic valuation model is not appropriate.

Usually, the earnings per share (EPS) and dividends per share (DPS) grow simultaneously (for the definition of EPS, see Appendix 9A). However, if the dividend policy changes over time, the dividends and earnings may reveal a different growth rate. This discussion focuses on the cases where both the EPS and the DPS grow at the same rate. Suppose we observe in a given year a change in the growth rate of the DPS, say an increase from 5% to 9%. Does this increase imply that the stock's price should also increase? To answer the question, we need to have a closer look at the potential sources of growth in the firm and, in particular, the sources of possible changes in the firm's growth rate.

The DPS grows by (a) reinvestment of the retained earnings, even in normal-profit projects, and (b) undertaking projects with extraordinary profits even if all reclaimed earnings are paid as dividends. Of course, if both (a) and (b) occur, the growth rate is

---

[5] This model was originally developed by M.J. Gordon, 'Dividends, earnings and stock prices', *Review of Economics and Statistics*, 41, May 1959, pp. 99–105.

enhanced. Let us elaborate on these two sources of growth. They do not have the same impact on the stock price.

9.4.1 Source a: Reinvestment of earnings

Consider a firm with no extraordinarily profitable projects. Such firms are normal-growth firms. Given the riskiness of such firms, the stockholders require, say, $k\%$ return per year on their investment. Suppose the firm reinvests the retained earnings in projects yielding $k\%$, exactly as required by the stockholders. Thus, the net present value (NPV) of all accepted projects is zero. Can the firm's earnings and dividends grow in such a case? Yes, they can, because the firm pays only a portion of its earnings as dividends and has some cash left to reinvest in the firm. Moreover, paying less dividends and increasing the dollar amount invested in profitable projects leads to higher future earnings. A firm pursuing this dividend policy will achieve growth in earnings and dividends. In this case, the increase in investment is financed by internal sources, namely by cutting the current dividends. The lower the portion of earnings paid out as dividends, the greater the firm's future growth rate.

9.4.2 Source b: Opportunities for extraordinary profits

When firms have opportunities for extraordinary profits, they can increase the growth rate of the EPS and the DPS with no change in their dividend policy – that is, without reducing the current dividends. Firms with these opportunities are supergrowth firms. Such a firm reinvests the retained earnings in projects yielding more than $k\%$, which is the required rate of return by the stockholders, given the risk of the firm. Thus, the firm invests in projects with a positive NPV. Because the firm earns extra profits on these projects, it experiences increased growth in sales, earnings and dividends. It should be emphasized that the firm's profit increases with no change in risk; hence, the required rate of return by investors remains $k\%$.

It might seem as though supergrowth firms will always have a larger growth rate than normal-growth firms, but this is not always true. To illustrate, consider the following example. One firm may reinvest 90% of its profit at the required rate of return k and grow at $g = 10\%$, whereas another firm may reinvest only 20% of its profit in projects with extraordinary profits (those with a rate of return greater than k) and grow only at $g = 8\%$. The relatively low growth rate of the second firm results from the low proportion of the earnings retained. However, the firm with a 10% growth rate is classified as a normal-growth firm, whereas the firm with an 8% growth rate is classified as a supergrowth firm. In other words, the actual growth rate is determined by the rate of return on reinvested earnings, as well as the proportion of earnings reinvested in the firm. However, only the first factor – the profit on projects – determines whether the firm is classified as a normal-growth or a supergrowth firm.

Growth rates play a major role in stock valuation models based on the DCF principle. To examine whether an increase in g affects the stock price, the following sections analyze situations facing normal and supergrowth firms. They show that an increase in the growth rate caused by a cut in dividends changes the future dividends but does not lead to an increase in the current stock price, whereas an increase in the growth of dividends due to the availability of extraordinarily profitable projects does cause an increase in the current stock price.

9.4.3 Normal-growth firms

Let us look first at Exhibit 9.3(a). Year 0 stands for the current time, and P_0 is the current price. Similarly, Year 1 stands for the end of the first year. The normal-growth firm's earnings per share is £10, and the firm distributes £5 per share as dividends. The firm earns 10% on its investments, and the stockholder's required cost of equity is $k = 10\%$. Thus, all projects have zero NPV. The current stock price is P_0. In the second year the earnings grow to £10.5, because £5 per share earned in the first year is reinvested at 10%, yielding an additional £5 × 0.1 = £0.5 earnings per share. Because by assumption, the firm distributes 50% of its earnings as dividends, in the second year it pays dividends of £5.25, or $\frac{1}{2} \times £10.5$, per share. Thus, the earnings, dividends and hence the firm's stock price grow from the first year to the second year at a 5% growth rate.

By this process the earnings, dividends and stock price are expected to continue to grow at this rate in all other years. For example, the earnings of the second year are £10.5 × 1.05 = £11.025. Similarly, the dividend grows at 5%; hence, in the second year, the DPS is £5.25 × 1.05 = £5.5125.

Let us generalize these results. Denoting by b the proportion of the EPS retained in the firm (that is, not distributed as dividends) and by R the rate of return on the reinvested monies in the firm, called the reinvestment rate, then the growth rate is given by $g = b \times R$. Thus, if $b = 0.50$ and $R = 10\%$, the growth rate is $g = 0.5 \times 0.10 = 0.05$, or 5%, as the previous example reveals.

Exhibit 9.3 The growth rate in dividends, earnings and stock prices for normal-growth firms

(a) Growth rate of $g = 5\%$ with £5 first-year dividends

Year	EPS	DPS	Stock price
0			P_0
1	£10	£5	$P_0(1.05)$
2	£10.5	£5.25	$P_0(1.05)^2$
3	£11.025	£5.5125	$P_0(1.05)^3$
.	.	.	.
.	.	.	.
.	.	.	.

(b) Growth rate of $g = 9\%$ with £1 first-year dividends

Year	EPS	DPS	Stock price
0			P_0
1	£10	£1	$P_0(1.09)$
2	£10.9	£1.09	$P_0(1.09)^2$
3	£11.881	£1.1881	$P_0(1.09)^3$
.	.	.	.
.	.	.	.
.	.	.	.

Employing Equation 9.5, the stock price (P_0) corresponding to the example in Exhibit 9.3(a) is given by

$$P_0 = \frac{d_1}{k - g} = \frac{\$5}{0.10 - 0.05} = \frac{\$5}{0.05} = \$100$$

Note that although this firm earns 10% on its investment, the growth rate is only 5%, because only 50% of the EPS is retained. Exhibit 9.3(a) shows that a normal-growth firm will experience the same growth in EPS, DPS and its stock price.

Exhibit 9.3(b) still assumes a normal-growth firm – namely $k = 10\%$ and the firm reinvests 90% of its retained earnings in projects yielding 10%. The only difference between this case and the previous case is that the firm distributes only £1 (out of £10) as cash dividends and reinvests the retained earnings of £9 per share. The £9 per share is invested in projects yielding, as before, 10%; therefore, the dollar return on this reinvestment of the retained earnings is £0.90 (given by £9 × 0.1 = £0.90) per share.

Let us continue these computations for the second year: 10% of the EPS, or 0.1 × 10.9 = £1.09, is paid out as dividends in the second year. What is left is once again reinvested at 10%. Because the growth rate is 9% for all years, the EPS in the third year is £10.9 × 1.09 = £11.881, and the DPS is £1.09 × 1.09 = £1.1881; this growth rate continues forever. Note that in Exhibit 9.3(b), we have $b = 0.9$ and $R = k = 10\%$; hence, the growth rate is $g = bR = 0.9 \times 0.10 = 0.09$, or 9%. Comparing Exhibits 9.3(a) and 9.3(b), it is easy to see that by decreasing the dividends that are paid to the stockholders in the first year, more money is left to be reinvested. Hence, earnings and dividends grow at $g = 9\%$, in comparison with only $g = 5\%$ growth rate as in Exhibit 9.3(a). Therefore, when only 10% of earnings is paid out as dividends, the stock price at the end of the first year (P_1) should grow at 9% over the original price (P_0). Note that the increase in the stock price is not due to the availability of extraordinary projects. The firm reinvests, as before, in projects yielding 10%. However, by cutting the dividends from £5 per share to £1 per share, the dollar volume of the investment in projects increases, and hence the dividend growth increases.

Does the increase in the growth rate by moving from 5% to 9% affect the current stock price (P_0)? To answer this question, use Equation 9.5 in the case described in Exhibit 9.3(b) to obtain

$$P_0 = \frac{d_1}{k - g} = \frac{£1}{0.10 - 0.09} = \frac{£1}{0.01} = £100$$

From this result, you can see that an increase in the growth rate of the dividends *does not* increase the current stock price (P_0). It is true that in Exhibit 9.3(b) the future dividends grow at a faster rate than in Exhibit 9.3(a) (9% versus 5%). However, for the faster-growth case (9%), there is also a lower dividend base – a £1 first-year dividend versus a £5 first-year dividend. These two factors exactly cancel each other, and the stock price remains unchanged, at $P_0 = £100$. The price (P_1) at the end of the first period increases faster in Exhibit 9.3(b) than in Exhibit 9.3(a) because as less dividends are consumed, the money is kept in the firm. This higher stock price does not mean that the investor is better off, however. Although the investor gets more dividends and hence the price (P_1) is lower, the investor's total wealth is unaffected.

The intuitive economic explanation for this result is that stockholders require a $k = 10\%$ return on their investment. If the firm invests the retained earnings at 10%, then by investing more or less (that is, by changing the dividend level), the stockholders cannot be worse or better off. The reason is that the NPV of cash flows created by a 10% profit, discounted at 10%, is zero; therefore, no change in the current stock price occurs, and the stock price is unchanged at $P_0 = £100$.

To illustrate this argument, suppose you invest for two years in one of the two alternative firms given in Exhibit 9.3. If the firm pays out 50% of its earnings as dividends, at the end of two years you obtain $P_0 \times (1.05)^2 = £110.25$ plus the second-year dividend of £5.25 and the £5 dividend received in the first year. Assuming you can invest for a year at 10%, its value at the end of the first year is $5 \times 1.1 = £5.50$. You obtain £121 altogether (110.25 + 5.25 + 5.50). Now suppose that the firm pays out only 10% of its earnings as dividends. At the end of two years you obtain $P_0 \times (1.09)^2 = £118.81$ plus £1.09 (the second-year dividend) plus the first-year dividends that you can invest at 10%, £1(1.1) = £1.10 – again, £121 altogether. As you see, the sum is the same in both cases; hence, the current price, P_0, will be the same.

PRACTICE BOX

Problem

The stock of BP Amoco, the gas company, trades at £25, will pay £1.50 in dividends next year (d_1), and has a required rate of return by the stockholders of 9.5%. BP Amoco is a normal-growth firm.

1 What is the implied growth rate of dividends?
2 If BP Amoco lowers its dividend by 10%, what is the percentage change in the growth rate of dividends?

Solution

1. From Equation 9.5, solve for g:

$$P_0(k - g) = d_1$$

$$(k - g) = \frac{d_1}{P_0}$$

$$g = k - \frac{d_1}{P_0}$$

Thus,

$$g = 0.095 - \frac{£1.50}{£25} = 3.5\%$$

2. A 10% decline in dividends will result in a dividend payment next year of £1.50 × 0.9 = £1.35. For a normal-growth firm, the change does not affect the price, which remains at £25. Hence, because BP Amoco is a normal-growth firm,

$$g = 0.095 - \frac{£1.35}{£25} = 4.1\%$$

and the percentage change in the growth rate is 17.14%, or (4.1% − 3.5%)/3.5%. Therefore, growth rates are very sensitive to dividend policy.

9.4.4 Supergrowth firms

In Exhibit 9.4, the change in the growth rate is due to the availability to the firm of extraordinarily profitable projects, i.e. projects with a positive NPV. Suppose the stockholders still require $k = 10\%$ (the risk of the firm does not change), but the firm can invest its retained earnings at 18% rather than 10%. To be more specific, suppose the firm pays £5 per share in the first year as a cash dividend, and £5 per share is reinvested at 18%. In this case, the second-year EPS will be £10 + (£5 × 0.18) = £10.90. The second-year dividend, assuming that 50% of earnings are paid as dividends, is $d_2 = \frac{1}{2} \times £10.9 = £5.45$. Similarly, the EPS and dividends grow at 9% in all other years.[6] Once again, the general formula can be applied to validate this 9% growth rate. In this example, $b = 0.5$, the reinvestment rate is $R = 18\%$, and hence $g = 0.5 \times 0.18 = 0.09$ or 9%.

Because dividends and earnings grow at $g = 9\%$ per year, the stock price should also grow at 9% per year. Equation 9.5 in this case yields:

$$P_0 = \frac{d_1}{k - g} = \frac{£5}{0.10 - 0.09} = \frac{£5}{0.01} = £500$$

Unlike the comparison of stock prices corresponding to Exhibits 9.3(a) and (b), a comparison of stock prices corresponding to Exhibits 9.3(a) and 9.4 (in both cases, 50% of earnings is paid as dividends) reveals a dramatic jump in the current stock price (P_0), from £100 to £500. How can we account for this large price increase? By shifting from Exhibit 9.3(a) to Exhibit 9.3(b), we see that the change in the growth rate (from 5% to 9%) is due to a change in the dividend policy. The firm reduces its dividend and reinvests more in projects (at 10%); hence, the growth rate increases from 5% to 9% at the expense of a reduction in the base dividend from £5 to £1. As a result, no gain in the stock price is achieved, and it remains $P_0 = £100$. However, in the comparison of Exhibits 9.3(a) and 9.4, the growth rate increases once again from 5% to 9%, not at the expense of a reduction in the base dividend, which is kept in the first year at $d_1 = £5$, but due to an increase in the project profitability (from 10% to 18%) with no change in the firm's risk. This is an economic gain, so the price increase from £100 to £500 is a reaction to the newly available profitable projects and is not due to an increase in the dollar volume invested.

Exhibit 9.4 **The growth rate in dividends, earnings and stock prices for a supergrowth firm: 9% with £5 first-year dividends**

Year	EPS	DPS	Stock price
0			P_0
1	£10	£5	$P_0(1.09)$
2	£10.90	£5.45	$P_0(1.09)^2$
3	£11.88	£5.94	$P_0(1.09)^3$
.	.	.	.
.	.	.	.
.	.	.	.

[6] Reinvestment at 18% of 50% of the EPS induces a growth rate of 18% × $\frac{1}{2}$ = 9%.

The key difference between normal-growth and supergrowth firms is that with the normal-growth firm, both the stockholders and the firm can reinvest at $k = 10\%$. The supergrowth firm, in contrast, can reinvest at 18%, whereas stockholders can reinvest the dividends at only 10%. The availability of projects with a positive NPV induces an increase in the stock price from £100 to £500.

In summary, Exhibit 9.3 shows normal-growth firms with different dividend policies. Exhibit 9.4 represents a supergrowth firm, which can reinvest money at a rate of return greater than the minimum rate required by the stockholders. A change in the growth rate of a firm that is due to a change in the proportion of earnings paid as dividends not accompanied by an increase in project profitability does not affect the stock price (see Exhibit 9.3). A change in the growth rate that is induced by the availability of more profitable projects, as expected, affects the stock valuation and thus the investors' view on whether a stock is overpriced or underpriced.

9.4.5 Supergrowth firms for a limited time period

The large increase in the stock price, from £100 to £500, should not come as a surprise. The price jump might seem to be very large and not justified by an increase in the projects' profitability from 10% to 18%. However, recall that this extra profit (18% rather than 10%) is assumed by the constant dividend growth model to continue forever on all earnings retained. Thus, the present value of the extra profit $(18\% - 10\%)$ on all retained earnings is £400; hence, the stock price increases from £100 to £500.

Does it make sense to expect that the company can reinvest its earnings at 18% but investors require only 10% on their investment? The answer is absolutely yes. To see why, consider a firm that discovers a new drug (e.g. the recent Viagra pill) and is granted a patent on this new drug. The firm earns an 18% rate of return rather than the 10% it would make without this new drug. However, the firm's risk does not change, and the required rate of return by the stockholders remains 10%. Because the firm makes 18%, investors will buy the stock, so the price will go up until the rate of return on the stock is 10%.

Because the firm in this case invests at a rate of return higher than that required by the stockholders $(k < R)$, it is a supergrowth firm. However, this supergrowth cannot continue forever, as Equation 9.5 assumes. Most firms face a limited number of years of supergrowth. Competition restricts the future growth of the firm. When one firm has an extraordinary profit, competitors will enter the market. Prices of the product, as well as its profitability, then go down. When Apple and IBM first entered the personal computer market, for example, prices were very high and these firms enjoyed extra profits. After a few years, many competitors were attracted to this profitable business, the prices of personal computers fell dramatically, and the extra profit disappeared. Firms such as IBM and Apple were supergrowth firms for a few years. When the accelerated growth levels off, they become normal-growth firms, with earnings and dividends growing at normal, rather than abnormal, rates.

Firms involved in the research and development of a new drug often achieve supergrowth for a limited period. If a firm's research is successful, the firm can obtain a patent on the drug for a limited number of years, during which supergrowth prevails. After the patent expires, competitors will be allowed to produce the drug, and the original firm becomes a normal-growth firm. The constant dividend growth model thus needs to be adjusted to reflect this nonconstant growth.

Let's consider the general method of evaluating a stock characterized by a supergrowth rate for only a limited period of time. Suppose that at the end of the first year, the dividend is $d_1 = £5$ per share, and the firm indeed can reinvest the retained earnings from the first year in a very profitable project with a positive NPV. This high rate of return is only for one year. (If it is for more than one year, a similar, but more complex, analysis applies.) The earnings retained from all subsequent years are invested at the firm's normal rate of 10%. In this case, the growth rate is not constant. Thus, Equation 9.5 cannot be employed to evaluate the stocks, because this equation is appropriate only for constant-growth cash flows. In this specific example the supergrowth lasts only one year, so we can apply Equation 9.5'. P_0 is thus given by

$$P_0 = \frac{d_1}{1+k} + \frac{d_2}{(1+k)^2} + \frac{P_2}{(1+k)^2} \qquad (9.5')$$

Let us employ the data in Exhibit 9.5. In this example, the dividend for the first year is $d_1 = £5$. We assume that earnings and dividends grow for one year at 9% (the second year) and that beginning with the second year, dividends and earnings grow only at the normal growth of 5%. Therefore, for given dividends of $d_1 = £5$, $d_2 = £5 \times 1.09 = £5.45$, $d_3 = £5.45 \times 1.05 \cong £5.72$, and so on. (All future dividends after the second year grow at 5%.) Because $d_1 = £5$ (see Exhibit 9.5) and $k = 10\%$ (by assumption), if you know P_2, you can easily solve for P_0. However, P_2 can be found by using the constant dividend growth model, because after the second year the firm will grow at the normal and constant rate. According to Equation 9.5,

$$P_2 = \frac{d_3}{k-g} = \frac{£5.72}{0.10 - 0.05} = \frac{£5.72}{0.05} = £114.40$$

where $d_3 = £5.72$, which is $d_1 = £5$ growing at 9% in the second year and at 5% in all the years from the third year on (see Exhibit 9.5). Recall that P_2 is nothing but the present value of all dividends obtained in the third year and thereafter; hence, P_2 is the present value of $d_3, d_4, \ldots$. Because the growth rate after Year 2 is constant at 5% (normal growth), using Equation 9.5 to solve for P_2 is appropriate. Therefore, P_0 is given by:

$$P_0 = \frac{d_1}{1+k} + \frac{d_2}{(1+k)^2} + \frac{P_2}{(1+k)^2} = \frac{£5}{1.1} + \frac{£5.45}{1.1^2} + \frac{£114.40}{1.1^2} = £103.60$$

Hence, because of the supergrowth of d_2 in comparison with d_1, the stock price increases from £100 to only £103.60. This result is quite different from the large jump

Exhibit 9.5 Supergrowth firm for one year and normal growth thereafter: growth rate of $g_1 = 9\%$ for the first year and $g_2 = 5\%$ after the first year with £5 first-year dividends

Year	EPS	DPS	Stock price
0			P_0
1	£10	£5	$P_0(1.09)$
2	£10.90	£5.45	$P_0(1.09)(1.05)$
3	£11.44	£5.72	$P_0(1.09)(1.05)^2$
.	.	.	.
.	.	.	.
.	.	.	.

of £400 in the stock price that occurred before, when the extra profit of 18%, and hence the supergrowth of 9%, were assumed to continue forever.

From this example it can safely be concluded that the longer the number of years a firm can enjoy extraordinary profits (or the slower the competitors are), the bigger the jump in the stock price due to the availability of these profitable projects.

This example assumed supergrowth for one year and normal growth thereafter. The valuation formula can be generalized for a stock with a supergrowth for n years and normal growth thereafter. For example, if a firm has a patent that protects it for $n = 7$ years, it has supergrowth for seven years. After seven years, competitors produce the protected product, and the growth rate is expected to go down. The firm steps into a second economic cycle characterized by a normal growth rate.

In summary, a firm's dividends can grow because of a current reduction in dividends paid, or by the firm's reinvesting funds in profitable projects. A firm that has extraordinarily profitable projects (projects with positive NPVs) is called a supergrowth firm. Otherwise, it is a normal-growth firm, regardless of the actual growth rate of EPS and DPS. Most supergrowth firms cannot enjoy this extraordinary investment opportunity forever; hence, a supergrowth firm model for a limited time period seems to be the most relevant stock valuation model to value the stock of supergrowth firms. With accurate valuation models that realize that supergrowth cannot continue forever, investors are better able to assess the reasonableness of current stock prices.

9.4.6 Supergrowth firms and risk

For supergrowth firms, the high stock price is based on the fact that the firm reinvests at $R > k$. But, if it is realized that R is smaller than what is expected, investors may revise their estimate of R (and hence of g) which may have a devastating effect on stock prices. For example, assume that $d_1 = £1$, $b = 0.5$, $k = 0.10$ and $R = 0.15$. Thus,

$$P_0 = \frac{£1}{0.1 - 0.5 \times 0.15} = £40$$

Suppose due to new information that R is revised to be, say, 12%. Thus,

$$P_0 = \frac{£1}{0.1 - 0.5 \times 0.12} = £25$$

i.e. even a relatively small drop in g would induce a 37.5% drop in the stock price ($£25/£40 - 1 = -0.375$ or -37.5%).

The high price of Internet stocks is an example of supergrowth expectation. If investors realize that the rosy future expectation is not that rosy, a sharper fall in the price of these stocks may occur. Indeed, this is what happened in 2001.

This may explain the difference in the 'growth investors' and 'value investors' mentioned in the *Investment in the news* article. It is possible that the value investors simply do not like to be involved in such risky investments. Thus, they probably realize the importance of future growth, but by the same token realize the risk involved with changes in the estimation of future growth. The possible changes of the earnings estimate of normal growth firms do not have such impact on stock price, because the firm has stable and well-known activities with a well-known market share for its products. Thus, the value investors prefer a solid 10% average return rather than, say, 25% average return with no strong swings.

9.5   CDGM VALUATION WHEN ALL THE EARNINGS ARE PAID AS CASH DIVIDENDS FOR NORMAL-GROWTH FIRMS

If a firm is a normal-growth firm and distributes all its earnings as cash dividends, the stock price (P_0) is nothing but the present value of an annuity discounted at k%. As an example, assume EPS = £10, and hence d_1 = £10. However, because all EPS is distributed as dividends, the firm does not grow, and next year's expected EPS, as well as dividends, will be constant at £10.[7] In this case,

$$P_0 = \frac{d}{1+k} + \frac{d}{(1+k)^2} + \frac{d}{(1+k)^3} + \cdots = \sum_{t=1}^{\infty} \frac{d}{(1+k)^t} = \frac{d}{k}$$

Using the data above yields the following:

$$P_0 = £10/0.1 = £100$$

This is exactly the value obtained before, when some of the profit was retained and reinvested in the firm, as long as these retained earnings were invested at k = 10% and not in extraordinarily profitable projects (k = 18%).

9.6   FINDING THE COST OF EQUITY CAPITAL WITH THE CDGM

Valuation models can be used for purposes other than finding overvalued and undervalued securities. Recall from your first finance course that the discount rate (k) is the required cost of equity capital by the stockholders, given the firm's risk. The constant dividend growth model can be used to estimate the cost of equity. In this case we assume the stock price to be the 'correct' or equilibrium market price and solve for the unknown value (k). According to the constant dividend growth model,

$$P_0 = \frac{d_1}{k-g} \text{ or } k = \frac{d_1}{P_0} + g$$

Because d_0 and P_0 are observed in the market and we can estimate the expected growth rate (g), then $d_1 = d_0 (1 + g)$ can be calculated, and we can solve for the required cost of equity by the stockholders, which is simply the expected rate of profit on equity. In the example that corresponds to the constant dividend growth model (with no super-growth) described by Exhibit 9.3(a), we get d_1 = £5, P_0 = £100, and g = 5%. Hence,

$$k = \frac{d_1}{P_0} + g = \frac{£5}{£100} + 0.05 = 0.05 + 0.05 = 0.10 \text{ or } 10\%$$

Therefore, investors who determine the stock price in the market are expecting (or requiring) to earn 10% on this investment. Given the risk of the stock, if an investor's required rate of return is greater than 10%, then the investor should avoid this investment. However, if the investor's required rate of return is lower than 10%, then this stock is an attractive investment.

---

[7] The firm reinvests the depreciation, which makes it possible to create the perpetuity of £10 per share.

PRACTICE BOX

Problem

A firm pays a £5 dividend per share and has a growth rate of 10% for four years. The growth rate is only 5% from then on. If the discount rate is a constant $k = 8\%$, what is the stock price today?

Solution

The value of this common stock in four years (P_4) will be based on the standard constant dividend discount model:

$$P_4 = \frac{d_5}{k - g_2} = \frac{d_4(1 + g_2)}{k - g_2}$$

$$= \frac{d_0(1 + g_1)^4 (1 + g_2)}{k - g_2} = \frac{£5(1 + 0.1)^4 \times (1 + 0.05)}{0.08 - 0.05} \cong \frac{£7.6865}{0.03}$$

$$\cong £256.2167$$

where $d_0(1 + g_1)^4 = d_4$, or the dividend paid at the fourth year, and g_2 is the growth rate from the fifth year and following. The present value of this stock price plus the present value of the dividends for the first four years is

$$P_0 = \frac{d_0(1 + g_1)^1}{(1 + k)^1} + \frac{d_0(1 + g_1)^2}{(1 + k)^2} + \frac{d_0(1 + g_1)^3}{(1 + k)^3} + \frac{d_0(1 + g_1)^4 + P_4}{(1 + k)^4}$$

$$= \frac{£5.5}{(1 + 0.08)^1} + \frac{£6.05}{(1 + 0.08)^2} + \frac{£6.655}{(1 + 0.08)^3} + \frac{£7.3205 + £256.2167}{(1 + 0.08)^4}$$

$$\cong £5.0926 + £5.1869 + £5.2830 + £193.7077 \cong £209.28$$

The firm's managers, in contrast, can use the market stock price as the market's equilibrium price and from this deduce the market's required rate of return (k). The firm can use this value to estimate the weighted average cost of capital, which is the appropriate discount rate used in project evaluation. Thus, the valuation formulas for stocks discussed in this chapter can be used by investors to estimate the price of a stock, as well as by a firm's management to estimate the firm's cost of equity capital. Chapter 10 discusses how historical data can be used to estimate the growth rate (g).

9.7 PICKING STOCKS USING THE P/E RATIO

Price/earnings (P/E) ratios for every firm (also known as P/E *multiple* or simply the 'multiple') are published by most economic media (for example, *Wall Street Journal* and *Barron's*). Although the P/E ratio is not based on the DCF principle, it is widely quoted and published. For example, *Barron's* of 2 July 2001 report a P/E of 16 for Hilton, 25 for Chase Manhattan and 91 for Peoplesoft Company. What does this ratio measure and how can we account for these differences in the P/E ratios?

This section discusses under what circumstances the P/E ratio conveys valuable information, discusses the factors which determine this ratio, and warns against potential misuse of the P/E ratio. Unlike the 'Super Bowl method', the P/E ratio does have some economic basis. This section covers the predictive power and limitations of the P/E ratio.

The P/E ratio published in the *Wall Street Journal, Barron's* and other financial media is the previous day's closing stock price divided by the *last* reported four quarters of EPS (denoted E). For example, if the closing stock price is $P = £100$ and annual EPS is $£10$, then P/E $= £100/£10 = 10$. This P/E ratio shows that an investor has to wait 10 years to recover the $£100$ initial investment in the stock. Similarly, a P/E ratio of 5 implies that an investor has to wait five years to recover an investment. Note that P is the current price (namely, P_0), but it is denoted as P and not P_0 in the P/E ratio.

Investment analysts, when recommending buying stock, talk about the relatively low multiples, a term they use synonymously with P/E ratios. They use either the P/E ratio expressed in years or its reciprocal, the E/P ratio, in a percentage figure to evaluate the investment profitability. The P/E rule says that if the P/E ratio is too low, the market will rise, and if the P/E ratio is too high, the market will fall.

Are analysts justified in using the P/E ratio? Is the P/E ratio consistent with the present value of dividends model (see Equation 9.5)? The following discussion explores when the P/E rule can safely be used.

It has been stated that what is relevant for investment valuation is the future cash flows. However, in the P/E calculation, E is the last (past) EPS, not the future EPS or the future dividends. When you buy a stock, though, you buy it for the future earnings, not for the past earnings. Also, earnings are also not cash flows to the investor. Therefore, using the E/P ratio (or the P/E ratio), which is based on past earnings, is conceptually wrong. However, in the following two cases, the E/P ratio yields a precise measure of profitability that is equal to the one implied by the constant dividend growth model, which probably accounts for its popularity:

- *Case 1.* Constant earnings, when all earnings are distributed as cash dividends. In this case all annual earnings (past and future) are constant and equal to the annual dividends.
- *Case 2.* Constant growth in earnings and dividends, as long as the firm has a normal growth rate (and not a supergrowth rate) and every year it pays out a fixed proportion of its earnings as dividends. In this case, however, P/E$_1$ is a relevant measure of profitability when E_1 is next year's EPS. The common P/E ratio based on last year's earnings is still misleading.

Let us elaborate.

Case 1: Constant EPS

Suppose the EPS and the DPS are constant at $£10$ (hence also $d_1 = £10$) and the stock price is $P = £100$. Therefore, E/P $= d_1/P = £10/£100 = 10\%$. In this case, the E/P ratio is 10%, which is equal to $d_1/P + g$, because $g = 0$ and $d_1/P = 10\%$. This is a trivial case, because the past earnings are equal to the future earnings (and dividends); therefore, by looking at past earnings rather than future dividends, no harm is done. However, cases in which all earnings are distributed as dividends are rare; hence, the more realistic case is one in which some fixed portion of earnings is distributed as dividends.

Case 2: Normal-growth firm

Let us turn to more relevant cases by illustrating the two cases in Exhibit 9.3 which deal with normal-growth firms.

We will show that the expected rate of return measured by Equation 9.5 or by the P/E yield the same result. These two cases have the following cost of equity which is also the expected future rate of return.

(a) $k = \dfrac{d_1}{P_0} + g = \dfrac{£5}{£100} + 0.05 = 0.05 + 0.05 = 0.10$

(b) $k = \dfrac{d_1}{P_0} + g = \dfrac{£1}{£100} + 0.09 = 0.01 + 0.09 = 0.10$

Thus, the future profitability to the investor, using the constant dividend growth model, which is the correct method, is expected to be 10%. Indeed, when $E = £10$ is the next year's EPS, E/P = 0.10 in both cases, as £10/£100 = 0.10.

Hence, for normal growth firms the P/E ratio can be safely used. However, employing the P/E ratio (or the E/P ratio) for supergrowth firms is misleading. Comparing Exhibits 9.3(a) and 9.4 yields

For normal-growth firm: $\dfrac{E}{P_0} = \dfrac{£10}{£100} = 0.10$

For supergrowth firm: $\dfrac{E}{P_0} = \dfrac{£10}{£500} = 0.02$

Thus, using the P/E ratio (or its reciprocal E/P ratio), we get a precise figure for a normal-growth firm but a distorted figure for supergrowth firms. (Note that $k = 10\%$, not 2% – see Exhibit 9.4.)

Thus, although both firms – one with a normal growth rate and one with a supergrowth rate – yield the same rate of return of 10%, looking at the E/P ratio as an indicator of profitability leads to an error: 10% for the normal-growth firm and only 2% for the supergrowth firm. The reason for the bias is that for the supergrowth firm, the future earnings, which grow at an accelerated rate, are ignored in the E/P calculation, because that calculation is fully based on current (or past) earnings.

To stress the possible distortion of the P/E ratio, suppose the P/E of Microsoft is 63, namely E/P = 1/63 ≅ 1.59 %. Does that mean that the investor's required rate of return on equity is only 1.59%? No, it does not, because investors can earn a higher certain income by buying US Treasury bills. However, there are two possible interpretations of this low figure: (1) the firm is a supergrowth firm, so the P/E ratio is misleading as discussed above, or (2) the current EPS is low and does not represent the future average EPS. Thus, a random deviation in the EPS in a particular year leads to a biased P/E ratio. Which of these two interpretations is correct can be known only by carefully studying the firm's income statement. In the case of Microsoft, supergrowth is the explanation, and the last (or the next) year's EPS does not represent the future earnings. Finally, there is a technical disadvantage to the P/E ratio. When the EPS values are negative, they are undefined.

In an article which appears in the *Wall Street Journal*, there is a suggested formula on how to pick stocks by their P/E ratio and growth:

Michael Culp, research director, says the firm's focus is 'mostly on growth stocks – companies that can deliver double-digit earnings gains the next couple of years.' To make the recommended list, the company should have a price/earnings ratio of less than the growth rate, Mr. Culp says. For example, a company whose earnings are expected to grow 15% a year should sell for a P/E ratio of less than 15.[8]

---

[8] *Source*: 'Rating your broker's stock picks', Wall Street Journal, 15 August 1997, p. C.23. Reprinted by permission of *The Wall Street Journal*. © 1997 Dow Jones & Co., Inc. All Rights Reserved Worldwide.

Now we have the tools to analyze this recommendation regarding stock selection. Suppose that you consider investing in stocks of two firms, both in the same industry. Hence, they have the same risk and the same discount rate of $k = 10\%$. Consider the following relevant data for these two firms:

	Firm A	Firm B
EPS	£10	£10
DPS	£1	£8
Price of stock	£70	£100
Rates of return on retained earnings (R)	9%	15%
Proportion of EPS retained in the firm (b)	0.9	0.2
Growth rate (g) = bR	8.1%	3%
P/E ratio	7	10

Which stock would you recommend to buy? An investor using the criterion for picking stocks as recommended above would prefer Stock A over Stock B, because Stock A has a lower P/E ratio and a higher growth rate. Moreover, according to the selection criterion, Stock A should be accepted (P/E $<$ g) and Stock B should be rejected (P/E $>$ g). Let us see if this recommendation is consistent with the dividend cash flow valuation formulas in this chapter.

Employing Equation 9.5, we find the following values of Stock A and Stock B:

$$\text{Value of Stock A: } d_1/(k - g) = £1/(0.1 - 0.081) = £1/0.019 \cong £52.63$$

$$\text{Value of Stock B: } d_1/(k - g) = £8/(0.1 - 0.03) = £8/0.07 \cong £114.29$$

Thus, the reverse is true: Stock A should be rejected because its price is higher than its discounted cash flows, and Stock B should be bought because the value of its discounted cash flows is higher than its market price. Thus, what is wrong with the recommendation given above? It simply ignores the source of growth in EPS: Firm A reinvests 90% of its earnings in the firm and thus has 8.1% growth. This growth is achieved in spite of the fact that the money is reinvested in projects with negative NPV whose rate of return (9%) is smaller than the cost of capital (10%). Firm B, in contrast, reinvests at 15%. It is a supergrowth firm, which explains its relatively high value of £114.29. However, because it reinvests only 20% of its earnings, its growth rate is relatively low. Thus, looking at the P/E ratio and g, as the article recommends, and ignoring the source of the growth rate (g) is simply misleading. This example illustrates the risk of using the P/E ratio for firms that are not normal-growth firms.

The financial media generally publish the P/E ratio in which P is the current price and E is the *last* published EPS. Exhibits 9.3(a) and (b) show that $d/p + g = E/p$; that is, for normal-growth firms, the constant dividend growth model and the reciprocal of the P/E ratio provide the same expected rate of return. However, it is important to note that even in this specific case the two methods provide the same result only when E is the *next year's* EPS, that is, the future EPS (see Exhibits 9.3(a) and (b)). Indeed, the financial media sometimes publish not only the P/E ratio with last year's earnings per share, E, but also the P/E ratio where E is next year's EPS.

In summary, investors should always rely on a stock valuation method that takes into account the discounted future dividends. However, the P/E ratio (or the E/P ratio) can be safely used for stock valuation (and for estimating the cost of equity) in the following two cases: (1) when all earnings are paid as cash dividends, and the dividends (and earnings) are constant across all years; and (2) when some constant percentage of the earnings is paid as cash dividends every year, and dividends grow over the years at a constant and normal growth rate – that is, the firm does not face an extraordinarily profitable project.

Although the P/E ratio is not based on the DCF principle, its ease of use has made it attractive for many investors. Appendix 10A and Appendix 10B at the end of the next chapter suggest two additional methods for valuing the stock of nondividend-paying firms: the free cash flow model and the economic value-added model.

9.8 A WORD OF CAUTION: THE QUALITY OF REPORTED EARNINGS

The EPS, which is the key factor for many valuation models and, in particular, for the P/E ratio discussed above, as well as for growth estimates discussed in the next chapter, are based on an accounting figure (see Appendix 9A), hence can be manipulated by management. Management can manipulate reported earnings in many ways. To boost short-term earnings, for example, they can aggressively push merchandise onto distributors. Similarly, they can depress earnings by adding to reserves for delinquent accounts. If such distortions occur, a valuation of stock or growth estimates of *g* which are based on earnings may be misleading. *The New York Times* of 1 July 1999 reports that Microsoft accounting was under scrutiny by the SEC. The SEC investigates the company's accounting practices involving the status of the reserves. It was claimed that in 1995 the chief financial officer of the company sent an e-mail to Bill Gates saying: 'I believe we should do all we can to smooth our earnings and keep a steady state earnings model' (see *The New York Times*, 1 July 1999, p. C6). In 2002, in the Enron scandal, the external auditor, Arthur Andersen, was blamed for not revealing manipulation of the reported earnings (see Exhibit 9.6 on p. 281).

While there are accounting rules asserting how a company should record revenue, there is a lot of flexibility given to the management to determine how to apply these rules. However, the purpose of the reserves is to reflect a company's true revenue – how much it will actually end up collecting in a given period if customers return merchandise or fail to pay their bills. But this flexibility opens up a door to smoothing earnings, if not done right. In the specific case of Microsoft, the company may have reserved too much, which would mean that it may have understated its profit. Indeed, financial analysts use *quality of earnings* systems which are based on the difference between the reported earnings and the actual earnings as estimated by them. Low quantity implies that the reported EPS differs greatly from the firm's actual EPS.

Along with measures of quality, analysts have devised checklists for review, or red flags to look for, when assessing the quality of earnings. The first item on the checklist is typically the audit report. Auditors write a letter – known as the *independent auditor's report* – to shareholders and the board of directors, giving an opinion on the fairness of management's financial statements, then the auditor will express them in this letter. The independent auditor's report is a part of the annual report to shareholders required by the Securities and Exchange Commission.

Finally, recall that analysts use the income statement and reported EPS as a means to estimate the future earnings ability of a firm. When trying to arrive at the actual earnings ability of a firm, the analysts must make several adjustments. For example, earnings attributable to nonrecurring items, such as the sale of a subsidiary, should not be expected to be repeated. Therefore, they should not be included in the EPS calculation.

SUMMARY

■ *Explain how investors use stock valuation models.*
A sound valuation method must rely on discounted future dividends. Whereas the current dividend is known, future dividends can only be estimated. Therefore, we say that the stock price is the present value of all expected dividends.

A valuation formula should be based on the discounted cash flow (DCF), hence it discounts all future dividends. However, the same value is also obtained when the investment is assumed to be for *n* years only. In such a case, the current stock price is the present value of the *n* years' cash dividends plus the present value of the stock price that is sold after *n* years.

■ *Describe the assumptions underlying the constant dividend growth model.*
The most popular valuation model is the constant dividend growth model, which assumes that every year the firm pays a constant percentage of its earnings as dividends, and the rest of the earnings are retained in the firm. Normal-growth firms invest the retained earnings at the required cost of equity, hence the percentage of profits retained in the firm does not affect the current stock price.

■ *Value firms that are presently experiencing supergrowth.*
Although the constant dividend growth model can be employed for normal-growth and supergrowth firms, economic logic and historical data tell us that constant supergrowth cannot continue forever. (IBM, for example, was a symbol of supergrowth, but faced a decline in profit, and even had negative earnings in 1992 and 1993.) Therefore, in the case of a supergrowth firm, a more reasonable assumption is that the supergrowth will last only for a given number of years. Then competitors will reduce the firm's growth, and after this supergrowth period, normal growth will characterize the firm. In any case, no matter whether the firm experiences normal growth or supergrowth after this initial period of supergrowth, the valuation formula changes, but the valuation is still based on the discounted value of future dividends. One task facing an analyst is how long the supergrowth will last.

■ *Explain when the P/E ratio can be used safely.*
The popular use of the P/E ratio as an investment criterion is not based on the principle of discounted future cash flows; hence, it is conceptually wrong. However, the use of the P/E ratio yields the same results as the use of the present value of future dividends for normal growth firms in two cases provided that the reported earnings are not manipulated by the management and that next year's EPS rather than the last year's EPS is used in the P/E calculation. The two cases are (a) all earnings are paid as cash dividends, and these dividends (and earnings) are constant across all years; and (b) some constant percentage of the earnings is paid as cash dividends every year, and dividends grow at a constant and normal growth rate. For supergrowth firms, the P/E ratio leads to misleading results and sometimes even to absurd results. Thus, the P/E ratio should be used with great care.

■ *Explain that reported earnings can be manipulated (see Enron).*

KEY TERMS

Balance sheet	Dividend discount model	Multiple
Constant dividend growth	(DDM)	Normal-growth firm
model (CDGM)	Dividends per share (DPS)	Price/earnings
Direct method (for cash	Earnings per share	(P/E) ratio
flows)	(EPS)	Reinvestment rate, R
Discount rate	Income statement	Statement of
Discounted cash flow	Indirect method (for cash	cash flows
(DCF) principle	flows)	Supergrowth firm

QUESTIONS

9.1 Suppose that the stock price is $P_0 = \$50$, and the dividend per share next year is $d_1 = \$2$. The discount rate is $k = 10\%$. What is the expected stock price (P_1) one year from now?

9.2 You expect to get a dividend per share of $d_1 = \$10$ next year and $d_2 = \$15$ two years from now. The stock price two years from now is expected to be $P_2 = \$120$, and the current stock price is $P_0 = \$100$. What is the equilibrium discount rate?

9.3 A stock, on average, pays $10 per share every year, and the stock price two years from now is $110. The risk-free interest rate is $r = 5\%$. Can you determine the maximum value of the stock? Explain.

9.4 In 1990, the stock of IBM traded for $P_0 = \$100$ with $d_1 = \$6$ per share, $k = 12\%$, and $g = 6\%$. Because of sharp competition in the computer industry and mismanagement, the market revised the estimate of the growth rate, making it only 4%. What should the effect be on the stock market?

9.5 Suppose the dividend at the end of the first year is $d_1 = \$10$. The growth rate will be $g_1 = 8\%$ for the next n years and then, from $n + 1$ forever, the growth rate will be $g_2 = 5\%$. The discount rate is $k = 10\%$.

(a) What is the stock price if $n = 1$?
(b) What is the stock price if $n = 10$?
(c) What is the stock price if $n = $ infinity?

9.6 A normal-growth firm has earnings of $10 per share and dividends of $5 per share. The discount rate is $k = 10\%$.

(a) What is the stock price?
(b) What is the multiplier, P/E?

9.7 One stock offers $10 a year from the next year to infinity. Another stock offers $5 next year and a growth rate of 10% a year.

(a) In what year will the dividends from both firms be equal?
(b) What stock will have a higher price if the discount rate for both is $k = 10\%$?

9.8 Suppose Firm A is a normal-growth firm. The firm's dividend policy is to maintain a dividend growth rate that is 50% of the firm's cost of equity (k). It is given that the stock price is $100, and $d_1 = \$10$. What is the firm's cost of equity (k)?

9.9 The P/E ratio of a normal-growth firm is P/E = 10. The dividend is d_1 = $10, and the stock price is $20. What is the growth rate (g)?

9.10 Suppose that the stockholder's required cost of capital is 23%. The dividend on the firm's stock was $10 per share, which is estimated to grow in the future at 2% a year indefinitely. What is the present value of all future dividends?

9.11 In 1993, IBM cuts its quarterly dividends per share from more than 50 cents to 25 cents. Suppose the annual dividends next year will be $1. IBM stock was trading for about $40. Assuming a 10% cost of capital, what is the market's long-term estimate of the growth rate of dividends for IBM?

9.12 A firm's stock price is $50, and its EPS is $5. The firm changes its accounting procedures (for example, changes its method of valuing inventory). As a result, the EPS went up to $7. How should this change affect the P/E ratio? How should it affect the present value of dividends? How should it affect the stock price?

9.13 Demonstrate that if a firm pays out a constant proportion of its earnings as dividends and reinvests its retained earnings at the cost of capital (k), then the dividend model and the P/E ratio (actually the inverse E/P ratio) yield the same value for the stock.

9.14 Suppose the average P/E ratio in the United States was about 20 in 2001. In Japan the average P/E ratio was about 50. Does this fact mean that the Japanese stock market should be considered expensive and the US market inexpensive?

9.15 'Any comparison of P/E ratios in a given country may be meaningful. However, an international comparison of P/E ratios may yield paradoxical results, because various countries have various accounting reporting standards.' Discuss this assertion.

SELECTED REFERENCES

Bower, Richard S. 'The n-stage discount model and required return: a comment'. *Financial Review*, 27(1), 1992, pp. 141–9.

Chollet, P., and E. Ginglinger. 'The pricing of French unit seasoned equity offerings'. *European Financial Management*, 2001, Vol. 7.

Danielson, Morris G. 'A simple valuation model and growth expectation'. *Financial Analysts Journal*, May–June 1998, pp. 50–7.

Diermeier, Jeff and Bruno Solnik, 'Global pricing of equity'. *Financial Analysts Journal*, July/August 2001.

Fouse, William L. 'Allocating assets across country markets'. *Journal of Portfolio Management*, 18(2), 1992, pp. 20–7.

Gehr, Adam K., Jr. 'A bias in dividend discount models'. *Financial Analysts Journal*, 48(1), 1992, pp. 75–80.

Good, Walker R. 'When are price/earnings ratios too high or too low?' *Financial Analysts Journal*, July–August 1991, pp. 9–12.

Gordon, M.J. 'Dividends, earnings and stock prices'. *Review of Economics and Statistics*, 41, May 1959, pp. 99–105.

Hayes-Yelken, S., Larry J. Merville, and Xu Yexiao. 'Identifying the factor structure of equity returns'. *Journal of Portfolio Management*, Summer 2001, Vol. 27, No. 4.

Leibowitz, Martin L., and Stanley Kogelman. 'The growth illustration: the P/E "cost" of earnings growth'. *Financial Analysts Journal*, March–April 1994, pp. 36–48.

Appendix 9A INFORMATION CONTAINED IN THE FINANCIAL STATEMENTS

Some stock evaluation methods or investment strategies are based on accounting data or on a mix of market and accounting data, e.g. book to market value, price earning ratio, etc. Therefore, in this section we briefly discuss the main financial statements provided by firms.

Analysts who evaluate a stock commonly use the financial statement analysis for the following purposes:

1 Investors can compare accounting earnings for firms in an industry to locate firms with below-average (or above-average) performance.
2 Investors can compare accounting earnings over time for a specific firm to detect future problems.
3 Accounting values can be used to predict future economic values.
4 Accounting values for earnings and dividends can be used as inputs to dividend discount models.
5 Bond investors can use financial statements to assess the risk that a firm will go bankrupt or be unable to make scheduled interest payments or repay principal.
6 Accounting values may predict future rates of return in the stock market.

Firms provide three major financial statements for investors:

1 *The income statement.* The income statement reports the firm's sales, cost of goods sold, other expenses, earnings and so forth during a given accounting period, quarter or year.
2 *The balance sheet.* Unlike the income statement, the balance sheet provides a 'snapshot' of the firm's assets and liabilities at a given moment, for example on 31 December 2001.
3 *The statement of cash flows.* The statement of cash flows is based on actual cash inflows and outflows rather than on accrual accounting. From this statement analysts can learn about the sources of a firm's cash flow and how these cash flows are used to pay for capital expenditures, dividends, interest expenses and so forth.

9A.1 Balance sheet

A balance sheet shows the assets, liabilities and equity of a firm on a specific date. The balance sheet is based on the following:

$$\text{Assets} = \text{liabilities} + \text{owners' equity}$$

The information contained in the balance sheet helps answer questions such as these: What is the size of the firm? Are most assets current or fixed? How is the capital being invested? What is the firm's capital structure?

When analyzing a balance sheet, investors look for patterns. Do any significant patterns emerge over time? Is a particular firm deviating significantly from others within its industry? Good financial statement analysis will always look beyond the numbers. However, the numbers often suggest which areas require further investigation.

Exhibit 9A.1 presents Microsoft's balance sheet, which contains data for two years. It reports the firm's assets and liabilities at the reported date, in our example the end of the year.

The current assets include mainly cash, short-term investment, e.g. Treasury Bills, and inventory. The fixed assets include long-term investment, mainly the plant equipment less the accumulated depreciation.

Exhibit 9A.1 **Balance sheets**

June 30	(in millions)	
	1997	1998
Assets		
Current assets:		
Cash and short-term investments	$8,966	$13,927
Accounts receivable	980	1,460
Other	427	502
Total current assets	10,373	15,889
Property and equipment	1,465	1,505
Equity investments	2,346	4,703
Other assets	203	260
Total assets	$14,387	$22,357
Liabilities and stockholders' equity		
Current liabilities:		
Accounts payable	$721	$759
Accrued compensation	336	359
Income taxes payable	466	915
Unearned revenue	1,418	2,888
Other	669	809
Total current liabilities	3,610	5,730
Commitments and contingencies		
Stockholders' equity:		
Convertible preferred stock – shares authorized 100;		
shares issued and outstanding 13	980	980
Common stock and paid-in capital – shares authorized 8,000;		
shares issued and outstanding 2,408 and 2,470	4,509	8,025
Retained earnings	5,288	7,622
Total stockholders' equity	10,777	16,627
Total liabilities and stockholders' equity	$14,387	$22,357

Source: Website at http://www.microsoft.com/MSFT/history.htm. © 2001 Microsoft Corporation, One Microsoft Way, Redmond, Washington 98052-6300 USA. All rights reserved.

The liabilities and equity are the other side of the balance sheet. It contains current liabilities (short-term debt, accounts payable, etc.), long-term debt and shareholders' equity. The firm's equity is composed of the par value of the stocks – the additional paid in capital less Treasury stocks and the employer benefit trust.

Financial analysts generally use this data to calculate the EPS and the book value per share, which are needed for stock valuation.

Financial analysts generally investigate the changes in the various items in the balance sheet. Are the changes in cash, and is this a signal that something is wrong (the firm has less project to invest) or are they due to a temporary change in cash? Why are accounts receivable increasing? To answer these questions, the analyst must look at the explanations to the balance sheet that are normally part of the financial statements. If satisfied by the explanations, the analyst can conclude that this is a firm with no *long-term* liabilities. Hence, it is mostly an equity firm with regard to its long-term financial policy. Thus, Microsoft has relatively little financial risk.

9A.2 Income statement

The income statement shows the flow of sales, expenses and earnings during a specified period. The income statement is also known as the profit and loss (P&L) statement. It provides a summary of the revenues, cost of goods sold and expenses of a firm for an accounting period.

The income statement helps investors assess the abilities of management. Specifically, the income statement demonstrates how profitably the firm operated over a period of time. Related to profitability is management's ability to control expenses.

The information contained in the income statement helps answer several questions that investors have. What were the primary sources of income, cost of goods sold, and expenses? What is the value of research and development? Does research and development produce income? What is the 'true' earning power of the firm, where 'true' implies actual benefits accruing to the firm? In particular, by comparing several years, what is the trend in revenues, market share and profits? Answers to these questions are found in part in the income statement.

Exhibit 9A.2 shows the income statement of Microsoft. The income statement reports the revenue and then the various costs which are needed to create these sales. The net

Exhibit 9A.2 Income statements

	(in millions, except earnings per share)		
Year ended June 30	1996	1997	1998
Revenue	$8,671	$11,358	$14,484
Operating expenses:			
Cost of revenue	1,188	1,085	1,197
Research and development	1,432	1,925	2,502
Acquired in-process technology	–	–	296
Sales and marketing	2,657	2,856	3,412
General and administrative	316	362	433
Other expenses	19	259	230
Total operating expenses	5,612	6,487	8,070
Operating income	3,059	4,871	6,414
Interest income	320	443	703
Income before income taxes	3,379	5,314	7,117
Provision for income taxes	1,184	1,860	2,627
Net income	2,195	3,454	4,490
Preferred stock dividends	–	15	28
Net income available for common shareholders	$2,195	$3,439	$4,462
Earnings per share:[1]			
Basic	$0.93	$1.44	$1.83
Diluted	$0.86	$1.32	$1.67

[1] Earnings per share have been restated to reflect a two-for-one stock split in February 1998. See accompanying notes.

Source: Website at http://www.microsoft.com/MSFT/history.htm. © 2001 Microsoft Corporation, One Microsoft Way, Redmond, Washington 98052-6300 USA. All rights reserved.

income is divided by the number of shares to yield the EPS figure. Of particular interest to financial analysts is the series of EPS and DPS for several years from which a trend can be detected and the growth rate can be estimated. As we can see, Microsoft is a supergrowth firm with EPS growing from $0.86 in 1996 to $1.67 in 1998.

9A.3 Statement of cash flows

Accounting principles are very different from valuation methods. By accounting principles a firm may be profitable, yet by valuation methods it could be near bankruptcy. Suppose Boeing sells 747 jumbo aircraft for $500 million each. The production costs, which are all paid in cash, are $470 million. Would Boeing be profitable? Your answer depends on the method you use to evaluate this firm. An accountant would report on the income statement $30 million in earnings for each plane sold. Suppose now that the planes are sold not for cash but on credit for one year. Does this affect accounting earnings? No, the earnings will be reported in the year of the transaction as $500 million in revenues, even though the $500 million has not yet been received. Thus, the $500 million will be on the balance sheet as accounts receivable. Now suppose that the appropriate annual discount rate is 10%. Clearly, $500 million received one year from now is worth only $500 million/(1 + 0.10) $\cong$ $454.5 million (recall the time value of money). Because it cost $470 million to produce the planes, Boeing actually loses in economic terms (or in market value), even though the accounting statement shows a profit.

Although the reported earnings can be adjusted to reflect the true economic earnings, such distortions can be identified in the statement of cash flow that is also reported by the firm. In our example, if there are accounts receivable of $500 million, this sum will not be written as cash flow this year but rather in the next year, when they are actually received.

The statement of cash flows tells us all the sources of cash for the firm (including borrowing or a new issue of stock) and how the firm uses this cash for expenses, investment, paying dividends and so forth. The statement of cash flows has three components: operating activities, investing activities and financing activities. Operating activities include almost all items in the income statement, as well as balance sheet items that directly relate to earnings activities. Investing activities include buying or selling securities or revenue-generating assets, as well as activities related to lending money. Financing activities include activities related to borrowing money, as well as transactions related to owners' equity. The statement of cash flows is beneficial in assessing the ability of the firm to pay future dividends, fund future growth and service its debts.

The statement of cash flows documents the flow of cash through the firm during an accounting period. There are two methods for reporting the cash flows. The direct method shows the cash receipts and payments from operations. This approach gives the analyst a better understanding of how cash moves through a firm. The most popular method of reporting the cash flows, however, is the indirect method, which takes net income and adjusts for non-cash items in order to convert it to cash from operations. The indirect method reconciles net income with cash from operations. For example, Exhibit 9A.3 presents Microsoft's statement of cash flows, which starts with net income and reconciles the change in the cash asset account on the balance sheet.

For example, the net income of Microsoft in 1998 was $4,490 million. However, this does not mean that the firm obtained $4,490 million in cash inflows. Cash inflows could be more or less. For example, the firm had depreciation of $1,024 million. This is not a cash outflow but an accounting allocation. Therefore, we add it to the $4,490 million, as cash flow to the firm.

Exhibit 9A.3 **Cash flow statements**

Year ended June 30	(in millions)		
	1996	1997	1998
Operations			
Net income	$2,195	$3,454	$4,490
Depreciation and amortization	480	557	1,024
Write-off of acquired in-process technology	–	–	296
Unearned revenue	983	1,601	3,268
Recognition of unearned revenue from prior periods	(477)	(743)	(1,798)
Other current liabilities	584	321	208
Accounts receivable	(71)	(336)	(520)
Other current assets	25	(165)	(88)
Net cash from operations	3,719	4,689	6,880
Financing			
Common stock issued	504	744	959
Common stock repurchased	(1,385)	(3,101)	(2,468)
Put warrant proceeds	124	95	538
Preferred stock issued	–	980	–
Preferred stock dividends	–	(15)	(28)
Stock option income tax benefits	352	796	1,553
Net cash from (used for) financing	(405)	(501)	554
Investments			
Additions to property and equipment	(494)	(499)	(656)
Cash portion of Web TV purchase price	–	–	(190)
Equity investments and other	(625)	(1,669)	(1,598)
Short-term investments	(1,551)	(921)	(4,828)
Net cash used for investments	(2,670)	(3,089)	(7,272)
Net change in cash and equivalents	644	1,099	162
Effect of exchange rates on cash and equivalents	(5)	6	(29)
Cash and equivalents, beginning of year	1,962	2,601	3,706
Cash and equivalents, end of year	2,601	3,706	3,839
Short-term investments	4,339	5,260	10,088
Cash and short-term investments	$6,940	$8,966	$13,927

See accompanying notes.

In practice, we see from Exhibit 9A.3 that the cash flow calculations are more complex. The firm makes several adjustments to get a net cash inflow from operations in 1998 of $6,880 million. Similarly, there are cash flows from raising more capital, firm investing, etc. The end result is a cashflow of $13,927 million in 1998.

It is interesting to see from this analysis that the firm has a policy of repurchasing its stocks. Stock buybacks can be interpreted by investors in one of two ways. Either management has run out of projects with positive NPVs and seeks to give investors capital gains rather than taxable dividends, or management believes the stock is significantly underpriced. Instead of raising money by issuing more stock, Microsoft is using cash to repurchase its stocks. Because Microsoft policy has been consistent for the past few years, it probably reveals significant information. It is possible that management thinks that its stock is underpriced, and it is a good investment to repurchase the stock. Also, this repurchasing signals a strong cash balance, because the repurchase is financed not by borrowing but from the firm's past earnings. The repurchasing may also mean that the firm lacks other profitable (NPV > 0) investment opportunities. In the case of Microsoft it clearly indicates strong confidence in the stock by management and may be based on some positive information that management knows but investors do not.

9A.4 Earnings and Dividends Per Share (EPS and DPS)

The actual EPS generally is different from the reported EPS. Therefore, analysts employ various methods to measure these deviations. There are various reasons why management reports EPS which differ from the actual EPS. For example, in 1999 Microsoft was under scrutiny by the SEC, who claimed that Microsoft manipulated the EPS in order to 'smooth' the EPS time series. Many analysts have devised ranking systems that are referred to as quality of earnings. Low quality implies that the reported EPS number differs greatly from the firm's actual operating earnings. In the case of Enron, the analysts failed in their analysis and Wall Street was hit in early 2002 by the discovery that reported earnings had been distorted. This distortion cast doubt on the quality of earnings reporting by other companies, leading to a market decline during February 2002 (see Exhibit 9.6 below).

As investors analyze the financial statements, they seek information on the quality of earnings. They ask several questions about quality. For example, when managers can select among different accounting procedures, do they select conservative or liberal procedures? Can a firm actually pay out the reported EPS, or is it not yet fully realized? Recall the preceding example of Boeing, where the $500 million in sales are in accounts receivable, so they cannot be paid as dividends. Over time, does the firm have stable earnings, or are the earnings volatile? How hard is it to forecast future earnings? Analysts seek to establish their level of confidence in the reported EPS figure, generally measured by the standard deviation of the EPS.

Exhibit 9.6

Andersen chief shifts blame in Enron debacle

By Peter Spiegel in Washington

Joseph Berardino, Andersen's chief executive, on Tuesday blamed the structure of the accounting industry for contributing to the collapse of Enron, saying that audit rules barred Andersen accountants from warning the public about the energy giant's financial condition.

Mr Berardino urged lawmakers to change accounting regulations to allow auditors to grade the quality and risk of a company's financial statements. Currently, firms can only give a 'pass' or 'fail' to financial data submitted by the company.

'Some companies do the bare minimum to meet [accounting] requirements, while others are much more prudent in their accounting decisions and disclosures,' Mr Berardino told a congressional hearing. 'There are some companies that are pushing the envelope and investors don't know which one is which.'...

In his testimony before the same panel, Mr Berardino said his company repeatedly questioned Enron's accounting practices, pointing to a widely reported February 5 meeting of Andersen auditors in which some of Enron's practices were labelled 'intelligent gambling'.

But while accounting rules allowed auditors to raise their concerns with Enron's board, which Mr Berardino said they did regularly, they prevented any public disclosure unless there were clear-cut violations of accepted accounting principles.

'Our only option is to resign the engagement [but] resigning an engagement may destroy a company that is fundamentally sound,' he said. 'So those are our choices when faced with a client whose accounting treatments are risky: give it a pass or give it the death penalty.'...

Mr Berardino said Andersen was aware of Enron's now-infamous private partnerships, which enabled the company to take debts off its balance sheets, but insisted they were set up by Enron executives and investment bankers, with Andersen only giving passive judgments as to whether they passed accepted accounting principles.

He also said Andersen would set up a new ethics office which would investigate questionable audit reviews when concerns are raised about the integrity or independence of an accountant.

Source: Website at http://news.ft.com/ft/gx.cgi, 5 and 6 February 2002. Reprinted with permission.

Chapter 11

MARKET AND INDUSTRY ANALYSIS

Learning objectives

After studying this chapter you should be able to:

1 Identify and describe the macro-economic variables that measure economic health.

2 Describe the impact of government fiscal and monetary policy on investment decisions.

3 Describe the measures used to value the stock market as a whole.

4 Evaluate market sectors and specific industries.

INVESTMENT IN THE NEWS

Three bears suggest fears of a recession are make believe

The downturn, like two before, has not lasted long enough for despair to set in, says Philip Coggan

Once upon a time, it was easy to spot bear markets, and to understand why they occurred. Back in 1973–74, the world suffered from stagflation, an oil price surge and banking collapses – it was hardly surprising that share prices plunged.

But it is much less easy to put your finger on why equity markets are in such a bad state now. Unemployment is low – in the UK, it fell below 1m in February for the first time since 1975 – and inflation is under control. Central banks are cutting interest rates. Currency markets are relatively calm. The developed world is at peace. As the English comic Stanley Holloway put it, there are "no wrecks and nobody drowned".

There were rumours yesterday of a Japanese banking collapse. But market falls are often accompanied by such rumours and the weakness of Japan's financial system is hardly a big surprise.

The downturn in the market bears a distinct resemblance to two other episodes in the last 25 years – the stock market crash of 1987 and the bond market collapse of 1994.

Economists are still not agreed on what prompted the crash of 1987, when the Dow Jones Industrial Average fell 22 per cent in one day. But in retrospect, it seems clear that the anomaly was not the crash but the first half of 1987, when a speculative surge carried markets sharply higher. Investors priced the market for perfection and disappointment became inevitable.

In 1994, bond prices plunged when the Federal Reserve raised interest rates, after a long period at 3 per cent. For the previous three years, speculators had enjoyed easy pickings by borrowing at the short-term rate and investing in the higher yields available on long-term bonds; they had become complacent.

Note that in neither case did the market falls prove to be a useful economic signal. The 1987 crash was not followed by a slump; economic growth surged in

▶

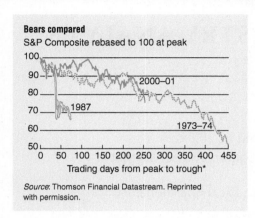

Bears compared

S&P Composite rebased to 100 at peak

Source: Thomson Financial Datastream. Reprinted with permission.

question of "buying on the dips". In a bear market, investors sell on the rallies.

In late 1999 and early 2000, investors became too optimistic about the potential for profits growth in the technology, media and telecommunication sectors.

Over the last year the TMT bubble has been deflated. The state of the economy is, in a sense, irrelevant since markets paid little attention to fundamentals on the way up. The TMT bubble was all about momentum – investors bought the stocks that had already moved higher. That same momentum is working against the sector on the way down.

So while the S&P 500 and some markets in Europe have met the first requirement for a bear market – a fall of 20 per cent – the downturn has not yet lasted long enough or caused sufficient despair to meet all the criteria.

For that to happen, the US slowdown needs to develop into a fully-fledged recession and, probably, the European economies have to slow sharply as well.

Source: *Financial Times*, 15 March 2001, p. 17.

1988. And 1994's fall in bond prices was not followed by a surge in inflation.

In each case, the bear phase was short-lived. A true bear market requires not only the conventional definition of a 20 per cent fall in prices, but also time. Investors need to become depressed by day after day of declines so that there is no longer any

* The graph shows, for example, that in 1987 the crash lasted for about 70 days and the S&P fell by more than 30%. The 1973 crisis lasted for about 455 days and the index fell by 50%.

W e see from the above *Investment in the news* article that spotting a trend in the stock market is very important but is a very difficult task. For example, the 1973–74 crises in the stock market had a macro-economic explanation (oil price crisis, stagflation, etc.). But how can we explain the one-day drop in the Dow Jones Industrial Average October 1987 crash? We see from this article that sometimes the health of the economy is directly related to stocks and bonds prices, but in other cases such a relationship is vague.

This chapter examines the major principles related to evaluating the overall health of a country's economy. It also looks at the role that government policy plays in economic health.

Why should investors analyze the whole economy, or even a given industry, when they are interested only in evaluating stocks or bonds? After all, investors are interested in the potential earnings of a specific firm, not the whole economy. Investors buy individual stocks, not industries or whole economies. Thus, it may seem that macro-economic analyses are not of much value to individual investors. However, as we see from the above article, this is not the case.

It is well known that the majority of the variation in a stock price can be explained by movements in the overall market.[1] Therefore, this chapter examines economic factors that influence the entire market, and hence also affect the prices of individual stocks. After accounting for market movements, the environment in which a firm operates – the

[1] See, for example, B. King, 'Market and industry factors in stock price behavior', *Journal of Business*, 39, January 1966, pp. 139–90.

firm's sector and industry – also explains a significant portion of a stock's price movement. For example, the expected low futures interest rate boosts stocks' price. The banking industry in particular benefits from low interest rates.

This chapter first reviews some basic economic principles and their influence on financial markets. It then establishes the necessary links between the economy and financial markets. Next it focuses on valuing the overall stock market, specifically by examining book value, dividends and earnings of broad stock market indexes. The chapter concludes with an overview of how to assess the relative value of market sectors and industries.

11.1 MACRO-ECONOMIC EVALUATION

A vibrant and growing economy needs a well-functioning capital market. In turn, when the economy is growing and firms are profitable, investors are willing to invest and thus provide the funds needed for capital expansion. All firms are influenced by the economic environment in which they operate. Therefore, the ability to forecast the overall economy is a key to being a successful portfolio manager.

However, the most important key is the ability to find economic factors that change *before* the stock market changes, not after the stock market changes. Identifying these economic factors enables the investor to buy stocks before stock prices rise or to sell them before they drop. Unfortunately, it is very difficult to identify such factors, because the stock market is a leading index (it reacts first) relative to most other economic indicators. Nevertheless, forecasting long-term economic trends and government policy and, in particular, the Central Bank policy regarding interest rate may be beneficial for long-run investors who consider investing in stocks or bonds.

11.1.1 Understanding gross domestic product

The most widely used measure of the health of the overall economy is the gross domestic product (GDP). The GDP is typically measured both quarterly and annually, and the government issues preliminary estimates throughout the year. The GDP, or the nominal GDP, as it is sometimes called, is the value of all goods and services produced in an economy in a particular time period. The US GDP is measured in dollars. Because inflation changes the value of dollars, economists adjust GDP values to include the effects of inflation. This inflation-adjusted measure, called the real GDP, allows economists and investors to compare the GDP over time, ignoring the impact of inflation. In the United States, statistics on the GDP and related measures of economic health are produced by the Bureau of Economic Analysis of the US Department of Commerce.

Gross national product (GNP) counts goods and services produced by US nationals in a foreign country but does not include goods and services produced by foreigners in the domestic country. Thus, a factory built in Spain by US citizens would count in the US GNP but not in Spain's GNP. The GDP, on the other hand, counts goods and services produced within the country's borders, ignoring who produced them. Thus, the factory built in Spain by US citizens would count as part of Spain's GDP but not as part of the US GDP.

Several measures of economic activity provide clues on the magnitude and direction of the real GDP. Exhibit 11.1 lists some of these measures, what component of the GDP they influence, and when these measures are announced. For example, the number of

Exhibit 11.1 **Measuring inflation and components of the GDP and when they are reported**

Component	Percentage of GDP	Economic measures	When available[a]
Consumption	69%	Car sales	After 3 days (biweekly)
		Retail sales	11th–14th
		Personal income/expenditures	22nd–31st
Investment	13	Housing starts/building permits	16th–20th
		Durable goods orders	22nd–28th
		New home sales	28th–4th
		Construction spending	1st (2 months prior)
		Factory orders/business inventories	30th–6th (2 months prior)
Government spending	19	Public construction	1st (2 months prior)
Net exports	−0.5	Merchandise trade balance	15th–17th (2 months prior)
GDP[b]	100[c]	Purchasing managers' index	1st
		Employment	1st–7th
		Industrial production capacity	14th–17th
Inflation		Producers price index	9th–16th
		Consumers price index	15th–21st

[a] Unless otherwise stated, the dates refer to the following month. See page 15 of the source.
[b] A negative figure implies that exports are smaller than imports.
[c] The sum is not exactly 100% because of rounding.

Source: W. Stansbury Carnes and Stephen D. Slifer, *The Atlas of Economic Indicators* (New York: HarperCollins Publishers, 1991).

cars sold is announced every two weeks about three days following the end of the second week. Clearly, car sales represent consumption, and they help give early clues as to whether consumers are loosening their purse strings. Consumers tend to purchase cars when they have confidence in the overall economy.

The value of these published economic measures depends heavily on how soon they are available. Car sales, for example, are very valuable, because they are published after only three days (as well as biweekly). Factory orders are not as valuable, because they are published only several months after the order day.

11.1.2 The business cycle and economic indicators

A business cycle is a period of expansion and contraction of aggregate economic activity measured by the real GDP. When the economy expands, stock prices rise, because firms are relatively profitable. The opposite is true in periods of contraction. Thus, predicting the business cycle is relevant for investors in the security market. Exhibit 11.2 illustrates the stages of a business cycle. The black line moving up through time represents long-run growth. As economic activity contracts, the real GDP dips below this growth rate. It reaches a low point known as the trough. Eventually the economy expands until it reaches the high point of the business cycle, known as the peak. An economy is in an expansion phase between a trough and before a peak; it is in a contraction phase after a peak and before a trough. Because business cycles do not occur regularly or predictably,

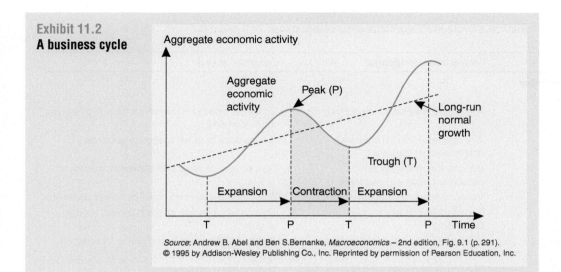

Exhibit 11.2
A business cycle

Aggregate economic activity

Aggregate
economic
activity

Peak (P)

Long-run
normal
growth

Trough (T)

Expansion Contraction Expansion

T P T P Time

Source: Andrew B. Abel and Ben S.Bernanke, *Macroeconomics* – 2nd edition, Fig. 9.1 (p. 291).
© 1995 by Addison-Wesley Publishing Co., Inc. Reprinted by permission of Pearson Education, Inc.

they are difficult to forecast. Even harder is predicting how financial markets will react to changes in the business cycle.

Because financial markets and business cycles are generally related, investors can be hurt if they forecast a business cycle incorrectly. For example, if an investor bought stocks that tend to move with the business cycle, known as *cyclical stocks*, and the economy suddenly deteriorated, then these stocks probably would incur substantial losses for the investor.

The National Bureau of Economic Research has constructed measures of business activity known as *composite indexes*, which are made up of selected economic data that vary depending on the purpose of the composite index.

The three main indexes (also called indicators – a technical measurement used to forecast the market's direction) are the leading, coincident and lagging indexes. Coincident indicators are indicators that are supposed to move directly with the business cycle. Leading indicators and lagging indicators are indicators that are supposed to lead and lag behind the business cycle. For example, the composite index of 11 leading indicators is a weighted average of 11 economic statistics that are supposed to lead the business cycle. Exhibit 11.3 gives these 11 components. Each index is given a specific reference number that helps analysts keep track of how a particular index or a composite index is constructed. Thus, each index can be identified uniquely by its number. For example, the average weekly hours worked in manufacturing is Series 1.

From time to time, the composition of these composite indexes is changed. We see from Exhibit 11.3 that the 11 series making up the leading index are statistics that would be expected to change first with changes in the business cycle. For example, Series 1, the average weekly hours worked by manufacturing labour, would tend to rise as businesses perceived that the economy was entering an expansion phase and demand was rising. It is interesting to note that Series 19, the index of stock prices (which is actually the Standard & Poor's 500 index), is one of the best-performing leading indicators of the business cycle.

Exhibit 11.3 **Business cycle indicators and their components**

Series	Type of index component	Explanation
Leading index components		
1	Average weekly hours, manufacturing	Length of working week increases with perceived future demand
5	Average weekly initial claims on unemployment insurance	Claims decline as an economy rebounds
8	Manufacturers' new orders, consumer goods and materials	New orders increase with a stronger economy
32	Vendor performance, slower deliveries	A stronger demand will result in slower deliveries
20	Contracts and orders for plant and equipment	New orders increase as the business outlook brightens
29	Index of new private housing units	People build houses based on the forecast of future prospects
92	Change in manufacturers' unfilled orders, durable goods	Unfilled orders indicate future GNP growth
99	Change in sensitive materials prices	The demand for certain materials increases as an economy expands
19	Index of stock prices, 500 common stocks	Stock prices are based on forecast *future* performance
106	Money supply, M2 (M1, M2 and M3) are three measures of the money supply as defined by the Federal Reserve. M1 represents all money that can be converted to cash immediately; M2 includes M1 plus savings accounts and time deposits; M3 is M2 plus the M3 is M2 plus the money market funds held by institutions	Economies are sensitive to the quantity of money available
83	Index of consumer expectations, University of Michigan	Consumers with bright expectations will spend more
Coincident index components		
41	Employees on nonagricultural payrolls	The number of persons employed moves with the business cycle
51	Personal income less transfer payments	Employee pay moves directly with the business cycle
47	Index of industrial production	Production moves directly with the demand for goods
57	Manufacturing and trade sales	Sales move directly with the business cycle
Lagging index components		
91	Average duration of unemployment	Length of unemployment declines after an economy rebounds
77	Ratio of manufacturing and trade inventories to sales	After an economy rebounds, sales increase and inventories decline
62	Change in labour cost per unit of output	Labour costs rise after an economy rebounds
109	Average prime rate charged by banks	Interest rates rise in response to business demand for funds

Exhibit 11.3 (continued)

Series	Type of index component	Explanation
101	Commercial and industrial loans outstanding	Borrowing increases after an economic rebound
95	Ratio of consumer instalment credit outstanding to personal income	People borrow a greater percentage of their income *after* an economic recovery
120	Change in Consumer Price Index for services	Price levels tend to rise only after an economy is expanding

11.1.3 Fiscal and monetary policy

The government uses fiscal policy and monetary policy to influence the level of real GDP in the economy and to promote GDP growth, relatively full employment and stable prices. The government can also intervene to avoid bankruptcy trends. For example, in November 1997, the fourth largest investment house in Japan declared bankruptcy. The Nikkei index dropped sharply, igniting fear of a bankruptcy chain reaction. The Japanese government immediately announced a reform plan to avoid the chain reaction, and the Nikkei index recovered in response to this plan. Thus, governments, in implementing their policies, can affect the business environment as well as the stock market.

The federal government and fiscal policy

Fiscal policy refers to the taxation and spending policies of the government designed to achieve GDP growth, relatively full employment and stable prices. Governments can stimulate growth in real GDP with tax incentives for investment. For example, a reduction in the corporate capital gains tax rates may motivate businesses to make capital expenditures. This increase in investment directly increases the GDP. Personal tax rates also affect the stock market. For example, if investors had been able to forecast that the Clinton administration would reduce the maximum capital gains tax from 28% to 20% (or even to 18% for a five-year holding period) in 1997, before this information was public or even before it was publicly discussed, they could have made money by purchasing stocks, because such an announcement usually induces an increase in stock market prices. Fiscal policy seeks to find the optimal strategy that maximizes GDP growth and employment and at the same time maintains stable prices.

The government can affect the unemployment rate in various ways. One method of stimulating a sluggish economy is for the government to hire unemployed persons to perform various tasks, such as building roads. Without tax increases, however, this government spending will produce budget deficits. Similar to a personal budget deficit, a governmental budget deficit occurs when a government spends more in a given period than it takes in as tax revenues. Budget deficits make prices unstable. If budget deficits are financed by printing money – something the United States has yet to do – the result is inflation. If budget deficits are financed by borrowing money, there is less capital for business investment.

Assessing the fiscal soundness of a country's government is a critical task for international portfolio analysis, as well as analysis of domestic portfolios. Even good companies have difficulty remaining profitable if they operate in a country whose government is irresponsible. Hence, one key assessment criterion for international investment is the integrity of the foreign government's fiscal policy.

■ The Federal Reserve Bank and monetary policy

In 1913, Congress created the Federal Reserve Bank (the Fed) to carry out monetary policy. Monetary policy refers to actions by a central bank to control the supply of money and interest rates that directly influence the financial markets. Like fiscal policy, monetary policy aims to achieve growth in the real GDP, relatively full employment and stable prices. The Fed's primary focus is on interest rates and money supply. Additionally, the Fed acts as a lender of last resort (when there is a cash drain on a bank) and guards against severe currency depreciation. The Fed will lend to banks, for example, when there are unusually large withdrawals. It will also try to support its currency in volatile foreign exchange markets. However, if the interest rate increase is moderate and expected and the Fed hints of more increases in the near future, the stock market may soar (see the *Investment in the news* article). Generally, when the Fed announces an interest rate increase, the stock market falls. Similarly, an interest rate decrease is accompanied by an increase in stock prices. Thus, analyzing the Fed's policy and being able to predict it ahead of time can turn out to be very profitable. To stimulate the economy the central bank decreases the interest rate. After the 11 September terrorist attack, in order to stimulate the economy, the Federal Reserve Bank cut interest rates several times and it was 1.75% as of February 2002. A relatively low interest rate makes consumers spend more money (even borrow money and spend it on goods), corporations enjoy an increase in demand, and more sales and more profit will generally push stock prices up. However, this is not always the case. The economy may be stuck in recession regardless of the low interest rate. In Japan, from 1999 the interest rates are very close to zero. Yet consumers refused to spend money and businesses declined to invest, a phenomenon known among economists as the 'liquidity trap'. This was the case in Japan in 1999 and it was feared that America would fall into the same trap. If this occurs, the central bank loses its power to steer the economy, i.e. a decrease in interest rate would not help either the economy or the stock prices. However, we would like to emphasize that the liquidity trap is the exception rather than the rule, and generally monetary policy is very powerful.

The Fed regulates the volume of bank reserves, affects the pace of money creation, and sets the percentage of funds that banks are required to hold as reserves. It rarely uses bank reserves as a policy tool in its efforts to manipulate the economy. Bank reserves are the percentage of deposits that banks must hold in noninterest-bearing assets (cash). Reserve requirements set by the Fed are one of the key tools in deciding how much money banks can lend. The higher the reserve requirement, the tighter the money, and therefore the slower the economic growth. In a recession, the Fed can decrease the reserve requirement to stimulate the economy. The tool used most often by the Fed to alter the money supply is its open market operations (these are activities by which the Federal Reserve Bank of New York carries out the instructions of the Federal Open Market Committee, which intends to regulate the money supply in the market). By buying and selling US Treasury securities directly in the bond market, the Fed can expand or contract the volume of bank reserves.

Exhibit 11.4 illustrates how the Federal Reserve system influences economic activity. Note that changes in bank reserves influence both the money supply and interest rates, which in turn influence both economic activity and inflation.

The Fed also establishes the bank discount rate, which is the rate the Fed charges banks when they borrow directly from it. Indirectly, the bank discount rate influences other interest rates. The federal funds rate is the rate charged for reserves borrowed between banks. The bank discount rate and the federal funds rate are highly correlated.

The ability of a central bank such as the Fed to maintain stable prices and stable interest rates is a key ingredient in providing an environment conducive to running business

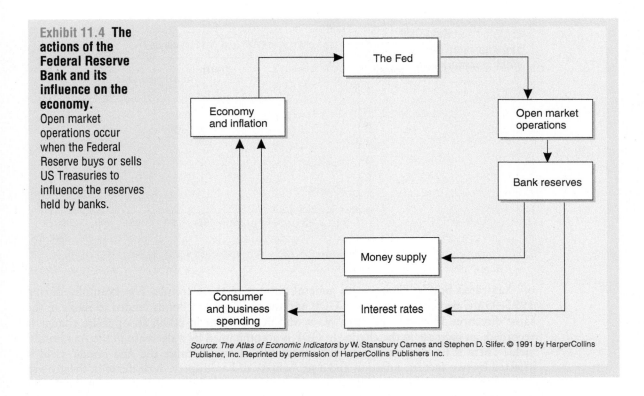

Exhibit 11.4 The actions of the Federal Reserve Bank and its influence on the economy. Open market operations occur when the Federal Reserve buys or sells US Treasuries to influence the reserves held by banks.

Source: The Atlas of Economic Indicators by W. Stansbury Carnes and Stephen D. Slifer. © 1991 by HarperCollins Publisher, Inc. Reprinted by permission of HarperCollins Publishers Inc.

profitably. Thus, investors need to assess the current abilities of Federal Reserve Bank authorities, as well as compare central bank operations across countries.

11.2 THE ECONOMY AND THE FINANCIAL MARKETS

This section examines the relationship between the overall economy and the bond and stock markets. An economy experiencing real growth in GDP will have a strong stock market. A strong economy implies that firms are working near capacity and profit margins are high. These higher earnings suggest higher stock prices. A productive country will also experience a strong demand for its currency as outside investors convert their currency and invest in the vibrant economy. A strong economy also implies a threat of some inflation, which is not favourable for the bond market. When firms are operating at capacity, the ability to raise prices (and to spark inflation) is always a consideration. Higher inflation translates into higher interest rates, which generally means falling bond prices.

Although we can make the intuitive link between the economy and the financial markets, what is the empirical evidence for such a link? Let's look at the actual experience of the United States.

11.2.1 Bond market

Exhibit 11.5 shows the relationship between changes in real GDP and the bond markets. Specifically, the exhibit compares changes in real GDP with the nominal yield to maturities

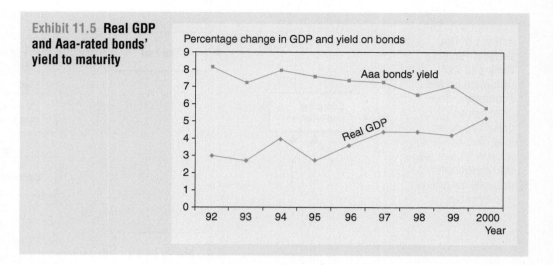

Exhibit 11.5 Real GDP and Aaa-rated bonds' yield to maturity

on Aaa-rated bonds. There is no general pattern in these trends. For example, during 1992–95 the percentage change in GDP and the yield on Aaa bonds tended to move in the same direction. However, in other years, and in particular in 2000, an opposite change is recorded: an increase in the change in GDP is accompanied by a decrease in the Aaa bonds' yield. There is no consistent pattern of these two curves, because the Aaa bonds' yield is affected by two factors: inflation and a probability of bankruptcy. A decrease in the growth rate of the GDP indicates a recession. Hence, the probability of firms going bankrupt increases, bond prices fall and the yield increases. Similarly, with an expansion of the economy, the increase in the change in the GDP decreases the probability of bankruptcy, bond prices increase and the yield decreases. Thus, in the absence of inflation, the two series given in Exhibit 11.5 should move in the opposite direction to that in 1999–2000. Inflation is another factor which affects yield. If the inflation rate is high, bond prices which guarantee a fixed interest will fall and the yield will go up to compensate investors for the inflation. The opposite occurs when the inflation rate decreases. However, inflation may go up or down. When inflation is up in a recession, the two forces of inflation and default risk join each other, and bond prices plummet. When the inflation and the economy are down (as in the early 1990s), there are conflicting forces and bond prices are relatively stable.

11.2.2 Stock market

The link between the stock market and real GDP growth is even less clear. However, there are several possible links between the business cycle and the stock market.

One link is based on earnings. In an expansion phase, firms typically have wider profit margins and hence are able to pay higher dividends or reinvest in projects with positive NPVs. Either way, investors are being well served, and stock prices tend to rise.

Another link, as already explained, is based on interest rates. Falling interest rates at the end of recessions tend to lift stocks. When the interest rate falls, the cost of capital (which is made up of the interest rate plus a risk premium – see Chapter 14) also falls. Recall from the constant dividend growth model that if the cost of capital (k) declines, then stock prices (P_0) rise.

Finally, as occurred in May 1999, the Fed increases the interest rate but due to innovation and improved productivity, many firms announce an increase in profit. The latter factor outweighs the first factor and the stock market soars.

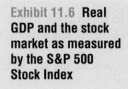

Exhibit 11.6 **Real GDP and the stock market as measured by the S&P 500 Stock Index**

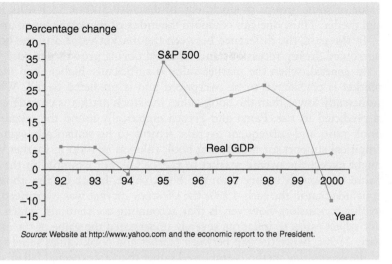

Source: Website at http://www.yahoo.com and the economic report to the President.

The stock market tends to move before the GDP, and although we would like to predict the stock market moves by looking at GDP changes in earlier periods, we cannot. The stock market is one of the best leading indicators of trends in real GDP, so tracking the GDP to get a preview of stock market trends is not of much use to an investor.

Exhibit 11.6 shows the relationship between real GDP and the US stock market for 1992–2000. There is a positive relationship between real GDP and the stock market; unfortunately, however, the stock market tends to lead the real change in GDP. If this is true, a sharp fall in the S&P 500 index in 2000 predicts a decrease in the GDP in 2001. Indeed, in August 2001 a slowdown in the US economy was reported. The annualized growth rates in the GDP were 1.3% and 0.2% in the first and second quarters of 2001, respectively. These changes in GDP are much lower than in the corresponding two quarters of 2000 (2.3% and 5.7%, respectively). In the third quarter of 2001, the GDP even became negative: −1.3%.

11.3 VALUING THE OVERALL STOCK MARKET

Once analysts have established an overall view of the future direction of the economy, they can assess how the overall stock market compares with this view. For example, if an analyst believes that an economy is headed for an extended expansionary period and overall valuation measures of the stock market indicate that the market is underpriced, then the analyst will have a bullish view of stocks in general. This section reviews three measures of the overall stock market's value: book value, dividends and earnings.

11.3.1 Book value

The ratio of a stock's price to its book value is sometimes used to predict up and down trends in the stock market. Book value is the accounting measure of the net worth of a firm. Indexes are constructed for book value in the same manner as for market value of stock. For example, a value-weighted index would sum up the book values of each firm rather than multiplying the number of shares times the stock price. An index of book value of some groups of stock, e.g. of the S&P 500 or S&P 400, is reported in the financial media. Thus, one can compare the index of market value to an index of book value.[2]

In the past, the difference between the market value and the book value has generally narrowed during recessions and widened during growth periods.

In general, when the market value is sufficiently higher than the book value, the stock market is considered to be overpriced and is predicted to fall. When the market value is sufficiently lower than the book value, the stock market is considered to be underpriced and is predicted to rise. Fama and French empirically found the relationship between price-to-book ratio and subsequent average returns to be statistically significant.[3] Hence, there is empirical support for monitoring book value in relation to market value to tell us when we might expect the overall market to rise or fall. For example, in the early 1990s the market value was much higher than the book value, hence by the above argument we would conclude that in the early 1990s the US stock market was overpriced. One counter-argument to this conclusion, however, is that accounting conventions, which in the United States do not adjust assets to inflation, severely understated the value of the assets on the books in the early 1990s, hence the gap between market and book values simply reflect the shortcomings of the accounting methods employed rather than an expected fall in stock prices.

11.3.2 Dividends

Dividends are a second tool used in appraising the overall stock market. Dividing the stock market index per share by the dollar dividend paid per share on an index such as the S&P 500 indicates how many years an investor has to wait until the investment is recovered by the paid dividends. The dividend divided by the price (the D/P ratio) is called the dividend yield. For example, in February 2002 the dividend yield was 1.4%. Normally, this value is compared with the interest rate to see which investment has higher cash flows. When the ratio of the price divided by the dividend is high, it generally indicates that the stock market is overpriced, and shifting to bonds is recommended. Exhibit 11.7 illustrates an overpriced stock market in the 1990s. Specifically, the graph plots the dividend yield (D/P) as well as the price/earnings (P/E) ratio, which is discussed in the next section. As the stock market of the 1990s rose (and dividends remained virtually constant), the dividend yield decreased. However, not everyone interpreted this as bad news for the stock market.

11.3.3 Earnings

Some experts claim that the P/E ratio is a good indicator of whether the stock market is overpriced or underpriced. Recall that a high P/E ratio means a low E/P ratio, or a low profit on investment. Exhibit 11.7 (see left vertical axis which corresponds to P/E ratio) gives the P/E ratio in the period 1975–2000 for the S&P 500. The P/E ratio climbed from about 10 in 1975 to about 23 in 1992 and then fell to a level of about 20 in 1996. In June 1997 the P/E was 24.35, and it continued to rise in 1998 to a level of 31.73 on 24 June 1998. The P/E ratio fell to a level of 26.2 on 7 June 1999. The decline in the P/E ratio continued also during 2000, to a level of 25.13 in February 2001 and rise to a level of 28.3 in February 2002.

---

[2] The S&P 400, an index of 400 industrial stocks, is one of the most widely used indexes for assessing the stock market as a whole. The S&P 500 includes the S&P 400, 40 financial stocks, 40 utility stocks, and 20 transportation stocks.

[3] See Eugene F. Fama and Kenneth R. French, 'The cross-section of expected stock returns', *Journal of Finance*, 47, June 1992, pp. 427–65.

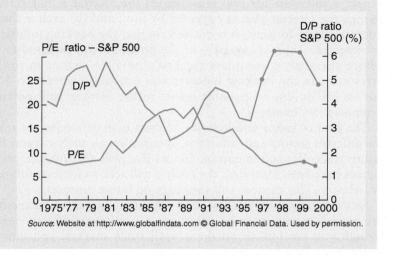

Exhibit 11.7

The S&P 500 P/E and D/P ratios as a measure of the overall market

Source: Website at http://www.globalfindata.com © Global Financial Data. Used by permission.

11.4 INDUSTRY ANALYSIS

There are periods when stocks of some industries flourish or drop significantly more than the whole market. The task of industry analysis is to forecast the activities of these specific industries. For example, when there is an oil crisis consumers spend less money on purchasing new cars, and the car industry is in a recession. Biotech stocks were very attractive with a high rate of return in 1991 and also in 1992, and then in the first quarter of 1998 most of the major Biotech stocks fell by 50–78%! Not approving some drugs by the FDA pushed the prices of the whole industry down. No matter if it is right or wrong, investors tend to shift from one industry to another, hence affecting the prices of stocks in various industries. When the Biotech stocks were hot, stock prices went up, which created optimization, which pushed the stocks further up. Not approving one or more new drugs by the FDA induces a decline in stock prices (due to shift to other stocks) which creates a momentum to further decline in the Biotech stocks. Thus, bad news affects the Biotech stocks which were always news driven. Also, when the whole stock market is down, and there is a chance of a rebound, investors tend to shift to cyclical stocks – those that tend to rebound fastest as the economy recovers. To buy the auto and manufacturing cyclical stocks, investors left the Biotech stocks which enhanced the fall in the stock prices of these firms.

The above analysis, as well as the *Investment in the news* article, indicate that not all industries react in the same way to changes in macro-economic phenomena, e.g. inflation, recession, economic recovery and change in the interest rate. The financial analyst's task is to analyze and forecast the forthcoming changes and to shift investment to those industries which will be most favoured due to the future changes. However, one should always recall portfolio theory asserting that diversification in various industries is important. For example, suppose that due to some change in the interest rates, one expects the banking industry to get the most enjoyment from the change. The financial analysts who forecast the change in the interest rate should shift some of the invested capital to the banking industry. However, we do not expect a full shift for two reasons: (a) the analyst is not certain that the Fed will change the interest rate as expected by him, and (b) even if the Fed does change the interest rate as forecast, it is not certain that the banking industry stocks will respond as expected. Thus, if say 10% of the portfolio was invested in the banking industry before the analyst considers the Fed's possible change in the investment rate, the investment in the banking industry will probably increase to 15–20%, but certainly not to 100%, due to possible errors in the forecast and portfolio consideration as explained in Chapter 6.

The goal of sector and industry analysis is to determine the relative attractiveness of the different sectors and industries. Specifically, an analyst wants to determine the risk – return trade-offs and important factors that will affect future performance. Once these factors have been identified, the analyst will seek to forecast future trends in each sector or industry. This exercise will shed light on future prospects.

Sector and industry analysis is an important element in successful investing. Although the overall market may be going up, a particular industry may decline. Thus even though you are bullish on the overall stock market, you must carefully assess the strengths and weaknesses of each industry.

11.4.1 The industrial life cycle

Many analysts believe that industries go through life cycles. A life cycle is a discernible pattern for an industry in which it is first born, then goes through an expansion phase of rapid growth, and finally reaches a period of maturation. Each industry is unique in how it progresses through each phase. Some industries, such as the biotechnology industry, develop rapidly; others, such as the natural gas industry, develop slowly. It is important for analysts to understand where in the industrial life cycle a particular industry is located, as future prospects depend on the remaining life of the industry.

External forces greatly influence a particular industry's progression through its life cycle. Political and regulatory changes influence the growth or decline of a given industry. For example, environmental legislation has spurred the growth of industries engaged in reducing pollution and cleaning toxic waste sites. Social and demographic forces also play an important role. For example, as the US population grows older with the ageing of the 'baby boomers', the pharmaceutical industry probably will experience stronger sales.

11.4.2 Demand and supply analysis

When analyzing a particular industry, it is helpful to break down the analysis based on factors that influence demand for the industry's products, as well as factors that influence the supply of the industry's raw materials. Analysts focus on real and nominal growth rates of the factors, as well as overall trends and cyclical variation.

On the demand side, analysts try to identify who the end users of products are and how they may change their behaviour in the future. Analysts are ever watchful for technological innovations that may have dramatic influences on demand for an industry's products. For example, a recent technological innovation is the ability to send interactive television signals via telephone wires. If this technology develops, the cable television industry will suddenly have as a competitor the telephone industry, which already has a direct connection to most homes.

On the supply side, analysts try to identify the degree of concentration within an industry. The concentration ratio is a measure of how much of the industry is dominated by the largest firms. How do these firms compete? Is the competition based on price, quality or warranties? For example, software firms and airline firms are both notorious for their price-cutting wars. Clearly, when a group of firms is willing to cut its prices drastically to gain market share, this could have an adverse impact on share prices.

11.4.3 Industry profitability

Industry analysts try to assess the future profitability of an industry. They use supply and demand analysis in an effort to understand how these different factors interact. Will any cost factors get out of control? Will price wars erupt that will seriously dampen profitability? What technological innovations are on the horizon that may redefine the entire industry? Will future governmental regulations dramatically alter how a particular industry functions? These are some of the important questions that analysts must address when examining an industry.

Analysts seek to forecast the future short-term and long-term profitability for an industry. Once they have estimated the future earnings potential, they can translate that estimate into an overall valuation of the industry. For example, analysts who believed that the outlook for the telephone systems industry was particularly bright relative to where stocks in this industry were trading would want to increase their holdings of telephone stocks.

A special case of industry effect has to do with the computer and Internet stocks. In July 1999, Microsoft, the largest corporation in the world, recorded a market value of more than $500 billion. The whole computer and Internet industry soared. Some pessimistic financial analysts predicted a crash in the Internet-computer industry. These gloomy forecasts became a reality in 2000 and 2001.

11.4.4 Selecting a stock from a given industry

Investors generally invest in a portfolio of securities composed from various industries. No matter what valuation model is employed, a comparison of stocks taken from various industries should be done with great caution. For example, it is meaningless to compare P/E ratios of two firms, one taken from the banking industry and one from the Internet industry. However, such a comparison is more meaningful within an industry characterized by similar risk, similar industry growth, etc.

Suppose that you would like to include one oil company in your portfolio. The data given in Exhibit 11.8 provide the relevant basis for comparing of firms which belong to the same industry.

From the P/E comparison it seems that Repsol is the less expensive stock with P/E = 18.4. Also, the price-to-book ratio of 2.8 is the lowest in the industry, indicating that this stock is a candidate to be included in the portfolio. The return on capital is 10.5%, the second highest in the industry. However, before making a final decision we need to analyze the growth rate of this firm (it may be the lowest in the industry, which explains the relatively low P/E ratio) as well as the quality of the management. However, we would like to emphasize that comparison of the various financial ratios needed for investment decision making is meaningful only when done within a given industry, because the industry risk and the industry prospect and probability along with the growth rate are very similar.

Exhibit 11.8 Drilling for value

Company	Country	Recent price (US$)	P/E	Est. 1999 EPS (US$)	Est. 2000 P/E	Price/ book	Price/ cash	Yield (%)	Return on capital (%)	Price change year to date (%)	Market value (US$m)
BP Amoco	UK	18.15	50.4	0.56	23.8	4.2	49.1	2.1	7.3	26.1	176,249
Chevron	US	92.75	34.5	3.08	23.8	3.6	14.9	2.6	9.2	11.8	60,619
Elf Aquitaine	France	146.39	31.6	5.17	22.4	3.3	8.0	2.4	8.1	42.6	40,309
ENI Group	Italy	6.31	20.8	0.34	15.5	3.4	9.3	2.6	NA	8.0	50,457
Exxon	US	79.81	35.3	2.67	25.9	4.4	17.6	2.1	13.2	9.1	193,768
Mobil	US	101.25	55.6	3.09	27.9	4.5	18.8	2.3	7.9	16.2	79,097
Repsol	Spain	18.68	18.4	1.07	15.1	2.8	8.4	2.5	10.5	18.2	16,816
Royal Dutch	Neth/UK	58.39	NM	1.62	29.2	3.6	21.9	2.6	9.0	32.0	125,202
Texaco	US	63.50	83.6	2.06	22.8	3.0	16.2	2.8	3.4	19.8	34,037
Total	France	125.64	33.3	4.83	21.5	3.1	14.1	2.5	6.7	39.7	44,019

As of 9 June 1999.
NA: Not available. NM: Not meaningful.

Source: John H. Christy, 'A bureaucrat with a head for oil', *Forbes*, 5 July 1999, pp. 54–6. Reprinted with permission of *Forbes* Global Magazine. © 2002 Forbes Global Inc.

SUMMARY

■ *Identify and describe the macro-economic variables that measure economic health.*
The key measure of economic health is the gross domestic product (GDP). The GDP is composed of consumption, investment, government spending and net trade. Real GDP (GDP adjusted to include the effects of inflation) is used, because inflation changes the value of dollars. Analysts attempting to establish relationships between macro-economic variables such as GDP and financial markets must incorporate a complex revision process into their analysis. Relationships that may appear based on final estimates of GDP may not appear based on advanced estimates of GDP.

■ *Describe the impact of government fiscal and monetary policy on investment decisions.*
Fiscal and monetary policy are key tools governments use to achieve GDP growth, relatively full employment and stable prices. Fiscal policy includes taxation and spending policies, whereas monetary policy includes actions taken by a central bank, such as controlling the money supply and manipulating interest rates. The effectiveness of a government is a key factor to consider when analyzing a country's financial market. Governments use both fiscal and monetary policies to stimulate economic growth, which directly affects financial markets.

■ *Describe the measures used to value the stock market as a whole.*
The three key measures of an overall stock market are book value, dividends and earnings. It is useful to compare the P/E ratio, dividend yield and book value over time to establish reasonable historical ranges. With these ranges established, investors can assess the relative value of the overall stock market.

■ *Evaluate market sectors and specific industries.*
A careful assessment of market sectors and specific industries helps investors allocate their portfolios effectively. A significant portion of a stock's volatility can be attributed to its industry. Thus, analysts seek to determine the future prospects within sectors and industries.

KEY TERMS

Bank discount rate	Federal funds rate	Monetary policy
Bank reserves	Fiscal policy	Nominal GDP
Budget deficit	Gross domestic product	Open market operations
Business cycle	(GDP)	Peak
Coincident indicator	Gross national product	Real GDP
Concentration ratio	(GNP)	Recession
Contraction	Lagging indicator	Trough
Dividend yield	Leading indicator	
Expansion	Life cycle	

QUESTIONS

11.1 Assume that Germany dramatically increased its interest rate. How should this increase affect the US stock market? How should it affect the US bond market?

11.2 Suppose the consumption in the United States increased by $10 billion, and this increase was in imported goods. How would this influence the GDP?

11.3 Suppose the Federal Reserve Board reduced the interest rate, and at the same time the price of bonds went down. Is this result what was predicted by macro-economic analysis? If not, how can you explain this result?

11.4 Suppose another oil crisis is predicted in the near future. How will this crisis affect car industry stocks? How will it affect food industry stocks? Explain your answer.

11.5 Some analysts claim that portfolio holdings of auto stocks, such as GM and Ford, as well as holdings of oil stocks, such as Exxon and Mobil, would be a good hedge against an oil crisis. Does this make any sense?

11.6 The price-to-book ratio is 40 in Japan and 25 in the United States. Do these ratios mean that there is a higher probability of a stock market crash in Japan? Explain your answer.

11.7 In some countries the book value of assets is adjusted every year to inflation. In the United States such an adjustment is not done. In your view, how would this adjustment affect the price-to-book ratio?

11.8 A financial analyst who analyzed CBM Corporation concludes that its earnings are expected to grow at 10% every year for the next 10 years. The analyst highly recommends buying this stock. After a week, the Federal Reserve increases the interest rate from 4% to $4^{1}/_{2}$%. The S&P 500 index drops by 8%. CBM drops by 4%. Explain these outcomes.

11.9 Suppose that for each $^{1}/_{4}$% increase in the interest rate, the stock market falls by 5%. In 2001 the Dow Jones Industrial Average is at 10,800 points, and the interest rate is at 4%. What would be the predicted value of the Dow if interest rates went up to 6%? What if interest rates went down to 2%?

11.10 A one-year bond is trading for $1,000, and the coupon is $50 paid annually. The face value is $1,000 and the maturity is one year. A stagflation (inflation along with a recession) erupts. The inflation was zero before and is now predicted to be 3%. The risk of bankruptcy increases from 0% to 10% on a yield-to-maturity basis. By how much will the bond price fall if investors demand the same average real rate of return as they had before? Do the calculations separately for inflation and recession, as well as for both.

11.11 Suppose you have the following two alternatives (A and B):

Year	Change in GDP A	Change in GDP B	Rates of return A	Rates of return B
1	5%			20%
2	0	5%	20%	−10
3	1	0	−10	5
		1	5	

(a) Analyze the two sets of figures.
(b) What set, A or B, is typical in the market? What set would investors like to have?

11.12 Suppose the government taxes consumers by taking 4 cents from each dollar of gas sold. The total taxes raised is $10 billion, and consumers reduce their spending by $5 billion. The government spends all of this $10 billion on developing a space station. What is the net change in GDP?

11.13 A low-dividend yield is predicted by practitioners as a sign of a bear market. Analyze the following figures:

Year	Dividend yield	Interest rate
1	6%	12%
2	5	8
3	4	6
4	2.9	2.5

Do analysts necessarily expect a crash in the stock market in Year 4? Explain your answer.

11.14 Suppose a firm has total assets of $100 million and liabilities of $20 million. There are 40 million shares outstanding. The price-to-book ratio is 2.0. What is the current stock price?

11.15 How will your results in Question 11.14 be affected by a 2-for-1 split if the split results in a price-to-book ratio of 2.2?

SELECTED REFERENCES

Abel, Andrew B., and Ben S. Bernanke. *Macro-economics*. Reading, MA: Addison-Wesley, 1992.

Baker, H. Kent. *Improving the Investment Decision Process – Better Use of Economic Inputs in Security Analysis and Portfolio Management*. Charlottesville, VA: Association for Investment Management and Research, 1992.

Black, Fischer. 'The ABCs of business cycles'. *Financial Analysts Journal*, November–December 1981, pp. 75–80.

Carnes, W. Stansbury, and Stephen D. Slifer. *The Atlas of Economic Indicators*. New York: HarperCollins Publishers, 1991.

Council of Economic Advisers. *Economic Report of the President*. Washington, DC: US Government Printing Office, various issues.

Fama, Eugene F., and Kenneth R. French. 'The cross-section of expected stock returns'. *Journal of Finance*, 47, June 1992, pp. 427–65.

King, Benjamin F. 'Market and industry factors in stock price behavior'. *Journal of Business*, 39, January 1966, pp. 139–90.

McFall, R. Lamm, Jr. 'Asset allocation implication of inflation protected securities'. *Journal of Portfolio Management*, Summer 1998, pp. 93–101.

Petrie, Thomas A. (ed.). *Industry Analysis – the Oil and Gas Industries*. Charlottesville, VA: Association for Investment Management and Research, 1993.

Treynor, Jack. 'Bulls, bears, and market bubbles'. *Financial Analysts Journal*, March–April 1998, pp. 69–74.

US Bureau of the Census. *Statistical Abstract of the United States*. Washington, DC: US Government Printing Office, various issues.

SUPPLEMENTARY REFERENCES

Bursch-Supan, A., and A. Brugiavini. 'Savings: The policy debate in Europe'. *Oxford Review of Economic Policy*, Spring 2001, Vol. 17, Issue 1.

Cavagalia, S., D. Cho, and B. Singer. 'Risks of sector rotation strategies'. *The Journal of Portfolio Management*, 2001, Vol. 27, No. 4.

Lusardi, A., J. Skinner, and S. Venti 'Saving puzzles and saving policies in the United States'. *Oxford Review of Economic Policy*, Spring 2001, Vol. 17, Issue 1.

Chapter 13

OPTIONS: BASIC CONCEPTS AND STRATEGIES

Learning objectives

After studying this chapter you should be able to:

1 Name the benefits of modern option contracts.
2 Understand the process of buying and selling of put and call options.
3 Explain the risk of holding naked options.
4 Describe the role of the Options Clearing Corporation (OCC).
5 Use payoff diagrams to determine the value of an option upon expiration.
6 Identify profitable option strategies based on beliefs about future asset price movements.
7 Explain the option price boundaries and put–call parity.
8 Explain the Black–Scholes valuation model and how to use it.

INVESTMENT IN THE NEWS

Options

An option contract enables the holder to buy or sell a fixed quantity of a security at a set, or striking price, within a specified period. A call gives the holder the right to buy the security, while a put gives the right to sell the security within the specified time. A buyer of a call option hopes to profit from a rise in the price of the underlying stock. The seller of a put expects the price of the underlying stock to hold above the striking price, thus enabling him to profit from the premium obtained from the sale of the put without having to buy the stock.

Source: Barron's, 2 July 2001, p. MW49.

As we can see from *Barron's* definition, the profit or loss on a call and a put option is derived from the stock price on which these options are written. A derivative security, like the above options, is any asset that derives its value from another asset. A derivative security is also called a contingent claim, because its claim is contingent on the value of the underlying security.

The basic concepts of derivatives are very simple. Derivatives seem to be like a bet on a Super Bowl, soccer or football game. However, if derivatives are merely bets, why are they of interest to investors or firms? Derivatives are important because they can be employed by both investors and firms to hedge risk. In addition, derivatives can be used for speculative reasons. In both cases, the investors who wish to speculate or to hedge risk should know the implied future cash flow of such derivatives.

Although derivatives can be considered as a simple bet, putting a value on such bets is complicated. How can investors determine the worth of a 'ticket' to play such a bet? This chapter examines the basic cash flow of options and the role that derivatives play in reducing risk, as well as the pricing of derivatives.

An option is a legal contract that gives its holder the right to buy or sell a specified amount of an underlying asset at a fixed or predetermined price. There are two basic types of options: call options and put options. A call option gives its holder the right to buy a specified amount of the underlying asset during some period in the future at a predetermined price. If you hold a call option on British Airways (BA) common stock and the option expires in three months with a predetermined price of £100, then you have the right to buy BA stock for £100 on or before the expiration date, regardless of the current market price. Similarly, a put option gives its holder the right to sell a specified amount of the underlying asset during some period in the future at a predetermined price. Although puts and calls can be based on the same underlying asset, such as shares of BA, they are separate securities.

13.1 THE DEVELOPMENT OF MODERN OPTION TRADING

Option contracts began to appear in the United States in the 1790s, shortly after the Buttonwood Agreement – the agreement that established the New York Stock Exchange.

Although options have been around for a long time, organized option trading did not occur until the passage of the Investment Act of 1934, which legalized option trading. Option trading was regulated by the Securities and Exchange Commission (SEC), and the Put and Call Brokers and Dealers Association was established in the early 1940s to assist option traders in their efforts to develop a market.

The Chicago Board of Trade (CBOT) created the Chicago Board Options Exchange (CBOE). The CBOE began option trading on 26 April 1973, at 10:00 a.m. eastern standard time. Initially, 16 call options were traded on common stocks (that is, the underlying assets were common stocks). Since 1973, the growth of the option market has been explosive. Nowadays, options are traded on many exchanges in the US and abroad. There are options on stocks, on indexes of stocks, on Treasury bonds, on foreign currency and on futures. Thus, the option market is very colourful.

13.2 BUYING AND SELLING OPTIONS

This section shows how investors buy and sell options. In the explanations of the transactions, the vocabulary used by option traders to describe the process is introduced.

13.2.1 The option buyer

An option buyer is the purchaser of an option contract. Recall that a call option gives its holder the right to buy the underlying asset at a predetermined price. Thus, if you bought a call option on Compaq common stock, by exercising the option contract you would be purchasing Compaq common stock (which is the underlying asset) at a predetermined price. This predetermined price is the strike price or exercise price. Likewise, if you bought a put option on British Airways common stock, by exercising the option contract you would be selling British Airways stock at the strike or exercise price. The buyer who holds an option – whether a call or a put option – takes a long position in an option.

Options trading is involved also with a required margin. When investors purchase a put or call they pay the price of the option in full and no purchase on margin is allowed. At most, the buyer will lose the investment. If, however, the investor writes a call or a put option, the loss is unlimited, and margin as well as maintenance margin are required.

13.2.2 The option seller

To purchase call and put options, there must be people willing to sell the options. Option sellers are called option writers, and they can write both call and put options. The option writer is the person from whom the option buyer purchases the option contract. Options trade between individual investors – the option writer and the option buyer. The option writer is obligated to honour the terms of the option contract if the buyer decides to exercise the option. The option writer takes a short position in an option (thus the writer has agreed to sell the underlying asset, as defined by the option contract).

It is worthwhile to distinguish between an option writer and a short seller of stock. A short seller of a stock sells stock that is not owned but rather is borrowed from a broker. Therefore, the short seller has an obligation to eventually repurchase the actual shares of stock so that the borrowed stock can be returned to the broker. An option writer, in contrast, may or may not actually have to supply or acquire the underlying asset.

13.2.3 The option contract

Some actual figures and possible transactions in call and put options will demonstrate how an option contract works. The relevant information on option prices is reported in several sources, including online services, satellite communications, newspapers and television. This section briefly explains how to read option quotes in newspapers such as the *Financial Times, Barron's* and *The Wall Street Journal*.

Consider the example of Cisco in Exhibit 13.1. The first column has the option name in abbreviated form, along with the closing price of the underlying security, which in this case is a stock. Cisco stock closed at 19.35 on this date. The option prices listed under call and put last prices headings are the prices for the last trade of the day, which could have been hours before the closing time, 4:15 p.m. eastern standard time. The option prices are given on a per-share basis, although option contracts are written in multiples of 100 shares. The second column gives the strike price (or exercise price) for the options. This column also includes the expiration date. The third column presents the type of option. Call options are identified either by 'c' or by no symbol at all, and 'p' stands for put option. The fourth column gives the number of option contracts traded (sales volume) on 1 July 2001. To demonstrate how to read an option quote, look at the bold Jan 40 put option. The Jan 40 strike price of the put option for Cisco last traded at $21.20. Because each option contract is for 100 shares of the stock, the cost of one option contract is $100 \times \$21.20 = \$2,120$.

The expiration date (or maturity date) of an option contract is the date on which the option expires or ceases to exist if the option contract is not exercised. For most stock options, the expiration date is the Friday before the third Saturday of the expiration month. Options on underlying assets other than stocks, such as interest rate options, have unique expiration dates. Eurodollar futures options expire on the Monday preceding the third Wednesday of the contract month. If the third Wednesday of March is, for example, 16 March, then the March contract expires on Monday 14 March.

The cost of purchasing an option contract is called the option premium. Specifically, the option premium is the price that the option buyer pays to the writer of the option. For example, if an option buyer pays $3.50 for the call option (Cisco Jan 20; see Exhibit 13.1), the total premium would be $3.50 \times 100 = \$350$, because each option contract is for 100 shares. This $350 premium is not just a good faith

Exhibit 13.1 Option price quotes as reported in *Barron's*

Company Exch Close	Strike Price		Sales Vol	Open Int	Week's High	Low	Last Price	Net Chg
42.90	Aug	40.00	2776	7469	7.10	3.30	7.00	+3.50
42.90	Jul	45.00	2752	3235	2.50	0.55	2.25	+1.60
Brocade	Jul	40.00	3771	7058	6.10	2.45	5.60	+2.20
43.45	Jul	45.00	3232	11610	3.10	1.10	3.00	+1.20
43.45	Jul	50.00	5566	6481	1.30	0.60	0.90	−0.10
CVS Corp	Aug	40.00	3268	2926	2.30	1.20	1.85	−14.55
Cabltrn	Jul	17.50	2505	5500	5.00	2.25	4.90	+2.80
22.85	Jul	20.00	3494	5308	2.75	0.80	2.75	+1.95
22.85	Jan	20.00	2729	5223	5.50	3.40	5.30	+1.80
22.85	Jan	25.00	2662	2310	3.20	2.10	2.95	+1.55
Cadence	Nov	20.00	3794	4070	2.00	2.00	2.00	−3.10
Calpine	Jul	40.00	5630	5583	2.10	1.00	1.30	−0.25
37.80	Jul	45.00	4969	7426	0.65	0.20	0.30	−0.15
CardnlHl	Aug	70.00p	3099	2938	3.70	1.30	3.70	+2.75
CaremkRx	Jul	15.00	3731	3230	2.10	1.10	2.00	+0.70
Caterp	Jul	55.00p	2693	2633	5.90	2.60	4.70	+2.05
50.05	Aug	55.00p	4026	5329	6.50	3.40	6.50	+3.75
50.05	Jan	55.00p	7520	7634	7.60	6.20	7.60	+1.60

▶

Exhibit 13.1 (continued)

Company Exch Close	Strike Price		Sales Vol	Open Int	Week's High	Week's Low	Last Price	Net Chg
AppleraBio	Aug	30.00	4021	4078	1.45	1.35	1.45	−0.10
Celestica	Sep	55.00	6846	7935	4.30	1.85	5.00	+2.95
Cendant	Aug	15.00	3338	17610	5.30	4.70	5.30	...
19.50	Jul	17.50	6358	4177	2.80	2.10	2.10	−0.60
19.50	Aug	17.50p	3750	30130	0.55	0.30	0.35	−0.10
19.50	Jul	20.00	4263	10607	0.85	0.45	0.50	−0.25
ChkPoint	Jul	45.00p	2503	3260	3.40	1.05	1.30	−1.60
50.99	Jul	50.00	2909	8543	6.70	2.70	4.30	+0.60
50.99	Jul	50.00p	2596	3858	5.80	2.25	3.00	−2.90
50.99	Jul	55.00	2533	3874	3.90	1.30	2.05	+0.15
Chevrn	Jul	95.00	2701	2220	2.25	0.20	0.40	−1.90
CienaCp	Jul	30.00p	2744	15694	1.55	0.55	0.95	+0.20
37.94	Jul	35.00p	4628	7571	3.40	1.10	2.20	+0.30
37.94	Jul	40.00	12452	10581	6.00	2.00	2.60	−2.50
37.94	Jul	40.00p	3247	7664	6.20	3.00	4.40	+0.70
37.94	Jul	45.00	14628	8522	3.90	0.90	1.35	−1.55
37.94	Aug	45.00	3175	1584	6.00	2.35	3.20	−1.60
37.94	Jul	50.00	5844	8646	2.30	0.45	0.65	−0.95
37.94	Jul	55.00	3478	8895	1.00	0.15	0.25	−0.50
37.94	Jul	70.00p	2717	3686	32.00	1.70	32.00	+3.10
37.94	Jul	80.00p	3768	1076	43.00	39.00	43.00	...
Cisco	Aug	12.50p	7292	12016	0.30	0.15	0.15	−0.10
19.35	Jul	15.00p	5244	39815	0.50	0.05	0.10	−0.35
19.35	Aug	15.00p	6550	6871	0.80	0.30	0.30	−0.50
19.35	Jan	15.00p	23758	35074	2.00	1.35	1.35	−0.65
19.35	Jul	17.50	38360	47986	2.70	1.35	1.75	+0.30
19.35	Jul	17.50p	14293	38638	1.25	0.35	0.65	−0.70
19.35	Aug	17.50p	12550	17155	1.75	0.90	1.20	−0.65
19.35	Oct	17.50	3945	18658	4.20	2.95	3.40	+0.60
19.35	Oct	17.50p	3181	34607	2.50	1.65	2.00	−0.55
19.35	Jul	20.00	50277	81710	1.05	0.45	0.45	−0.05
19.35	Jul	20.00p	6299	37153	3.00	1.00	2.00	−0.90
19.35	Aug	20.00	21676	39681	1.85	1.00	1.35	+0.25
19.35	Aug	20.00p	13712	10343	3.30	1.90	2.55	−0.55
19.35	Oct	20.00	5140	27502	2.80	1.85	2.55	+0.65
19.35	**Jan**	**20.00**	**3713**	**42542**	**3.70**	**2.65**	**3.50**	**+0.90**
19.35	Jul	22.50	13845	68760	0.30	0.10	0.20	...
19.35	Aug	22.50	10997	4566	0.90	0.45	0.55	...
19.35	Jan	22.50	3385	26834	2.80	1.85	2.55	+0.65
19.35	Jul	25.00	5183	81576	0.10	0.05	0.05	−0.05
19.35	Oct	25.00	5033	29385	1.15	0.55	0.85	+0.05
19.35	Jan	25.00	25064	59993	1.95	1.30	1.85	+0.50
19.35	Jul	30.00p	22361	14450	12.30	10.80	10.80	−1.70
19.35	Jul	35.00p	3514	1589	17.20	15.70	15.70	−1.80
19.35	Jul	40.00p	9500	1379	22.20	2.10	20.70	−1.80
19.35	**Jan**	**40.00p**	**5124**	**2223**	**22.30**	**20.80**	**21.20**	**−1.30**
19.35	Jan	45.00p	4801	1550	27.00	26.40	27.00	−1.50
19.35	Jan	55.00p	5950	437	37.00	35.70	35.70	−1.00
19.35	Jan	60.00p	11755	2844	42.20	40.70	40.70	−1.80
19.35	Jan	65.00p	7150	2106	47.20	45.70	45.70	−1.80
19.35	Jan	70.00p	6000	1725	52.20	50.70	50.70	+1.40

Source: *Barron's*, 2 July 2001, p. MW50. Barron's Online by *Barron's*. © 2001 by Dow Jones & Co., Inc. Reproduced with permission of Dow Jones & Co., Inc. in the format *Fundamentals of Investments* via Copyright Clearance Center.

deposit or a down payment but rather a nonrefundable fee. The option price refers to the current market price of the option. The option premium and the option price are the same at the time of the option transaction ($350 in the above example). However, after the time of purchase, the option premium is $350, whereas the option price can change with current market conditions. For example, if the stock price rallies, the option price may rise to $800 per contract, whereas the option premium is still $350. The option premium refers to the option price when first purchased, not the current market price.

A distinction is made between when an option contract is initiated and when the contract is closed. An opening transaction occurs when a new position is established. A closing transaction occurs when an already established position is eliminated. For example, suppose you purchased one Cisco Jan 20 call to open on 2 July for a premium of 3^1/_2$ per share. After two months you decide to sell one Cisco Jan 20 call for a market price that happens to be $6 per share. The opening transaction takes place when you purchase the Cisco Jan 20 call. When you sell the call option, the transaction will be closed. Hence, after selling the options, you have no option position, and you have 2^1/_2$ per-share profit ($6 − 3^1/_2$) before transaction costs. Therefore, after the sale of one Cisco Jan 20 call on 2 September you would have no outstanding position, because the sale of the previous purchase is offsetting.

Another distinction related to option contracts involves when the contract can be exercised: European-style versus American-style options. European-style options can be exercised only on specific dates. For example, contracts that can be exercised only on the last day of the contract, such as foreign exchange options, are traded on the Philadelphia Stock Exchange. American-style options, in contrast, can be exercised any time on or before the expiration date of the contract. The holder of an American option has the freedom to decide when, if ever, the option contract will be exercised. Note that these terms do not refer to, or even reflect, geographical location (that is, Europe or the United States). Most stock options are American-style options, and many index options and interest rate options are European-style options.

Exhibit 13.2 illustrates quotes on long-term options on individual stocks, as well as options on various financial products: options on various indexes (for example, Dow Jones or S&P 100 and S&P 500), foreign currency, etc. As an example of an option on an index, the quote of a DJIA index put option (December 2001) with a strike price of $100 is $2.70 (see the 'Last Price' column). As an example of a quote on options on foreign currency, the call option to buy a euro until Sept 2001 with a strike price of 86 American cents per euro costs 0.11 cents. (The current exchange rate is 84 cents per euro.)

13.2.4 Investing in options versus investing in stock

Suppose Bill Ups, an eternal optimist, believes the price of Compaq stock will rise sharply over the next three months. Compaq stock is currently trading at $63.6875 per share. How can Bill profit from his hunch? He could simply buy Compaq stock: one round lot (100 shares) would cost him $63.6875 × 100 = $6,368.75. Alternatively, he could buy call options on Compaq stock at a much lower initial cost. He would profit more on options if his prediction was correct. For example, if a three-month call option was $5.25 with a strike price of $65, he would pay only $525 to take a long position in 100 call options on shares of Compaq at the expiration date. If Compaq rose to $75, then a 100 long position of call options in Compaq will result in a profit of

Exhibit 13.2 Various listed option quotations

Equity Options

Company Exch Close	Strike Price	Sales Vol	Open Int	Week's High	Low	Last Price	Net Chg
ADC Tel	Aug 5.00p	45255	638	0.25	0.10	0.10	-0.10
AES Cp	Aug 40.00p	4543	9641	2.60	2.00	2.35	-0.65
43.05	Aug 45.00	3988	1866	3.00	1.55	2.60	+0.90
A M R	Jul 35.00	2428	1405	1.75	0.55	1.55	+0.15
AmOnline	Jan 45.00p	3212	22464	3.30	2.75	2.75	-0.25
53.00	Jul 50.00	4509	36423	4.60	1.50	3.80	-0.60
53.00	Jul 50.00p	5738	21997	1.30	0.65	0.70	-0.30
53.00	Aug 50.00p	2734	3545	2.05	1.55	1.60	-0.15
53.00	Jul 55.00	16289	67047	1.50	0.60	0.85	-0.50
53.00	Jul 55.00p	3100	7406	3.80	2.55	2.70	-0.30
53.00	Aug 55.00	6665	8581	2.45	1.25	1.80	-0.30
53.00	Jul 60.00	4278	43058	0.30	0.05	0.10	-0.15
53.00	Oct 60.00	17632	39408	2.25	1.55	1.90	-0.15
ASML Hld	Aug 25.00	3631	1510	1.20	0.95	0.95	-0.05
ATT Wrls	Jul 17.50	3901	10421	0.60	0.15	0.40	+0.15
16.35	Jul 17.50p	4256	5723	2.30	1.30	1.45	-0.55
16.35	Oct 17.50	2757	3294	1.55	1.00	1.50	+0.25
AT&T	Jul 15.00	6011	10786	6.90	6.40	6.90	+1.10
22.00	Jul 15.00p	6000	8562	0.05	0.05	0.05	-0.30
22.00	Jul 20.00p	2917	15548	0.60	0.20	0.20	-0.25
22.00	Aug 20.00	3183	3931	2.45	1.70	2.45	+0.45
22.00	Aug 20.00p	15700	42132	1.05	0.50	0.50	-0.35
22.00	Jan 20.00	3120	20920	3.50	2.80	3.50	+0.50
22.00	Aug 22.50	3498	18791	0.45	0.15	0.40	+0.15
22.00	Aug 22.50	3411	6143	0.90	0.35	0.85	+0.10
AdvFibCm	Aug 15.00	2550	2000	7.60	7.30	7.50	...
A M D	Oct 17.50p	46554	15730	1.25	0.85	0.85	-0.50
28.90	Oct 20.00p	3165	4418	1.85	0.90	1.00	-0.15
28.90	Jul 25.00	7243	16005	5.50	2.05	4.40	+2.30
28.90	Oct 25.00p	5390	12271	2.15	0.40	0.60	-1.90
28.90	Oct 25.00	4807	10021	4.10	2.15	2.15	-1.95
28.90	Jul 27.50	4688	6878	3.40	1.00	2.75	+1.50
28.90	Jul 27.50p	11653	5321	3.80	0.90	1.20	-2.70
28.90	Jul 30.00	6755	18458	1.75	0.55	1.20	+0.65
28.90	Jul 30.00p	4067	16121	5.70	1.70	2.35	-3.75
28.90	Jul 32.50	2932	8180	0.80	0.25	0.50	+0.15

Interest Rate Options

CBOE

Yields

Company Exch Close	Strike Price	Sales Vol	Open Int	High	Low	Last	Net Chg	Yield
10yrTN	Aug 50.00	125	1251	8.24	15.07	15.07	...	570.00
10yrTN	Sep 45.00	450	2255	2.10	42.31	42.31	...	570.00
10yrTN	Mar 47.50 p	50	2511	.10	11.10	11.10	...	570.00
10yrTN	Mar 55.00	3	1061	7.06	17.06	17.06	-10.05	570.00

Call Vol.	1,725	Open Int.	2,707
Put Vol.	204	Open Int.	1,963

Index Options

Company Exch Close	Strike Price	Sales Vol	Open Int	Week's High	Low	Last Price	Net Chg
Am BioT	Jul 770.00	400	339	0.25	0.05	0.10	-1.10
Bank Idx	Aug 900.00	300	1	31.10	31.10	31.10	...
909.97	Aug 900.00p	300	...	30.10	30.10	30.10	...
909.97	Jul 905.00	301	302	25.80	23.00	24.70	+8.70
DJ Inds	Sep 90.00p	161	13657	0.65	0.35	0.35	-0.05
105.02	Dec 90.00p	2490	15804	1.45	0.90	1.05	-0.10
105.02	Jul 92.00p	2396	1871	0.10	0.05	0.05	-0.20
105.02	Jun 92.00p	902	1628	2.80	2.50	2.50	-0.40
105.02	Sep 94.00p	350	832	1.05	0.75	0.75	-0.25
105.02	Jul 96.00p	1135	7589	0.30	0.20	0.20	-0.05
105.02	Sep 96.00p	3614	11893	1.30	0.95	0.80	-0.05
105.02	Dec 96.00p	1205	8782	2.40	2.10	2.00	-0.40
105.02	Jul 100.00p	1350	12675	0.80	0.30	0.30	-0.20
105.02	Aug 100.00p	788	3917	1.35	0.80	0.95	+0.10
105.02	Sep 100.00	220	1588	8.70	6.80	8.00	-0.60
105.02	Sep 100.00p	1517	8290	2.25	1.45	1.50	-0.25
105.02	**Dec 100.00p**	**182**	**13180**	**3.70**	**2.70**	**2.70**	**20.25**
105.02	Jul 101.00p	342	434	0.95	0.40	0.45	-0.40
105.02	Jul 102.00p	2071	2000	1.20	0.45	0.50	-0.30
105.02	Aug 102.00p	556	1285	2.05	1.20	1.35	-0.20
105.02	Sep 102.00p	221	2652	2.85	1.80	2.20	...
105.02	Jul 103.00	1552	515	3.80	2.70	3.50	...
105.02	Jul 103.00p	401	432	1.55	0.65	0.65	...
105.02	Jul 104.00	853	757	3.30	2.10	2.40	-1.60
105.02	Jul 104.00p	5426	12519	2.00	0.80	0.95	-0.30
105.02	Aug 104.00	892	708	4.60	3.10	3.40	-0.90
105.02	Aug 104.00p	661	2524	2.80	1.75	1.75	-0.10
105.02	Sep 104.00p	2834	19082	3.60	2.35	2.60	-0.30
105.02	Dec 104.00p	190	4938	5.10	4.00	4.00	-0.30
105.02	Jul 105.00	1710	763	2.85	1.40	1.85	-0.80
105.02	Jul 105.00p	766	736	2.40	1.15	1.55	+0.15
105.02	Jul 106.00	3764	2820	2.25	1.15	1.25	-0.90
105.02	Jul 106.00p	1649	8437	3.00	1.50	2.10	+0.15
105.02	Aug 106.00	492	938	3.10	2.05	2.50	-0.80
105.02	Aug 106.00p	489	1166	3.50	2.45	2.60	-0.30
105.02	Sep 106.00	4324	12709	4.50	3.10	3.60	-0.80
105.02	Sep 106.00p	3187	11281	4.40	3.30	3.40	-0.20
105.02	Jul 107.00	4642	3314	1.60	0.85	1.10	-0.60
105.02	Jul 107.00p	11834	6896	3.60	1.90	2.35	-0.10
105.02	Jul 108.00	4060	5107	1.25	0.50	0.75	-0.45
105.02	Jul 108.00p	24695	14473	4.30	2.35	3.10	...
105.02	Aug 108.00	506	1185	2.40	1.50	1.50	-0.75
105.02	Aug 108.00p	1175	6705	4.90	3.30	3.90	-0.10
105.02	Sep 108.00p	250	8182	5.80	4.00	4.20	-0.30

Foreign Currency Options

Philadelphia Exchange

50,000 Australian Dollars-cents per unit.

31,250 Brit. Pound-cents per unit.

50,000 Canadian Dollars-cents per unit.

62,500 Euro-cents per unit

6,250,000J. Yen-100ths of a cent per unit.

Currency	Strike	Sales Vol	Open Int	Week's High	Low	Last Price	Net Chg	Close
ADollr	Sep 52.00	4	18	0.08	0.08	0.08	...	54.26
BPound	Sep 130.00 p	125	525	0.01	0.01	0.01	...	147.69
CDollr	Sep 65.00	4	4	0.12	0.12	0.12	...	66.48
CDollr	Dec 65.00	37	37	0.15	0.15	0.15	...	66.48
CDollr	Dec 66.00 p	84	109	0.13	0.12	0.13	...	66.48
CDollr	Mar 63.50	5	5	0.27	0.27	0.27	...	66.48
CDollr	Mar 65.00	2	4	0.17	0.17	0.17	...	66.48
CDollr	Mar 66.00	62	62	0.15	0.15	0.15	...	66.48
Euro	Jul 82.00 p	4	51	0.01	0.00	0.01	-0.00	88.15
Euro	Jul 84.00 p	27	20	0.05	0.01	0.03	...	88.15
Euro	Jul 86.00	34	117	0.05	0.02	0.02	-0.06	88.15
Euro	Jul 86.00 p	8	28	0.07	0.07	0.07	...	88.15
Euro	Jul 86.00 p	11	25	0.17	0.09	0.17	+0.03	88.15
Euro	Jul 88.00	10	22	0.03	0.03	0.03	-0.04	88.15
Euro	Sep 80.00 p	33	50	0.03	0.03	0.03	-0.01	88.15
Euro	Sep 84.00 p	2	36	0.08	0.08	0.08	...	88.15
Euro	**Sep 86.00**	**2**	**10**	**0.11**	**0.11**	**0.11**	**20.30**	**88.15**
Euro	Sep 90.00	3	20	0.05	0.05	0.05	...	88.15
Euro	Sep 91.00	50	50	0.02	0.02	0.02	...	...
Euro	Sep 92.00	100	100	0.01	0.01	0.01	...	88.15
Euro	Sep 96.00	200	226	0.01	0.01	0.01	...	88.15
Euro	Sep 98.00	1	63	1.19	1.19	1.19	-0.09	88.15
JYen	Jul 80.00 p	45	96	0.04	0.04	0.04	...	92.53
JYen	Jul 81.00 p	20	22	0.11	0.11	0.11	-0.01	92.53
JYen	Jul 82.00 p	20	46	0.15	0.15	0.15	...	92.53
JYen	Sep 80.00	15	15	0.20	0.20	0.20	...	92.53
JYen	Sep 80.00 p	5	330	0.12	0.12	0.12	+0.06	92.53
JYen	Sep 80.50 p	7	7	0.12	0.12	0.12	...	92.53
JYen	Sep 81.00	15	30	0.16	0.16	0.16	...	92.53
JYen	Sep 81.00 p	10	65	0.17	0.17	0.17	+0.10	92.53

($75 − $65) × 100 = $1,000. A $1,000 profit on a $525 investment results in a rate of return of ($1,000/$525) × 100 = 190%. The rate of return from merely buying the stock is only about ($7,500 − $6,368.75)/$6,368.75 = 17.8%. Clearly, Bill would rather have the 190% rate of return. Thus, call options provide a low-cost way of taking large positions in stock at a lower cost than buying the stock directly. The profit on options is taxable; the tax calculation is explained in Appendix 13A.

Now suppose Jane Downs, an eternal pessimist, believes Compaq's stock price will fall over the next six months. Short selling the stock is risky, requires margin money, and may not be allowable for regulatory reasons (depending on the nature of the invested funds). Rather than short sell stock, Jane could buy a put option. Recall that a put option gives its holder the right to sell the underlying asset at a predetermined price. Put options cost less than the margin required to short sell the stock, and the loss is limited to the purchase price of the put.

For example, assume the price of a six-month put option with a strike price of $60 is $2. Jane would pay only $200 to take a short position in 100 shares of Compaq. If, at the expiration date, Compaq fell to $50, then the put option would have a profit of ($60 − $50) × 100 = $1,000. A $1,000 profit on a $200 investment results in a rate of return of ($1,000/$200) × 100 = 500%. Clearly, investors bearish on Compaq's stock would be attracted to put options.

With such tremendous gains available to option buyers, why would anyone wish to write options? The primary benefit is that option writers receive the option premium. If the asset price moves against the option buyer, then there are no future costs to the option writer.

PRACTICE BOX

Problem

Consider the call option price for Genentec, Inc., of $2 with the strike price of $25. The stock price never goes above $20 before the maturity (the expiration date) of the option. What is the profit or loss to the call writer? What is the profit or loss to the call buyer? What is the call option worth at expiration? Why? What is the premium? (Recall that each option contract is for 100 shares, and the option price is quoted on a per-share basis.)

Solution

The premium of the option is $2. Because the stock price never exceeds the strike price, the call option expires worthless. (You would not wish to buy a stock at a price higher than it is currently trading in the market.) The call writer will keep the entire option premium of $2 × 100 = $200. The call buyer will lose the entire option premium of $200.

13.2.5 The underlying asset and the option

Options are categorized by the relationship that exists between the current market price of the underlying asset and the option's exercise price. Let S_0 represent the current market price of the underlying asset (for example, the stock price) and X represent the option exercise price. An in-the-money option is an option that would generate a positive cash flow if it were exercised *now*. That is, a call option is an in-the-money option if the market price of the underlying asset is greater than the strike price ($S_0 > X$) of the option contract. If the option is American style, an investor could exercise the call option, pay X dollars for the stock, and turn around and sell the stock for S_0, generating a positive cash flow of $S_0 - X$. For put options, an in-the-money option is an option in which the price received for exercising the option, X, is greater than the current price of the stock ($X > S_0$). An out-of-the-money option is the exact opposite of an in-the-money option. That is, for calls, $X > S_0$ (for puts, it is out-of-the-money if $X < S_0$). In the case of out-of-the-money options, there is no incentive to exercise the put or call. At-the-money options occur when the current price of the stock is exactly equal to the exercise price, $S_0 = X$.

Sometimes option traders refer to *deep in-the-money options* or *deep out-of-the-money options*. The word *deep* emphasizes that the distance between S_0 and X is relatively large. For example, for a deep in-the-money call option, S_0 is much higher than X. In the case of deep out-of-the-money call options, S_0 is much lower than X.

A call option written when the investor does not own the underlying asset is a naked position. A covered position is a call option written when the underlying asset is already owned. Writing a call option without owning the underlying asset is very risky and hence exposes the writer to great risk.

13.3   OVERVIEW OF OPTION MARKETS

Option trading occurs on exchanges, over the counter, and directly between buyers and sellers. There are many different exchanges on which options are traded. The most active option exchanges are the Chicago Board Options Exchange (CBOE), the American Stock Exchange (AMEX), the Chicago Board of Trade (CBOT), the Philadelphia Stock Exchange (PHLX), the Chicago Mercantile Exchange (CME) and the Pacific Stock Exchange (PSE). On the CBOE alone, the total volume of contracts traded increased over 600% in the years 1997 to 2001: see Exhibit 13.3.

Option transactions are similar to stock transactions. For example, if John Q decides to buy call options on Compaq, he would call his broker and state his desires. The broker would communicate this order to the appropriate option exchange, where the trade would occur either with an investor wanting to sell call options on Compaq or with the market maker (see Chapter 3).

The Options Clearing Corporation (OCC) maintains the records of option trades and is one of the major clearing corporations (organizations that facilitate the validation, delivery and settlement of security transactions). The OCC is owned and backed by several exchanges (such as the CBOE, AMEX, NYSE and PHLX). Hence, the OCC is a very creditworthy corporation. It issues all option contracts and guarantees both sides of

Exhibit 13.3 Option contract volume on the CBOE

Date	Call volume	Put volume	Total volume
1 December 1995	326,385	239,526	565,911
2 December 1996	375,228	200,637	575,865
1 December 1997	443,900	264,396	708,296
30 July 2001	3,136,695	1,926,657	5,063,352

the contracts. Thus, the option buyer does not have to evaluate the credit risk of the option writer. Also, all option contracts have standardized features that make them easier to resell, thus enhancing the option contract's liquidity. The OCC provides a prospectus for each contract, which details the regulations related to trading options and processes all transactions related to option trading.

Suppose that you purchase a call option with an exercise price of $50. The stock price subsequently increases to $200. Who guarantees that the call writer will pay you the difference (that is, $200 − $50 = $150)? The OCC requires that the call writer (as well as all other option writers) provide collateral, known as margin. The margin requirements, which are explained in detail in Appendix 13B, ensure that the option writer will pay the option buyer if the events indeed occur in the buyer's favour.

13.4 OPTION VALUES AT EXPIRATION

This section examines the value of options at expiration. In this examination, it is helpful to use graphs with lines that plot the future possible values of the underlying asset. These graphs, called *payoff diagrams*, are used in Section 13.4.2 to compare the objectives of different option-based trading strategies. This section first examines option values and then explains the mechanics of payoff diagrams.

13.4.1 Option prices: intrinsic and time value components

Option prices can be broken down into two components: intrinsic value and time value. The intrinsic value of an option is the value of the option if it is immediately exercised (assuming it is an American-style option) or zero. That is, the intrinsic value for calls (IV_c) is

$$IV_c = \max(0, S_0 - X) \tag{13.1}$$

The intrinsic value for puts (IV_p) is

$$IV_p = \max(0, X - S_0) \tag{13.2}$$

As the stock price changes, the intrinsic value of the option may change as well. It remains zero if the option remains out of the money. The time value of an option is whatever value an option currently has above its intrinsic value. Even if an option is out of the money, the chance that the stock price may change and the option may end up in the money gives the option time value. Most often, the term *time value* refers to discounting future cash flows. When related to options, time value has a different meaning. It is the value of the option related to the chance that the option may go in the money (or further in the money, if it is already in the money).

Let C_0 and P_0 represent the call and put premiums, respectively. Then the time value of a call (TV_c) is

$$TV_c = C_0 - IV_c \tag{13.3}$$

The time value of a put (TV_p) is

$$TV_p = P_0 - IV_p \tag{13.4}$$

Clearly, from the definition of *time value* and *intrinsic value*, we can represent option prices as follows:

$$C_0 = IV_c + TV_c = \max(0, S_0 - X) + TV_c$$

and

$$P_0 = \mathrm{IV_p} + \mathrm{TV_p} = \max(0, X_0 - S_0) + \mathrm{TV_p}$$

For example, suppose the current price of GNE stock now is \$28 ($S_0 = \$28$). If the current price of a GNE July 25 call, C_0, is \$6\frac{1}{2}$ ($C_0 = \$6\frac{1}{2}$, $X = 25$), then the call's intrinsic value, $\mathrm{IV_c}$, is \$28 − \$25 = \$3, and the time value, $\mathrm{TV_c}$, is \$6\frac{1}{2} − \$3 = \$3\frac{1}{2}$. If the GNE July 25 put is trading at \$$\frac{3}{4}$, then the put's intrinsic value, $\mathrm{IV_p}$, is max(0, 25 − 28) = \$0, and the time value, $\mathrm{TV_p}$, is \$$\frac{3}{4}$ − \$0 = \$$\frac{3}{4}$.

PRACTICE BOX

Problem

Suppose you are given the following option quotes for United Airlines:

Stock price	Strike price	Calls			Puts		
		Oct.	Nov.	Dec.	Oct.	Nov.	Dec.
114	110	$4\frac{1}{4}$	$7\frac{1}{2}$	$8\frac{1}{4}$	$\frac{3}{8}$	$2\frac{1}{4}$	3
114	115	$\frac{7}{8}$	$3\frac{7}{8}$	5	$1\frac{3}{4}$	$4\frac{1}{2}$	$5\frac{1}{4}$
114	120	$\frac{1}{8}$	2	$2\frac{1}{2}$	$6\frac{1}{8}$	$7\frac{3}{4}$	$8\frac{1}{4}$

Compute the intrinsic value and time value for each option.

Solution

The intrinsic value is the dollar amount of an in-the-money option. For calls only, the 114 strikes are \$4 in the money. For puts, the 115 strikes are \$1 in the money, and the 120 strikes are \$6 in the money. Thus, we can construct the following table for intrinsic value:

Strike price	Calls			Puts		
	Oct.	Nov.	Dec.	Oct.	Nov.	Dec.
110	4	4[a]	4	0	0	0
115	0	0	0	1	1	1
120	0	0	0	6	6[b]	6

[a] $\mathrm{IV_c} = \max(0, S_0 - X) = \max(0, \$114 - \$110) = \$4.$
[b] $\mathrm{IV_p} = \max(0, X - S_0) = \max(0, \$120 - \$114) = \$6.$

The time value is nothing but the option value minus the intrinsic value. We can construct the following table of time value:

Strike price	Calls			Puts		
	Oct.	Nov.	Dec.	Oct.	Nov.	Dec.
110	$\frac{1}{4}$	$3\frac{1}{2}$[a]	$4\frac{1}{4}$	$\frac{3}{8}$	$2\frac{1}{4}$	3
115	$\frac{7}{8}$	$3\frac{7}{8}$	5	$\frac{3}{4}$	$3\frac{1}{2}$[b]	$4\frac{1}{4}$
120	$\frac{1}{8}$	2	$2\frac{1}{2}$	$\frac{1}{8}$	$1\frac{3}{4}$	$2\frac{1}{4}$

[a] $\mathrm{TV_c} = C_0 - \mathrm{IVc} = \$7\frac{1}{2} - \$4 = \$3\frac{1}{2}.$
[b] $\mathrm{TV_p} = P_0 - \mathrm{IV_p} = \$7\frac{3}{4} - \$6 = \$1\frac{3}{4}.$

13.4.2 Payoff diagrams

A payoff diagram relates to various values at the expiration date of the options. It is a graph that illustrates (1) the relationship among the values of securities (the value line), (2) the dollar profit or loss (the P/L line), or (3) both the value line and the P/L line.

Let us illustrate these concepts with a call option on Apple with a strike price of $50 ($X = \$50$) and a call price of $5 ($C_0 = \$5$). The value line in Exhibit 13.4(a) illustrates the value of the call option at its expiration date. If the stock price falls below $50 at expiration, then the option is worthless. For example, if the stock price is selling for $30 at maturity, the call price is $0. If the stock price rises above $50 at expiration, the option is in the money and has a positive price. Specifically, for every dollar the stock is above $50, the option is worth an additional dollar. If the stock price rises to $70 at expiration, then the call option has a value of $70 - \$50 = \$20$, because at expiration we receive the right to buy the stock for $50 when its market value is $70. Hence, we buy the stock via the option contract for $50 and sell the stock received for $70, with a profit of $20. Thus, the value line is zero on the horizontal axis up to the strike price. At the strike price it becomes a positive 45-degree line. From the value line we see clearly that a call option is very profitable when the underlying stock price goes up.

If an option expires in the money, then it has intrinsic value. The option investment is said to *break even* if the proceeds from the exercise of the option at expiration are just equal to the original option premium. For example, when the stock price at maturity date is $S_t = \$55$ and $X = \$50$, then we just break even because $C_0 = \$5$.

Exhibit 13.4(b) illustrates the P/L line for this $5 call, at a strike price of $50. If the stock price falls below $50 at expiration, then the option is worthless, and the investor who bought a call option loses the $5 option premium. For every dollar the stock rises above $50, the investor makes an additional dollar. With a $5 premium, the stock must rise to $55 in order to break even on the contract. For every additional dollar above $55, the option provides an additional dollar of profit. Hence, if the stock price reaches $70 at maturity, then the profit from this option is $70 - (\$50 + \$5) = \$15$.

We now examine the profit or loss of a call option at expiration from the call writer's point of view. Exhibit 13.5 illustrates the payoff diagram of writing a call option on Apple stock with a strike price of $50 and a call premium ($C_0$) of $5. Recall that when you short a call, you receive the cash flow C_0, which is the call premium. The P/L line is equal to $+5$ as long as the stock price at expiration is less than $50, and then it starts declining at -45 degrees, because for an $1 increase in price the call writer loses $1. For example, if the stock price falls to $30, then the call writer keeps the call premium of $5 and has no obligations at maturity, because the option buyer will not exercise the call option. However, if the stock price rises to $70 at maturity, then the writer loses $20 at expiration and has a dollar loss of $-\$20 + \$5 = -\$15$. Clearly, call writers face large liabilities when the stock price rises sharply.

In a similar fashion, Exhibit 13.6 presents the P/L line for buying a put option for $5 at a strike price of $50. Recall that buying a put option, in the case of stocks, gives the buyer the right to sell a stock at the strike price. Hence, a put option is more valuable as the price of the stock declines. In contrast, the value of the put option at expiration is zero if the put option expires out of the money (when the stock price is above $50, in this case).

The dollar P/L line is $-\$5$ for stock price above, $50, because the buyer of the put option in this example pays $5 for the put which expires worthless. For puts, the breakeven point is when the strike price less the stock price is equal to the purchase price, which in our case is $50 - \$45 = \$5$, i.e. for a stock price of $45 the put buyer exactly breaks even. For example, if the stock price rises to $70 at maturity, the put option is worth $0, and the dollar loss is $5 (the put price). If the stock price falls to $30 at maturity, the put option is worth $50 - \$30 = \$20$, and the dollar profit will be $20 - \$5 = \$15$. Thus, buying a put option is similar to buying a call option, except money is earned when the stock price falls. The put P/L diagram can be viewed as the

Exhibit 13.4 Payoff diagrams for buying a call option (strike price: $50, call price: $5)

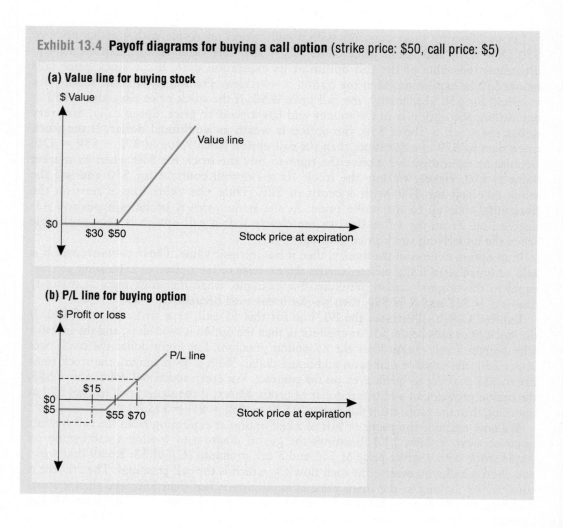

(a) Value line for buying stock

(b) P/L line for buying option

Exhibit 13.5 Payoff diagram for writing a call option (strike price = $50, call price = $5)

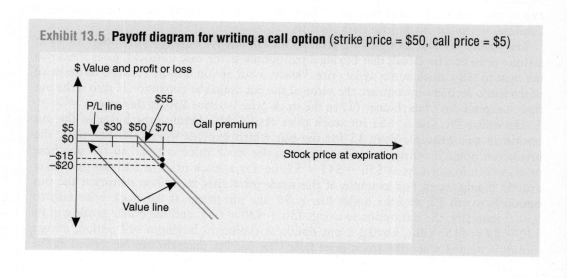

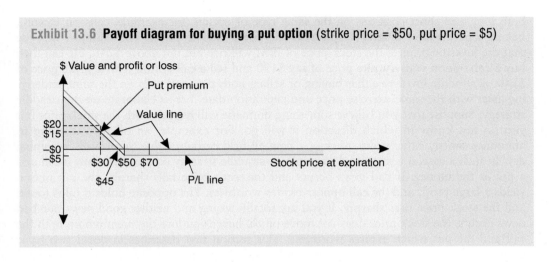

Exhibit 13.6 **Payoff diagram for buying a put option** (strike price = $50, put price = $5)

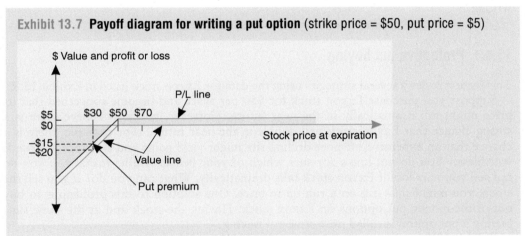

Exhibit 13.7 **Payoff diagram for writing a put option** (strike price = $50, put price = $5)

mirror image of the call P/L diagram, except the mirror is placed vertically on the strike price. (Note there is no requirement that the put price equal the call price. We adopted these values to simplify the discussion.)

Exhibit 13.7 presents the P/L lines for writing put options. Recall that put writing obligates an investor to buy a stock from the put buyer at a specified price. Hence, as the stock price falls, the put buyer will want to exercise the option and sell stock at X. Therefore, the put writer loses as the stock price declines. If the stock price falls to, say, $30 the put writer has to pay $50 - $30 = $20 but as he or she obtains a premium of $5 for selling this put option, the net loss is only $15. The lines in Exhibit 13.7 are the mirror image of those in Exhibit 13.6, where the mirror is placed on the horizontal axis.

13.5 INVESTMENT STRATEGIES USING OPTIONS

There are many possible investment strategies composed of various combinations of call and put options as well as the underlying asset. For example, a spread involves holding both long and short positions on the same type of option (for example, calls on Exxon), but the options have different expiration dates and exercise prices. For example, suppose that the investor believes the stock price of IBM will rise but not above $240. He can then buy a call option with a strike price of say $190 and sell a call option with a strike price of $240. A straddle involves either buying or selling both puts and calls on the same underlying asset with the same exercise price and expiration date. Let us elaborate on the straddle strategy. Suppose that you believe something dramatic will happen with the stock price but you do not know in which direction it will go. For example, an oil firm is going to announce shortly either a discovery of a new oil field or failure due to all wells becoming dry. In such a case, it is suggested to employ a straddle strategy composed of buy a call and a put at the money. If bad news occurs and the stock price falls sharply, the put option yields a large profit and the call option expires worthless. The opposite holds if oil is found and the stock price rises sharply. If you are totally wrong and neither good news nor bad news occurs, the stock price does not move much, hence you lose the premium on both the call and the put which expires worthless. This section first describes in detail two basic option-based strategies which are commonly used: protective put buying and covered call writing.

13.5.1 Protective put buying

This section reviews several strategies using the data for Exxon stock listed in Exhibit 13.8.

Suppose you purchase Exxon stock for $50 per share and become concerned that its price might fall dramatically in the near future. However, you also believe there is a strong chance that Exxon stock will double in the near future. (For example, there is a chance that an expensive offshore drilling site might yield gains and a chance the site is worthless.) You do not know for sure which of your beliefs will be realized. If you do not sell you may lose if Exxon stock falls dramatically. What can you do? If you sell the stock, you might miss out on a run up in price. One solution to this problem is to buy out-of-the-money put options on Exxon stock. Having the stock and at the same time buying a put option is called protective put buying.

Exhibit 13.9(a) shows the P/L line of buying the stock and the P/L line of buying a $45 strike, $1.50-per-share put option. Recall that a put option will benefit investors when the stock price falls. If the stock price remains at $50 per share, then the investor has no profit or loss on the stock and has a $1.5-per-share loss on the put option, because it expired out of the money. At a stock price of $45, the investor has a total

---

Exhibit 13.8 Exxon stock data

Strike price	Call price	Put price
$X_L = \$45$	$C_{0,L} = \$8$	$P_{0,L} = \$1\frac{1}{2}$
$X = \$50$	$C_0 = \$5$	$P_0 = \$3\frac{1}{2}$
$X_H = \$55$	$C_{0,H} = \$3$	$P_{0,H} = \$6\frac{1}{2}$

Current stock price is $S_0 = \$50$.
L stands for a lower strike price, and H stands for a higher strike price.

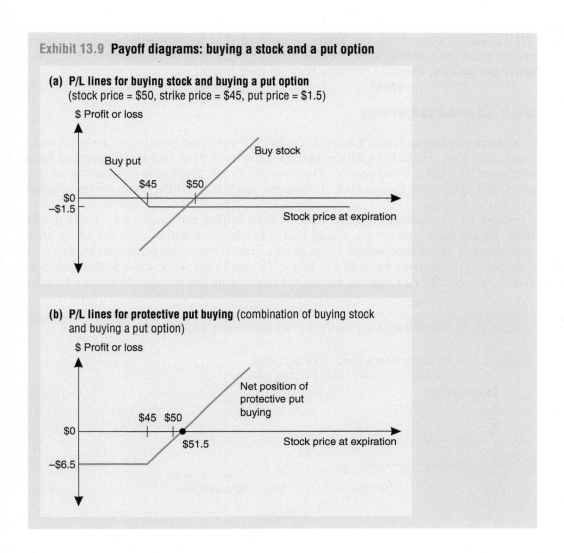

Exhibit 13.9 Payoff diagrams: buying a stock and a put option

(a) P/L lines for buying stock and buying a put option
(stock price = $50, strike price = $45, put price = $1.5)

$ Profit or loss

Buy put

Buy stock

$45 $50

$0
−$1.5

Stock price at expiration

(b) P/L lines for protective put buying (combination of buying stock and buying a put option)

$ Profit or loss

$45 $50

Net position of protective put buying

$0

$51.5

Stock price at expiration

−$6.5

loss of $6.5, because the stock position has a loss of $50 − $45 = $5 and the put position is still not in the money, resulting in a $1.5-per-share loss. The maximum loss is $6.5 because below a $45 stock price, for every additional dollar lost on the stock position, the put position gains a dollar, resulting in no overall change in the protective put buying portfolio. For any stock price above $45, for every additional dollar gained on the stock position, the put is worthless and adds a constant loss of $1.5 to the protective put buying position. Thus one dollar increase in the stock price above $45 results in one dollar gain for the protective put buying portfolio. Exhibit 13.9(b) illustrates the net position for protective put buying. Note that for a stock price of $51.5, the net profit is zero, as $1.5 is earned on the stock but the investor loses $1.5, which is the premium on the put option. Notice that the net position is very similar to the P/L line derived when simply buying a call option. The only actual difference between protective put buying and buying a call option relates to the timing of cash flows and the required discounting of these cash flows. Payoff diagrams ignore the time value of money.

It should be clear from the above discussion that by purchasing a put option, investors can dramatically alter the risk–return profile of their investments. With protective put options, investors can set a floor on their losses.

13.5.2 Covered call writing

Now suppose you purchased Exxon stock for $50 per share, wanted to generate additional cash flow, and did not believe that Exxon's stock price had much potential for a substantial rise. What could you do? One solution to this problem is to write out-of-the-money call options on Exxon stock. Having the stock and writing a call option is called covered call writing.

Exhibit 13.10 illustrates the P/L lines of both buying the stock and writing a $55 strike, $3-per-share call option. Recall that a call buyer benefits when the stock price rises; hence, a call writer suffers a loss in this case. If the stock price rises to $55 (the strike price), the investor has a $55 − $50 = $5 gain in the stock and a $3 (the call premium) gain on the call option, because it expired at the money. Notice in Exhibit

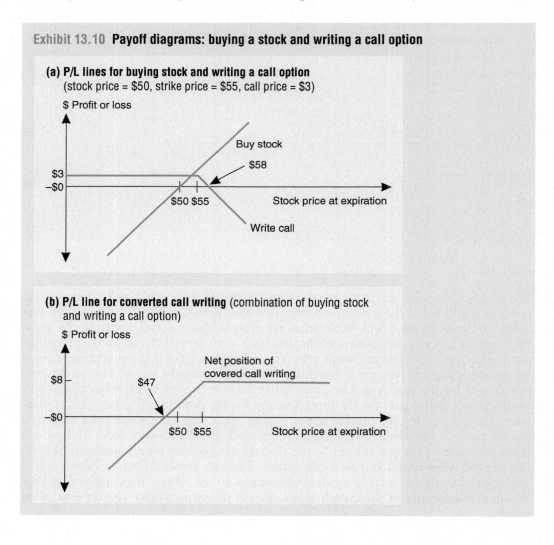

Exhibit 13.10 Payoff diagrams: buying a stock and writing a call option

(a) P/L lines for buying stock and writing a call option
(stock price = $50, strike price = $55, call price = $3)

(b) P/L line for converted call writing (combination of buying stock and writing a call option)

13.10(a) that above a $55 stock price, for every additional dollar gained on the stock position, the call option position loses a dollar. Hence, the profit is greatest at $8 ($5 from the stock and $3 from selling the option). Below a $55 stock price the call option is worthless; hence for every additional dollar reduction in the stock position, the call position's cash flow does not change and the net position loses a dollar.

Exhibit 13.10(b) illustrates the net position of covered call writing. Notice that the net position is very similar in its shape to the P/L line derived when just writing a put option. Again, the actual differences relate to the timing of the cash flows. Covered call writing dramatically alters the risk–return profile of a stock position; it sets a ceiling on the potential gain. Investors are willing to accept this ceiling in return for receiving the call premium.

13.6 OPTION VALUATION

At expiration date the value of the option is easy to determine: it is either zero if is out of the money, or the stock price less the strike price if it is in the money. The difficult problem is to determine the option price before the expiration date. Black and Scholes (B&S) provide such a valuation formula (see Section 13.8).

This section covers the pricing of options and how investors can detect whether an option is underpriced or overpriced. Option pricing heavily relies on the no-arbitrage argument – that is, in equilibrium, no arbitrage profit prevails.

Understanding the price behaviour of options requires a knowledge of options arbitrage. When there are arbitrage opportunities available, they do not last long. With the lightning-fast computer technology available today, investors need to be quick to exploit arbitrage opportunities. Arbitrage is basically a 'free lunch', which occurs rarely and does not last very long.

Although there are many possible definitions of arbitrage, this text focuses on two popular definitions. An arbitrage opportunity exists when either (1) a portfolio can be constructed at zero cost (by selling some securities short) that has future positive cash flows but absolutely zero probability of negative cash flows, or (2) a portfolio can be constructed for a negative cost (that is, the investor receives money today) that has no risk of future losses. In equilibrium, arbitrage opportunities do not exist. The existence of arbitrage profit thus represents disequilibrium. Option prices are determined for the most part by option traders eliminating arbitrage opportunities.

This section examines the pricing of European-style options (that is, options where early exercise is not allowed). First, we examine the option pricing boundaries that all option prices must satisfy. Option prices remain within the boundaries because of arbitrage forces in the market. Then we discuss the Black–Scholes pricing approach to determining the equilibrium price of an option. Finally, we examine a risk management strategy called *portfolio insurance*, which uses this approach.

Most of the illustrations in this section relate to pricing stock options. However, the same principles demonstrated in this chapter apply to pricing options on any underlying asset, such as stock index options, futures or foreign currency options.

13.6.1 Option boundaries

Option boundaries provide a helpful first step in the quest to understand option price behaviour. Option boundary conditions represent the range where we would anticipate

Exhibit 13.11 Closing price options based on Microsoft

(a) Closing price quotes

Stock price	Strike price	Calls			Puts		
		31 day	91 day	182 day	31 day	91 day	182 day
100	90	10.80	12.85	15.47	0.42	1.74	3.26
100	95	6.76	9.39	12.31	1.35	3.21	4.97
100	100	3.70	6.57	9.62	3.27	5.33	7.16
100	105	1.74	4.41	7.38	6.30	8.11	9.80
100	110	0.70	2.84	5.57	10.24	11.47	12.86

(b) Lower bounds

Stock price	Strike price	Calls			Puts		
		31 day	91 day	182 day	31 day	91 day	182 day
100	90	10.37	11.09	12.16	0.0	0.0	0.0
100	95	5.39	6.15	7.28	0.0	0.0	0.0
100	100	0.41	1.21	2.40	0.0	0.0	0.0
100	105	0.0	0.0	0.0	4.57	3.73	2.48
100	110	0.0	0.0	0.0	9.55	8.67	7.36

The closing price quotes are based on the Black–Scholes option pricing model discussed later in this chapter. They assume a 5% interest rate and a standard deviation of 30%.

finding option prices. Option prices must satisfy certain boundaries; otherwise, investors could make an infinite profit at no risk. (This arbitrage activity would push the option price inside these bounds.) The derivation of option prices is based on the assumption that there are sophisticated investors in the market. Whenever these investors see arbitrage opportunities, they exploit them. This trading activity causes prices to change until the arbitrage profits disappear and option prices lie within the designated boundaries.

Exhibit 13.11 is a hypothetical closed market quote sheet for a market maker in Microsoft options. How are we to make sense out of all these numbers? Are these reasonable prices? Are they overpriced? Are they underpriced? Finding option boundaries helps to answer these questions.

An arbitrageur would like to find option prices that are either too high or too low. The analysis in this section establishes ways of assessing the validity of option market prices. The section first examines call option boundaries and then put option boundaries.

13.6.2 Call option boundaries

For a call option, there is both an upper and a lower boundary for the current call price. If the call price is above the upper boundary or below the lower boundary, then an arbitrageur will be able to make money with no risk. This section first examines call option boundaries and then describes what happens when option prices get outside them.

Lower boundary

The prices of a European-style call option (c_0) must lie above the following boundary:

$$c_0 \geq \max\left[0, S_0 - \frac{X}{(1 + r)^t}\right] \qquad (13.5)$$

where S_0 is the price of a security or underlying asset today; X is the strike or exercise price; t is the time to maturity until the expiration date (in fraction of years); and r is the annual risk-free interest rate, which is assumed to be constant.

In Exhibit 13.12 we establish an investment strategy which will guarantee an arbitrage profit as long as Equation 13.5 does not hold. The trading strategy presented in Exhibit 13.12 will establish the lower boundary by examining cash flows at time 0 and maturity date t. (We assume that any trade opened at time 0 is closed at t.) Note that we separate the future into two possibilities: $S_t \geq X$ and $S_t < X$. More information on the exact value of S_t is not needed.

Column 1 of Exhibit 13.12 identifies the exact trading strategy to adopt at time 0 (today). As a cash flow table, columns 2, 3 and 4 contain dollar cash flows. Column 2 shows the dollar cash flows today from following the trading strategy in column 1. (Recall that when you short sell the stock, you receive money.) The net cash flow at the bottom of this column is found by summing the cash flows in the 'Today' column (the required investment). The question mark (?) indicates that we investigate whether the investment will be positive, zero or negative if arbitrage profits are absent. Columns 3 and 4 depict the cash flow when $S_t > X$ (column 3) and when $S_t \leq X$ (column 4).

According to Exhibit 13.12, if the cash flow today (0) is positive (that is, the question mark in the exhibit is positive), then an arbitrage profit opportunity (sometimes called a money machine) prevails. That is, we are able to generate a positive cash flow today with no risk of future loss (and possibly a positive future cash flow). The last column of this table is positive by assumption ($S_t \leq X$). Thus, to avoid this arbitrage or money machine, we must find the cash flow today to be negative. Therefore, we must have, in equilibrium,

$$-c_0 + S_0 - \frac{X}{(1+r)^t} \leq 0$$

Exhibit 13.12 The lower boundary for call options: a cash flow table

	Cash flows		
(1)	(2)	(3)	(4)
Trading strategy	Today (0)	At expiration	
		$S_t > X$	$S_t \leq X$
Buy one call option	$-c_0$	$S_t - X$	0
Sell short one share of stock	$+S_0$	$-S_t$	$-S_t$
Lend $X/(1 + r)^t$	$-X/(1 + r)^t$	X	X
Net cash flow	$-c_0 + S_0$	0	$X - S_t$ (zero or positive)
	$-X/(1 + r)^t = ?$		

C_0 = the current call price, S_0 = the current stock price, S_t = the stock price at expiration, X = the strike price, r = the risk-free interest rate, and t = the time to maturity in fractions of a year.

which implies that

$$c_0 \geq S_0 - \frac{X}{(1+r)^t}$$

How do the actions of the arbitrageur influence market prices? If $-c_0 + S_0 - X/(1 + r)^t$ is positive, everyone will want to buy call options, short sell the stock, and borrow to create this money machine. These actions will push the price of the call up and the price of the stock down until the cash flow is nonpositive (0). Also, because of limited liability of an option, the option price cannot be negative ($c_0 \geq 0$). Recall that the option buyer does not have to exercise the options. We can conclude that the inequality given in Equation 13.5 holds.

■ Upper boundary

Using similar arguments, we can demonstrate that the price of a European-style call option must lie below the underlying stock price:

$$c_0 \leq S_0 \tag{13.6}$$

Intuitively, we would not pay more for an option to buy a security than we would pay for the underlying security if we purchased it directly. For example, why should we pay \$100 for the right to buy the stock when we could buy it directly in the market for $S_t = \$90$? Thus, a call option is always worth less than the underlying security on which the option is written.

Exhibit 13.13 illustrates the boundaries for call options. Note that if we have an American-style call option and it is exercised, the value is $S_0 - X$. Because $c_0 > S_0 - [X/(1 + r)^t] > S_0 - X$, it never pays to exercise the call option before maturity. (You are better off selling the option.) Thus, the boundaries of European-style call options also apply to American-style options.

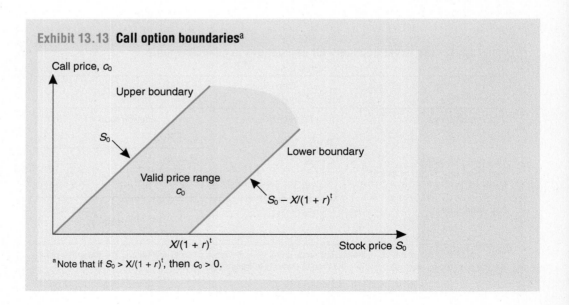

Exhibit 13.13 Call option boundaries[a]

Call price, c_0

Upper boundary

S_0

Lower boundary

Valid price range c_0

$S_0 - X/(1 + r)^t$

$X/(1 + r)^t$

Stock price S_0

[a]Note that if $S_0 > X/(1 + r)^t$, then $c_0 > 0$.

Exhibit 13.14 The lower boundary for put options: a cash flow table

(1)	(2)	(3)	(4)
	Cash flows		
Trading strategy	Today (0)	At expiration	
		$S_t \geq X$	$S_t < X$
Buy one put option	$-p_0$	0	$X - S_t$
Borrow $$X/(1 + r)^t$	$+X/(1 + r)^t$	$-X$	$-X$
Buy one share of stock	$-S_0$	$+S_t$	$+S_t$
Net cash flow	$-p_0 + X/(1 + r)^t - S_0 = ?$	$S_t - X$ (zero or positive)	0

p_0 = the current put price, S_0 = the current stock price, S_t = the stock price at expiration, X = the strike price, r = the risk-free interest rate, and t = the time to maturity in fractions of a year.

13.6.3 Put option boundaries

■ Lower boundary

As with call options, European-style put options have pricing boundaries. The lower boundary for the put price (p_0) is

$$p_0 \geq \max\left[0, \frac{X}{(1+r)^t} - S_0\right] \tag{13.7}$$

The trading strategy employed to demonstrate the lower boundary of a put option consists of three parts: (1) borrowing the amount $$X/(1 + r)^t$, (2) buying one share of stock, and (3) buying one put option. Exhibit 13.14 illustrates the cash flows. The next-to-last column of this table is nonnegative (0) by assumption ($S_t \geq X$). Therefore, if the cash flow today (0) is positive (? > 0), then this is an arbitrage opportunity. We are able to generate a positive cash flow today with no risk of future loss (and possibly a positive future cash flow). Thus, to avoid this arbitrage, we must find the cash flow today to be negative. We must have

$$-p_0 + X/(1 + r)^t - S_0 \leq 0$$

which implies

$$p_0 \geq X/(1 + r)^t - S_0$$

If we observe that $-p_0 + X/(1 + r)^t - S_0$ is positive, everyone will want to buy put options, buy the stock, and lend to create this money machine. Buying the stock and the put option will drive the stock price and the put price up, and eventually any arbitrage profits will vanish.

■ Upper boundary

The most you can lose from writing a put option (or earn by buying a put option) is the strike price (see Equation 13.8). This occurs when the stock price falls to zero. Because this loss occurs at maturity and not on the day the put option is purchased, the put option price must be below the discounted value of the strike price:

$$p_0 \leq \frac{X}{(1 + r)^t} \tag{13.8}$$

Why would you pay more for an option than the present value of its maximum pay-off? The answer is that you would not. For example, a one-year put option ($t = 1$) with a strike price of $100 at a 5% risk-free rate has an upper boundary of $\$100/(1 + 0.05)^1$ = $95.24. Investors will not pay more than $95.24 for a put option that gives them the right to make at most $100 one year from now.

Exhibit 13.15 illustrates the boundaries for put options. Again, the valid range of prices is still wide. We must investigate option pricing further to find out whether we can make a more precise assertion regarding the option price. We turn now to examine the relationship between stock, put option and call option prices.

Unlike with the call options analysis, with put options there may be value associated with an early exercise. Thus, American-style put options may have a higher

PRACTICE BOX

Problem

Based on the following information from *Barron's*, verify that the closing prices of Borland's put and call options satisfy the boundary conditions. The time to maturity is one month ($t = \frac{1}{12}$), Borland's stock price is $\$41\frac{7}{8}$, and the annual risk-free interest rate is 3%. Are there any arbitrage opportunities?

Expiration date and strike price	Closing Price ($)
Borland Oct 40 call	$3\frac{3}{4}$
Borland Oct 40 put	$1\frac{3}{4}$
Borland Oct 45 call	$1\frac{5}{8}$
Borland Oct 45 put	$4\frac{1}{4}$
Borland Oct 50 call	$\frac{1}{2}$
Borland Oct 50 put	$8\frac{1}{4}$

Solution

Clearly, none of these prices approaches the upper bounds ($\$41\frac{7}{8}$ for calls and $40, $45 and $50 discounted for one month at the risk-free rate for puts). We now examine the lower bounds. The discount factor is $1/(1 + r)^t = 1/(1 + 0.03)^{1/12} = 0.9975$. Thus, for $X = \$40$ we have $\$40 \times 0.9975 = \$39.9$; for $X = \$45$ we have $\$45 \times 0.9975 = \$44.8875$; and for $X = \$50$ we have $\$50 \times 0.9975 = \$49.875$.

Let us consider calls first. When $X = \$40$, we have a lower boundary of $\$41.875 - \$39.9$ = $1.975, which is lower than the closing price of $\$3\frac{3}{4}$. When $X = \$45$, we note that $\$44.8875 > \$41.875$, and the lower boundary is zero. This is also true when $X = \$50$. In both cases, the lower boundary holds.

The boundaries for puts (using Equation 13.8) are as follows:

$$X = \$40: p_0 = 0$$
$$X = \$45: p_0 = \$44.8875 - \$41.875 = \$3.0125$$
$$X = \$50: p_0 = \$49.875 - \$41.875 = \$8.0$$

We see that each lower boundary is below the put option prices. Thus, based on these observations, there are no arbitrage opportunities.

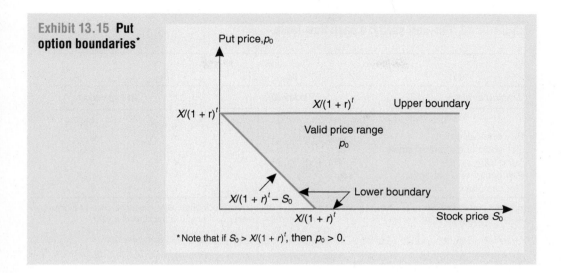

Exhibit 13.15 Put option boundaries*

*Note that if $S_0 > X/(1 + r)^t$, then $p_0 > 0$.

value than European-style put options. To illustrate, suppose that you buy a put option on a firm that is under financial distress, and its stock price is, say, 1 cent. If the strike price is, say, $10, you had better exercise your right, get the cash flow (of $10 less 1 cent), and deposit the money in the bank to earn interest on this cash flow. The interest received may be more than the maximum additional profit from holding the put option (1 cent at most if the stock price drops to zero) until maturity. Thus, unlike with call options, with put options there is economic value for the possibility of an early exercise. We therefore expect the market value of American-style put options to be higher than the market value of similar European-style put options.

13.7 PUT–CALL PARITY

Put–call parity is very useful in establishing pricing relationships between securities such as calls and puts. The notion of put–call parity (PCP) was first published by Russell Sage in the late nineteenth century. Put–call parity establishes an exact relationship among the current stock price, the call price and the put price. In other words, put–call parity establishes the relationship among the underlying security, the risk-free interest rate, and call and put options that have the same strike price. Given any three of the following four securities – (1) the underlying security, (2) zero-coupon bonds (borrowing or lending), (3) a call option and (4) a put option – we can synthetically create the fourth. That is, by creating a portfolio of three assets, we can duplicate the cash flow of the fourth asset. Put–call parity can be written as follows:

$$c_0 = S_0 - \frac{X}{(1 + t)^t} + p_0 \qquad (13.9)$$

Again, we assume that any trade opened at time 0 is closed at the option maturity date (t). Exhibit 13.16 establishes the validity of Equation 13.9.

As in Exhibit 13.14, the first column of Exhibit 13.16 identifies a trading strategy adopted at time 0 (today). The other three columns show the relevant cash flows. The

Exhibit 13.16 Put–call parity: a cash flow table

(1)	(2)	(3)	(4)
	Cash flows		
	Today (0)	At expiration	
Trading strategy		$S_t \geq X$	$S_t < X$
Buy one call option	$-c_0$	$S_t - X$	0
Sell short one share of stock	$+S_0$	$-S_t$	$-S_t$
Lend $X/(1 + r)^t$	$-X/(1 + r)^t$	X	X
Sell (write) one put option	$+p_0$	0	$-(X - S_t)$
Net cash flow	$-c_0 + S_0 - X/(1 + r)^t + p_0$	0	0

c_0 = the current call price, p_0 = the current put price, S_0 = the current stock price, S_t = the stock price at expiration, X = the strike price, r = the risk-free interest rate, and t = the time to maturity in fractions of a year.

net cash flows are simply the sum of all cash flows from the investment. For example, the net cash flow in column 2 represents the required investment today (if negative) or the cash inflow to the investor (if positive).

Exhibit 13.16 shows that the future net cash flow from this portfolio is zero regardless of the future stock price. (That is, the sums of columns 3 and 4 are zero.) Hence, from capital budgeting, we know that the discounted value of these payoffs (which are zero) is definitely zero (regardless of the discount rate used). Therefore, the cash flow today must be zero, or else there exists a 'money machine'. If the net cash flow today is positive, everyone would want such an investment; the demand for the call options would increase their price, selling short the stock would decrease the price of the stock, and selling the put would decrease the put price. This selling will continue until the cash flow at time 0 is zero and any arbitrage profit vanishes.

PRACTICE BOX

Problem

Using the information in the previous problem on Borland, evaluate whether the put–call parity holds when the strike price is $X = \$40$.

Solution

From Equation 13.9 we know that

$$c_0 - p_0 = S_0 - \frac{X}{(1 + r)^t}$$

and we have $c_0 = \$3^3/_4$, $p_0 = \$1^3/_4$, $S_0 = \$41^7/_8$, $X = \$40$, $r = 3\%$ and $t = 1/_{12}$. We need to evaluate whether the following equality exists:

$$\$3.75 - \$1.75 \cong \$41.875 - \$39.9$$

$$\$2 \neq \$1.975$$

Thus, put–call parity does not hold precisely. However, it would probably be impossible to profit from this discrepancy because of transaction costs. In practice, put–call parity holds very closely.

13.8 BLACK–SCHOLES OPTION PRICING MODEL (BSOPM)

The Black–Scholes option pricing model (BSOPM) was developed in a famous paper published by Fischer Black and Myron Scholes in 1973 in the *Journal of Political Economy*. The BSOPM was distinct from other, similar models proposed in the late 1960s and early 1970s in that the option price does not depend on the expected returns of the underlying stock. Moreover, the model is based on a creation of a fully hedged position; thus, the riskless asset is employed to discount the future cash flows.

To better understand the usefulness and limitations of the BSOPM, let us examine the primary assumptions required for the BSOPM to be developed:

1 The market is frictionless.
2 Investors are price takers.
3 Short selling is allowed, with full use of the proceeds.
4 Borrowing and lending occur at the risk-free rate, which is continuously compounded.
5 Stock price movements are such that past price movements cannot be used to forecast future price changes.

A frictionless market is a market where trading is costless; there are no taxes, bid–ask spreads, brokerage commissions, and so forth. The second assumption means that no single investor can significantly influence prices. As discussed in Chapter 3, short selling is selling stock that you do not own with the understanding that you will return stock to the lender in the future.

The assumption that the risk-free interest rate is compounded continuously is made for convenience and conforms with standard practice. The fifth assumption determines the stock price distribution. The assumption that the stock price movement in the future cannot be predicted from the past is used by Black and Scholes, when obtaining the BSOPM.

13.8.1 Call options

Black and Scholes used the assumptions to develop a model for pricing call options. At first glance, the BSOPM looks difficult. However, a familiarity with the symbols and steps required to systematically solve pricing problems, as well as software packages, makes the BSOPM easier to use.

The BSOPM for call options is as follows:

$$c = SN(d_1) - Xe^{-r_c t}N(d_2) \tag{13.10}$$

where

$$d_1 = \frac{\ln(S/X) + [r_c + (\sigma^2)/2]t}{\sigma\sqrt{t}}$$

$$d_2 = \frac{\ln(S/X) - [r_c + (\sigma^2/2)]t}{\sigma\sqrt{t}} = d_1 - \sigma\sqrt{t}$$

$N(d)$ is the cumulative area of the *standard normal distribution*. For example, if $d_1 = 1.645$, then using the normal distribution, the cumulative areas up to 1.645 (which is the intersection of 1.600 in the vertical column and 0.045 on the horizontal column of Exhibit 13.17) are 95%. Hence, $N(d_1) = 0.95$ (see Exhibit 13.17). Thus, the area under the normal curve right to d_1 is 0.05. Suppose that $\sigma = 24.5\%$, or 0.245, and

Exhibit 13.17 Values for N(d) given d

d	0.0000	0.0050	0.0100	0.0150	0.0200	0.0250	0.0300	0.0350	0.0400	0.0450	0.0500	0.0550	0.0600	0.0650	0.0700	0.0750	0.0800	0.0850	0.0900	0.0950
													Second decimal of d							
-2.9000	0.0019	0.0018	0.0018	0.0018	0.0018	0.0017	0.0017	0.0017	0.0016	0.0016	0.0016	0.0016	0.0015	0.0015	0.0015	0.0015	0.0014	0.0014	0.0014	0.0014
-2.8000	0.0026	0.0025	0.0025	0.0024	0.0024	0.0024	0.0023	0.0023	0.0023	0.0022	0.0022	0.0022	0.0021	0.0021	0.0021	0.0020	0.0020	0.0020	0.0019	0.0019
-2.7000	0.0035	0.0034	0.0034	0.0033	0.0033	0.0032	0.0032	0.0031	0.0031	0.0030	0.0030	0.0029	0.0029	0.0028	0.0028	0.0028	0.0027	0.0027	0.0026	0.0026
-2.6000	0.0047	0.0046	0.0045	0.0045	0.0044	0.0043	0.0043	0.0042	0.0041	0.0041	0.0040	0.0040	0.0039	0.0038	0.0038	0.0037	0.0037	0.0036	0.0036	0.0035
-2.5000	0.0062	0.0061	0.0060	0.0060	0.0059	0.0058	0.0057	0.0056	0.0055	0.0055	0.0054	0.0053	0.0052	0.0052	0.0051	0.0050	0.0049	0.0049	0.0048	0.0047
-2.4000	0.0082	0.0081	0.0080	0.0079	0.0078	0.0077	0.0075	0.0074	0.0073	0.0072	0.0071	0.0070	0.0069	0.0069	0.0068	0.0067	0.0066	0.0065	0.0064	0.0063
-2.3000	0.0107	0.0106	0.0104	0.0103	0.0102	0.0100	0.0099	0.0098	0.0096	0.0095	0.0094	0.0093	0.0091	0.0090	0.0089	0.0088	0.0087	0.0085	0.0084	0.0083
-2.2000	0.0139	0.0137	0.0136	0.0134	0.0132	0.0130	0.0129	0.0127	0.0125	0.0124	0.0122	0.0121	0.0119	0.0118	0.0116	0.0115	0.0113	0.0112	0.0110	0.0109
-2.1000	0.0179	0.0176	0.0174	0.0172	0.0170	0.0168	0.0166	0.0164	0.0162	0.0160	0.0158	0.0156	0.0154	0.0152	0.0150	0.0148	0.0146	0.0144	0.0143	0.0141
-2.0000	0.0228	0.0225	0.0222	0.0220	0.0217	0.0214	0.0212	0.0209	0.0207	0.0204	0.0202	0.0199	0.0197	0.0195	0.0192	0.0190	0.0188	0.0185	0.0183	0.0181
-1.9000	0.0287	0.0284	0.0281	0.0277	0.0274	0.0271	0.0268	0.0265	0.0262	0.0259	0.0256	0.0253	0.0250	0.0247	0.0244	0.0241	0.0239	0.0236	0.0233	0.0230
-1.8000	0.0359	0.0355	0.0351	0.0348	0.0344	0.0340	0.0336	0.0333	0.0329	0.0325	0.0322	0.0318	0.0314	0.0311	0.0307	0.0304	0.0301	0.0297	0.0294	0.0290
-1.7000	0.0446	0.0441	0.0436	0.0432	0.0427	0.0423	0.0418	0.0414	0.0409	0.0405	0.0401	0.0396	0.0392	0.0388	0.0384	0.0379	0.0375	0.0371	0.0367	0.0363
-1.6000	0.0548	0.0542	0.0537	0.0532	0.0526	0.0521	0.0516	0.0510	0.0505	0.0500	0.0495	0.0490	0.0485	0.0480	0.0475	0.0470	0.0465	0.0460	0.0455	0.0450
-1.5000	0.0668	0.0662	0.0655	0.0649	0.0643	0.0636	0.0630	0.0624	0.0618	0.0612	0.0606	0.0600	0.0594	0.0588	0.0582	0.0576	0.0571	0.0565	0.0559	0.0554
-1.4000	0.0808	0.0800	0.0793	0.0785	0.0778	0.0771	0.0764	0.0756	0.0749	0.0742	0.0735	0.0728	0.0721	0.0715	0.0708	0.0701	0.0694	0.0688	0.0681	0.0675
-1.3000	0.0968	0.0959	0.0951	0.0943	0.0934	0.0926	0.0918	0.0909	0.0901	0.0893	0.0885	0.0877	0.0869	0.0861	0.0853	0.0846	0.0838	0.0830	0.0823	0.0815
-1.2000	0.1151	0.1141	0.1131	0.1122	0.1112	0.1103	0.1093	0.1084	0.1075	0.1066	0.1056	0.1047	0.1038	0.1029	0.1020	0.1012	0.1003	0.0994	0.0985	0.0977
-1.1000	0.1357	0.1346	0.1335	0.1324	0.1314	0.1303	0.1292	0.1282	0.1271	0.1261	0.1251	0.1240	0.1230	0.1220	0.1210	0.1200	0.1190	0.1180	0.1170	0.1160
-1.0000	0.1587	0.1574	0.1562	0.1551	0.1539	0.1527	0.1515	0.1503	0.1492	0.1480	0.1469	0.1457	0.1446	0.1434	0.1423	0.1412	0.1401	0.1390	0.1379	0.1368
-0.9000	0.1841	0.1827	0.1814	0.1801	0.1788	0.1775	0.1762	0.1749	0.1736	0.1723	0.1711	0.1698	0.1685	0.1673	0.1660	0.1648	0.1635	0.1623	0.1611	0.1599
-0.8000	0.2119	0.2104	0.2090	0.2075	0.2061	0.2047	0.2033	0.2019	0.2005	0.1991	0.1977	0.1963	0.1949	0.1935	0.1921	0.1908	0.1894	0.1881	0.1867	0.1854
-0.7000	0.2420	0.2404	0.2389	0.2373	0.2358	0.2342	0.2327	0.2312	0.2296	0.2281	0.2266	0.2251	0.2236	0.2221	0.2206	0.2192	0.2177	0.2162	0.2148	0.2133
-0.6000	0.2743	0.2726	0.2709	0.2693	0.2676	0.2660	0.2643	0.2627	0.2611	0.2595	0.2578	0.2562	0.2546	0.2530	0.2514	0.2498	0.2483	0.2467	0.2451	0.2435
-0.5000	0.3085	0.3068	0.3050	0.3033	0.3015	0.2998	0.2981	0.2963	0.2946	0.2929	0.2912	0.2894	0.2877	0.2860	0.2843	0.2826	0.2810	0.2793	0.2776	0.2759
-0.4000	0.3446	0.3427	0.3409	0.3391	0.3372	0.3354	0.3336	0.3318	0.3300	0.3282	0.3264	0.3246	0.3228	0.3210	0.3192	0.3174	0.3156	0.3138	0.3121	0.3103
-0.3000	0.3821	0.3802	0.3783	0.3764	0.3745	0.3726	0.3707	0.3688	0.3669	0.3650	0.3632	0.3613	0.3594	0.3576	0.3557	0.3538	0.3520	0.3501	0.3483	0.3464
-0.2000	0.4207	0.4188	0.4168	0.4149	0.4129	0.4110	0.4090	0.4071	0.4052	0.4032	0.4013	0.3994	0.3974	0.3955	0.3936	0.3917	0.3897	0.3878	0.3859	0.3840
-0.1000	0.4602	0.4582	0.4562	0.4542	0.4522	0.4503	0.4483	0.4463	0.4443	0.4424	0.4404	0.4384	0.4364	0.4345	0.4325	0.4305	0.4286	0.4266	0.4247	0.4227

Exhibit 13.17 (continued)

Second decimal of d

d	0.0000	0.0050	0.0100	0.0150	0.0200	0.0250	0.0300	0.0350	0.0400	0.0450	0.0500	0.0550	0.0600	0.0650	0.0700	0.0750	0.0800	0.0850	0.0900	0.0950
0.0000	0.5000	0.5020	0.5040	0.5060	0.5080	0.5100	0.5120	0.5140	0.5160	0.5179	0.5199	0.5219	0.5239	0.5259	0.5279	0.5299	0.5319	0.5339	0.5359	0.5378
0.1000	0.5398	0.5418	0.5438	0.5458	0.5478	0.5497	0.5517	0.5537	0.5557	0.5576	0.5596	0.5616	0.5636	0.5655	0.5675	0.5695	0.5714	0.5734	0.5753	0.5773
0.2000	0.5793	0.5812	0.5832	0.5851	0.5871	0.5890	0.5910	0.5929	0.5948	0.5968	0.5987	0.6006	0.6026	0.6045	0.6064	0.6083	0.6103	0.6122	0.6141	0.6160
0.3000	0.6179	0.6198	0.6217	0.6236	0.6255	0.6274	0.6293	0.6312	0.6331	0.6350	0.6368	0.6387	0.6406	0.6424	0.6443	0.6462	0.6480	0.6499	0.6517	0.6536
0.4000	0.6554	0.6573	0.6591	0.6609	0.6628	0.6646	0.6664	0.6682	0.6700	0.6718	0.6736	0.6754	0.6772	0.6790	0.6808	0.6826	0.6844	0.6862	0.6879	0.6897
0.5000	0.6915	0.6932	0.6950	0.6967	0.6985	0.7002	0.7019	0.7037	0.7054	0.7071	0.7088	0.7106	0.7123	0.7140	0.7157	0.7174	0.7190	0.7207	0.7224	0.7241
0.6000	0.7257	0.7274	0.7291	0.7307	0.7324	0.7340	0.7357	0.7373	0.7389	0.7405	0.7422	0.7438	0.7454	0.7470	0.7486	0.7502	0.7517	0.7533	0.7549	0.7565
0.7000	0.7580	0.7596	0.7611	0.7627	0.7642	0.7658	0.7673	0.7688	0.7703	0.7719	0.7734	0.7749	0.7764	0.7779	0.7794	0.7808	0.7823	0.7838	0.7852	0.7867
0.8000	0.7881	0.7896	0.7910	0.7925	0.7939	0.7953	0.7967	0.7981	0.7995	0.8009	0.8023	0.8037	0.8051	0.8065	0.8078	0.8092	0.8106	0.8119	0.8133	0.8146
0.9000	0.8159	0.8173	0.8186	0.8199	0.8212	0.8225	0.8238	0.8251	0.8264	0.8277	0.8289	0.8302	0.8315	0.8327	0.8340	0.8352	0.8365	0.8377	0.8389	0.8401
1.0000	0.8413	0.8426	0.8438	0.8449	0.8461	0.8473	0.8485	0.8497	0.8508	0.8520	0.8531	0.8543	0.8554	0.8566	0.8577	0.8588	0.8599	0.8610	0.8621	0.8632
1.1000	0.8643	0.8654	0.8665	0.8676	0.8686	0.8697	0.8708	0.8718	0.8729	0.8739	0.8749	0.8760	0.8770	0.8780	0.8790	0.8800	0.8810	0.8820	0.8830	0.8840
1.2000	0.8849	0.8859	0.8869	0.8878	0.8888	0.8897	0.8907	0.8916	0.8925	0.8934	0.8944	0.8953	0.8962	0.8971	0.8980	0.8988	0.8997	0.9006	0.9015	0.9023
1.3000	0.9032	0.9041	0.9049	0.9057	0.9066	0.9074	0.9082	0.9091	0.9099	0.9107	0.9115	0.9123	0.9131	0.9139	0.9147	0.9154	0.9162	0.9170	0.9177	0.9185
1.4000	0.9192	0.9200	0.9207	0.9215	0.9222	0.9229	0.9236	0.9244	0.9251	0.9258	0.9265	0.9272	0.9279	0.9285	0.9292	0.9299	0.9306	0.9312	0.9319	0.9325
1.5000	0.9332	0.9338	0.9345	0.9351	0.9357	0.9364	0.9370	0.9376	0.9382	0.9388	0.9394	0.9400	0.9406	0.9412	0.9418	0.9424	0.9429	0.9435	0.9441	0.9446
1.6000	0.9452	0.9458	0.9463	0.9468	0.9474	0.9479	0.9484	0.9490	0.9495	0.9500	0.9505	0.9510	0.9515	0.9520	0.9525	0.9530	0.9535	0.9540	0.9545	0.9550
1.7000	0.9554	0.9559	0.9564	0.9568	0.9573	0.9577	0.9582	0.9586	0.9591	0.9595	0.9599	0.9604	0.9608	0.9612	0.9616	0.9621	0.9625	0.9629	0.9633	0.9637
1.8000	0.9641	0.9645	0.9649	0.9652	0.9656	0.9660	0.9664	0.9667	0.9671	0.9675	0.9678	0.9682	0.9686	0.9689	0.9693	0.9696	0.9699	0.9703	0.9706	0.9710
1.9000	0.9713	0.9716	0.9719	0.9723	0.9726	0.9729	0.9732	0.9735	0.9738	0.9741	0.9744	0.9747	0.9750	0.9753	0.9756	0.9759	0.9761	0.9764	0.9767	0.9770
2.0000	0.9772	0.9775	0.9778	0.9780	0.9783	0.9786	0.9788	0.9791	0.9793	0.9796	0.9798	0.9801	0.9803	0.9805	0.9808	0.9810	0.9812	0.9815	0.9817	0.9819
2.1000	0.9821	0.9824	0.9826	0.9828	0.9830	0.9832	0.9834	0.9836	0.9838	0.9840	0.9842	0.9844	0.9846	0.9848	0.9850	0.9852	0.9854	0.9856	0.9857	0.9859
2.2000	0.9861	0.9863	0.9864	0.9866	0.9868	0.9870	0.9871	0.9873	0.9875	0.9876	0.9878	0.9879	0.9881	0.9882	0.9884	0.9885	0.9887	0.9888	0.9890	0.9891
2.3000	0.9893	0.9894	0.9896	0.9897	0.9898	0.9900	0.9901	0.9902	0.9904	0.9905	0.9906	0.9907	0.9909	0.9910	0.9911	0.9912	0.9913	0.9915	0.9916	0.9917
2.4000	0.9918	0.9919	0.9920	0.9921	0.9922	0.9923	0.9925	0.9926	0.9927	0.9928	0.9929	0.9930	0.9931	0.9931	0.9932	0.9933	0.9934	0.9935	0.9936	0.9937
2.5000	0.9938	0.9939	0.9940	0.9940	0.9941	0.9942	0.9943	0.9944	0.9945	0.9945	0.9946	0.9947	0.9948	0.9948	0.9949	0.9950	0.9951	0.9951	0.9952	0.9953
2.6000	0.9953	0.9954	0.9955	0.9955	0.9956	0.9957	0.9957	0.9958	0.9959	0.9959	0.9960	0.9960	0.9961	0.9962	0.9962	0.9963	0.9963	0.9964	0.9964	0.9965
2.7000	0.9965	0.9966	0.9966	0.9967	0.9967	0.9968	0.9968	0.9969	0.9969	0.9970	0.9970	0.9971	0.9971	0.9972	0.9972	0.9972	0.9973	0.9973	0.9974	0.9974
2.8000	0.9974	0.9975	0.9975	0.9976	0.9976	0.9976	0.9977	0.9977	0.9977	0.9978	0.9978	0.9978	0.9979	0.9979	0.9979	0.9980	0.9980	0.9980	0.9981	0.9981
2.9000	0.9981	0.9982	0.9982	0.9982	0.9982	0.9983	0.9983	0.9983	0.9984	0.9984	0.9984	0.9984	0.9985	0.9985	0.9985	0.9985	0.9986	0.9986	0.9986	0.9986

$t = 1$. Then $d_2 = d_1 - \sigma\sqrt{t} = 1.645 - 0.245 = 1.400$, and the cumulative area up to $d_2 = 1.400$ is about 92%. Hence, $N(d_2) \cong 0.92$, and the area right of d_2 is about 0.08. Thus, the area between d_2 and d_1 is about 3%, or 0.03.

The other parameters of Equation 13.10 are as follows: ln( ) is the natural logarithm; σ is the continuously compounded, annualized standard deviation of stock returns; r_c is the continuously compounded, annual risk-free interest rate; t is the time to maturity as a fraction of a year (with some software, we need to plug in t as the number of days to expiration); X is the strike price; S is the current stock price; and e is the base of natural logarithms and is equal to 2.7128. Thus, we need five variables (σ, r_c, t, X and S) to calculate the price of a call option using the BSOPM (for the calculation of r_c and σ on a continuous basis, see Appendix 13C and Appendix 13D, respectively).

Calculating the call option price is easy with the available software. All we have to do is to insert S, X, σ, r_c and t (in some software, t is given in days to expiration – for example, 182 days – rather than as a fraction of a year) and the call option price, c, then appears on the screen. However, tables with $N(d_1)$ and $N(d_2)$ are also available. We can use them along with a calculator to derive c. For example, suppose we are given the following parameters: $S = \$100.0$, $X = \$100.0$, $\sigma = 30\%$, $r_c = 7\%$ and $t = 182$ days (about $^1/_2$ year). The use of a software package reveals that $c = \$10.12$.

Using EXCEL and inserting d_1 and d_2, we obtain (without a need for tables) the values of $N(d_1)$ and $N(d_2)$. Then it is simple to obtain c by inserting these values in Equation 13.10.

13.8.2 Put options

The appropriate formula for put options can be found using the BSOPM for call options and put-call parity. Rearranging Equation 13.9 (with continuous compounding rather than discrete compounding) yields the following:

$$P = C - S + Xe^{-r_c t} \tag{13.11}$$

13.8.3 Estimating inputs to the BSOPM

There are five input parameters in the BSOPM: S, X, t, r_c and σ. The current stock price (S) is easily obtainable by calling a broker, by some Internet sites, or by contacting an information service, such as Reuters or Telerate. The strike price (X) is specified in the options contract and published in the financial media, such as the *Wall Street Journal* and *Barron's*.

Time to maturity (t) is the fraction of the year remaining until the option expires. There is some debate on whether the year should be measured in business days (days when the market is open, which is approximately 20 days per month) or calendar days. The consensus appears to be calendar days. Hence, if there are 73 calendar days before expiration, then $t = 73/365 = 0.20$ (assuming that the year is not a leap year).

The risk-free interest rate (r_c) is slightly more difficult to estimate. We know that we should use fixed-income securities that are default-free, such as US or UK Treasury bills. Thus, the appropriate rate to employ is the continuously compounded yield to maturity closest to the option maturity date. For example, if the option is for $t = ^1/_5$ of a year, then we want a Treasury bill that pays $1 in $^1/_5$ of a year that is trading now for P_B (the price of the bill). Mathematically, we have the following relationship:

$$P_B = 1 \times e^{-r_c \times 1/5} = e^{-r_c/5}$$

or

$$\ln(p_B) = -r_c /5$$

and, solving for r_c,

$$r_c = -\frac{\ln(P_B)}{t} = -\frac{\ln(P_B)}{1/5}$$

Thus, for the observed price P_B, we can solve for r_c. Appendix 13D elaborates on the relationship between the discrete and continuous interest rates.

The last and most difficult parameter to estimate is the volatility of stock returns, which is measured by σ. There are several methods to estimate volatility, including the use of historical return data. Recall that the standard deviation of returns is calculated based on the following equation:

$$\sigma = \sqrt{\frac{1}{n} \sum_{t=1}^{n} (R_t - \overline{R})^2}$$

where R_t is the continuously compounded rate of return.

An alternative method is estimating the implied volatility of stock returns by basically turning the BSOPM around and finding the volatility that gives the current option price. However, this procedure assumes that the call price is given as observed in the market. Calculating manually the implied volatility is difficult, but software that computes these values swiftly is available.

The B&S formula has its problems too, as asserted by Kyle Rosen, a portfolio manager:

'Black–Scholes works great when the markets are quiet, but when turmoil hits, it gets thrown out the window.' Prices explode too fast, as they did Monday, for anyone to sit patiently plugging numbers into a model. And the quickest reflexes in the world can't change things, particularly if accurate quotes aren't available, as was the case during the fast-moving markets, and if it takes more than an hour to open trading in an option, such as it did on the Philadelphia Stock Exchange on Tuesday and Thursday in Dell Computer.'

Source: Sandra Ward, *Barron's*, 3 November 1997, p. MW17. Reprinted by permission of *Barron's*, © 1997 Dow Jones & Co., Inc. All Rights Reserved Worldwide.

13.8.4 Valuing portfolio insurance using the BSOPM

One benefit of the BSOPM is the ability to estimate the cost of engaging in various risk management strategies. Recall that protective put buying is the strategy of buying puts on the underlying portfolio and is one form of portfolio insurance. Portfolio insurance is any strategy in which the maximum loss is set or determined in advance.

Suppose you are a portfolio manager responsible for a $100 million stock portfolio that closely resembles the Standard & Poor's 500 (S&P 500) stock index. Because of an unprecedented rise in stock prices, you are concerned that recent gains will be lost in another 'crash' like the ones that occurred in October 1987, October 1997, August 1998 and November 2001. Of course, if you wanted to guarantee no loss at all, you would have to pay a high price for the insurance. For example, you might buy a put option on your portfolio with a strike price of $100 million. Then, no matter what the value of your portfolio became, you would be guaranteed to have a value no less than your original $100 million minus the cost of the put option.

More realistically, suppose you allow for some loss – say, not more than 10%. Suppose it is now August, and you are considering 'insuring' your portfolio risk for

182 days. How much should such a put option cost? If current interest rates are around 7% and the S&P 500 index has a volatility of 20%, how much should the insurance cost? Without option pricing analysis, this would be a difficult problem to solve.

Because this type of portfolio insurance is nothing more than buying a put option, you can employ the BSOPM for puts. The inputs are $S = \$100$ million, $X = \$90$ million (or 10% loss), $r_c = 7\%$, $\sigma = 20\%$ and $t = 182$ days (or about $1/2$ year).

Using a software package, you find that according to the BSOPM, the insurance policy should cost \$1,127,709.50. Hence, the fair value for this insurance policy is \$1,127,709.50, or about only 1.1% of the portfolio value. Thus, if there is a crash in the market and the market value of your portfolio goes down to \$70 million, you sell the put option for \$20 million (which is the strike, \$90 million less \$70 million). After the cost of the put option, you have $\$90,000,000 - \$1,127,709.50 = \$88,872,290.50$. If, in contrast, the value of the portfolio goes up to \$110 million the option expires worthless. What is left in this case is $\$110,000,000 - \$1,127,709.50 = \$108,872,290.50$. Thus, you have established a floor on your losses at the cost of some of the gains if prices rise.

SUMMARY

■ *Name the benefits of modern option contracts.*
Although options have been around for a long time, they were not actively traded until 1973. In that year the Chicago Board Options Exchange introduced an option contract that was standardized, was transferable, and provided insurance against defaults of option writers. Since 1973, the growth of option trading has been phenomenal.

■ *Understand the process of buying and selling of put and call options.*
An option buyer has the right, but not the obligation, to exercise the option in the future. A call option buyer has the right to buy stock in the future at a stated price, whereas a put option buyer has the right to sell stock in the future at a stated price. An active secondary market allows option investors to get out of an option trade if they so desire and accept the current market price.

■ *Explain the risk of holding naked options.*
Writing a call option without owning the underlying asset is very risky and hence exposes the writer to great risk.

■ *Describe the role of option clearing corporations.*
Clearing corporations protect option buyers from the consequences of a default by an option writer. They also issue option contracts, maintain appropriate records, and process all the necessary financial transactions.

■ *Explain how margin requirements on option writers protect buyers from default.*
Option clearing corporations require option writers to post and maintain adequate collateral to cover potential losses. The OCC issues all options contracts and guarantees both sides of the contracts. The OCC is owned by several exchanges, such as the CBOE, AMEX and NYSE.

■ *Use payoff diagrams to determine the value of an option upon expiration.*
The value of an option at expiration is its intrinsic value. With this observation, investors can examine a wide array of alternative risk–return trade-offs using payoff diagrams. A payoff diagram is a graphical means of illustrating the relationship among the dollar profit or loss (the P/L line), when the price of the underlying asset changes.

■ *Identify profitable option strategies based on beliefs about future asset price movements.*
Protective put buying sets a floor on potential losses, whereas covered call writing sets a
ceiling on potential gains.

KEY TERMS

American-style option	In-the-money option	Out-of-the-money option
At-the-money option	Intrinsic value	Payoff diagram
Call option	Long position	Portfolio insurance
Closing transaction	Maturity date	Protective put buying
Contingent claim	Money machine	Put option
Covered call writing	Naked position	Put–call parity (PCP)
Covered position	Opening transaction	Short position
Derivative security	Option	Spread
European-style option	Option buyer	Straddle
Exercising (an option)	Option premium	Strike price
Exercise price	Option writer	Time value
Expiration date	Options arbitrage	Underlying asset
Frictionless market	Options Clearing	
Implied volatility	Corporation (OCC)	

QUESTIONS

13.1   Why was option trading thin between 1934 and 1973?

13.2   Why was 1973 such a pivotal year in option trading history?

13.3   What is the difference between an opening option transaction and a closing option transaction?

13.4   What is the difference between European-style options and American-style options?

13.5   If $S_0 = \$100$ and $X = \$90$, are puts in the money or out of the money? What about calls?

13.6   Can option prices be negative? Explain your answer.

13.7   If $S_0 = \$120$ and $X = \$130$, what is the intrinsic value of puts and calls? Given that the call price is c_0 and the put price is p_0, write the time value of the put and call in terms of p_0 and c_0.

13.8   Is it possible that a put and a call option on the same stock with the same strike price would have the same time value? Could they have the same intrinsic value?

13.9   Using payoff diagrams, describe the difference between being long a call at the money and being short a put at the money.

13.10 'A call buyer who buys a call for $c = \$10$ does not need to deposit any initial margin.' Do you agree with this assertion? Explain.

13.11 Describe in nonfinance terms (to your non-business major friend) what could be the motivation behind selling naked positions in options.

Questions 13.12 through 13.16 are based on the information about Microsoft in the following table:

Microsoft's option data

Option and NY close	Strike price	Calls–settle			Puts–settle		
		June	July	October	June	July	October
$100^3/_4$	$95	$5^7/_8$	$8^3/_4$	$12^3/_8$	$1/_{16}$	$2^3/_8$	$5^1/_2$
$100^3/_4$	100	$1^5/_8$	$5^1/_2$	$10^3/_8$	$3/_4$	4	$7^5/_8$
$100^3/_4$	105	$1/_8$	$3^1/_4$	$8^5/_8$	$4^1/_2$	$6^3/_4$	$11^1/_8$

13.12 Draw the payoff diagram (profit and loss line only) for long July calls for all strike prices ($95, $100 and $105) on one graph. Be sure to identify the exact breakeven point. Describe the relative costs and benefits of each strategy.

13.13 Draw the payoff diagram (profit and loss line only) for long July puts for all three strike prices ($95, $100 and $105) on one graph. Be sure to identify the exact breakeven point. Describe the relative costs and benefits of each strategy.

13.14 Create two tables similar to the one given for Microsoft, except that one table has the time value, and the other table has the intrinsic value. What general inferences can you draw about time value from your table?

13.15 Suppose the stock price is $100 and the call price is $5 with a strike price of $105. What is the profit or loss on the following two strategies when the stock price goes up to $110 *and* when the stock goes down to $90?

(a) Write a call option.
(b) Write a covered call option; that is, write a call and buy a stock.

13.16 Suppose the call price is $c_0 = \$10$, the stock price is $100, and the strike price is $X = \$95$.

(a) Calculate the initial margin for selling a call option.
(b) Suppose now that the stock price goes up to $120, and the call price falls to $1. What is the maintenance margin required?

13.17 Refer to the following table. Suppose you buy a call option for $6^3/_4$ that matures in June with a strike price of $65.

Pfizer stock price	Strike price	Calls–settle June
$69^1/_2$	65	$6^3/_4$
$69^1/_2$	70	$3^1/_2$
$69^1/_2$	75	$1^3/_4$

(a) What is your dollar profit if the stock price in June is $70? What if it is $50?
(b) Calculate the rate of return.

13.18 Referring to the following table, suppose you buy a put option for that matures in June with a strike price of $65.

Pfizer stock price	Strike price	Puts–settle June
$69^1/_2$	65	$1^5/_8$
$69^1/_2$	70	$3^1/_2$
$69^1/_2$	75	$6^3/_4$

(a) What is your dollar profit if the stock price in June is $70? What if it is $50?
(b) Calculate the rate of return.

13.19 Referring to the data in Question 13.18, suppose that in June the stock price falls to $60. Calculate your dollar profit and rate of return for the following strategies:

(a) Buy one stock for $69\frac{1}{2}$ and one put option with a June maturity and a strike price of $65.

(b) Buy one stock and two put options with a June maturity and a strike price of $65.

13.20 Repeat Question 13.19, but this time in June the stock price jumps to $75. Compare and analyse the results of Questions 13.18 and 13.19.

13.21 Prove that $c_0 \leq S_0$ is the call price's upper boundary, using an arbitrage table.

13.22 Prove that $p_0 \geq$ max $[0, X/(1 + r)^t - S_0]$ is the put price's lower boundary, using an arbitrage table.

13.23 Prove that $p_0 \leq X/(1 + r)^t$, the put price's lower boundary, using an arbitrage table.

13.24 Is the value of $N(d_1)$ always greater than the value of $N(d_2)$? Explain.

13.25 Suppose you work for an express mail service that will purchase 10 million gallons of gasoline in three months. Assume that a gallon of gas costs $1.00 wholesale, and you wish to guarantee a maximum price of $1.10. Also, you feel that gasoline price volatility is about 25%, and the six-month interest rate is 7% (annualized). Assuming that the BSOPM is valid, how much would it cost to hedge 10 million gallons of gas with options? What is the appropriate option strategy? (Assume that a gas option contract exists on an exchange.)

13.26 What is the price of a call option if $S_0 = \$25$, $X = \$20$, $r = 10\%$, $t = \frac{1}{2}$, and the put option value is $p = \$1.50$? (Make whatever assumptions are necessary.)

13.27 Suppose the interest rate decreases from 5% to 1%. How should this affect the lower boundary of a call option when $S_0 = \$100$, $X = \$80$, and $t = \frac{1}{2}$? How will this affect the lower boundary for a put option?

13.28 Based on the following information from *Barron's*, verify that the closing prices of Coke's put and call options satisfy the boundary conditions. The time to maturity is five months ($t = \frac{5}{12}$), Coke's stock price is $41, and the annual risk-free interest rate is 3%.

Expiration date and strike price	Closing price
Coke May 40 call	$3\frac{3}{4}$
Coke May 40 put	$1\frac{1}{2}$
Coke May 45 call	1
Coke May 45 put	$4\frac{1}{4}$

13.29 Suppose there are puts and calls on IBM stock with the same strike price and the same maturity. You observe that $c_0 = p_0$, and the interest rate for the period remaining until expiration is 5%. Is the call option in the money, at the money or out of the money? Is the put option in the money or out of the money? Explain.

13.30 Suppose $\sigma = 35\%$, $S_0 = \$100$, $X = \$100$, $r_c = 5\%$ and $t = \frac{1}{2}$. Calculate the Black–Scholes call and put option prices.

13.31 Suppose the standard deviation is $\sigma = 35\%$, $S_0 = \$58$, $X = \$55$, $r_c = 4\%$ and $t = \frac{1}{2}$. Calculate the Black–Scholes call and put option prices.

13.32 Suppose the standard deviation is $\sigma = 30\%$, $S_0 = \$100$, $X = \$100$, $r_c = 5\%$ and $t = \frac{1}{2}$. Calculate the Black–Scholes call and put option prices.

13.33 Suppose you manage a portfolio of $100 million. You estimate that there is a probability of 20% that the portfolio value will go to $80 million next year and a probability of 80% that it will go to $120 million. If the value is less than $90 million, you will be fired. How can you protect yourself with put options?

SELECTED REFERENCES

Chance, Don M. *An Introduction to Options and Futures*. 2nd edn. New York: Dryden Press, 1991.
This text provides a good introduction to options and other derivative securities.

Danielsen, Barley R., and Sorin M. Sorescu. 'Why do option introductions depress stock prices? A study of diminishing short-sale constraints'. *Journal of Financial and Quantitative Analysis*, forthcoming.

Hull, John, C. *Options, Futures and Other Derivative Securities*. 2nd edn. Englewood Cliffs, NJ: Prentice-Hall, 1993.
This text presents a more advanced introduction to options and other derivative securities.

Isakov, D. and B. Morard. 'Improving portfolio performance with option strategies: evidence from Switzerland'. *European Financial Management*, Vol. 7, 2001.

Peoa, I., G. Rubio, and G. Serna. 'Smiles, bid-ask spreads and option pricing,' *European Financial Management*, Vol. 7, Issue 3, 2001.

Yang, H.L., and T.K. Siu. 'Coherent risk measures for derivatives under Black-Scholes economy'. *European Financial Management*, Vol. 7, Issue 3, 2001.

SUPPLEMENTARY REFERENCES

Black, Fischer, and Myron Scholes. 'The pricing of options and corporate liabilities'. *Journal of Political Economy*, 81, May–June 1973, pp. 637–54.

Bookstaber, Richard M. *Option Pricing and Investment Strategy*. 3rd edn. Chicago: Probus Publishing, 1991.

Cox, John C., Stephen A. Ross, and Mark Rubinstein. 'Option pricing: a simplified approach'. *Journal of Financial Economics*, 7, September 1979, pp. 229–63.

Cox, John C. and Mark Rubinstein. *Options Markets*. Englewood Cliffs, NJ: Prentice-Hall, 1985.

Fabozzi, Frank J. (ed.) *The Handbook of Fixed-Income Options Pricing, Strategies & Applications*. Chicago: Probus Publishing, 1989.

Foglewski, Stephen, William L. Silber, and Marti G. Subrahmanyam (eds). *Financial Options from Theory to Practice*. Homewood, IL: Business One Irwin, 1990.

Gibson, Rajna, *Option Valuation Analyzing and Pricing Standardized Option Contracts*. New York: McGraw-Hill, 1991.

Konishi, Atsuo, and Ravi E. Dattatreva (eds.). *The Handbook of Derivative Instruments*. Chicago: Probus Publishing, 1991.

McLean, Stuart K. (ed.). *The European Options and Futures Markets*. Chicago: Probus Publishing, 1991.

Merton, Robert. 'Theory of rational option pricing'. *Bell Journal of Economics and Management Science*, 4, Spring 1973, pp. 141–83.

Options Institute (ed.). *Options: Essential Concepts and Trading Strategies*. Homewood, IL: Business One Irwin, 1990.

Robertson, Malcolm J. *Directory of World Futures and Options*. Englewood Cliffs, NJ: Prentice-Hall, 1990.

Smith, Clifford W., Jr., and Charles W. Smithson. *The Handbook of Financial Engineering*. New York: Harper Business, 1990.

Smith, Clifford W., Jr., Charles W. Smithson, and D. Wilford Sykes. *Managing Financial Risk*. New York: Harper & Row, 1990.

Tsiveriotis, K., and N. Chriss. 'Pricing with a difference'. *Risk*, February 1998.

Appendix 13A   TAXES

The tax consequences of option trading depend on a number of factors, such as the tax status of the investor, the underlying interest involved, whether the option is exercised or not, whether the position is a covered or an uncovered position, and whether the position is subject to a closing transaction. Taxes are usually paid in the year in which the position is closed. As with all tax laws, however, there are exceptions. For example, index options are mark to market (gains and losses are taxed even if the position is still held) at year-end for tax purposes. As a result, the paper profits and losses are taxed in each year (as opposed to waiting until an offsetting position is taken, as is true with options on individual stocks, such as IBM, AT&T, and so forth).

Suppose you purchased an index option for $500 in June of Year 1 that matures in June of Year 2 (see Exhibit 13A.1). On 31 December the index option is worth $1,100; thus, you have taxable income of $600 ($1,100 − $500) even if you do not sell it. Now further suppose that in Year 2 the option expires worthless. In this case, you have a tax loss of $1,100 ($500 purchase price + $600 gain in Year 1) in Year 2.

Exhibit 13A.1 Example of tax liabilities from option trading with 28% tax bracket

(a) Index options

Date	Action	Option value	Cash flow
June, Year 1	Buy 1 index option	$500	−$500
December, Year 1	Mark to market for tax purposes	1,100	−168[a]
June, Year 2	Option matures out of the money	0	308[b]

[a] −$168 = 0.28($1,100 − $500). Tax on paper gain at year end.
[b] $308 = 0.28 × $1,100. Tax credit on loss of the $1,100.

(b) Stock cost basis via call option

Action	Cost per share
Buy call option ABC 120	$8 + commission
Exercise option	$120
Cost basis for future tax calculation	**$128 + commission**

As Exhibit 13A.1 shows, with options on individual stocks, taxes are paid when the options are sold. However, when options on individual stocks are exercised, the option premium is used to adjust the cost basis, and no taxes are paid until the underlying asset is sold. For example, suppose you paid $8 per share for an option on ABC with a strike price of $120. At the expiration date you exercise your option and purchase ABC at $120. Your cost basis is $128 + commission (see Exhibit 13A.1(b)). Hence, taxable gains will occur only if ABC is subsequently sold for a price above $128 plus commissions.

Appendix 13B   MARGIN REQUIREMENTS

Suppose an investor purchased 100 call option contracts for \$5 per share (the total cost would be \$50,000 = \$5 $\times$ 100 shares per contract $\times$ 100 contracts), and the stock was in the money \$20 on the expiration date (that is $S_0 - X = \$20$). Then the 100 option contracts would be worth \$200,000 (\$20 $\times$ 100 shares per contract $\times$ 100 contracts). Will the call writer pay cash to the OCC as a result of the price increase? Yes!

Clearing corporations such as the OCC protect themselves against option writers' defaulting by requiring Clearing Members to provide collateral known as *margin*. These Members in turn require margin from their customers. Margin requirements reduce the incentive of the option writers to default on their obligations. If the writer has posted a substantial amount of collateral, then the writer is less likely to default. The risk of default is intimately related to the volatility of the underlying asset. The more volatile the asset, the higher the risk of default by option writers. For example, in the crashes of October 1987, 1989 and 1997, there were several defaults by option writers. (However, do not forget that option buyers were protected by the guarantees provided by option clearinghouses such as the OCC.)

The risk of default is limited to option writers. The Federal Reserve Board (the regulatory body for US option transactions) allows options to be purchased on margin (by borrowing money). The Federal Reserve Board regulates margin requirements through Regulation T, which covers the extension of credit to customers by security brokers, dealers and members of the national securities exchanges. Regulation T establishes initial margin requirements and defines which securities are eligible to be traded on margin. The brokerage firms have the discretion to require higher margins if they wish. Option buyers must pay for the option in full; this totally eliminates the possibility of default by the option buyer. Thus, option buyers could never default on the contract, because option contracts give the option buyers the right but not the obligation, to do something in the future. Specifically, an option buyer at most could lose the option premium, but the buyer had to pay that up front.

The *initial margin* is money that option writers send to the OCC when they initially sell the specific options. The *maintenance margin* is the dollar amount that must be kept at the OCC throughout the life of the contract. The maintenance margin changes as asset prices change.

Exhibit 13B.1 compares the initial and maintenance requirements for margin accounts for different types of contracts traded on the CBOE. Recall that margin accounts are required to keep securities (or cash) on deposit with the broker as collateral. In the options market, margin implies the money deposited by the option writer as collateral for the potential future liability. As Exhibit 13B.1 illustrates, margin requirements are complex and differ across different types of securities and purposes (long, short and spreads). Margin requirements change with market conditions.

As an illustration, consider writing one call option on the S&P 100 stock index. The option contract is actually for 100 times the index. Index options are *cash settled*, which means that cash, rather than securities in the amount of the intrinsic value of the options, is exchanged at expiration. For example, if the index rises to 470 and the strike price is 370, the index call writer must pay \$10,000 [100(\$470 − \$370)].

The formula for finding the margin requirement of the option writer based on Exhibit 13B.1 (see 'Short puts – Index' row and 'Initial margin' column) is as follows:

$$\text{Margin} = \max(A, B)$$

where

Exhibit 13B.1 Initial and maintenance margin requirements

	Option Type	Cash Account Initial Requirement	Margin Account Initial (Maintenance) Requirement
Long Put or Long Call *9 months or less until expiration*	Equity, Broad and Narrow Based Indexes, Interest Rate Options, Long CAPS.	Pay for option in full.	Pay for option in full.
Long Put or Long Call *More than 9 months until expiration*	Equity, Broad and Narrow Based Indexes only [For all other options types, the requirement is the same as for 9 months or less option (above).]	Pay for option in full.	Listed 75% of the total cost (market value) of the option.
Short Put or Short Call	Equity, Broad and Narrow Based Indexes, Interest Rate Composite, Currency and Cross Rate.	Deposit cash or cash equivalents equal to the exercise price or put option deposit letter for short put. Deposit appropriate escrow agreement for short call. Sales proceeds not released until deposit is made. Short Calls are not permitted for Interest Rate options.	100% of the option proceeds plus • 20% of the underlying stock value. • 15% of the underlying broad-based index value. • 20% of the underlying narrow-based index value. • 10% of the underlying aggregate interest rate composite value. • 4% of the underlying currency value (also applies to Cross Rate options). Less out-of-the-money amount, if any, to a minimum for puts (calls) at option proceeds plus • 10% of the exercise price (underlying stock value). • 10% of the exercise price (underlying broad-based index value). • 10% of the exercise price (underlying narrow-based index value). • 5% of the exercise price (underlying aggregate interest rate composite value). • 75% of the exercise price (underlying currency value) (also applies to Cross Rate options). Currency or Cross Rate option requirement may be satisfied with a letter of credit from an approved bank. Cross Rate margin is calculated in the base currency of the contract.
	Capped Index.	Deposit cash, cash equivalents or appropriate escrow receipt equal to the cap interval times the index multiplier.	The lesser of: A: The cap interval times the index multiplier, or B: 100% of the option proceeds plus 15% of the underlying index value less the out-of-the-money amount, if any, to a minimum for puts (calls) of the premium plus 10% of the exercise price (underlying index value).
Short Put and Short Call (Short Capped Index and Short Index permitted)	Equity, Broad and Narrow Based Indexes, Capped Index, Interest Rate Composite, Currency and Rate.	Deposit an escrow agreement for each option. See requirement for appropriate short put/call. Not permitted for Interest Rate options.	For the same underlying • Equity • Capped Index • Currency • Index • Interest Rate Composite • Cross Rate With the same multiplier, short put or short call requirement, whichever is greater, plus the option proceeds of the other side.
Put Spread or Call Spread (long side expires with or after short side, long Capped index vs. short options cannot receive spread treatment	Equity, Broad and Narrow Based Indexes, Capped Index, Interest Rate Composite, Currency and Cross Rate.	Not permitted for American Style options.	For the same underlying • Equity • Capped Index • Currency • Index • Interest Rate Composite • Cross Rate With the same multiplier, the amount by which long put (short call) aggregate exercise price is below short put (long call) aggregate exercise price; long side must be paid for in full.
	Broad and Narrow Based Indexes.	All options must be cash settled European Style options, and all must expire at the same time. Deposit and maintain cash or cash equivalents equal to the amount by which the long put (short call) aggregate exercise price is below the short put (long call) aggregate exercise price. Long side must be paid in full.	See above.
Short Call and Long Underlying (not permitted for CAPS or Interest Rate Composite options)	Equity, Currency and Cross Rate.	Pay for the underlying position in full.	No requirement on short call. 50% requirement on long stock position. 100% requirement on currency position.
	Broad and Narrow Based Indexes.	Not permitted.	No requirement on short call 50% requirement on long underlying stock basket; or unit investment trust or open and mutual fund approved by the Exchanges.
Short Put and Short Underlying (not permitted for CAPS, Interest Rate Composite, Currency or Cross Rate options)	Equity, Broad and Narrow Based Indexes.	Not permitted	No requirement on short put. Short sale proceeds plus 50% requirement on short stock position.

Source: *Pocket Options Margin Guide*. Reprinted with permission of The Options Clearing Corporation.

$$A = c_0 + (0.15 \times 100 \times \text{index}_0) - [100 \times \max(0, X - \text{index}_0)]$$

$$B = c_0 + (0.10 \times 100 \times \text{index}_0)$$

where c_0 is the call price (per 100 units), and $100 \times \max(0, X - \text{index}_0)$ is the out-of-the-money amount. For example, suppose we observe the S&P index at 365, along with a call option with a strike price of $370 and a call price of $900. In this example,

$$A = \$900 + (0.15 \times 100 \times \$365) - \max[0, 100 \times (\$370 - \$365)]$$

$$= \$900 + \$5{,}475 - \$500 = \$5{,}875$$

$$B = \$900 + (0.10 \times 100 \times \$365) = \$900 + \$3{,}650 = \$4{,}550$$

Hence, the margin is

$$\text{Margin} = \max(\$5{,}875, \$4{,}550) = \$5{,}875$$

To write one call option contract on the S&P index, we are required to post margin of $5,875. This margin is quite a bit more than the possible proceeds of $900. The reason is that if stock prices rise, the option writer must pay the option buyer the difference between the index value and the exercise price. Exhibit 13B.1 shows that for the above specific short positions in options, the maintenance margin is the same as the initial margin. The equations for both A and B above are directly influenced by the value of the index. As the index rises, so does the margin required. For example, if the index rises to 375 and the call price rises to $1,500, then the required maintenance margin is

$$A = \$1{,}500 + (0.15 \times 100 \times \$375) - \max[0, 100 \times (\$370 - \$375)]$$

$$= \$1{,}500 + \$5{,}625 - 0 = \$7{,}125$$

$$B = \$1{,}500 + (0.10 \times 100 \times \$375) = \$1{,}500 + \$3{,}750 = \$5{,}250$$

Hence, the margin required is

$$\text{Margin} = \max(\$7{,}125, \$5{,}250) = \$7{,}125$$

Thus, the option writer must place additional monies as margin. Specifically, $7,125 − $5,875 = $1,250 more must be placed as margin.

Appendix 13C CONTINUOUSLY COMPOUNDED INTEREST RATES

This appendix compares annually compounded interest rates with continuously compounded interest rates. The Black–Scholes option pricing model (BSOPM) uses continuously compounded interest rates. *Annual compounding* implicitly assumes that interest is paid annually. *Continuous compounding assumes* that interest is paid continuously – that is, more frequently than every second. If we let PV denote present value and FV denote future value, then Equations 13C.1 and 13C.2 express the relationship between PV and FV via annual compounding (r) and continuous compounding (r_c), respectively:

$$FV = PV(1 + r)^t \qquad \text{(annual)} \qquad \text{(13C.1)}$$

$$FV = PVe^{r_c t} \qquad \text{(continuous)} \qquad \text{(13C.2)}$$

where e stands for the exponential. Solving for the compound rate, r and r_c, we have

$$r = \left(\frac{FV}{PV}\right)^{1/t} - 1 \qquad \text{(13C.3)}$$

$$r_c = \frac{\ln\left(\dfrac{FV}{PV}\right)}{t} \qquad \text{(13C.4)}$$

where ln() is the natural logarithm.

For example, suppose that $t = {}^1/_2$ year (hence, $1/t = 2$), FV = \$105 and PV = \$100. What is the relationship between r_c and r?

$$r = \left(\frac{105.0}{100.0}\right)^2 - 1$$

$$= 0.1025 \text{ or } 10.25\%$$

$$r_c = \frac{\ln\left(\dfrac{105.0}{100.0}\right)}{{}^1/_2}$$

$$= \ln(1.05)/(0.5) = 0.04879/0.5$$

$$\cong 0.09758 \text{ or } 9.758\%$$

Hence, continuous compounding is another method of accounting for the time value of money. Continuous compounding is used in calculating option prices, because it most closely relates to the underlying assumptions of the BSOPM, which assumes a continuous change in the hedge ratio (as illustrated in the binomial option pricing model).

Appendix 13D CALCULATING CONTINUOUSLY COMPOUNDED STANDARD DEVIATIONS

Recall from Chapter 6 that the standard deviation of stock rates of return is calculated by the following equation:

$$\sigma = \sqrt{\frac{1}{n}\sum_{t=1}^{n}(R_{i,t} - \overline{R}_i)^2} \tag{13D.1}$$

where $R_{i,t}$ is the rate of return on stock i during period t, $\overline{R}_i$ is the average rate of return on stock i, and n is the number of historical observations. Chapter 5 presented the interim rate of return (modified for stocks) as follows:

$$R_{i,t} = \frac{P_{i,t} - P_{i,t-1} + D_{i,t}}{P_{i,t-1}} \tag{13D.2}$$

where $P_{i,t}$ is the price of stock i at t, $P_{i,t-1}$ is the price of stock i at $t-1$, and $D_{i,t}$ is the dividend of stock i, if any, paid at t. The only difference in calculating the standard deviation with continuous compounding is the equation to calculate $R_{i,t}$. With continuous compounding, the proper equation for calculating rates of return is

$$R_{i,t} = \ln\left(\frac{P_{i,t} + D_{i,t}}{P_{i,t-1}}\right) \tag{13D.3}$$

where ln( ) is the natural logarithm.

Exhibit 13D.1 Illustration of continuously compounded rates of return compared with annually compounded rates of return

Year	Index	Continuously compounded rates of return[a]	Annually compounded rates of return[b]
1	100.0		
2	138.8	0.328	0.388
3	216.6	0.445	0.561
4	556.9	0.944	1.571
5	332.7	−0.515	−0.403
6	136.0	−0.895	−0.591
7	274.1	0.701	1.015
8	373.0	−0.308	0.361
9	317.6	−0.161	−0.149
10	360.9	0.128	0.136
11	634.4	0.564	0.758
Mean		0.185	0.365
Standard deviation		0.536	0.624

[a] Based on $R_{i,t} = \ln\left(\dfrac{P_{i,t} + D_{i,t}}{P_{i,t}}\right)$

[b] Based on $R_{i,t} = \dfrac{P_{i,t} - P_{i,t-1} + D_{i,t}}{P_{i,t-1}}$

Note that this index is without dividends included, so $D_{i,t}$ is always zero.

It can be shown that for sufficiently short time periods (or small changes in the stock price), the rates of return given by Equations 13D.2 and 13D.3 are about the same. However, for long holding periods (greater than one week), the differences are more substantial.

To illustrate the magnitude of the differences in the two methods of estimating the standard deviation, let us consider the annual price information of a stock index. The second column in Exhibit 13D.1 gives the index values for a recent decade. The third column gives the continuously compounded rates of return, and the fourth column gives the annually compounded rates of return. As the exhibit shows, the differences between the standard deviations can be sizable. This case was based on data from Hong Kong stocks, which are very volatile. The holding period was assumed to be one year, which is fairly long. The less volatile the assets in question and the shorter the holding period, the smaller the differences will be between these methods.

Chapter 14

RISK AND RETURN: THE LINEAR RELATIONSHIPS AND THE CAPITAL ASSET PRICING MODEL

Learning objectives

After studying this chapter you should be able to:

1 Define and explain how to measure beta.

2 Understand why beta is the appropriate measure of risk.

3 Understand why the security market line (SML) and the capital asset pricing model (CAPM) describe the equilibrium relationship between risk and expected rate of return.

4 Understand how practitioners who believe in market inefficiency use alpha and beta to select underpriced stocks.

5 Understand the single index model (SIM) and the multifactor model.

6 Understand the arbitrage pricing theory (APT).

INVESTMENT IN THE NEWS

Hollywood or bust

Dana Giacchetto at Cassandra shoots to profit for his A-list clients

NEW YORK. On a sunny midsummer morning, Sandra Bullock is shooting *28 Days on Broadway* outside Dana Giacchetto's SoHo loft. It could be a perfect time for Giacchetto – money manager to the stars and Leonardo DiCaprio's lad about town when he comes to the Big Apple – to troll for clients.

But he's blasé about the bustle on his doorstep. Giacchetto is holed up in the eighth floor office of his investment boutique. The Cassandra Group Inc., flitting from phone to laptop, keeping tabs on his trades and the stock market...To pick stocks, he looks at three things – technical charts of the stock's historical movement, the company's record on hitting earnings projections and the 'beta,' which measures how volatile a stock is.

Source: Alex Frew McMillan, CNNfn, 17 July 1999.

Three things are taken into account in stock selection by the professional investor, Dana Giacchetto: technical charts (that will be covered in Chapter 18), earnings projections (covered in Chapters 9 and 10) and beta, which measures how volatile the stock is. This chapter is devoted mainly to beta as a measure of risk, to the risk–return relationship called the Capital Asset Pricing Model (CAPM), developed by William Sharpe and John Lintner for which Sharpe won the 1990 Nobel Prize in economics, and to the arbitrage pricing theory (APT).

In Chapter 6 we saw that investors will choose a portfolio taken from the capital market line (CML) regardless of their risk preferences (see Equation 6.4). It has also been shown that the risk of an efficient portfolio is measured by its standard deviation or variance. In this chapter, it will be shown that beta is the correct measure for risk for individual assets and portfolios alike, regardless of whether or not these portfolios are efficient. However, for efficient portfolios, the investor can use either the standard deviation or beta (which will be defined below) to size up risk without affecting the ranking of the portfolios by their risk. Because beta corresponds to individual securities as well as portfolios, this chapter uses the word *asset* where it refers to both individual assets and portfolios. When the discussion refers to individual assets only, it explicitly states this.

14.1 BETA AS A MEASURE OF RISK

How can we size up risk of an individual asset, e.g. Marks and Spencer stock, or even an inefficient portfolio, e.g. a mutual fund which may be located below the CML (for the CML definition, see Chapter 6)? As asserted in the *Investment in the news* article opening this chapter, beta (denoted by the Greek letter β) measures risk. Actually it measures the risk of individual assets, an inefficient portfolio as well as an efficient portfolio.

14.1.1 How to calculate beta

First, let us define beta and demonstrate how to calculate it. The beta of Asset i, denoted by β_i, is defined as

$$\beta_i = \frac{\text{Cov}(R_i, R_m)}{\sigma_m^2} \tag{14.1}$$

where R_i is the rate of return on the ith asset, R_m is the rate of return on the market portfolio (portfolio m, see Chapter 6) and Cov is the covariance as defined in Chapter 6. Thus, beta measures the co-movement of the return on Asset i and the return on the market portfolio. In practice, the market portfolio is not observable and it is common to take as a proxy to it some broad index, e.g. the FTSE 100, the S&P 500, the Dow Jones, etc.

With historical data when equal probability is assigned to each period, beta can be calculated as follows:[1]

$$\beta_i = \frac{\frac{1}{N}\left(\sum_{t=1}^{N} R_{i,t} \times R_{m,t}\right) - \overline{R}_i \overline{R}_m}{\frac{1}{N}\left(\sum_{t=1}^{N} R_{m,t}^2\right) - \overline{R}_m^2} \tag{14.2}$$

where N denotes the number of observations and t denotes historical periods (for example, years, months and so forth). Obviously, beta also can be calculated for portfolios (efficient and inefficient alike) and mutual funds.

14.1.2 The meaning of beta – characteristic lines

Why does beta measure risk? We provide here an intuitive explanation and in Section 14.4 we prove that beta sizes up risk. Note that β (or β_i, where i stands for Asset i) is nothing but the slope of the regression line given by[2]

$$R_{i_t} = \alpha_i + \beta_i R_{m_t} + e_{i_t} \tag{14.3}$$

where R_{i_t} is the rate of return on the ith stock in period t, α_i is the intercept of the line, R_{m_t} is the rate of return on the market portfolio for the same period t, and e_{i_t} is the deviation from the regression line of the observation corresponding to period t, called the error term. In practice, the error term is not directly observable. However, it can be calculated from Equation 14.3, because R_{i_t} and R_{m_t} are directly observable, and α_i and β_i

---

[1] Recall from Chapter 6 that

$$\text{Cov}(R_i, R_m) = E[(R_i - \overline{R}_i)(R_m - \overline{R}_m)] = \frac{1}{N}\sum_{t=1}^{N}(R_{i,t} - \overline{R}_i)(R_{m,t} - \overline{R}_m)$$

which can be rewritten as

$$\text{Cov}(R_i, R_m) = \frac{1}{N}\sum_{t=1}^{N}(R_{i,t} \times R_{m,t}) - \overline{R}_i\overline{R}_m$$

Similarly, the denominator of Equation 14.2 is the variance because

$$\text{Variance}(R_m) = \frac{1}{N}\sum_{t=1}^{N}(R_{m,t} - \overline{R}_m)^2 = \frac{1}{N}\sum_{t=1}^{N}R_{m,t}^2 - \overline{R}_m^2$$

[2] In running the following kind of regression:

$$y = \alpha + \beta x + e$$

the slope of the regression line is β, given by

$$\beta = \frac{\text{Cov}(x, y)}{\sigma_x^2}$$

Thus, for $y = R_i$ and $x = R_m$, we get

$$\beta_i = \frac{\text{Cov}(R_i, R_m)}{\sigma_m^2}$$

Also, a well-known statistical result is

$$\alpha = \overline{y} - \beta\overline{x}$$

and in our specific case we have

$$\alpha_i = \overline{R}_i - \beta\overline{R}_m$$

PRACTICE BOX

Problem

The rate of return for three years on the market portfolio (market return) and on Exxon stock is as follows:

Year	Exxon stock	Market return
1	0.12	0.10
2	0.20	0.15
3	0.10	0.08

Calculate the beta of Exxon where the probability of each annual outcome is $1/3$.

Solution

Let Exxon's rates of return be denoted by R_i and the market's rate of return be denoted by R_m. Construct the following table:

Year	R_i	R_m	$R_i \times R_m$	R_m^2
1	0.12	0.10	0.012	0.0100
2	0.20	0.15	0.030	0.0225
3	0.10	0.08	0.008	0.0064
Sum	0.42	0.33	0.050	0.0389
Average	0.14	0.11	0.0167	0.0130

Using Equation 14.2 we get

$$\beta_i = \frac{0.0167 - 0.14 \times 0.11}{0.013 - 0.11^2} = \frac{0.0013}{0.0009} \cong 1.44$$

are estimated.[3] The regression line describing the relationship between R_i and R_m is called the characteristic line.[4] The slope of the regression line is equal to β_i and it measures the risk of the ith asset. The following discussion sheds more light on this risk measure.

If you hold a well-diversified portfolio, you can eliminate a large portion of the risk by diversification; however, the risk of the fluctuations in the whole market as measured by the fluctuations in the market portfolio cannot be eliminated. Exhibit 14.1 shows the 10 biggest one-day percentage declines of the Dow Jones Industrial Average (until the year 2000). Even if you hold the market portfolio (e.g. the S&P 500 index), you cannot avoid the fluctuations of the whole market. For example, on 19 October 1987, the whole

---

[3] We will show later on in the chapter that when the regressions are conducted in terms of excess return, alpha (α) has an economic meaning; it measures the return in excess of the risk-adjusted return as implied by the CAPM and therefore is called the *abnormal return* (see Section 14.5).

[4] The characteristic line measures the expected rate of return on the ith asset for a given R_m. A point on the line is given by $R_{i_t} = \alpha_i + \beta_i R_{m_t}$ (i.e. the error term is assumed to be zero). For example, if $R_{m_t} = 10\%$, and $\beta = 2$ and $\alpha = 5\%$, we have $R_{i_t} = 5\% + (2 \times 10\%) = 25\%$. However, if R_{m_t} changed from 10% to 14%, the average rate of return on the stock would be $R_{i_t} = 5\% + (2 \times 14\%) = 33\%$, and the *change* in the expected rate of return would be 8%, as a beta of 2 would predict.

Exhibit 14.1 Biggest one-day declines in the DJIA

Days with greatest percentage loss in index points

Rank	Date	Close	Net change	% change
1	19 October 1987	1738.74	−508.00	−22.61
2	28 October 1929	260.64	−38.33	−12.82
3	29 October 1929	230.07	−30.57	−11.73
4	6 November 1929	232.13	−25.55	−9.92
5	18 December 1929	58.27	−5.57	−8.72
6	12 August 1932	63.11	−5.79*	−8.40
7	14 March 1907	76.23	−6.89	−8.29
8	26 October 1987	1793.93	−156.83	−8.04
9	21 July 1933	88.71	−7.55	−7.84
10	18 October 1937	125.73	−10.57	−7.75

Source: Website at http://www.dowjones.com. Wall Street Journal Online (Staff produced copy only). © 2001 by Dow Jones & Co., Inc. Reproduced with permission of Dow Jones & Co., Inc. in the format *Fundamentals of Investments* via the Copyright Clearance Center.

stock market went down by more than 20%. No matter how well diversified your portfolio was on 19 October 1987, or any of the other days shown in Exhibit 14.1, you could not have avoided this loss.

Similarly, no amount of diversification can avoid the risk of economic recession. Thus, macro-economic factors such as unemployment, the trade balance, budget deficits, changes in interest rates (see Chapter 11) or events such as war can significantly affect the market rate of return. This risk cannot be diversified away, because it affects the whole market. Beta of an asset captures this macro-economic risk, and therefore it is also called market risk.

To illustrate, suppose that the Central Bank suddenly increases sharply the interest rate. The whole market falls by, say, 10%. If beta of a stock is 2, the stock price is expected to fall by 20%. Suppose that on the same day the firm announces its research and development failure to discover a new drug. The stock price falls by an additional 5%. Thus, the 5% in our example corresponds to the error term e_i in Exhibit 14.2 and it is the firm's specific risk or the firm's specific variability. The firm's specific factor could be due to the discovery of new oil fields, firing the CEO, etc. (see also Section 14.3).

Beta measures the slope of the line given by Equation 14.3; it measures the sensitivity of the ith stock to market fluctuations which cannot be diversified away. For example, if $\beta_i = 2$, when the market rate of return increases by 1%, this stock's rate of return is expected to go up by 2% on average. However, when the market rate of return goes down by 1%, the stock's rate of return is expected to fall by 2%. Thus, this stock is considered to be an aggressive stock, or a stock that is more risky than the market portfolio. This stock, on average, fluctuates twice as much as the market portfolio. Similarly, if $\beta_i = \frac{1}{2}$, the stock fluctuates half as much as the market and is considered to be not very risky; it is called a defensive stock. A defensive stock 'defends' the investor from large losses but also denies the investor large gains. Finally, if $\beta_i = 1$, the stock moves exactly with the market on average. It is called a neutral stock.

Exhibit 14.2(a) presents pairs of rates of return on the market portfolio and on the ith stock, where each pair of points corresponds to a given period (e.g. year, month), along with the regression line that best fits this 'cloud' of points, that is, the corresponding characteristic line. The intercept of the line is α_i, the slope is β_i and the vertical

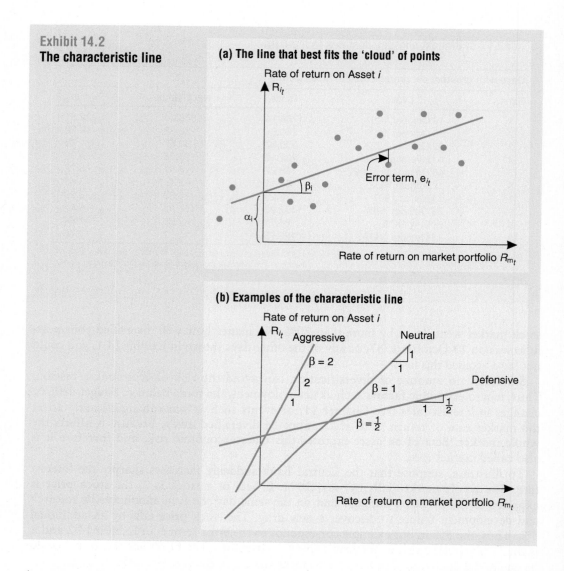

Exhibit 14.2
The characteristic line

(a) The line that best fits the 'cloud' of points

Rate of return on Asset i

R_{it}

Error term, e_{it}

β_i

α_i

Rate of return on market portfolio R_{mt}

(b) Examples of the characteristic line

Rate of return on Asset i

R_{it} Aggressive   Neutral

$\beta = 2$ 1
                     1

2   Defensive
1        $\beta = 1$
                          1    $\frac{1}{2}$
                     1

$\beta = \frac{1}{2}$

Rate of return on market portfolio R_{mt}

deviations of the points from the line are the error terms, e_{it}. The closer the points are to the line, the better the fit of the regression line to the various points.

Exhibit 14.2(b) describes characteristic lines corresponding to aggressive, defensive and neutral stocks. Hi-tech firms, such as Apple Computer and Microsoft, are considered to be aggressive stocks. When the market is up by $x\%$, they usually go up by more than $x\%$; when the market is down by $x\%$, they usually go down by more than $x\%$. The stocks of utilities such as Florida Gas or British Petrolium are considered to be defensive. When the market is up by $x\%$, the demand for gas or electricity increases, but by less than $x\%$. When the market is down by $x\%$, the demand for gas and electricity goes down less sharply than the overall demand for other products; hence, the stock of these firms decreases by less than $x\%$. Thus, beta measures the sensitivity of the ith stock (or the portfolio) rate of return to changes in the market portfolio rates of return.

Note that apart from beta, other risk factors are reported, e.g. the financial strength. Thus, although beta is the theoretical measure of risk (as we see from Exhibit 14.3 in the following pages), practitioners complement it by another measure of risk called financial strength.

There are several important rules corresponding to beta.

Rule 1: Beta of the market portfolio, m, is equal to 1.
To see this, recall that a covariance of one variable with itself is the variance. Thus, $\text{Cov}(R_m, R_m) = \sigma_m^2$, hence

$$\beta_m = \frac{\text{Cov}(R_m, R_m)}{\sigma_m^2} = \frac{\sigma_m^2}{\sigma_m^2} = 1$$

Rule 2: Beta of the riskless asset is zero.
To see this, recall that the riskless interest rate is constant and a covariance of a constant with other variables is always equal to zero.[5]

Rule 3: $\beta_p = \Sigma w_i \beta_i$ where β_p is the portfolio beta, w_i is the weight of the ith asset in the portfolio and β_i is the ith asset beta.

Let us elaborate. The portfolio rate of return is given by $R_p = \sum_{i=1}^{n} w_i R_i$,

where R_p is the rate of return on the portfolio and w_i the investment weight in the portfolio of the ith asset whose return is R_i.

Therefore, the portfolio beta, β_p, is given by:[6]

$$\beta_p = \frac{\text{Cov}(R_p, R_m)}{\sigma_m^2} = \frac{\text{Cov}\left(\sum w_i R_i, R_m\right)}{\sigma_m^2} = \frac{\sum w_i \text{Cov}(R_i, R_m)}{\sigma_m^2} = \sum w_i \beta_i$$

Rule 4: The percentage contribution of the ith asset to the market portfolio risk is $w_i \beta_i$.
To see this, recall, by Rule 1, that for the market portfolio $\beta_m = 1$. Also, by Rule 3, for the market portfolio we have $\beta_m = \Sigma w_i \beta_i = 1$. Hence, $w_i \beta_i$ is the percentage contribution of the ith asset to the market portfolio risk which is equal to 1.

Rule 5: Beta of an efficient portfolio (see Chapter 6) located on the CML is given by

$$\beta_p = 1 - w$$

where w is the investment proportion in the riskless asset and $(1 - w)$ is the investment proportion in the market portfolio, m.
To see this, recall from Chapter 6 that all efficient portfolios are combinations of portfolio m and the riskless asset. Namely,

$$R_p = wr + (1 - w) R_m$$

And because r is constant, wr has zero covariance with R_m. Therefore, we have

$$\beta_p = \frac{\text{Cov}(R_p, R_m)}{\sigma_m^2} = \frac{(1 - w)\text{Cov}(R_m, R_m)}{\sigma_m^2} = (1 - w)\frac{\sigma_m^2}{\sigma_m^2} = 1 - w$$

We will use some of these rules in the rest of the chapter.

---

[5] $\text{Cov}(r, R_m) = E[(r - Er)(R_m - ER_m)]$, but because $Er = r$ the covariance is equal to zero (see Chapter 6).
[6] We employ the statistical rule asserting that $\text{Cov}(ax + by, R_m) = a\,\text{Cov}(x, R_m) + b\,\text{Cov}(y, R_m)$.

Exhibit 14.3 Using beta as a measure of risk in practice

Page	Ticker	Company	Recent price	P/E	Yield (%)	Beta	Financial strength
1682	AZO	AutoZone Inc.	29	20.1	Nil	1.10	B ++
Industry sector: Retail (Special Lines)							
2198	BMCS	BMC Software	66	29.9	Nil	1.30	B ++
Industry sector: Computer Software & Svcs							
904	ETH	Ethan Allen Interiors	39	20.0	0.3	1.30	B +
Industry sector: Furn./Home Furnishings							
681	HBOC	HBO & Co.	48	45.7	0.2	1.30	B ++
Industry sector: Healthcare Information							
1881	HAL	Halliburton Co.	49	24.9	1.0	0.90	B ++
Industry sector: Oilfield Services/Equip.							
317	LDRY	Landry's Seafood	24	20.7	Nil	1.35	B +
Industry sector: Restaurant							
1064	LLTC	Linear Technology	57	26.5	0.4	1.40	A
Industry sector: Semiconductor							
2153	KRB	MBNA Corp.	27	20.8	1.2	1.55	B ++
Industry sector: Financial Services							

Source: The Value Line Investment Survey, 9 January 1998, p. 6424. Reprinted with permission.

14.1.3 The use of beta in practice

Beta is commonly used in many publications as a measure of the risk of an investment (or as an index for safety). Beta is a risk index for portfolios (mutual funds), as well as for individual securities. The larger the beta, the more risky the corresponding asset or portfolio. Exhibit 14.3 illustrates how beta is used as a risk measure by Value Line.

14.1.4 US market portfolio and the world market portfolio

At this stage, one should ask, what is the composition of the market portfolio m? Conceptually, it should include all available risky assets. Should international securities markets be included in Portfolio m? In other words, can we get a steeper CML by diversifying internationally? In principle, the answer is yes, we can gain from international diversification. In the age of electronic communications, the world market has become one large market, and it is easy to invest in the securities of foreign countries. However, most macro-economic shocks affect all markets. For example, the 1987 crash or the 2000 crisis was not just a US or UK phenomenon but a world phenomenon. Still, as long as correlations between markets are not perfect, the investor can benefit from international diversification.

International diversification achieves two objectives: (1) it increases the number of assets available, and (2) it decreases, but does not eliminate, the market portfolio risk. It is possible to reduce the market portfolio fluctuations by investing in the world market portfolio, but certainly these fluctuations cannot be completely eliminated. Thus, in principle, when calculating beta, portfolio m should be taken as the world market, not just the US market. However, for practical reasons, in calculating beta, only the US market is used (or at best, the US market plus the UK market and other markets in

Western Europe and Japan, which have accessible databases on rates of return). We will elaborate on the gain from international diversification in Chapter 15.

14.2   THE SECURITY MARKET LINE (SML)

In Chapter 6, we describe the CML, which provides the linear relationship between expected return and risk (standard deviation) that holds only for efficient portfolios. Here we show the existence of a linear relationship, called the security market line (SML), between expected return and risk (beta) of individual assets as well as portfolios, regardless of whether they are efficient or not. For an *efficient portfolio*, both beta and sigma measure risk and indeed the SML and CML coincide.

So far, we explain intuitively that beta is the risk of an individual asset. However, how is the expected return on an individual asset related to beta? Answering such a question requires the introduction of a new concept, the *security market line* (SML). Each asset has its own risk–return profile. If the expected return exactly compensates investors for the risk exposure, we say that the market is in equilibrium. There is no incentive to sell or buy stocks, and no investors will wish to change their portfolio compositions. When the market is in equilibrium, all assets are correctly priced, and there are no 'bargains' in the market.

The asset pricing model that determines the equilibrium relationship between the expected return and risk of individual assets, as well as portfolios, is called the capital asset pricing model (CAPM). The induced linear relationship between expected return and beta that follows from the CAPM is called the security market line (SML). Although we use the terms SML and CAPM interchangeably for the linear risk–return relationship, keep in mind that the CAPM is an equilibrium pricing model, whereas the SML is the end result of this model. We first describe the SML and then discuss the CAPM.

The main results of the CAPM are summarized in the SML linear relationship, which describes the risk–return relationship of individual assets as well as portfolios, whether they are efficient or not. The SML is summarized by Rule 6.

Rule 6: To find the expected return on the ith asset, first calculate its beta. Multiply it by the market risk premium $[E(R_m) - r]$, and add to it the riskless interest rate. Thus, the following linear risk–return relationship should hold in equilibrium:[7]

$$E(R_i) \qquad = \qquad r \qquad + [E(R_m) - r]\beta_i \qquad (14.4)$$

expected rate of return = risk-free rate + risk premium

where $E(R_i)$ = the expected rate of return on the ith asset, $E(R_m)$ = the expected rate of return of the market portfolio, r = the risk-free interest rate, and β_i = the risk of the ith asset (or its beta). The SML asserts that the expected rate of return on asset i is equal to the risk-free rate plus a risk premium. This risk premium is equal to the market risk premium $[E(R_m) - r]$ multiplied by the asset's beta.

---

[7] The linear relationship between $E(R_i)$ and β_i holds for any security or portfolio as long as portfolio m is mean–variance efficient. However, to develop the equilibrium model, we must assume that all investors are risk averse and that they select their portfolios according to the mean–variance rule. In addition, we must assume homogeneous expectations among investors, the absence of transaction costs, and the availability of the risk-free asset. Under these assumptions, all investors hold portfolio m (the separation property), from which the CAPM follows.

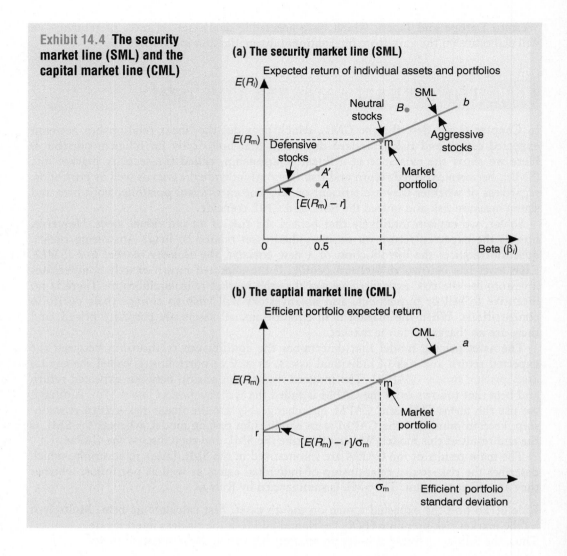

Exhibit 14.4 **The security market line (SML) and the capital market line (CML)**

(a) The security market line (SML)

Expected return of individual assets and portfolios

(b) The captial market line (CML)

Efficient portfolio expected return

Exhibit 14.4(a) demonstrates the SML. Note first that if $\beta_i = 0$, the ith asset is similar to the risk-free asset. Indeed, if we substitute zero for β_i in Equation 14.4, we obtain $E(R_i) = r$. Thus, as expected, the return on a risk-free asset is r. Second, if $\beta_i = 1$ then $E(R_i) = E(R_m)$. In this case, the asset's price fluctuates, on average, in tandem with the market, therefore the asset has the same risk as the market and hence yields, on average, the same rate of return as the market portfolio, $E(R_m)$. If the stock is a defensive stock ($\beta_i < 1$), the expected return will be smaller than $E(R_m)$. When $\beta_i > 1$, the stock is aggressive – that is, more risky than the market portfolio. Therefore, in equilibrium, the aggressive stock will be characterized by a higher expected return than the market.

Because $E(R_m) - r$, the slope of line rb in Exhibit 14.4(a), is the same for all stocks, we conclude that the higher β_i is, the greater the risk and thus the higher the required risk premium. Therefore, for a high β_i, the corresponding $E(R_i)$ will also be relatively large.

Why is the risk–return linear relationship called a pricing model, although no prices appear in Equation 14.4? Suppose that according to Equation 14.4, $E(R_i) = 15\%$, and

> **PRACTICE BOX**
>
> **Problem**
> Suppose the mean rate of return on the market is 10% and the risk-free interest rate is 5%. Given that beta is 2.48 for Hilton Stock, what is the expected rate of return on Hilton stock?
>
> **Solution**
> Based on Equation 14.4, the expected rate of return is
>
> $$E(R_i) = 5\% + [(10\% - 5\%) \times 2.48] \cong 17.4\%$$

the stock's expected price at the end of the investment period is $E(P_1) = \$115$. Assuming no dividends, what is the current stock price? It must be $P_0 = \$100$, because $15\% = (\$115 - \$100)/\$100$. Suppose now that for some reason, the stock's beta increases so that $E(R_i)$ as implied by the CAPM (or by SML, which is a result of the CAPM) increases to $E(R_i) = 20\%$. Assume that there is no change in the expected price at the end of the period; hence, $E(P_1)$ remains $\$115$. (One can also relax this assumption without affecting the analysis.) The current price (P_0) must now decrease until

$$E(R_i) = 20\% = (\$115 - P_0)/P_0$$

or

$$(0.2 \times P_0) + P_0 = \$115$$

or

$$P_0 \times (0.2 + 1) = \$115$$

Therefore $P_0 = \$115/1.2 \cong \$95.83$. Thus, according to the CAPM, a change in $E(R_i)$ causes a change in the current price of the asset – hence the name capital asset *pricing* model. The expected return $E(R_i)$ as implied by the CAPM is also called the *required* rate of return, because it is the return that investors require in equilibrium as compensation for the risk exposure. In Section 14.4 below we show that under certain assumptions the CAPM and the SML hold, which justify beta as a risk index.

14.3 SYSTEMATIC AND UNSYSTEMATIC RISK

When a portfolio composed of a large number of assets is held, the firm's variance has almost no role in determining the asset's risk premium. To elaborate, let us recall Equation 14.3:

$$R_{i_t} = \alpha_i + \beta_i R_{m_t} + e_{i_t}$$

The variance of R_i is as follows:[8]

$$\sigma_i^2 = \beta_i^2 \sigma_m^2 + \sigma_{e_i}^2 \tag{14.5}$$

---

[8] Because α_i and β_i are constant (α_i is the intercept of the line), their variances are zero. We take the variance of both sides to obtain Equation 14.5. Note that we also employ the rule, Variance $(ax) = a^2 \times$ variance (x), where a is constant, and use the fact that in regression analysis by construction, $\text{Cov}(e_i, R_m) = 0$. Hence, we have only two terms appearing in Equation 14.5, where $\sigma_{e_i}^2$ is the variance of e_i.

Thus, the variance σ_i^2 can be broken down into two terms. The first term, $\beta_i^2 \sigma_m^2$, is the firm's systematic risk component, which represents the part of the stock's variance that is attributable to overall market volatility. The second term, $\sigma_{e_i}^2$, is the firm's unsystematic risk component, which represents the part of the stock's variance that is *not* attributable to overall market volatility. The component $\sigma_{e_i}^2$ is the variance of the error term e_i, and σ_{e_i} is its standard deviation. The unsystematic risk component is related to the firm's specific volatility. If all points fall exactly on the regression line (the error term e_i is zero for all points; see Exhibit 14.2), then $\sigma_{e_i}^2 = 0$. The farther the points are from the regression line, the larger is $\sigma_{e_i}^2$, which measures the dispersion of the points around the regression line (see Exhibit 14.2).

Note that β_i appears only in the systematic risk component. Therefore, we can conclude that only the systematic part of the firm's variance is relevant in determining expected rates of return and, hence, the required risk premium. The CAPM does not account for the component, $\sigma_{e_i}^2$, which implies that this risk is irrelevant. It is irrelevant because it can be eliminated by holding a well-diversified portfolio. Obviously, $\sigma_{e_i}^2$ is irrelevant for asset pricing only if a well-diversified portfolio is held. If an investor holds only one stock in his portfolio, β is irrelevant and σ_i^2 (which includes $\sigma_{e_i}^2$ as one component) is the correct measure of risk.

If we divide both sides of Equation 14.5 by σ_i^2, we have the following:

$$1 = \frac{\beta_i^2 \sigma_m^2}{\sigma_i^2} + \frac{\sigma_{e_i}^2}{\sigma_i^2}$$

where the first term is the *proportion* of the total risk of a security that is systematic, and the second term is the proportion that is unsystematic.

14.4 THE CAPITAL ASSET PRICING MODEL (CAPM)[9]

So far we have provided an intuitive explanation why beta measures the risk. Namely, beta measures the volatility of a given asset relative to the volatility of the market portfolio. In Chapter 6, we show that at the optimum, all investors should hold the market portfolio whose risk is measured by its standard deviation. Therefore, the market portfolio's standard deviation is the risk exposure. We will show here that beta of an individual asset is its contribution to the market portfolio risk held, and therefore is identified as the individual's asset risk: the higher the beta, the higher the required rate of return from the asset.

The SML describes the relationship between the expected return and beta of assets. Suppose that there is an asset which is not on the SML: is it overpriced? Underpriced? We show in this section that all assets in equilibrium must fall on the SML. Any deviation from the SML will be corrected in equilibrium. This implies that beta is the risk index, because by the SML the higher the beta, the higher the expected return, $E(R_i)$. However, to achieve this result we must make some assumptions. Under these assumptions the CAPM holds, and the SML is the resulting equilibrium as determined by the CAPM.

---

[9] For a detailed proof of the CAPM, see William F. Sharpe, 'Capital asset prices: a theory of market equilibrium', *Journal of Finance*, September 1964, pp. 425–42, and John Lintner, 'Security prices and maximal gains from diversification', *Journal of Finance*, December 1965, pp. 587–615. Sharpe won the 1990 Nobel Prize in economics in part because of this paper.

To derive the CAPM, we must make the following assumptions: (1) investors make their investment decisions according to the mean–variance rule; (2) investors incur no transaction costs that would prevent sufficient diversification to achieve Portfolio m; (3) investors can borrow and lend at the riskless rate, r; and (4) there are no taxes. Given these assumptions, the CAPM would place all risky individual assets and portfolios on line rb in Exhibit 14.4(a), that is, on the SML. However, these assumptions are needed to derive the CML given in Exhibit 14.4(b) from which the CAPM of Exhibit 14.4(b) is taken. Indeed, if we show that all assets lie on the SML, Equation 14.4 holds, and so does the CAPM. The CAPM can be proven in the following two steps.

Step 1: Efficient portfolios

Relying on the assumption that investors make their own decisions by the mean–variance rule, we showed in Chapter 6 that the investors will mix portfolio m and the riskless asset. The fact that there are no transaction costs allows us to diversify among many assets, i.e. to hold the market portfolio or an efficient portfolio located on the CML (see Chapter 6 and Exhibit 14.4(b)). We show first that for *efficient portfolios* the SML and CML coincide. Thus, the SML holds for efficient portfolios. In the second step we show that the SML holds also for individual assets or inefficient portfolios.

In the first step, we prove that the SML holds for all efficient portfolios whose returns are R_p. Thus, we claim that all points on line rb (see Exhibit 14.4(a)) are attainable by mixing portfolio m, whose beta is equal to 1, and the risk-free asset. Thus, all efficient portfolios (combinations of portfolio m and the riskless asset (see Chapter 6)) are located on the SML given by line rb in Exhibit 14.4(a).

To see this, construct an efficient portfolio, R_p:

$$R_p = wr + (1 - w)R_m$$

where w is the investment weight in the risk-free asset and $(1 - w)$ is the investment weight in the market portfolio. The expected return on this efficient portfolio is

$$E(R_p) = wr + (1 - w)E(R_m)$$

and its beta is (see Rule 5):

$$\beta_p = 1 - w$$

Substituting $w = 1 - \beta_p$ and $1 - w = \beta_p$ in the above equation for $E(R_p)$, we obtain the following:

$$E(R_p) = (1 - \beta_p)r + \beta_p E(R_m)$$

or

$$E(R_p) = r + [E(R_m) - r]\beta_p$$

Because r and $[E(R_m) - r]$ are the intercept and slope of the SML, the pair $[E(R_p), \beta_p]$ lies on the SML. By altering the investment proportion w, we can select any point $[E(R_p), \beta_p]$ lying on the SML (line rb in Exhibit 14.4(a)). Thus any point on line rb is a feasible investment: it can be achieved by mixing the market portfolio of the CML, m, and the riskless asset.

Step 2: Individual assets

From Step 1 we can conclude that all points on line rb of Exhibit 14.4(a) can be achieved by mixing portfolio m with the riskless asset. Now we show that in equilibrium all assets, efficient or inefficient, must also lie on the line rb.

To see why this claim holds, consider Asset A, whose beta is $\beta_A = 0.5$, which is located below the SML (see Exhibit 14.4(a)). No investor would be willing to hold Asset A, because by mixing portfolio m and the risk-free asset, investors could achieve point A′ (see Step 1 above). In the specific example with $\beta = 0.5$, the mix would be achieved by investing 50% in m and 50% in r (we obtain a portfolio whose beta is 0.5 because $\beta_p = \frac{1}{2} \times 1 = \frac{1}{2}$: see Rule 5 above). Because Asset A′ has the same risk as Asset A ($\beta_{A'} = \beta_A = 0.5$) but a higher expected return, investors who held Asset A would prefer to sell Asset A and buy Asset A′. As a result, the price of Asset A will go down and its expected rate of return will go up until, in equilibrium, point A shifts upward to line rb. Only when point A is located on line rb will equilibrium be restored and there will be no further incentive to sell Asset A and buy Asset A′.

By the same argument, no asset, such as Asset B, can be above line rb, because in this case all investors would sell Portfolio m and hold this superior asset (see Exhibit 14.4(a)). The price of Portfolio m (or of the securities making up Portfolio m) will fall, and the price of Asset B will increase until equilibrium is restored, with all assets located on line rb. When all assets are on line rb, Equation 14.4 holds. This proves that in equilibrium, the linear relationship between expected return and risk (the SML) holds also for individual assets or inefficient portfolios.

Note that in the above proof of the CAPM and the resulting SML, we do not assume that beta is a measure of risk; it emerges as a result. We assume only the CAPM assumptions, from which we can conclude that all investors will select a portfolio located on the CML (see Chapter 6). Then we show that all efficient portfolios are located also on the SML, hence we can switch (for efficient portfolio) from sigma to beta as an index for risk. Thus, we prove that for an efficient portfolio beta (as well as sigma) can serve as the risk index. Finally, we show that in equilibrium all assets (efficient or inefficient) must be located on the SML, hence beta (but not sigma) is a risk index for individual assets as well as for inefficient portfolios.

Finally, once beta is accepted as a measure of risk, it follows from the CAPM that for any two assets i and j, the following must hold in equilibrium:

$$\frac{ER_i - r}{\beta_i} = \frac{ER_j - r}{\beta_j}$$

or the risk premium for a unit of risk must be the same across all assets. To see this recall that, by the SML,

$$ER_i = r + (ER_m - r)\beta_i$$

or

$$\frac{ER_i - r}{\beta_i} = ER_m - r$$

and for stock j the same holds:

$$\frac{ER_j - r}{\beta_j} = ER_m - r$$

hence

$$\frac{ER_i - r}{\beta_i} = \frac{ER_i - r}{\beta_j} = ER_m - r$$

This CAPM relationship is summarized in Rule 7.

Rule 7: In the CAPM equilibrium, the asset's risk premium divided by its beta must be equal across all assets.

14.5 USING THE CAPM FOR STOCK SELECTION

14.5.1 The abnormal return

How are alpha of Equation 14.3 and the CAPM employed in securities selection? If Equation 14.4 holds for all assets, it implies that all assets are located on the SML. In such a case, we say that the market is in equilibrium or that there are no inefficiencies in the market. The expected return on such stocks is exactly determined by their risk.

For example, if $E(R_m) = 15\%$, $r = 5\%$ and $\beta_i = 1.5$, then according to the CAPM, the expected return on the ith stock is (see Equation 14.4)

$$E(R_i) = 5\% + [(15\% - 5\%) \times 1.5] = 20\%$$

Thus, this stock lies on the SML. It is a good investment, although certainly not a bargain. The investor is fully compensated for the risk exposure. However, what if we expect to have $E(R_i) = 25\%$, with no change in β_i? We say that this stock has a 5% excess return or abnormal return above and beyond the compensation for the risk involved in investing in such a stock (the return on the stock is more than expected by the CAPM, thus it has an abnormal return). If the market is not in equilibrium, and if this excess return persists for a long time, we say that the market is *inefficient* (see Chapter 16). Of course, investors should grab such a stock.

This strategy is exactly the strategy employed by many practitioners for picking stocks. Let us elaborate. According to the CAPM, in equilibrium all assets are located on the SML: there are no deviations, hence there is no abnormal return and the following should hold (see Equation 14.4):

$$E(R_i) - r = [E(R_m) - r]\beta_i$$

However, if there are excess returns in the market, there is a deviation from the line, and the equation becomes

$$E(R_i) - r = \alpha_i + [E(R_m) - r]\beta_i$$

where α_i is the deviation of the ith stock from the SML which is exactly the 'excess return'. Thus, α_i measures the abnormal return of the ith stock. In the previous example, α_i is 5%. Of course, in practice the expected return, $E(R_i)$, as well as β_i, is unknown and is estimated from historical data.[10]

Of course, if the CAPM is an accurate model and the market is efficient, this excess return will instantly disappear. The trick is to be the first one to discover the high-alpha stocks (see Exhibit 14.5 for reported α and β) and buy them before everyone else does, thus forcing the stock prices up (recall the $100 bill found on the pavement – see the Preface).

---

[10] In Equation 14.3, α_i can be estimated by running the regression of R_i on R_m. One can also run the regression of $R_i - r_t$ on $R_m - r_t$ and estimate alpha where these two variables are stated in terms of excess return in comparison with the risk-free interest rate. Generally we refer to alpha when excess returns are employed. Therefore, if $\alpha_i > 0$ a positive abnormal return is observed, and if $\alpha_i < 0$ a negative abnormal return is observed.

Exhibit 14.5 The use of alpha and beta in practice

Risk and rating statistics	High	Low	Average
CDA rating	94	4	52
Beta (vs. S&P)	2.41	0.01	0.84
Beta (vs. category)	2.82	0.01	1.00
Standard deviation	10.06	0.12	3.52
Alpha	7.2	−3.6	−0.5
R^2	100	2	88

Source: Thomson Financial.

It is also interesting to note that the suggested strategy does not rely solely on the CAPM. Once the high-alpha stocks are selected, fundamental analysis is used in choosing stocks from this group. Thus, practitioners feel that the CAPM is useful but has its short-comings. They do not rely solely on the CAPM in making portfolio investment decisions. Indeed, we can see in Exhibit 14.5 that apart from alpha and beta, many other variables are reported which are probably employed in stock picking.

14.5.2 Using alpha and beta in practice

Exhibit 14.5 shows that practitioners use beta, as well as alpha, and consider these two parameters very informative. Thus, practitioners consider beta (and the CAPM) to be a useful risk index. Exhibit 14.5 shows the α, β, σ and R^2 of mutual funds. The table also provides risk-rating statistics. The 'highs' and 'lows' refer to funds with abnormal results. The CDA rating is a composite percentile rating from 1 to 99 based on a fund's performance over past market cycles.

In Exhibit 14.5, two calculations of beta are presented. The first uses the regression line of the fund calculated using the S&P index as the market portfolio. The other uses a category portfolio as a proxy for the market portfolio; a category portfolio is the average return on all funds (in the long-term growth class).

Alpha appears next; alpha is estimated by running a regression of $R_{i_t} - r_t$ on $R_{m_t} - r_t$ (see footnote 10). Funds with a positive alpha outperformed the market, or revealed an abnormal return.

14.6 SHORTCOMINGS OF THE CAPM

We can test the CAPM by estimating Equation 14.4 with past data, substituting histori-cal values for $E(R_i)$ and β_i. Of course, we do not expect to get an exact relationship, and we anticipate deviations from the line. Thus, it is possible to test the CAPM using the following equation:

$$\overline{R}_i = \gamma_0 + \gamma_1 \hat{\beta}_i + e_i$$

where $\overline{R}_i$ is the historical average return on the ith asset, γ_0 is the historical intercept, $\hat{\beta}_i$ is the historical estimate of the stock's beta, and e_i is the deviation from the line. The 'hat' emphasizes that this is an estimate of the true beta. γ_0 and γ_1 are the regression coefficients (if the CAPM is true, we should have that $\gamma_0 = r_f$ and $\gamma_1 = [E(R_m) - r_f]$: see Equation 14.4).

Many empirical studies have tested the CAPM. Most of them show that γ_1 is positive and significant (that is, there is a positive association between average return and risk). However, the fit is not as good as would be expected from the CAPM. (With individual stocks, R^2, which describes how well the model fits, was approximately 20%, which means that only 20% of this association could be explained by beta.) Recently, a study by Fama and French (see footnote 11) claimed that γ_1 is not significantly different from zero, which means that a positive association between beta and average return could not be found. In other words, Fama and French claim that beta is not the appropriate risk index, which casts doubt on the validity of the CAPM. Other researchers disagree with this conclusion and show a positive relationship between average return and beta.[11] In particular, Amihud, Christensen and Mendelson use an advanced econometric technique to show that expected return and beta are positively associated even when the same data set used by Fama and French is used. In their words, 'beta is still alive and well'.[12]

Roll showed that it is very difficult, if not impossible, to empirically test the CAPM.[13] Roll also showed that if beta is calculated with an efficient portfolio (a portfolio taken from the efficient frontier), then there is always a perfect positive association between average return and beta ($R^2 = 1$). Thus, the fact that empirical studies show a less than perfect linear association indicates only that an inefficient portfolio (a portfolio interior to the efficient frontier, i.e. a portfolio located below the CML – see Exhibit 14.4(b)) has been selected as a proxy to the market portfolio. According to Roll, the only testable question is whether the market portfolio is mean–variance efficient – that is, whether the market portfolio lies on the frontier or not. However, such a test is technically impossible with existing computers, because it involves using thousands of securities to solve for the efficient frontier.

Roll and Ross claim that the empirical findings regarding the CAPM are very sensitive to the proxy of the market portfolio that is employed to calculate the beta of each individual security.[14] They claim:

> This implies that an index proxy can conceivably be substantially inefficient and still produce a strong cross-sectional regression between expected returns and betas or it can conceivably be close to the efficient frontier and yet produce zero cross-section relation.[15]

They conclude:

> The empirical findings are not by themselves sufficient cause for rejection of the theory.[16]

---

[11] For more details on studies showing a positive association between mean return and beta, see M. Miller and M. Scholes, 'Rate of return in relation to risk: a reexamination of some recent findings', in M. Jensen (ed.), *Studies in the Theory of Capital Markets* (New York: Praeger, 1972); H. Levy, 'Equilibrium in an imperfect market: a constraint on the number of securities', *American Economic Review*, 68, September 1978, pp. 643–58; and Y. Amihud, B.J. Christensen and H. Mendelson, 'Further evidence on the risk–return relationship', working paper, Stanford University, 1992. An example of a study showing no association between risk and return is E. Fama and F. French, 'The cross-section of expected stocks returns', *Journal of Finance*, 47, 1992, pp. 427–66.

[12] Amihud, Christensen and Mendelson, p. 1.

[13] R. Roll, 'A critique of the asset pricing theory's test, Part I: On past and potential testability of theory', *Journal of Financial Economics*, 4, 1977, pp. 129–76.

[14] R. Roll and S. Ross, 'On the cross-section relation between expected return and betas', *Journal of Finance*, 49, March 1994, pp. 101–122.

[15] *Ibid*, p. 109.

[16] *Ibid*, p. 115.

Thus, some claim that beta is dead, and some claim that beta is alive and well. It seems that this controversy is not going to end soon. However, as have seen, practitioners employ beta as a measure of risk, hence they think that beta is alive but not well. Because it is not well, they employ additional investment criteria and do not rely solely on the CAPM.

It is obvious that some of the assumptions of the CAPM do not hold. For example, there are transaction costs, and in general the larger the number of shares bought, the lower the percentage paid in transaction costs. Investors, and in particular small investors, hold only a relatively small number of stocks in their portfolios; hence, they do not invest in portfolio m. Therefore, some extensions of the CAPM which relax these unrealistic assumptions are called for.

For the case in which there is only a limited number of stocks in the optimum portfolio, Levy, Markowitz, Merton and Sharpe himself suggest an alternative model that is similar to the CAPM but that allows investors to hold a relatively small number of assets in their portfolios.[17] This model is called the General Capital Asset Pricing Model (GCAPM); it is general in the sense that once the transaction costs are eliminated from the model, the CAPM is obtained as a specific case of the GCAPM. Under this model, each investor holds a different portfolio; therefore, each portfolio has a different beta (which is measured against the portfolio held). The beta of the ith asset is obtained as a weighted average of all these betas.

In summary, the CAPM provides insight into the risk–return relationship, but it has its shortcomings.[18] An investor cannot rely solely on the CAPM, and practitioners realize this. Therefore, despite the wide use of the CAPM, as well as the use of beta as a measure of risk and alpha as a measure of excess return, practitioners require additional tools in choosing their investment portfolios. Indeed, practitioners use the CAPM as a screening tool to divide all stocks into high-alpha and low-alpha groups. Their final investment decisions, however, rely on the analysis of dividends, price-to-book ratios, growth, earnings surprises and so forth.

14.7 THE SINGLE INDEX MODEL (SIM)

The single index model (SIM) suggested by Sharpe[19] has two important roles. First, it facilitates the derivation of the mean–variance frontier, and secondly, it paves the way to the arbitrage pricing theory (APT) developed by Ross (see Section 14.8).[20] The APT is an equilibrium model similar to the CAPM, but relies on another set of assumptions.

---

[17] For more details on the GCAPM, see H. Levy, 'Equilibrium in an imperfect market: a constraint on the number of securities in a portfolio', *American Economic Review*, 68, 1978, pp. 613–58; Harry M. Markowitz, 'Risk adjustment', *Journal of Accounting, Auditing and Finance*, Winter/Spring 1990; Robert C. Merton, 'A simple model of capital market equilibrium with incomplete information', *Journal of Finance*, 42, 1987, pp. 483–510; and W.F. Sharpe, 'Capital asset prices with and without negative holdings', *Journal of Finance*, 46, June 1991, pp. 489–510.

[18] See H. Levy, 'Risk and return: an experimental analysis', *International Economic Review*, February 1997. This paper uses an investment experiment to show that both the CAPM and the GCAPM are not 'dead' and can be used in risk–return equilibrium model analysis.

[19] See W.F. Sharpe, 'A simplified model for portfolio analysis', *Management Science*, January 1963, pp. 277–93.

[20] See S. Ross, 'Mutual fund separation in financial theory – the separating distributions', *Journal of Economic Theory*, April 1978; S. Ross, 'The arbitrage theory of capital asset pricing', *Economica*, 1976.

14.7.1 Common-factor and firm-specific rates of returns

The SIM has some basic assumptions about the way rates of return are generated. According to the SIM, two factors are responsible for a given stock's rate of return: the percentage change in some index (or the common factor) and changes related to firm-specific events. The index could be any variable that is correlated with security rates of return, such as the inflation rate, gross domestic product (GDP), or even the S&P 500 or FTSE 100 index.

The SIM assumes that the rate of return on Asset i is given by

$$R_i = \alpha_i + \beta_i I + e_i \qquad (14.6)$$

where R_i is the rate of return on Asset i, I is the *percentage change* in some index that is common to all stocks, and e_i is the change in Asset i's rate of return related to firm-specific events. In the CAPM, beta is related to the market portfolio, and hence I is chosen to be the market portfolio. Like beta in the CAPM, in the SIM β_i measures the sensitivity of the ith asset's return to changes in the index (I).

For example, if $\beta_i = 2$ and I is the GDP, it means that if the GDP goes up by 1%, R_i, on average, will go up by 2%. The term α_i is the intercept that measures the anticipated return when $I = 0$.

The term e_i is the random deviation from the straight line given by $R_i = \alpha_i + \beta_i I$. It can be either above the line (positive) or below the line (negative), and it is zero on average.[21] The straight line in Exhibit 14.6 has an intercept of α_i and a slope of β_i. If all points (R_i) are exactly on the line, then all deviations (e_i) are zero. However, in general, some points are located above the line and some below it. Hence, there are positive as well as negative deviations.

The index (I) and the sensitivity factor (β_i) determine the expected rate of return on Asset i.

For example, suppose the common index determining stock prices is the rate of return on the FTSE 100 index, and the stock under consideration is British Airways (BA).

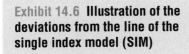

Exhibit 14.6 Illustration of the deviations from the line of the single index model (SIM)

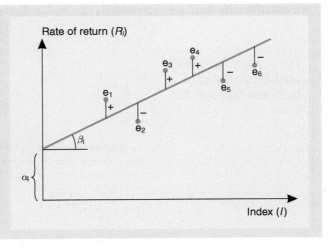

---

[21] If the mean of e_i is not zero, we can always add the mean of e_i to α_i, then the mean of the deviations left is, by construction, zero. Also when we run a regression to estimate β_i, the sample mean $\bar{e}_i$ is zero.

Moreover, suppose $\alpha_{BA} = 1\%$ and $\beta_{BA} = 2$. Then the following relationship holds for BA:

$$R_{BA} = 1\% + 2I + e_{BA}$$

Suppose that in a given year, $I = 10\%$ (namely, the FTSE index goes up by 10%). If no information regarding e_{BA} is available, the best estimate is that $e_{BA} = 0$. Then the rate of return on BA in this specific year is expected to be

$$R_{BA} = 1\% + (2 \times 10\%) + 0 = 21\%$$

Now suppose that I goes up by 12%. Would we predict the rate of return on BA to go up? Absolutely:

$$R_{BA} = 1\% + (2 \times 12\%) + 0 = 25\%$$

This is our best prediction when nothing is known about the firm-specific component (e_{BA}). The *realized return* (in contrast to the expected return) on BA, however, can be larger or smaller than 25%, depending on the sign of the actual deviation of e_{BA} from the straight line. For example, suppose that when the FTSE index goes up by 12%, BA also announces that it failed to develop a new personal computer model. This firm-specific news (news that relates to the firm specifically and not to the whole market) will make e_i negative; hence, BA stock will show an actual return lower than 25%. For example, if $e_{BA} = -10\%$, we get

$$R_{BA} = 1\% + (2 \times 12\%) - 10\% = 15\%$$

Thus, what determines the *actual* or realized future return on each asset is the common index change (I), beta, and the firm-specific factor e_i. On average, we expect the firm-specific factor to be zero. In any given period, however, it can be either negative or positive, depending on whether the news is good or bad.

If an investor can predict the common index as well as the firm-specific news, the investor can predict the rate of return on the stock. Unfortunately, these types of predictions are hard to make.

Exhibit 14.7 demonstrates graphically the component of the return that is due to the common index and the component that is due to the firm-specific risk (e_i) for AT&T. We assume that $\alpha_{AT\&T} = 1\%$ and $\beta_{AT\&T} = 0.5$. If the index (say, the S&P 500) shows

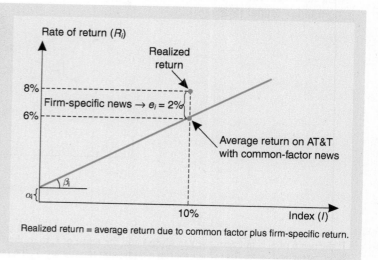

Exhibit 14.7 The return components: common factor and firm-specific factor

Realized return = average return due to common factor plus firm-specific return.

in a given year a return of 10%, then we expect *on average* that the return on AT&T in this year will be 6%:

$$R_{AT\&T} = 1\% + (^1/_2 \times 10\%) = 6\%$$

However, suppose that AT&T announces some positive information – for example, a new service that will greatly increase its profit. This firm-specific event will cause a deviation from our prediction that is based on the index only. For example, the deviation (e_i) would be positive, say 2% (see Exhibit 14.7). Therefore, the *realized rate of return*, given the information on the index as well as AT&T specific news, is

$$R_{AT\&T} = 1\% + (^1/_2 \times 10\%) + 2\% = 8\%$$

which can be rewritten in more general terms as follows:

$$R_i = \alpha_i \quad + \quad \beta_i \times I \quad + \quad e_i$$
$$\text{constant} + \text{common factor news} + \text{Firm-specific news}$$

One of the main benefits of the SIM in solving for mean–variance efficient portfolios located on the efficient frontier is the reduction in the number of inputs that must be estimated. Chapter 6 showed that in order to solve for the mean–variance efficient set, we have to minimize the portfolio's variance for a given mean return. The portfolio's variance, in turn, is a function of all possible covariances. If we have 100 stocks, for example, we first have to calculate the covariance of all possible pairs of the 100 assets. In this case, the number is $100!/(98! \times 2!) = 4,950$, which is quite a large number to handle.[22] The SIM is a simplified model that drastically decreases the necessary number of calculations of covariances. Using Equation 14.6, the covariance of Assets i and j is

$$\text{Cov}(R_i, R_j) = \text{Cov}(\alpha_i + \beta_i I + e_i, \alpha_j + \beta_j I + e_j)$$

The SIM assumes that Firm i's specific news is independent of Firm j's specific news. This means that if some success or failure occurs at BA, it does not affect the chance of success or failure at Marks & Spencer. In statistical terms, this assumption implies that $\text{Cov}(e_i, e_j) = 0$. Also, the deviation from the lines for e_i is assumed to be independent of the common factor, namely $\text{Cov}(I, e_i) = 0$. With these assumptions, the covariance of these two stocks is reduced to the following:[23]

$$\text{Cov}(R_i, R_j) = \beta_i \beta_j \sigma_i^2 \tag{14.7}$$

Thus, if we have 100 stocks and we estimate 100 values of β_i and σ_i^2 we get all possible covariances. Therefore, with the SIM we have to estimate only 100 betas (and σ_i^2) to get all 4,950 covariances needed without the assumptions of the SIM.[24]

---

[22] All combinations of selecting two assets out of 100 assets are given by the following formula:

$$C_2^{100} = \frac{100!}{(100-2)!2!}$$

where C_2^{100} denotes the combination of two taken from a population of 100, and ! denotes a factorial. For example. $4! = 4 \times 3 \times 2 \times 1 = 24$. If we know the weights, then there is no problem calculating the variance of the portfolio, because we simply calculate the variance of the given portfolio corresponding to the known weights. However, when we are trying to determine the optimal weights to select, we need all of these covariances.

[23] Recall that α_i, α_j and β_i, β_j are constants, and that the deviation from the line e_i is assumed to be independent of the index level I. That is, $\text{Cov}(I, e_i) = 0$ and $\text{Cov}(I, I) = \sigma_i^2$. Because α_i and α_j are constants, and e_i and e_j are independent, we have $\text{Cov}(R_i, R_j) = \text{Cov}(\alpha_i + \beta_i I + e_i, \alpha_j + \beta_j I + e_j) = \text{Cov}(\beta_i I, \beta_j I)$, namely, $\text{Cov}(R_i, R_j) = \beta_i \beta_j \sigma_i^2$.

[24] See Footnote 22.

Thus, the assumptions of the SIM, and in particular the assumption that $\text{Cov}(e_i, e_j) = 0$, greatly reduce the number of estimates needed for the derivation of the efficient frontier.

The SIM is similar in its structure to the arbitrage pricing model we discuss next. To see this, recall that the expected value of the firm's specific term is zero: $E(e_i) = 0$. Taking the expected value from both sides of Equation 14.6 yields

$$E(R_i) = \alpha_i + \beta_i \times E(I)$$

or

$$\alpha_i = E(R_i) - \beta_i \times E(I)$$

Substituting this expression for α_i in Equation 14.6, we get

$$R_i = \{E(R_i) - \beta_i \times E(I)\} + (\beta_i \times I) + e_i$$

which can be rewritten as

$$R_i = E(R_i) + \beta_i[I - E(I)] + e_i$$

This form of the SIM is exactly how the arbitrage pricing theory advocates that rates of return be generated. However, to derive equilibrium prices by the APT, some additional assumptions are needed. We now turn to the arbitrage pricing theory.

14.8   THE ARBITRAGE PRICING THEORY (APT)

The arbitrage pricing theory (APT), like the CAPM, is an equilibrium pricing model. The APT, developed by Stephen Ross, reaches conclusions similar to those of the CAPM. However, the APT is based on a different set of assumptions. Recall that in deriving the CAPM, we assume that all investors make their investment decisions by a mean–variance rule. With this assumption, investors maximize the slope of the capital market line (CML), seeking the highest expected return for a given level of standard deviation. In deriving the APT risk–return relationship, Ross does not assume risk aversion or rely on the mean–variance rule. Rather, he explains the linear relationship between expected return and risk as arising because in equilibrium there are no arbitrage opportunities in security markets. If investors can find a portfolio that earns with certainty a positive return with a zero net initial investment, all investors will seek this attractive investment. As a result, the price of this investment will change until, in equilibrium, the positive return drops to zero, and such attractive investments vanish from the market. Indeed, the prices of all such bargains increase until no arbitrage profit opportunities are available. When this occurs, the linear risk–return relationship, which is very similar to the SML, holds.

14.8.1 Examples of arbitrage

Consider first the simplest case of arbitrage, where you can borrow $100 at Bank A at 5%, and you can deposit the money in a second fully insured Bank B to earn 6%. In this simple example, you have a zero out-of-pocket investment at t_0 and a profit of $1 at the end of the year (t_1). If such a financial situation existed, it would be an arbitrage opportunity. If you could borrow an unlimited amount of money at 5% and lend it at 6%, the potential profit would be infinite. Such a case is called a money machine; one has a machine, so to speak, to create money.

Although in general such situations do not exist in the market, the simple example illustrates the concept of an arbitrage opportunity. You create a financial transaction such that with zero net investment, you earn a positive return. If such a situation exists, arbitrage profit is available, and the financial transaction by which this profit is achieved is called an arbitrage transaction.

An essential property needed for the derivation of the APT is the allowance of short selling of securities. Recall that when investors sell a security short, they sell shares they do not own. The process of short selling is as follows. The investor borrows the shares from a broker and then sells the shares in the market to receive the proceeds from the sale. At some future date, the investor must buy the stocks in the market to replace the shares borrowed.

To illustrate how an investor can create an arbitrage profit using short-selling transactions, suppose you have three securities, A, B and C, with returns as given in Exhibit 14.8. For simplicity, assume that each share is trading at $100, so the profit or loss in dollars is also the percentage return on your investment. For example, making $10 on a $100 investment means a 10% rate of return. It is obvious from Exhibit 14.8 that Stock B does not always earn a better return than Stock A – Stock B yields a lower return in a recession and in a stable economy than does Stock A. In addition, Stock C does not always earn a better return than Stock A. Stock C yields a lower return than Stock A when the economy booms.

Although neither Stock B nor Stock C is always better than Stock A, you can create a portfolio of B and C such that arbitrage opportunities are available. Recall that when an investor short sells an asset, the dollar profit to the short-seller is reversed. If the profit is −$2 (see Stock A in a recession), this means the stock dropped by 2%. However, because the short-seller sells it today and returns the stock to the broker after buying it back at a lower price, the short-seller's profit is +$2. Suppose you borrow a share from the broker and sell it for $100. (The broker just lends you a share and hence you do not pay any money.) After a month, the stock drops to $98 (a +2% rate of return). You buy it back for $98, return the stock to the broker, and make a profit of +$2.

We will show below that holding a portfolio of Stocks B and C and selling short Stock A produces an arbitrage profit. Suppose you sell short two shares of Stock A for $200, take the $200 proceeds from the short sale, and buy one share of Stock C for $100 and one share of Stock B for $100. The return from the transaction in dollars is given in Exhibit 14.9. If a recession occurs, then stock A will lose −$2. However, you were short two shares of Stock A, and you have a gain of $2 \times 2 = \$4$, as illustrated in the second column of Exhibit 14.9. Buying one share of Stocks B and C in a recession will result in a $4 loss on Stock B and no profit or loss on Stock C, as illustrated in the third column of Exhibit 14.9. A similar calculation shows a profit of $14 on Stocks B and C in a stable economy and a profit of $22 if the economy booms. Hence, the total net return from the arbitrage transaction is $+\$4 - \$4 = \$0$ if recession

Exhibit 14.8 **Profit and loss on an investment**	Securities		
State of the economy	A	B	C
Recession	−$2	−$4	$0
Stable	6	4	10
Boom	10	16	6

Exhibit 14.9 **Arbitrage profit with short sales**

Cash flow from transaction

State of the economy	Short sale of two shares of Stock A	Portfolio of one share of Stock B and one share of Stock C	Total net return from the arbitrage transaction
Recession	2 × ($2) = $4	(1 × −$4) + (1 × −$0) = $4	+$4 − $4 = 0
Stable	2 × (−$6) = −$12	(1 × $4) + (1 × $10) = $14	−$12 + $14 = $2
Boom	2 × (−$10) = −$20	(1 × $16) + (1 × $6) = $22	−$20 + $22 = $2

occurs. Following similar logic, you have a $2 gain if either a stable or a boom economy exists.

The initial investment on the transaction described in Exhibit 14.9 is zero (ignoring any trading costs), because the investor sells short two shares of stock A, gets the $200 proceeds, and invests $100 in Stock B and $100 in Stock C. The investor's future net return is always nonnegative regardless of the state of the economy. The investor gains either nothing (in a recession) or $2 (in a stable or boom economy). This is clearly an arbitrage opportunity. Why not double the transaction to $400 and make a potential profit of $4 (or $0), or invest $2,000 in Stocks B and C to make a profit of $20 (or $0), or even invest $1 million in Stocks B and C to make an arbitrage profit of $10,000 (or $0). The investor will continue to sell Stock A short and buy Stocks B and C to earn arbitrage profits. With these three stocks we have a money machine. However, by the APT this is impossible to hold in equilibrium.

With many such transactions in large amounts, there will be selling pressure on Stock A and buying pressure on Stocks B and C. Therefore, the price of Stock A will fall (hence the investor will get less from the short sale), and the price of Stocks B and C will go up (hence the investor will pay more for Stocks A and B) until eventually no arbitrage opportunities are available. The arbitrage will disappear because with these new prices the investor has to pay out-of-pocket money to create the transaction suggested above. For example, if the investor pays $1 for the suggested position (e.g. the price of A falls to $99.75 and the price of B and C increases to $100.25) and a recession occurs, the income is zero (see Exhibit 14.8), and the investor loses because he could earn a riskless interest on the investment of $1. Obviously, the larger the investment, the larger the loss. Thus, with these new prices of the three stocks, arbitrage profit vanishes.

14.8.2 The APT: assumptions and risk–return relationship

Recall that by the definition of an arbitrage opportunity, with a zero investment, the future return on the portfolio must be nonnegative. Ross employs this argument to derive the APT. Because prices change when arbitrage exists, he explores which asset prices should be in equilibrium in order to eliminate arbitrage opportunities. The mean return and risk of each asset also change until arbitrage opportunities disappear. In short, when arbitrage transactions are available, the economy is not in equilibrium. This is why the APT is an equilibrium pricing model. Thus, the APT investigates the market equilibrium prices when all arbitrage transactions are eliminated. This section examines the assumptions and resulting asset pricing of the APT.

The assumptions underlying the APT follow:

1 Rates of return depend on some common factors and some 'noise', which is firm specific. This return dependency is called a return-generating process.
2 A very large number of assets exist in the economy.
3 Short sales are allowed, and the proceeds are available to the short-sellers.
4 There are no transaction costs.
5 Investors prefer more wealth to less.

Note that unlike the CAPM, there is no need to assume that investors choose the investment by the mean–variance rule.

According to the APT, the rates of return on Security i, R_i, in a given period (say, a month) are generated by the following process:

$$R_i = E(R_i) + \beta_i[I - E(I)] + e_i \qquad (14.8)$$

where R_i is the rate of return on Security i ($i = 1, 2, \ldots, n$), I is the value of the factor (or index) generating the return R_i (that is, the percentage change in some index, as in the SIM), and $E(I)$ is the mean of this factor. Because only one factor is involved, this model is called the *one-factor model*. The coefficient β_i measures the sensitivity of changes in R_i as a result of changes in I. The term e_i is the 'noise', or the deviation from the line that is the firm specific factor; that is, whereas all firms have the same common factor I, each has a different e_i.

The assumed return-generating process is identical to the return process predicted by the SIM (see Section 14.7). However, whereas the SIM's main purpose is to provide an easy way to calculate all possible pairs of correlations, the return-generating process given by Equation 14.8 is constructed for the purpose of deriving the risk–return linear relationship (similar to the CAPM); hence, further assumptions beyond the return-generating process are needed to derive the APT results.

The most important characteristic of this return-generating process is that I is a common factor to all risky assets, just as it is in the SIM. Because this factor is common to all assets, its fluctuations cannot be diversified away. The common factor could be the inflation rate in the economy, the unemployment rate, the interest rate on government bonds, the gross national product (GNP), or even, as in the CAPM, the rate of return on the market portfolio R_m. Note that the APT uses $I - E(I)$ instead of simply I. This is called the 'surprise' factor. For example, if we expect the inflation rate to increase on average by, say, $E(I) = 10\%$, and it actually increases by $I = 12\%$, we have a 2% surprise, or unexpected, factor. Thus, the APT measures the difference between expectations and actual outcome rather than simply actual outcome.

The larger an asset's beta, the larger the effect of the surprise on the asset's return. Another possible surprise is firm specific and is given by e_i, which is predicted to be zero before the firm-specific news is declared. As with the SIM, this firm-specific news could be the resignation of the chairman of General Motors, an increase in the dividends of AT&T, or a new drug discovery by Johnson & Johnson. Thus, like the SIM we have a common factor's surprise, $I - E(I)$, and a firm's specific surprise, e_i.

14.8.3 The linear APT relationship

To examine the relationship between risk and expected return implied by the APT, we first examine a unique portfolio that has a zero beta and requires no investment due to short selling. Thus, the determination of asset prices by the APT relies on the following rule.

Rule 8: Zero beta, zero investment portfolios must yield zero return.

The main result of the APT is the implied linear risk–return relationship similar to the SML. The proof of this relationship relies on Rule 1. Suppose we invest a proportion of our wealth (w_i) in the ith asset. Then, by multiplying all terms in Equation 14.8 by w_i and summing up for all n assets held in the portfolio, we get

$$\sum_{i=1}^{n} w_i R_i = \sum_{i=1}^{n} w_i E(R_i) + [I - E(I)] \sum_{i=1}^{n} w_i \beta_i + \sum_{i=1}^{n} w_i e_i$$

Because $\sum_{i=1}^{n} w_i R_i = R_p$ is the return on the created portfolio whose mean return is $\sum_{i=1}^{n} w_i E(R_i) = E(R_p)$, the above equation can be rewritten as follows:

$$R_p = E(R_p) + [I - E(I)] \sum_{i=1}^{n} w_i \beta_i + \sum_{i=1}^{n} w_i e_i$$

For *a very large portfolio* composed of many securities (that is, n is very large), the noise factors tend to cancel each other, so we can safely assume that $\sum_{i=1}^{n} w_i e_i \cong 0$. Therefore, for a very large portfolio, R_p is given by

$$R_p = E(R_p) + [I - E(I)] \sum_{i=1}^{n} w_i \beta_i$$

where $\sum_{i=1}^{n} w_i \beta_i$ is the portfolio beta, which is actually the average of all the assets' betas weighted by their proportion (w_i) in the portfolio. Thus, the rate of return on a portfolio by the APT is equal to the expected return plus an adjustment for unanticipated changes in the common factor. Deviation of the portfolio return from what was expected is a function of the portfolio beta and the magnitude of the unanticipated change in the common factor.

Now suppose you can create a portfolio with *zero investment* and with *zero risk*, namely, $\sum_{i=1}^{n} w_i = 0$ and $\sum_{i=1}^{n} w_i \beta_i = 0$. Such a portfolio is called a zero beta portfolio. What should the return be on such a portfolio? According to the above equation, the return must be $R_p = E(R_p)$, because the second term on the right-hand side is zero. Note that the rate of return on such a portfolio is equal to its mean [$E(R_p)$], and because $E(R_p)$ is constant the return R_p has *no variability*. Because by assumption this is a zero investment portfolio, the expected return must be equal to zero (see Rule 8); otherwise, we have an arbitrage opportunity. For example, if the zero beta, zero investment portfolio had positive dollar returns, then this would be a money machine because you can earn positive return with no risk. Alternatively, if this portfolio had negative dollar returns, then an investor could construct another portfolio with exactly opposite weights (i.e. short this portfolio) that would result in positive dollar returns.

With no arbitrage opportunities and using the zero beta and zero investment portfolio, Ross demonstrated that the mean return on the ith asset, $E(R_i)$, is related to β_i in a linear fashion as follows:

$$E(R_i) = \alpha_0 + \alpha_1 \beta_i \tag{14.9}$$

where α_0 and α_1 are constant across securities. This result is very similar to the CAPM. Indeed, when we use the market portfolio as the index, we get $\alpha_0 = r$, and $\alpha_1 = E(R_m) - r$, with the APT and CAPM yielding identical results.

But how can one construct zero beta portfolio with zero investment? For simplicity, we demonstrate how to do this with three stocks; however, recall that in order for the ATP to hold, we need many assets to be included in the portfolio. To show that Equation 14.9 is intact, let us look at the following three stocks. (For simplicity, assume each stock has the same market price.)

	Stock		
	A	B	C
Mean return, $E(R_i)$	8%	13%	?
Beta, β_i	1	2	3

Our goal is to select a mean rate of return on Stock C such that we can construct a zero investment, zero risk portfolio of Stocks A, B and C with no arbitrage opportunities. Suppose we plot A and B and connect them by a straight line. What mean rate of return should hold such that also Stock C will place it on line AB? We will show that when the mean rate of return of Stock C is determined such that no arbitrage exists, point C will be on the straight line connecting points B and A. Namely, all points are located on a straight line, which illustrates that the APT linear relationship given by Equation 14.9 is intact.

If we select investment proportions $w_A = 1$, $w_B = -2$ and $w_C = 1$, then[25]

$$\sum_{i=1}^{n} w_i = 1 - 2 + 1 = 0$$

and

$$\sum_{i=1}^{n} w_i \times \beta_i = (1 \times 1) + (2 \times (-2)) + 3 \times 1 = 0$$

Thus, we have constructed a zero investment and zero risk portfolio.

According to Rule 8 the portfolio with zero beta and zero investment should not provide arbitrage profit, so we must have[26]

$$1 \times 8\% - 2 \times 13\% + 1 \times E(R_{\hat{C}}) = 0$$

Therefore, $E(R_{\hat{C}}) = 26\% - 8\% = 18\%$. If $E(R_{\hat{C}}) = 18\%$, there is no arbitrage profit. Let us elaborate. Suppose that $E(R_{\hat{C}}) = 20\%$. Then we can earn the following on a portfolio with a zero risk and zero investment:

$$R_p = E(R_p) = 1 \times 8\% - 2 \times 13\% + 1 \times 20\% = 2\%$$

---

[25] To obtain the weights, we solve two equations with two unknowns (w_1 and w_2):

$$w_1 + w_2 + (1 - w_1 - w_2) = 0$$

and

$$(w_1 \times 1) + (w_2 \times 2) + ((1 - w_1 - w_2) \times 3) = 0$$

Note that a negative weight implies short selling.

[26] The equation claiming that $R_p = E(R_p) = 0$ is generally not true for only three stocks, because for three stocks, we would not expect that the sum of the error terms would actually be zero. We really need a large number of stocks to demonstrate the APT. Thus, here we assume that the sum of the error terms is zero (as if we had an infinite number of assets) but demonstrate the linear relationship by focusing on only three points. This greatly simplifies the demonstration.

Hence, there are arbitrage opportunities. Holding such a portfolio creates a positive certain profit with no investment. This is impossible in equilibrium, because it constitutes a 'money machine'. Similarly, if $E(R_{\hat{C}})$ is lower than 18%, say 15%, with zero investment and risk, we get a negative return of

$$R_p = E(R_p) = 1 \times 8\% - 2 \times 13\% + 1 \times 15\% = -3\%$$

Then, by short selling such a portfolio with zero investment, we get a positive return, which is again a money machine.[27] To sum up, in equilibrium with no arbitrage possibilities, we must have $E(R_{\hat{C}}) = 18\%$. We will use this result later in the APT linear relationship demonstration.

Now what is left to show is that the point given by $E(R_C) = 18\%$ and $\beta_C = 3$, which characterizes Stock C when there are no arbitrage opportunities, indeed lies on the same straight line as Stocks A and B, as asserted by the APT. Exhibit 14.10 demonstrates the straight line connecting points A and B with the relevant parameters taken from the example. The slope of the line is $(13\% - 8\%)/(2 - 1) = 5\%$, which is the line KB (the rise) divided by the line KA (the run). The intercept of this line can be found by inserting the parameters of point A (or point B) and employing the straight-line formula with a slope of 5%:

$$E(R_i) = \alpha_0 + (5\% \times \beta_i)$$

Because for Stock A we have $E(R_A) = 8\%$ and $\beta_A = 1$, we get $8\% = \alpha_0 + (5\% \times 1)$; thus, $\alpha_0 = 3\%$. Therefore, the straight line connecting Stocks A and B is given by $E(R_i) = 3\% + (5\% \times \beta_i)$, where $\alpha_0 = 3\%$ and $\alpha_1 = 5\%$. Because one can pass a straight line between any two points, these findings so far neither support nor refute the APT. The crucial test of the APT is whether Stock C with $E(R_C) = 18\%$ and $\beta_C = 3$, which are the necessary parameters to eliminate an arbitrage profit, also lies on the same line. To test this, we substitute 18% for $E(R_C)$ and 3 for β_C, and check whether there is an identity with this straight-line parameter:

$$18\% = \alpha_0 + \alpha_1 \times 3$$

Indeed, with $\alpha_0 = 3\%$ and $\alpha_1 = 5\%$, we have

$$3\% + (5\% \times 3) = 18\%$$

which implies that the third point, corresponding to Stock C, also lies on the same straight line. If $E(R_C)$ is greater than 18% (say, 23%), the point is above the line (see point C_1 in Exhibit 14.10). If $E(R_C)$ is lower than 18% (say, 13%), the point is below the line (see point C_2 in Exhibit 14.10).

Because a mean return of exactly 18% for Stock C eliminates an arbitrage possibility, and all three stocks lie on the same straight line, we conclude that when arbitrage opportunities are eliminated, we get the following linear relationship for the three stocks under consideration:

$$E(R_i) = \alpha_0 + \alpha_1\beta_i$$

where α_0 and α_1 are the intercept and the slope of the APT line, respectively. This is similar to the CAPM risk–return relationship. When arbitrage opportunities are

---

[27] Recall that when you short sell a portfolio with zero initial investment, you get no proceeds from the short sale. If you hold a portfolio of two assets (say, $w_1 = +1$, $w_2 = -1$ and $\Sigma w_i = 0$), then by short selling it you get $w_1 = -1$, $w_2 = +1$, and again $\Sigma w_i = 0$. Thus, selling a zero investment portfolio remains a zero investment strategy.

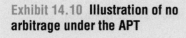

Exhibit 14.10 Illustration of no arbitrage under the APT

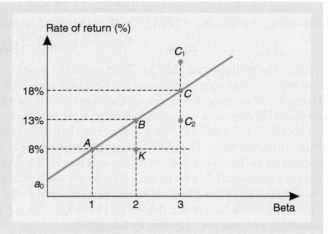

available, not all stocks will lie on this line; hence, it will not describe the relationship between $E(R_i)$ and β_i. When all arbitrage opportunities vanish, all assets must lie on this straight line.

The APT linear relationship has been illustrated with three stocks, but the same principle holds with a portfolio having any number of stocks. As long as one of the stocks is not on the straight line, an arbitrage profit can be made. To eliminate such an arbitrage profit, all $[E(R_i),\beta_i]$ points must lie on the one straight line. We assumed a zero investment, zero beta portfolio to derive the APT, but the linear relationship derived holds for any individual asset, no matter what the beta is and, of course, for nonzero investments. For example, if $\alpha_0 = 5\%$ and $\alpha_1 = 10\%$, and the beta of Xerox is 2, we expect to earn on an investment in Xerox $5\% + (10\% \times 2) = 25\%$. Thus, every \$1 investment in Xerox is expected to grow to \$1.25. Similarly, if beta is zero, every dollar invested is expected to grow to \$1.05.

Let us now turn to the intuitive explanation of the linear risk–return relationship and to the meaning of the coefficients α_0 and α_1. First, because the APT assumes that a large portfolio is held, the variance of the unsystematic risk of each asset is not important.[28] This by no means implies that unsystematic risk does not exist. However, investors will not change the required risk premium from the asset due to the 'noise', because this part of the risk is eliminated in a large portfolio. If two stocks have the same beta, but one has a large unsystematic risk and the other has zero unsystematic risk, both will be priced the same and hence have the same average return.

14.9 THE APT AND THE CAPM

When the common factor in the APT model is the market portfolio – for example, the S&P 500 index – then $\alpha_1 = E(R_m) - r$, the risk premium of the market portfolio. In this instance, the APT and the CAPM yield the same results. To see this, select the market portfolio as the common factor, where the beta of the market portfolio is +1; it would

---

[28] Unsystematic and systematic risk have the same interpretation with the APT as with the SIM.

be located on the line shown in Exhibit 14.10 (see point A). The line can be found as follows: $\alpha_0 = r$ and $\alpha_1 = [E(R_m) - r]/1$ (the slope of the line). From Equation 14.9,

$$E(R_i) = r + [E(R_m) - r]\beta_i$$

which is the well-known CAPM. Thus, with the market portfolio as the common factor, if we assume that large portfolios are held and some specific return-generating process is driving returns, then we arrive at the same result as the CAPM. However, the CAPM and the APT rely on a completely different set of assumptions.

The CAPM is built on the assumption that investors are risk averse and follow the mean–variance rule. The APT does not require these assumptions. Thus, the APT is considered to be much less restrictive. That is, the APT can apply to markets where investors are not risk averse or where more than portfolio mean and variance matter. The CAPM predicts that all investors will hold the same market portfolio; there is no such prediction with the APT. However, the APT assumes some specific return-generating process not required by the CAPM.

The APT also can be extended to include more than one common factor in the return-generating process. The major disadvantage of the APT is that it fails to tell us exactly what the common factors are. Many researchers have attempted to establish the appropriate number of factors, as well as exactly which variables are the best to use as the factors. Similarly, if there is only one factor, the APT fails to tell what that factor is.

14.10 MULTIFACTOR APT MODEL

So far, we have assumed that only one factor, I, generates the return on the various assets. It is possible, however, that several macro-economic factors generate the return on the assets, such as the inflation rate and the unemployment rate. Denoting the jth factor by I_j whose mean is $E(I_j)$, the multifactor model assumes that rates of return on the ith asset are generated by the following process:

$$R_i = E(R_i) + \beta_{i1}[I_1 - E(I_1)] + \beta_{i2}[I_2 - E(I_2)] + \ldots + \beta_{iK}[I_K - E(I_K)] + e_i$$

where there are K factors, and β_{ij} is the sensitivity of the return of the ith stock to the I_j factor ($j = 1, 2, \ldots, K$). The same no-arbitrage-opportunity approach can be used where we have zero investment ($\Sigma w_i = 0$) with zero betas for each of the above factors. Thus, $\Sigma w_i \beta_{i1} = 0$, $\Sigma w_i \beta_{i2} = 0$, and so forth, and there is no arbitrage opportunity. Following this procedure, we get a linear relationship similar to the one-factor APT of the following form:

$$E(R_i) = \alpha_0 + \alpha_1\beta_1 + \alpha_2\beta_2 + \ldots + \alpha_K\beta_K$$

which is a generalization of the APT when K factors, rather than one factor, are generating the returns. α_0 is the rate of return expected if all betas are zero (the risk-free rate), α_i is the market price of the risk related to factor i on a per-unit basis, and β_i is the sensitivity of the security to factor i.

In practice, the relevant risk factors are selected based on their historical influence on returns. For example, Berry, Burmeister and McElroy suggest the following factors:

1 Unanticipated changes in bond default premiums (government bonds versus corporate bonds).
2 Unanticipated changes in the term structure (20-year government bonds versus one-month Treasury bills).
3 Unanticipated changes in inflation.

4 Unanticipated changes in the growth rate of corporate profits.
5 Unanticipated changes in residual market risk (the part of the S&P 500 return not explained by the previous four factors).[29]

The remaining task in applying this five-factor model is to estimate the market price of risk for each factor. Although the market price of risk is difficult to estimate, this task is not impossible. Clearly, the multifactor APT model is much more flexible than the CAPM.

SUMMARY

■ *Understand why beta is the appropriate measure of risk.*
Beta – the slope of the characteristic line – is a risk measure that takes into account the variance of the asset under consideration, as well as the covariances with all other assets included in the portfolio. Beta is the correct risk measure of individual assets as well as portfolios.

■ *Understand why the security market line (SML) and the capital asset pricing model (CAPM) describe the equilibrium relationship between risk and expected rate of return.*
In equilibrium, all assets, individual stocks and portfolios lie on a straight line called the security market line (SML). According to the CAPM, the higher asset risk (beta) is, the higher the expected rate of return will be. In equilibrium, all assets are correctly priced, and one cannot find 'bargains'. Any deviation from the SML implies that the market is not in the CAPM equilibrium.

■ *Understand that if a well-diversified portfolio is held, only the systematic risk which cannot be washed out by diversification determines the risk premium.*
The nonsystematic risk is irrelevant. Show that for efficient portfolios the CML (of Chapter 6) coincides with the SML. Hence, for efficient portfolios, sigma as well as beta can serve as measured risk.

■ *Show that all assets must be located on the SML including individual assets and inefficient portfolios.*
Hence, beta is a measure of risk of all assets.

■ *Understand how practitioners who believe in market inefficiency use alpha and beta to select underpriced stocks.*
Practitioners use the CAPM's beta (systematic risk) as a measure of risk but believe that the market is not always in equilibrium. Therefore, they try to find underpriced stocks (that is, stocks that are located above the SML). These stocks are characterized by a relatively large alpha.

■ *Explain the single index model (SIM) and why it reduces the efficient frontier computations.*

■ *Explain the arbitrage pricing theory (APT), its assumptions and the resulting linear relationship.*
The primary assumption of the APT is that security returns are generated by a linear factor model. The APT is based on a no-arbitrage condition. That is, an investor should

---

[29] See Michael A. Berry, Edwin Burmeister and Marjorie B. McElroy, 'Sorting out risks using known APT factors', *Financial Analysts Journal*, March–April 1988, pp. 29–42.

not be able to build a zero risk, zero investment portfolio that has positive returns. However, the APT assumes that there are many assets in the economy and that there is some specific return-generating process:

$$E(R_i) = \alpha_0 + \alpha_1\beta_1 + \alpha_2\beta_2 + \ldots + \alpha_K\beta_K$$

■ *Compare and contrast the relationship between the CAPM and the APT.*
The APT is an alternative equilibrium pricing model that is built on different assumptions from the CAPM. Specifically, the APT does not assume that investors make decisions according to the mean–variance rule; also, investors do not have to be risk averse.

KEY TERMS

Abnormal return	Characteristic line	Market portfolio
Aggressive stock	Common factor	Market risk
Alpha	Defensive stock	Neutral stock
Arbitrage	Efficient portfolio	Security market line (SML)
Arbitrage pricing theory (APT)	Error term	Single index model (SIM)
Beta	Excess return	Systematic risk
Capital asset pricing model (CAPM)	Firm-specific news	Unsystematic risk
Capital market line (CML)	Firm's specific risk	Zero beta portfolio
	General capital asset pricing model (GCAPM)	

QUESTIONS

14.1   The rates of return on GM and on the market portfolio (R_m) for the last four years follow:

Year	GM	R_m
1	−5%	+10%
2	20	15
3	−2	−6
4	+30	+25

(a) Calculate the beta.
(b) Calculate the systematic and unsystematic risk, as well as the proportion of each in the variance of GM stock.

14.2   It is given that $E(R_m) = 10\%$, $\sigma_m = 10\%$ and $r = 5\%$. Draw the CML.

14.3   According to the CML, we have

$$E(R_p) = r + \frac{E(R_m) - r}{\sigma_m}\sigma_p$$

which holds for efficient portfolios (p). According to the SML, we have

$$E(R_p) = r + [E(R_m) - r]\beta_p$$

which holds for efficient portfolios as well as inefficient portfolios and individual assets. Show that for efficient portfolios, these two formulas are equivalent (hence, no contradiction arises).

14.4   Suppose there are two portfolios on the CML denoted by x and y. Calculate the correlation of x with y.

14.5   You have the following information: the stock is an aggressive stock, the systematic risk is 0.016, and the market portfolio has the following rates of return:

Year	Rate of return
1	5%
2	20%
3	10%

Calculate the stock's beta.

14.6   Suppose you receive the following rates of return on Assets X and Y:

Probability	X	Y
$1/2$	5%	3%
$1/2$	5%	20%

Calculate the expected rate of return and variance of each asset, as well as the covariance of X and Y. Explain your results.

14.7   (a) Suppose there are only two stocks in the market. The portfolio is composed of $1/2$ of Asset A and $1/2$ of Asset B. The standard deviations are $\sigma_A = 10\%$ and $\sigma_B = 20\%$. The covariance is $Cov(R_A, R_B) = 0.02$. What is the percentage contribution of each asset to the portfolio variance?

(b) Suppose that the means are $E(R_A) = 10\%$ and $E(R_B) = 10\%$, and the risk-free interest rate is 5%. Is the market in equilibrium? Does the CAPM hold with these parameters?

14.8   (a) Prove that the beta of the market portfolio is equal to 1.

(b) Calculate the beta of the market portfolio with the following data:

Year	Rate of return on the market portfolio
1	5%
2	10
3	20

14.9   Suppose that in the regression line

$$R_{i_t} = \alpha_i + \beta_i R_{m_t} + e_{i_t}$$

all residuals are $e_{i_t} = 0$. 'The beta, then, must be equal to 1.' Evaluate this statement. Demonstrate your answer graphically.

14.10   (a) Suppose there are two stocks, A and B, with $\beta_B = \beta_A$. 'Then, if the CAPM holds, it must be true that $E(R_B) = 2E(R_A)$.' Do you agree? Demonstrate your answer with $\beta_A = 1$, $\beta_B = 2$, $E(R_m) = 10\%$ and $r = 5\%$.

(b) How would you change your answer to (a) if $r = 0$?

14.11   Suppose that the CAPM holds and $\beta_i = 0.9$, $E(R_i) = 10\%$ and $E(R_m) = 10.5\%$. Calculate the risk-free interest rate (r).

14.12   Suppose you have the following data for Stock A and the market portfolio:

Year	Rate of return on Stock A	Rate of return on the market
1	5%	8%
2	3	-2
3	20	30

(a) Calculate β_A.
(b) Calculate σ_A^2.
(c) Calculate the systematic and nonsystematic risk component. Discuss these rules in proportional terms.

14.13 Suppose you have the following figures:

Year	Stock A return	Market portfolio return
1	10%	5%
2	5	2.5
3	20	10

(a) Calculate the unsystematic risk component.
(b) Calculate the correlation between R_A and R_m.
(c) Prove that when the unsystematic risk is zero and the beta is positive, then the correlation coefficient is $+1$.

SELECTED REFERENCES

Bansal, Ravi, David A. Hsieh, and S. Viswanathan. 'A new approach to international arbitrage pricing'. *Journal of Finance*, 48, December 1993, pp. 1719–47.

Berry, Michael A., Edwin Burmeister, and Marjorie B. McElroy. 'Sorting out risks using known APT factors'. *Financial Analysts Journal*, March–April 1988, pp. 29–42.

Grundy, Kevin, and Burton Malkiel. 'Reports of beta's death have been greatly exaggerated'. *Journal of Portfolio Management*, Spring 1996, pp. 36–45.

Lintner, John. 'Security prices and maximal gains from diversification'. *Journal of Finance*, December 1965, pp. 587–615.

Merton, Robert. 'An intertemporal capital asset pricing model'. *Economica*, 41, September 1973, pp. 867–80.

Roll, R. 'A critique of the asset pricing theory's tests, Part I: On past and potential testability of the theory'. *Journal of Financial Economics*, 4, March 1977, pp. 129–76.

Ross, S.A. 'The arbitrage theory of capital pricing'. *Journal of Economic Theory*, December 1976, pp. 341–60.

Sharpe, William F. 'A simplied model for portfolio analysis'. *Management Science*, January 1963, pp. 277–93.

Sharpe, William F. 'Capital asset prices: a theory of market equilibrium'. *Journal of Finance*, September 1964, pp. 425–42.

Shleifer, Andrei, and Robert W. Vishry. 'The Limits of Arbitrage'. *Journal of Finance*, March 1997, pp. 35–55.

SUPPLEMENTARY REFERENCES

Beliossi, G. 'Take the long and short route'. *Risk*, November 2000, Vol. 13, No. 11.

Lundin, M., and Satchell, S. 'The long and the short of it'. *Risk*, August 2000, Vol. 13, No. 8.

Miller, Edward M. 'Why the low returns to beta and other forms of risk?' *The Journal of Portfolio Management*, Winter, 2001.

Chapter 16

EFFICIENT MARKETS: THEORY AND EVIDENCE

Learning objectives

After studying this chapter you should be able to:

1 Define an efficient market.
2 Identify the types of information related to each form of the efficient market hypothesis.
3 Compare the investment strategies in efficient markets with investment strategies in inefficient markets.
4 Describe the findings of researchers who tested each form of the efficient market theory.
5 Define anomaly, and identify the common types of anomalies.

INVESTMENT IN THE NEWS

The Efficient Market

What is Efficient Market Theory?
Evidence to support the Efficient Market Theory
Ways to beat market averages
Why people try to beat the market

What is the Efficient Market Theory?

Assumptions

- The market is full of intelligent investors
- Information useful for determining prices is available to everyone nearly simultaneously

Under these conditions it is very difficult to beat the market averages

Another way to look at it,

Everyone thinks they can beat the market averages.

But by definition, not everyone can beat the market averages
- Half do better
- Half do worse

▶

Evidence to support the Efficient Market Theory

There are about 100,000 full-time investment professionals who follow perhaps 3,000 stocks

Since each follows about 30 stocks, there are 1,000 professionals following each stock.

A fund that blindly invests in an index that matches the Standard & Poors 500 has outperformed about 75 percent of all actively managed stock mutual funds. The low fees charged by the index fund are a key factor in this superior performance

Ways to beat market averages

Dumb luck:

Forbes dartboard portfolio roundly beats market averages and most professionals

By accepting more risk:

Peter Lynch has a great record of beating the averages. But in the 1987 crash, when most stock funds lost 16 percent of their value, Lynch's Magellan fund lost 32 percent of its value

Why people try to beat the market?

Because of compounding, beating the market by a little over time can dramatically increase your wealth

It's fun!

Source: Numen Lumen website, www.numen-lumen.com, 23 August 1999; body text © 1997 by David Luhman.

This chapter's *Investment in the news* claims that if the market is efficient (and there is evidence that it is efficient), then the 100,000 full-time professionals are probably wasting time and money: the index fund is doing better than most of the managed funds. The only way to beat the average, apart from luck, is to take more risk.

In studying the impact of information on stock prices, we refer to the efficient market theory (EMT).[1] Basically, the theory claims that stock prices reflect all available information that is relevant for the stock, and that no investor can earn an abnormal return (or an excess return after adjusting for risk) by trying to find buying or selling opportunities in the market. For example, if an investor could analyze the historical prices of IBM stock and develop a buy–sell rule that will yield a positive, risk-adjusted return, this would contradict the EMT. This chapter explores the various ways to interpret the EMT.

In general, academics support the EMT, whereas practitioners do not. Indeed, practitioners on Wall Street use investment strategies that rely on market *inefficiency*. Recently, however, some academics who preached for decades in support of the EMT have found empirical evidence favouring market inefficiency.[2] Chapter 18 describes some widely used valuation methods that assume market inefficiency, at least to a certain degree.

---

[1] The EMT is also widely referred to as the *efficient market hypothesis* (EMH).

[2] See Eugene F. Fama and Kenneth R. French, 'The cross-section of expected stock returns', *Journal of Finance*, 47, June 1992, pp. 427–66.

Your own perception of the EMT will govern, in large part, the particular investment philosophy you adopt. The objective of this book is not to persuade you to adopt one school of thought over another but rather to give you the analytical tools needed to reach your own conclusions. This chapter examines the investment implications and appropriate investment strategies to use if markets are efficient or, alternatively, inefficient. It also surveys the available empirical evidence regarding market efficiency.

16.1   EFFICIENT MARKET DEFINED

How efficiently do markets process information? An investigation of the effect of information on security prices must begin with a definition of an efficient market. A well-functioning financial market in which prices reflect all relevant information is said to be an efficient market. Another way to state this is that the EMT claims that security prices reflect all relevant information; that is, the current market price of a security incorporates all relevant information. If a financial market is efficient, then the best estimate of the true worth of a security is given by its current market price.

A large number of analysts are assessing the true value of stocks. The analysts try to find stocks whose market prices are substantially different from their true values. If the analysts find such 'mispriced' securities, they buy or sell them, driving the market price instantaneously towards the true value of the security. Hence, in an efficient market competition in the stock market pushes prices to their 'true' value. Thus, stock prices change every day, every hour, even every second as new information flows into the marketplace.

Is the market efficient? Are there 'bargains' in the market? Actually, it is almost impossible to test purely whether the market is efficient, which explains why there are no clear winners in the market efficiency dispute. Most of the tests of market efficiency are joint tests – that is, one is testing jointly whether the model measuring risk-adjusted returns is appropriate and whether markets are efficient. Thus, one of the reasons for the market efficiency dispute is that tests of market efficiency are *joint tests* of the assumed model *and* of market efficiency.

To illustrate, suppose that an analyst claims he observes the historical price movement of IBM stock, and based on these historical figures, he reaches the conclusion that IBM stock is a bargain (that is, it is underpriced). Suppose he buys IBM stock, and his annual realized rate of return on the stock is 12%. Can we then conclude that the market is inefficient? Did the analyst succeed in exploiting the information on historical prices to make an extraordinary return? To reach such a conclusion, we first need to find out the risk involved with the investment in IBM stock and figure out whether there is an abnormal return adjusted for this risk. For example, suppose that we use the CAPM (see Chapter 14) and IBM's beta to estimate the expected rate of return on IBM to be 11%. In such a case, the analyst has an *extraordinary profit* of 1%. This extraordinary profit is also called an abnormal rate of return. It seems that based on this result, we might claim that the market is inefficient. However, what if the CAPM is an incorrect model, and therefore the 11% estimate of the required expected return was wrong? Then we may come to the wrong conclusion regarding market efficiency, because we employed an incorrect model to measure the 'normal' rate of return.

Thus, in testing for market efficiency, first we should estimate what should be the normal rate of return on an asset, which is also called the risk-adjusted rate of return. For that purpose, we need a model asserting what the risk is and what the corresponding risk premium should be. Then we compare the realized return by the analyst's investment policy to this normal return. If the realized return is significantly higher than the normal return, researchers generally assert that the market is inefficient, because the analyst made abnormal or excess returns.

However, by this procedure, we see that we have a joint hypothesis and therefore should conduct a joint test of the model and of market efficiency. To illustrate, suppose that the CAPM is wrong, and the variance of the rate of return, rather than beta, is the correct measure of risk. We may conclude that with this risk measure, the required rate of return is 12% in the IBM example. Now the analyst does not make any profit after adjusting for risk. Thus, testing market efficiency is based on a normal return as a benchmark. Because this normal return is deduced from some model, empirical tests are joint tests of the model and of market efficiency. Therefore, we cannot claim unequivocally that the market is efficient, even if empirical tests seem to reveal market efficiency (that is, that there are no abnormal returns).

16.2   WHAT CONSTITUTES THE APPROPRIATE INFORMATION SET?

A great deal of information is available in the stock market: historical stock prices, earnings and dividends, macro-economic data, private information known only to insiders, and other information that seems irrelevant for stock valuation (for example, the age and eye colour of a firm's chief executive officer). At one extreme, it might be argued that all information is useful in earning an abnormal return. An investor can use all available information and make an extraordinary profit. In other words, it pays to analyze available information in making a security selection.

At the other extreme, it might be argued that the observed prices reflect all information that exists. That is, everything that can be known about a security is already incorporated in its price. For example, even the poor health of an important member of upper management would be reflected in the stock price. From this point of view, any data collection or economic analysis is a waste of time.

Clearly, these two extremes are irrational and probably irrelevant in price determination. However, somewhere between these two extremes lies a reasonable set of the information employed in determining stock prices. Along the journey across the continuum from 'no information' to 'all information' lie three milestones or information sets: historical, public and private information. The efficient market theory, which describes the impact of information on the market prices of securities, can be analyzed in terms of these specific information sets and their impact on price determination. These three sets of information correspond to weak, semistrong and strong EMT. Let us elaborate.

16.2.1 Weak form of the EMT

The first form of the efficient market theory is the weak form of the EMT.[3] According to the weak form of the EMT, today's stock prices reflect all information about the historical prices of the stock, so historical prices are not useful for investment decisions.

---

[3] See Roberts (1967), as quoted in Burton Malkiel, 'Efficient market hypothesis', in John Eatwell, Murray Milgate and Peter Newman (eds), *The New Palgrave: Finance* (New York: Macmillan Press, 1989). In 1991 Fama suggested broadening this category to include other variables used in determining return predictability.

Thus, trading technique based on historical prices, well known as technical analysis (see Chapter 18), is not useful according to the weak form efficiency. However, other information – for example, historical earnings – may be useful in earning an abnormal profit. If this is true, then an investor could not use historical stock price information to find mispriced stocks and thus profit from buying or selling these stocks. The stock prices already would have adjusted for this information. Technical analysts try to use historical price information to locate mispriced stocks. Therefore, under the weak form of the EMT, we would not expect them to find opportunities that generate abnormal returns using these techniques. Investors would just earn the normal profit for the risk taken.

If the weak form of the EMT holds, and thus prices are independent of the pattern of historical stock prices, we say that price *changes* will appear to follow a random walk.[4] A random walk is a statistical concept that predicts that the next outcome in a series does not depend on its prior outcomes. A simple way that illustrates the random walk notion is with a flipping of a coin. For example, although the first three tosses may be heads, these outcomes do not affect the probability of head or tail in the next toss. The result in the next toss has no memory; it does not depend on previous results.

Because risky securities offer positive expected returns, we would anticipate stock prices to rise over time. Despite this trend, price changes may still follow a random walk. For example, suppose we have a security presently trading at $100. We know that in each period, the price will rise by 12% with a 75% probability, or fall by 10% with a 25% probability. In this case, on average, three out of four times (75%) the return will be 12%, whereas only one out of four times (25%) the return will be −10%. The expected return in this case is $E(R)$:

$$E(R) = 0.75(12\%) + 0.25(-10\%) = 6.5\%$$

Although the expected return is 6.5%, the particular outcome observed in a given year is random. Hence, even in this case, we say that the security follows a random walk.

Going back to the coin-tossing example, suppose you flip a biased coin with a probability of heads of $^3/_4$ and a probability of tails of $^1/_4$.[5] Do the results of the first three tosses affect the result of the next toss? Absolutely not. This process has no memory, and the probabilities are still $^3/_4$ for heads and $^1/_4$ for tails.

16.2.2 Semistrong form of the EMT

The second form of the efficient market theory is the semistrong form of the EMT. According to the semistrong form of the EMT, prices reflect all relevant publicly available information. In addition to historical stock prices, publicly available information includes financial statements, notes to the financial statements, and supplementary information required by accounting regulations. Publicly available information also includes other external financial and regulatory filings such as property taxes paid, as well as market-related data such as the level of interest rates and the stock's beta.

According to the semistrong form of the EMT, an investor could not earn abnormal returns on trading strategies built on publicly available information. Thus, if the market

---

[4] Technically, stocks, on average, will move up by the stock's expected return. Hence, the random walk concept is applied after adjusting for the expected return.

[5] A biased coin is typically heavier on one side. Hence, tossing it results in outcomes different from 50–50.

is semistrong efficient, a diligent study of financial statements is of no economic value. The idea behind this view is that, once this information becomes public, all investors react instantaneously and push the price to reflect all public information. For example, hearing on CNN that Enron manipulated its reported earnings is too late, because the stock price will already have dropped and so you cannot then sell the stock at the relatively high price that prevailed before the news became public. Thus, when you read the *Wall Street Journal* with your morning coffee and see some public information, such as a new drug discovery or a financial crisis in Asia, it is too late for you to earn an abnormal profit. The price at which you can buy or sell the stock already reflects this information.

In contrast to proponents of the semistrong form of the EMT, there are investors who think they can profit from a careful study of publicly available data – particularly accounting data. These investors practice fundamental analysis and use the information in financial statements and other public sources to identify mispriced stock. The two factors commonly employed to identify underpriced stock in a fundamental analysis are the price/earnings (P/E) ratio and the market-to-book-value (M/B) ratio, where M is the market value (stock price) and B is the book value per share.

16.2.3 Strong form of the EMT

The third form of the efficient market theory is the strong form of the EMT. The strong form states that current prices already reflect all publicly and privately available information. Thus, the strong form includes all relevant historical price information and all relevant publicly available information, as well as information known only to a select few such as management, the board of directors and private bankers. For example, suppose a member of the board of directors of Intel knows that the firm has decided to take over another firm. The board member's spouse then buys shares of Intel stock before the takeover becomes public information. This would be considered trading on inside information, and is illegal. If the strong EMT form were true, then insiders would not profit from trading on their information. There is much evidence that the market is not strong-form efficient, because there is money to be gained from trading on inside information (although such trading is illegal). Insiders who know about future takeovers or acquisitions can earn large profits. However, it is illegal to trade on private information, and many inside traders have received prison sentences for doing so.

Because semistrong form information is a subset of strong form information, and weak form information is a subset of semistrong information, it is clear that if the market is weak form inefficient, it is also semistrong and strong form inefficient; if it is semistrong form inefficient it is also strong form inefficient. Exhibit 16.1 summarizes the discussion thus far from the viewpoint of an analyst. If an analyst believed that the weak form of the EMT was not true, then the analyst should be able to earn abnormal returns based on historical price data, as well as public and private data. If an analyst believed that the market was weak form inefficient, but not the semistrong form of the EMT, then the analyst should be able to earn excess returns based on public and private data but not based on historical prices. If an analyst believed that the semistrong form, but not the strong form, of the EMT was true, then the analyst should be able to earn excess returns only based on private information (which is illegal to trade upon). Finally, if an analyst believed that the strong form of the EMT was true, then no excess returns would be possible, no matter what information the analyst could access. Clearly, investment strategy is directly linked to the analyst's view of the EMT.

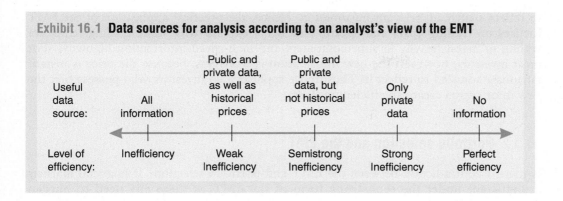

Exhibit 16.1 **Data sources for analysis according to an analyst's view of the EMT**

Useful data source:	All information	Public and private data, as well as historical prices	Public and private data, but not historical prices	Only private data	No information
Level of efficiency:	Inefficiency	Weak Inefficiency	Semistrong Inefficiency	Strong Inefficiency	Perfect efficiency

16.3 INVESTMENT STRATEGY IN AN EFFICIENT MARKET

It seems reasonable that markets do process historical and public data with relative efficiency, and this is the view of many academic investment theorists as well as practitioners who sell index funds which are unmanaged funds. Thus, this section examines how to structure a successful investment strategy in the semistrong form of the EMT. It first examines how resources are allocated in this market. Next, it examines portfolio selection and the usefulness of employing the expected risk–return trade-off when markets are efficient. It also distinguishes between passive and active portfolio management strategies.

16.3.1 Resource allocation and the EMT

If relatively more money is allocated to firms that have profitable capital budgeting projects and relatively less money is allocated to firms with poor projects, we say that money is allocated in the market in an effective manner. In efficient markets, resources are allocated to the various firms in an effective manner, because those firms with good prospects will be able to raise additional capital in the primary market on relatively good terms. That is, in constructing their portfolios, investors will allocate more money to those firms they deem a relatively good investment. For example, suppose IBM has a good new computer or Pfizer develops a new drug (such as Viagra). When this information becomes public, investors will allocate more of their money to IBM or Pfizer, and its stock price will instantaneously go up.

Thus, a firm with good projects will have a higher stock price and can issue stocks on better terms in the market. In contrast, a firm with poor projects (one that is expected to go bankrupt) would be unable to raise money through either a stock issue or a bond issue. Thus, the information on the firm's projects is reflected in the stock prices; the rosier the estimated future is, the higher the stock price.

This observation regarding the link between resource allocation and the EMT illustrates a seeming paradox. In order for markets to be efficient, new firm information should affect the stock price. Hence, some investors have to be paying attention to firm information. However, the EMT suggests there is no benefit to monitoring firm information. This paradox is solved once we understand that in practice, those investors with the least costly access to information capitalize on minor mispricing, which drives prices to reflect swiftly all relevant information. Hence, the practical application of the EMT focuses on trading costs and speed. This helps explain why some trading firms are willing to invest heavily in supercomputers and high-speed information highways. For most investors, however, the new information is worthless, because the price is instantaneously adjusted to reflect it. Thus, those sophisticated investors who possess first the new information create an efficient market.

16.3.2 Portfolio selection and the EMT

Is there a contradiction between the EMT and portfolio selection? If financial markets are efficient under the semistrong form of the EMT, is there any need to burden ourselves with portfolio diversification? Under the semistrong form of the EMT, the analysis conducted by technicians (who do technical analysis) and fundamentalists (who do fundamental analysis) will not generate excess returns. There are no 'bargains' in the market, and stock selection techniques are worthless. What is left for portfolio managers is portfolio diversification, which pays off even in efficient markets.

To demonstrate this idea, suppose that two stocks, 1 and 2, each trade for $10. You flip two coins, one corresponding to each stock. If a head comes up, the stock price increases to $13; if a tail appears, the stock price falls to $9. Of course, these stock price changes conform to semistrong-form market efficiency, because the price changes are dependent on a random coin toss and do not depend on historical or public information. If you do not diversify between the two stocks, the future mean and variance of each stock, for your $10 investment, are as follows:

$$\text{Mean: } (^{1}\!/_{2} \times \$13) + (^{1}\!/_{2} \times \$9) = \$11$$

$$\text{Variance: } \sigma^2 = {}^{1}\!/_{2} (13 - 11)^2 + {}^{1}\!/_{2} (9 - 11)^2 = 4$$

$$\sigma = \$2$$

Can you gain from diversification in such a market that obeys the EMT? The answer is yes. To see why, assume you invest $5 in Stock 1 and $5 in Stock 2. Because the two stocks are independent (you toss two coins, separately, one for each stock), you get the following returns:

Stock 1		Stock 2		Portfolio
$^{1}\!/_{2} \times \$13$	+	$^{1}\!/_{2} \times \$13 =$		$13 (with a probability of $^{1}\!/_{4}$)
$^{1}\!/_{2} \times \$13$	+	$^{1}\!/_{2} \times \$9 =$		$11 (with a probability of $^{1}\!/_{4}$)
$^{1}\!/_{2} \times \$9$	+	$^{1}\!/_{2} \times \$13 =$		$11 (with a probability of $^{1}\!/_{4}$)
$^{1}\!/_{2} \times \$9$	+	$^{1}\!/_{2} \times \$9 =$		$9 (with a probability of $^{1}\!/_{4}$)

where $^{1}\!/_{2}$ represents the proportion of investment in each stock ($5/$10 = $^{1}\!/_{2}$). The portfolio mean return is

$$(^{1}\!/_{4} \times 13) + (^{1}\!/_{4} \times 11) + (^{1}\!/_{4} \times 11) + (^{1}\!/_{4} \times 9) = \$11$$

which is exactly the same as investing in just Stock 1 or Stock 2 alone. Note, however, that the variance of the portfolio is lower:

$$\sigma^2 = {}^{1}\!/_{4} (13 - 11)^2 + {}^{1}\!/_{4} (11 - 11)^2 + {}^{1}\!/_{4} (11 - 11)^2 + {}^{1}\!/_{4} (9 - 11)^2 = 2$$

$$\sigma \cong \$1.41$$

Thus, you reduce the risk by diversifying.

Some believe that the semistrong form of the EMT implies that all stocks are correctly priced, and therefore you can select stocks at random – for example, by throwing a dart at a list of stocks obtained from the financial pages. This is not correct. Although you cannot predict which stock will go up and which will go down in the future, by diversification you can reduce your risk. If you ignore this diversification, you are exposing yourself to higher risk with no compensation in the form of a higher expected return. Note that in the previous example, your variance decreased through diversification, but your expected return remained the same, at $11.

The previous example can be extended to many assets with positive and negative correlations. For example, suppose you have a stock with a high variance but a low beta (for example, $\beta_i = 0.5$). According to the CAPM, the mean rate of return on the stock will be relatively low, because this stock has a low correlation with other securities, and hence portfolio risk is reduced. If you do not diversify and thus hold only one stock (or only a few stocks), you pay a relatively high price for the stock; you expose yourself to high risk (variance) and do not enjoy the benefits of the risk reduction possibilities that are due to the negative correlation, i.e. the low beta is irrelevant in the lack of diversification.

In summary, if the semistrong form of the EMT holds, technical and fundamental analysis are economically worthless. However, portfolio analysis remains important; in fact, more effort should be allocated to portfolio analysis. If the market is inefficient, then both security analysis (to find 'bargains' in the market) and portfolio analysis (to reduce risk) are economically important.

16.3.3 **Passive versus active portfolio management**

Portfolio managers face two main tasks:

1 *How to diversify among the various assets.* Finding the desired investment proportions and adhering to them or changing them as the S&P index changes weights, i.e. by computer rather than by human judgement, is called passive investment strategy.
2 *When to change the investment proportions in the various assets.* Managers try to predict whether the stock market or the bond market will be stronger, say, next month, and actively change the investment proportions according to their predictions. Such a management strategy is called active investment strategy. Managers may increase the proportion of stocks from 40% to 60% today, and reverse this proportion next month, reducing the stock proportion to 40% or even less.

If the market is efficient, only the passive management strategy is relevant, because according to the semistrong form of the EMT, publicly available information (for example, the budget deficit, the amount of money in the market, reported earnings by firms or unemployment) is not useful in predicting whether stocks or bonds will be better in the future. In such a case, portfolio managers do not have 'timing ability', or the ability to predict when is the best time to move from heavy bond investment to more stock investment or vice versa. Nearly all investors know that when interest rates go down more than expected, the stock market typically rallies. However, can they predict what the interest rate will be next month? If you believe in the semistrong form of the EMT, you cannot predict the interest rate changes; hence you cannot benefit from active investment strategies. The best investment strategy is simply to find some investment proportions and adopt a passive investment strategy; a portfolio manager should not try to outsmart the market.

Funds known as index funds do not engage in active rebalancing strategies. For example, the Vanguard Index 500 Portfolio holds stocks in the same proportions as the Standard & Poor's 500 stock price index. Thus, if you buy this fund, you really buy the index, and the manager does not make any attempt to outperform the S&P 500 index. Because index funds do not have a large turnover and do not need to spend money on economic analyses, they incur expenses of about 0.2%; for managed funds (funds that invest not just in indexes but in stocks, bonds, options, futures, currencies, etc., thus offering the investor the advantage of professional management), these fees are much larger (usually around 1.3%).

The *Investment in the news* article asserts that index funds outperform 75% of the mutual funds, indicating that active management on average is useless and even reduces returns.

16.4 INVESTMENT STRATEGY IN AN INEFFICIENT MARKET

In an inefficient market, the appropriate investment strategy is different than when the market is efficient. The particular strategy to pursue depends on the level of efficiency (or inefficiency). Investors who believe in the weak form of the EMT but not the semistrong form might locate mispriced securities using fundamental analysis. Hence, the investors who are the best at analyzing the data will earn an abnormal return.

Similarly, investors who do not believe in the weak form of the EMT would even benefit from some technical trading rules based on past historical prices, as well as fundamental analysis. Finally, investors who believe in the strong form of the EMT believe they cannot benefit even if they are insiders. Those insiders who do not believe in the strong form of the EMT can earn abnormal profits. However, they have to consider the risk–return profile, where they risk being sent to prison!

16.5 EMPIRICAL EVIDENCE RELATED TO THE EMT

Does actual price behaviour support the EMT? The existing evidence is vast; this text will survey just a few studies to answer this question.

However, before we look at the empirical tests of the various forms of market efficiency, it is worth noting another set of classifications that has been suggested by Fama.[6] His classifications are derived from the empirical tests conducted to figure out whether the market is efficient. The first category includes *tests for return predictability*, which includes historical prices and other variables such as dividends, interest rates, firm size, and so on. If one can use these variables to predict stock price or to make an abnormal return, we say that the market is inefficient. The second category includes event studies, which test whether an abnormal rate of return exists because of an announcement of an event such as an increase in dividends, or a merger. Once again, if one can make an abnormal return using this information, the market is inefficient. The third category includes *tests for private information*, which are similar to the tests for insider information discussed earlier.

---

[6] See Eugene F. Fama, 'Efficient capital markets: 2', *Journal of Finance*, 46, December 1991, pp. 1575–617.

This chapter will adhere to the original classifications of market efficiency. Nevertheless, keep in mind that these classifications are arbitrary and can be changed without changing the empirical tests for market efficiency. The names change, but not the content of the tests.

The objective of this section is to assess how efficient the market actually is in practice. To organize our investigation, we categorize the evidence according to how it is related to the three forms of the EMT (weak, semistrong and strong).

16.5.1 Evidence related to the weak form of the EMT

A large number of empirical studies have tested the weak form of the EMT; some are summarized in Exhibit 16.2. In general, the early research provides strong evidence in favour of markets' being weak-form efficient. More recent evidence has uncovered many anomalies, which are events that are not anticipated and that offer investors a chance to earn abnormal profits. (Researchers were so convinced that the EMT was true that they felt any contrary evidence must be an anomaly; some of these findings were referred to as *enigmas*.)

Two primary techniques are used to test the validity of the weak-form proposition: analysis of technical trading rules for abnormal rates of return, and statistical tests on historical data to locate significant patterns.

■ Analysis of technical trading rules for abnormal rates of return

To measure whether a given strategy or a technical rule is beneficial, we need first to define more precisely abnormal return. Abnormal rates of return, as defined earlier, are the rates of return that are above what we would expect to earn given the level of risk taken.

To calculate abnormal returns, we must first determine normal returns. We can use the CAPM, the SIM or the APT (see Chapter 14) to find normal returns. Let us demonstrate with the CAPM. By the CAPM, the expected return on Asset i (a security or a portfolio) is

$$E(R_i) = r + [E(R_m) - r]\beta_i \tag{16.1}$$

where r is the risk-free interest rate, $E(R_m)$ is the expected rate of return on the market portfolio, and β_i is the beta coefficient (defined as $\dfrac{\mathrm{Cov}(R_i, R_m)}{\sigma_m^2}$). Thus, the normal expected rate of return is given by $E(R_i)$. The abnormal rate of return (AR_i) is defined as

$$\mathrm{AR}_i = R_i - E(R_i) = R_i - \{r + [E(R_m) - r]\beta_i\} \tag{16.2}$$

or, in words,

Abnormal rate of return = Actual rate of return − Normal rate of return

where R_i is the realized or actual return on the ith stock. Because $E(R_m)$ and β_i are unknown parameters, they are usually estimated by using historical data. Hence, the normal return is estimated first, and then the abnormal return is estimated. This technique is commonly employed in the event studies explained next.

Many research studies of market efficiency examine the behaviour of these abnormal rates of return over time and in particular, the cumulative effect. Researchers measure this using the cumulative abnormal rate of return (CAR_i), the sum of all abnormal rates

Exhibit 16.2 Summary of evidence related to the weak form of the efficient market theory

Authors	Year	Assets studied	Weak form efficient?	Comments
Bachelier	1900	French securities	Yes	Tried to test whether the French government securities options and futures market was efficient
Roberts	1959	US stocks	Yes	Found that stock prices resemble random patterns
Osborne	1959	US stocks	Yes	Found that stock prices are similar to random movement of physical particles in water (Brownian motion)
Granger, Morgenstern	1963	US stocks	Yes	Employed spectral analysis (a powerful statistical tool that identifies patterns), but still found no significant patterns
Fama	1965	US stocks	Yes	Examined serial correlations and other statistical tools to check for patterns, and found no significant patterns
Fama, Blume	1966	US stocks	Yes	Examined technical trading rules and found no abnormal profits
Solnik	1973	Stocks in 9 countries	Yes	Used serial correlations and found no profitable investment strategies
Merton	1980	US stocks	No	Found that changes in variance are somewhat predicable from past data
French	1980	US stocks	No	Identified a weekend effect
Keim	1983	US stocks	No	Identified a January effect
Gultekin, Gultekin	1983	International markets	No	Identified seasonal patterns
Jaffe, Westerfield	1984	International markets	No	Identified seasonal patterns
Lehmann	1990	US stocks	No	Identified reversal effects
Serletis, Sondergard	1995	Canadian stocks	Yes	Using tests of the 1980s, it was found that efficiency holds for Canadian stocks
Masih, Masih	1996	Daily spot exchange rates	No	Tested spot rates and found that they suggest violation of market efficiency
Yu	1996	East Asian exchanges	No	Found that exchange rates contain predictive power about stock movements in Hong Kong
McQueen, Thorley	1997	Gold	No	Found that prior returns on an equally weighted portfolio of gold stocks predict gold returns

of return for the whole investment period, which is calculated for a particular trading strategy as follows:

$$CAR_i = \sum_{t=1}^{m} AR_{i,t} \qquad (16.3)$$

where m is the number of periods (which are usually days). If the cumulative abnormal rates of return are significantly positive, then we conclude that abnormal returns are possible following some strategy, and the EMT is wrong. An alternative conclusion would be that the risk of the portfolio was not appropriately estimated by its beta. Therefore, as discussed before, we face a joint hypothesis regarding EMT and the model used to measure the normal rate of return.

The CAR method is commonly employed in event studies. An *event study* is a technique to measure the impact of a particular event on a firm's stock price. It measures the response of the stock price to the event – for example, an announcement of an increase in cash dividends. Suppose that a firm announces an increase in cash dividends, and the stock price on the same day goes up by 2%. Is this an abnormal profit? The answer is not clear, because many other economic phenomena that may affect the stock price may occur on the same day – an announcement of a decrease in the interest rate, a new peace treaty, and so on. The aim of event study methodology is to measure the increase in price that is due solely to the event itself. Therefore, we measure the average abnormal return of many firms which increased their dividends on various dates, hence the name *event study*: in our example we test the event of an increase in dividends.

Because β_i is unknown, we cannot directly employ Equation 16.2 to measure AR_i. Therefore, in an event study, we commonly employ the single index model when the factor is some stock index (for example, the S&P 500 index). The event date is denoted by t. Then the abnormal rate of return on day t (see Equation 16.2) is estimated by e_t, given by the equation

$$R_t = a + bR_{m,t} + e_t$$

Namely, the abnormal return is estimated by e_t, given by

$$e_t = R_t - a - bR_{m,t}$$

where R_t and $R_{m,t}$ are the rates of return on the announcement date of the firm's stock and on the market portfolio (for example, the S&P 500 index), respectively, and a and b are the intercept and the slope, respectively, of the regression line of R_t regressed against $R_{m,t}$. In order not to contaminate the estimates of a and b by the event itself, generally some period before the announcement date is taken – for example, 60 months (starting 65 months before the announcement date) – and a regression of R_t on $R_{m,t}$ is conducted in this period to estimate a and b. Also, because there may be leaks of information before the event and a continuing effect after the event, it is common to measure the abnormal return corresponding to a few days surrounding the event date as well.

As mentioned above, to make sure that e_t measures the abnormal rate of return and not another economic factor occurring on the same date, many firms that increase the cash dividends from different dates in the past are included in the study. Thus, by having various periods, the effects of other economic factors tend to cancel each other. Thus, $\bar{e}_t$ which is the average of e_t across many firms, is the estimate of the abnormal return, AR_i across all firms on the various announcement dates (t). Having the average abnormal return ($\bar{e}_t$) of all the firms included in the study on the announcement date (which differs across firms but is still denoted by t) allows us to employ Equation 16.3 to calculate the average cumulative abnormal rate of return.

If the average abnormal return ($\bar{e}_t$) or the average cumulative abnormal rate of return is significantly different from zero, we say that the announcement itself provides an abnormal return, and the market is semistrong inefficient. If the average abnormal return is significant before the announcement date as well, we conclude that information was leaked before the announcement date. Finally, if the average abnormal return is significant after the event, we conclude that investors can earn an abnormal rate of return after the information is in the public domain for a few days, which strongly contradicts the market semistrong efficiency. However, do not forget that the event study has a joint test, and the commonly strong conclusion may be misleading, because the model employed to measure the normal return may be wrong!

The empirical evidence generally rejects the notion that abnormal returns are generated from simple trading rules which are based on historical prices. However, there are many trading rules, some of which are privately held; hence, not all rules have been tested and we cannot definitely assert that the market is weak form efficient.

▪ Statistical tests of historical data for significant patterns

A second way to test the validity of the weak form of the EMT is to conduct statistical tests on historical data to locate significant patterns. For example, autocorrelations or serial correlations can be examined to assess whether past returns had predictive power in determining future returns.[7] Alternatively, nonparametric tests can be employed to assess whether negative returns are followed by positive returns or vice versa.[8] Although some evidence suggests that weak patterns do exist, they are not strong enough to profit when transaction costs are taken into consideration.

Looking again at Exhibit 16.2, one pattern is clear. Early evidence appears to support the weak form of the EMT, but more recent evidence appears to reject it. Numerous patterns have been identified that suggest that markets do not even adhere to the weak form of the EMT.

16.5.2 Evidence related to the semistrong form of the EMT

When investigating whether the semistrong form of the EMT is true, researchers try to determine whether investors using fundamental analysis could earn abnormal returns. If these investors cannot earn abnormal returns consistently, then the semistrong form is true. Exhibit 16.3 lists some studies of the semistrong form of the EMT and their conclusions.

The evidence related to the semistrong form of the EMT investigates information obtained through fundamental analysis. Fundamental analysis focuses on the analysis of a firm's specific information and its stock prices. The most common information analyzed is the reported earnings per share (EPS). Thus, fundamental analysis seeks to determine whether there is a link between basic information about a company (such as earnings per share) and its stock price.

The key to understanding the relationship between earnings per share and stock prices lies in what was expected by the market. That is, we should ask, how different are the earnings from what was expected? Rendleman, Jones and Latané used this measure to analyze the validity of the semistrong form of the EMT, examining the cumulative abnormal rates of return for 10 groups of stocks.[9] The stock groups were constructed by rankings based on the following equation:

$$\text{SUE} = \frac{\text{EPS} - E(\text{EPS})}{\text{SEE}} \tag{16.4}$$

---

[7] Autocorrelations or serial correlations look at how correlated past changes are with current changes. If past changes are highly correlated (positive or negative), they can be used to predict future changes.

[8] Nonparametric tests are statistical techniques that seek to determine whether patterns exist in a given set of data.

[9] Richard J. Rendleman, Charles P. Jones and Henry A. Latané, 'Empirical anomalies based on unexpected earnings and the importance of risk adjustments', *Journal of Financial Economics*, 10, 1982, pp. 269–87.

PRACTICE BOX

Problem

Suppose you know that the expected daily rate of return of Morgan, Inc., common stock is 0.0453%. You also observe the following daily rates of return around Day 3. Assume that the firm announced an increase in dividends on Day 3.

Date	Rate of return
1	−0.5%
2	0.3
3	5.0
4	3.0
5	0.05

Calculate the cumulative abnormal rates of return.

Solution

Given that $E(R_i) = 0.0453\%$, construct the following table:

Date	Rate of return	$AR_{i,t}$	$CAR_{i,t}$
1	−0.5%	−0.5453 %	−0.5453%
2	0.3	0.2547[a]	−0.2906[b]
3	5.0	4.9547	4.6641
4	3.0	2.9547	7.6188
5	0.05	0.0047	7.6235

[a] $0.2547 = 0.3 − 0.0453$.
[b] $−0.2906 = −0.5453 + 0.2547$.

The main implication of these results is not that there was a 5% return on Day 3 when the dividends announcement is made. The main implication is that there was a 3.0% return the day after, which could have resulted in abnormal profits. Thus, investors can buy the stock at Day 3 and still make money at Day 4. This example illustrates the concept of abnormal returns. However, five observations of one security are not enough to draw any conclusions.

where SUE = standardized unexpected earnings, EPS = earnings per share, $E(EPS)$ = expected earnings per share, and SEE = the standard error of the estimate. The denominator helps adjust for some industries' having more or less volatility than other industries. For example, utility firms have a fairly predictable EPS, whereas software firms have a very unpredictable EPS. Thus, a 5% difference in the actual EPS from the expected EPS may be interpreted as dramatic by investors in a utility firm's stock but interpreted as insignificant by investors in software companies. The SEE would be greater for the software firm, reducing the SUE. After adjusting for this difference in earnings volatility, 10 groups of stocks were formed, where Group 1 represents firms with the lowest SUE, Group 2 represents firms with the next-to-lowest SUE, and so forth. Thus, Group 10 represents stocks with the highest SUE.

Exhibit 16.4 illustrates the results. Clearly, market prices react to unexpected earnings announcements as cumulative average excess returns move up or down due to the announcements. In contradiction to the EMT, however, the best (Group 10) and worst

Exhibit 16.3 Summary of evidence related to the semistrong form of the efficient market theory

Authors	Year	Assets studied	Semistrong form efficient?	Comments
Fama, Fisher, Jensen, Roll	1969	US stocks	Yes	Stock splits – no gains after announcements
Scholes	1972	US stocks	Yes	Large secondary offerings – price decline is permanent when insiders are selling
Jaffe	1974	US stocks	No	Insiders can profit from public information about insider trading
Ball	1978	US stocks	No	Earnings announcement reactions take considerable time
Watts	1978	US stocks	No	Reproduced work of Ball (1978) with better techniques and found same results
Dodd	1981	US stocks	Yes	No abnormal profits after merger announcement
Rendleman, Jones, Latané	1982	US stocks	No	Similar results to Ball (1978)
Roll	1984	Orange juice futures	Yes/No	Inefficient due to exchange limits; otherwise efficient
Seyhun	1986	US stocks	Yes	Insiders cannot profit from public information about insider trading
Fama, French	1992	US stocks	No	Investors can profit from information on the firm's size and the market-to-book-value ratio
Peterson	1995	US stocks	Yes	Abnormal returns associated with 'stock highlights' published by Value Line found consistent with EMT
Bernard, Seyhun	1997	US stocks	No	Using a stochastic dominance approach to test market efficiency following earnings announcements showed the market is inefficient
Blose, Shieh	1997	US stocks	No	Positive correlation found between Tobin's Q and stock price reaction to capital investment announcements, where Tobin's Q is defined as the ratio of the market value of the firm's assets to its replacement value

(Group 1) continue to move up and down, respectively, after the announcement. Thus, the information on the surprise in the past can be employed to make profits in the future. This is good evidence against the semistrong form of the EMT.

In response to this research, as well as other studies, the *Wall Street Journal* has now begun to publish 'Quarterly earnings surprises'. Investors may benefit from this information as Exhibit 16.4 reveals.

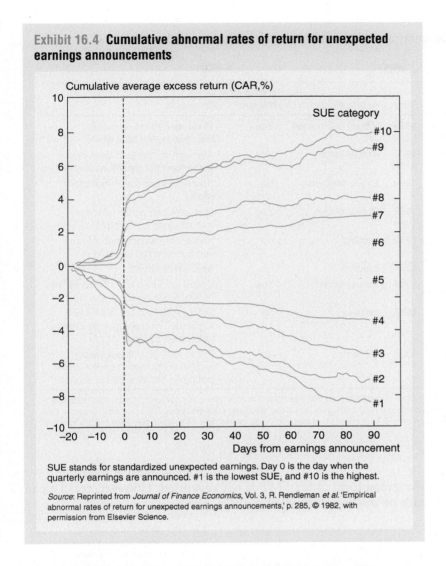

Exhibit 16.4 Cumulative abnormal rates of return for unexpected earnings announcements

SUE stands for standardized unexpected earnings. Day 0 is the day when the quarterly earnings are announced. #1 is the lowest SUE, and #10 is the highest.

Source: Reprinted from *Journal of Finance Economics*, Vol. 3, R. Rendleman *et al.* 'Empirical abnormal rates of return for unexpected earnings announcements,' p. 285, © 1982, with permission from Elsevier Science.

16.5.3 Evidence related to the strong form of the EMT

The evidence against the strong form of the EMT is irrefutable; some of this research is summarized in Exhibit 16.5. Several studies have found that insiders can profit significantly from the valuable information they possess. Exactly where you draw the line between private information and public information may influence your position on the strong form of the EMT. For example, Liu, Smith and Syed (1990) found significant price changes on stocks discussed in the 'Heard on the Street' column in the *Wall Street Journal*. When reporters find this information, is it private or public at that point? Clearly, after publication it is public information. However, reporters know this information before it is published, yet they are not insiders. Technically, however, it is inside information prior to publication.

If the strong form of the EMT is correct, then insiders should not be able to generate abnormal returns from their trading decisions. The evidence presented in this section is very convincing: insiders (but not mutual funds managers) can generate abnormal

Exhibit 16.5 Summary of evidence related to the strong form of the efficient market theory

Authors	Year	Assets studied	Strong form efficient?	Comments
Cowles	1933	Money managers[a]	Yes	Professionals do no better than the market as a whole
Friend, Brown, Herman, Vickers	1962	Mutual funds[a]	Yes	Average mutual fund does not outperform the market as a whole
Neiderhoffer, Osborn	1966	NYSE specialist	No	Specialists generate significant profits
Jensen	1968 1969	Mutual funds[a]	Yes	Risk-adjusted performance of mutual funds is no better
Scholes	1972	Insiders	No	Insiders have access to information not reflected in prices
Jaffe	1974	Insiders	No	Insiders can profit
Henriksson	1984	Mutual funds[a]	Yes	Before load fees but after expenses, mutual funds do about average
Seyhun	1986	Insiders	No	Before load fees but after other expenses, mutual funds do slightly better than average
Liu, Smith, Syed	1990	US stocks	No	Prices change with publication of articles in the 'Heard on the Street' column in the *Wall Street Journal*

[a] Many assumed that money and mutual fund managers were in possession of inside information. Hence, examining the performance of mutual fund managers was a test of strong-form efficiency. The evidence suggests that mutual fund managers are not in possession of material inside information (or at least they cannot profit from it if they have it).

profits, and hence the strong form of the EMT is not supported. However, recall again that it is illegal to trade on insider information.

16.6 MARKET ANOMALIES

The EMT has some widely known and well-documented violations. Recall that a market anomaly is any event that can be exploited to produce abnormal profits. Anomalies exist in any form of the EMT but in most cases relate to the semistrong form of the EMT.

Market anomalies imply market inefficiency. However, because all market efficiency tests are joint tests, it is possible that these anomalies are actually not anomalies but rather that we do not have a powerful model to explain them. This explanation is convincing, particularly in cases where anomalies persist for a long time. Why don't they disappear, as investors are well familiar with them? Exhibit 16.6 identifies four categories of anomalies: seasonal, event, firm and accounting anomalies.

Firm anomalies are anomalies that result from firm-specific characteristics. For example, small firms tend to outperform large ones on a risk-adjusted basis, an anomaly called the size effect. A similar anomaly is the neglected firm effect: the fewer analysts tracking a particular security, the larger the average return. This anomaly may be an instance of the size effect, because neglected firms tend to be small.

Exhibit 16.6 Summary of market anomalies

Anomaly	Description/implication
Firm anomalies	
Size	Returns on small firms tend to be higher, even on a risk-adjusted basis
Closed-end mutual funds	Returns on closed-end funds that trade at a discount tend to be higher
Neglect	Firms that are not followed by many analysts tend to yield higher returns
Institutional holdings	Firms that are owned by few institutions tend to have higher returns
Seasonal anomalies	
January	Security prices tend to be up in January, especially the first few days (as well as the last days of December)
Weekend	Securities tend to be up on Fridays and down on Mondays
Time of day	Securities tend to be up in the first 45 minutes and the last 15 minutes of the day
End of month	Last trading day of the month tends to be up
Seasonal	Firms with highly seasonal sales tend to be up during high sales periods
Holidays	Returns tend to be positive on the last trading day before a holiday
Event anomalies	
Analysts' recommendations	The more analysts recommending purchase of a stock, the more likely it will go down
Insider trading	The more insiders buying a stock, the more likely it is to go up
Listings	Security prices rise after it is announced that a firm will be listed on an exchange
Value Line rating changes	Security prices continue to rise after Value Line places a security in its #1 category
Accounting anomalies	
P/E ratio	Stocks with low P/E ratios tend to have higher returns
Earnings surprises	Stocks with larger-than-anticipated earnings announcements tend to continue to rise even after the announcement
Price/sales ratio	If the price-to-sales ratio is low, then the stock tends to outperform
Price/book ratio	If the price-to-book value is low, then the stock tends to outperform
Dividend yield	If the dividend yield is high, then the stock tends to outperform
Earnings momentum	Stocks of firms whose growth rate of earnings is rising tend to outperform

Fama and French analyze the market-to-book-value (M/B) ratio of stocks as a predictor of returns across securities.[10] The terms *book value* and *market value* relate to the book value and market value of the firm's equity. Fama and French classified all the

---

[10] Eugene F. Fama and Kenneth R. French, 'The cross section of expected returns', *Journal of Finance*, 47, 1992, pp. 427–65.

stocks included in their sample into 10 deciles, according to the M/B ratio. They found that the decile with the lowest M/B ratio had an average monthly rate of return of 1.65%, whereas the decile with the highest M/B ratio had a return of only 0.72% per month. Exhibit 16.7 shows their findings regarding the M/B anomaly.

A seasonal anomaly is an anomaly that depends solely on time. For example, the January anomaly (or January effect) is the tendency for stock prices to be abnormally up in January (and late December).

Exhibit 16.8 demonstrates the January effect for various assets for the periods 1926 to 1996 and 1987 to 1996. For the long period 1926 to 1996 (Exhibit 16.8(a)), the January effect is striking for small stocks, which had an average monthly rate of return of about 7% in January and less than 2% in most other months. For the S&P 500 index there is no January effect; a larger rate of return is recorded in July and August, and a similar rate of return is recorded in December. For the other assets categories (Treasury bills, long-term corporate bonds, long-term government bonds and intermediate-term government bonds), there is no January effect.

Exhibit 16.8(b) is the same as Exhibit 16.8(a) except that the averages of the rates of return are for only 10 years, 1987 to 1996. Although the rate of return on small stocks in January is higher than in any other month, the January effect was dramatically reduced. The January effect does not exist for the other assets. It is possible that investors, being more aware of the January effect in the recent period, bought the stocks earlier in the year (in December) in an attempt to gain in January. This possibility provides only a partial explanation for the reduction in the January effect in the last

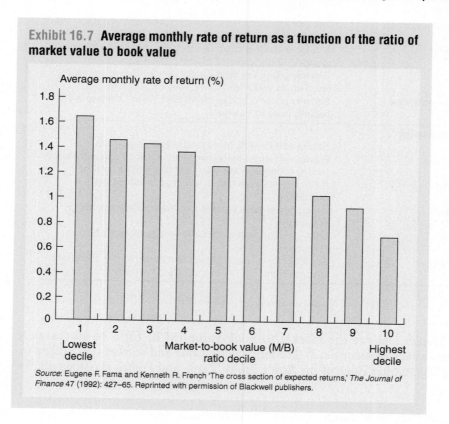

Exhibit 16.7 **Average monthly rate of return as a function of the ratio of market value to book value**

Source: Eugene F. Fama and Kenneth R. French 'The cross section of expected returns,' *The Journal of Finance* 47 (1992): 427–65. Reprinted with permission of Blackwell publishers.

Exhibit 16.8 The January anomaly

(a) Average monthly returns, 1926 to 1996

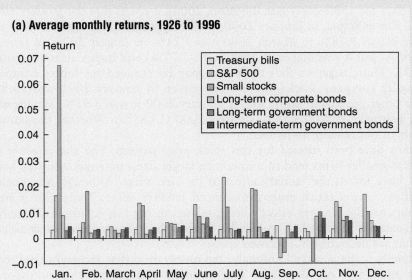

(b) Average monthly returns, 1987 to 1996

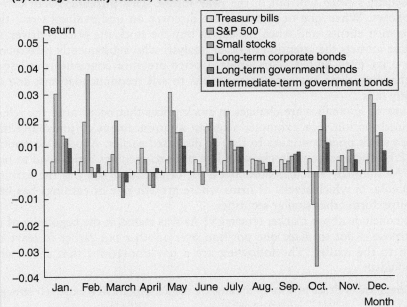

Source: Stocks, Bonds, Bills, and Inflation® Yearbook, © Ibbotson Associates, Inc. Based on copyrighted works by Ibbotson and Sinquefield. All rights reserved. Used with permission.

decade, because in February, May and December there is also a relatively high rate of return on the S&P index and on small stocks, which is not explained by this argument. Looking at the data for 1997–2001 (see Ibbotson, 2000), it seems that the January effect is still a puzzle. For example, in January 2000, the average return on the S&P 500 was −5.02%, while it was 9.78% in March 2000 and 6.21% in August 2000. In January 2001 it was 3.55%, but it was higher in April 2001 (7.77%) and higher relative to other months in 2001. Thus, it seems that the effect may be reduced for larger company stocks. For smaller company stocks, the average return in January 2001 was 13.8%, higher than for other months in 2001, but in January 2000 it was 5.95%, significantly lower than for February 2000 (23.58%) or June 2000 (13.68%). Whether the January effect disappears or not remains to be seen.

Several reasons have been offered for this stock price pattern. The size effect is the phenomenon that smaller firms tend to outperform larger firms on a risk-adjusted basis. Several studies have linked the January effect to the size effect. Although it is unclear why, smaller firms have a much more pronounced January effect. There also is some empirical support for the January effect's being related to tax-loss selling in December. By selling in December stocks that have fallen during the year, an investor is able to realize losses that are deductible for income taxes.

Another anomaly is the weekend anomaly, the observation that securities tend to be up on Fridays and down on Mondays. This anomaly is even more pronounced at holiday weekends.

Event anomalies are price changes that occur after some easily identified event, such as a listing announcement. Security prices of firms rise after it is announced that the firm's stock will be listed on the NYSE. Another event anomaly is analysts' recommendations. The more analysts there are recommending a particular security, the more likely it is that the security's price will fall in the near future. This puzzling result can be explained as follows. When one or two analysts discover an undervalued stock they recommend it to their clients, and when the clients buy the stock the price is driven up. This price increase attracts the attention of other analysts who subsequently recommend it, pushing the price even higher. This upward price pressure continues until some analysts start changing their buy recommendations to sell recommendations, and the price subsequently falls.

Finally, accounting anomalies are changes in stock prices that occur after the release of accounting information. For example, after an announcement of unusually high earnings, a firm's stock price continues to rise, as discussed earlier. Another accounting anomaly is the P/E ratio anomaly. Stocks with low price-to-earnings ratios tend to have higher returns. An anomaly that has attracted a lot of attention lately is the earnings momentum anomaly, in which stocks of firms whose growth rate of earnings has been rising tend to outperform other similar securities.

What can we conclude about market efficiency? As was stated at the beginning of the chapter, the purpose is not to place one position over another but rather to leave the final conclusion to the reader. The following are a few quotations that show what others have concluded:

In general, the empirical evidence in favor of the efficient market hypothesis is extremely strong.[11]

It's very hard to support the popular academic theory that the market is irrational [that is, that the EMT is true] when you know somebody who just made a twentyfold profit in Kentucky

---

[11] Burton Malkiel, 'Efficient market hypothesis', in John Eatwell, Murray Milgate and Peter Newman (eds), *The New Palgrave: Finance* (New York: Macmillan Press, 1989), p. 131.

Fried Chicken, and furthermore, who explained in advance why the stock was going to rise. My distrust of theorizers and prognosticators continues to the present day.[12]

Event studies are the cleanest evidence we have on efficiency....With few exceptions, the evidence is supportive.[13]

They [market inefficiencies] exist because we [practitioners] do not root out their basic causes. These causes are easy enough to identify, if one looks with enough dispassion and rigor. If the academics point to them, the rest of us can respond and...walk by.[14]

As you can see, disagreement regarding market efficiency still exists.

SUMMARY

■ *Define an efficient market.*
A well-functioning financial market in which prices reflect all relevant information is said to be efficient.

■ *Identify the types of information related to security prices in each form of the efficient market hypothesis.*
The efficient market theory (EMT) has three forms: the weak, the semistrong and the strong forms. The weak form of the EMT states that stock prices reflect information revealed by the historical price sequence. The semistrong form of the EMT states that stock prices reflect all relevant publicly available information. The strong form of the EMT states that prices reflect all publicly and privately available information.

■ *Compare investment strategies in efficient markets with investment strategies in inefficient markets.*
The existence of efficient capital markets has several important implications. Most important is that scarce resources are allocated in an efficient manner. Also, technical analysis is useless if at least the weak form of the EMT is true, and fundamental analysis is useless if at least the semistrong form of the EMT is true. Finally, no matter what form of the EMT an investor adheres to, portfolio selection benefits still hold. Thus, even under the EMT, portfolio selection is still important.

■ *Describe the findings of researchers who tested each form of the efficient market theory.*
Researchers have gathered empirical evidence related to the weak, semistrong and strong forms of the EMT. The evidence against the strong form is the most conclusive; some insiders are clearly able to make abnormal returns. The evidence related to the weak and semistrong forms is mixed; some technical trading strategies and some fundamental trading strategies have generated abnormal returns in the past.

■ *Define anomaly, and identify the common types of anomalies.*
An anomaly offers investors a chance to earn abnormal profits. Most of the anomalies that have been documented can be categorized in one of the following groups: firm, seasonal, event or accounting anomalies.

---

[12] Peter Lynch, *One Up on Wall Street* (New York: Penguin Books, 1989), p. 35.
[13] Eugene F. Fama, 'Efficient capital markets: 2', *Journal of Finance*, 46, December 1991, p. 1602.
[14] Dean LeBaron, 'Reflections on market inefficiency', *Financial Analysts Journal*, 39, May–June 1983, pp. 16–17, 23. Reprinted in Charles D. Ellis (ed.), *Classics 2: Another Investor's Anthology* (Homewood, IL: AIMR and Business One Irwin, 1991), p. 239.

KEY TERMS

Abnormal rate of return
Accounting anomaly
Active investment strategy
Anomaly
Cumulative abnormal rate
 of return (CAR)
Efficient market
Efficient market theory
 (EMT)
Event anomaly
Event study
Excess returns

Firm anomaly
Fundamental analysis
Historical prices
Index fund
Joint hypothesis
Market-to-book-value
 (M/B) ratio
Neglected firm effect
Normal rate of return
Passive investment
 strategy
Price/earnings (P/E) ratio

Random walk
Risk-adjusted rate of
 return
Seasonal anomaly
Semistrong form of the
 EMT
Size effect
Strong form of the EMT
Technical analysis
Timing ability
Weak form of the EMT

QUESTIONS

16.1   Explain why it is important to determine how efficient the markets are.

16.2   Suppose you flip a coin. Whenever a head shows up, the stock price goes up by 10%.
Whenever a tail shows up, the stock market drops by 5%. Are the stock rates of return
following a random walk? Explain.

16.3   The rates of return on two stocks have the following values:

Day	Stock A	Stock B
1	+10%	+10%
2	−5	+10
3	+10	−5
4	−5	−5
5	+10	+10
6	−5	−5
7	+10	+10

16.4   (a) The rates of return of a given stock are serially correlated. Does this conform with the
         EMT?

   (b) The rates of return on two stocks are correlated. Does this conform with the EMT?

16.5   IBM reported $7 EPS for the second quarter – lower than expected. The stock price on the
publication date (t_0) was $P_0 = \$90$. In the five days after the announcement, the prices
were $P_1 = \$89$, $P_2 = \$88$, $P_3 = \$85$, $P_4 = \$84$ and $P_5 = \$83$. In this period the market
went up. Does this evidence tend to support or refute semistrong efficiency? Why?

16.6   The market-to-book value (M/B) ratio of a given stock is as follows:

Quarter	M/B	Stock price
1	1.2	$100
2	0.9	90
3	1.3	95
4	1.0	80

What can be learned from this regarding market efficiency?

16.7 A firm's beta is 0.5, the riskless interest rate is 10% and the mean annual rate of return on the market portfolio is 0.2. The annual rates of return on the firm's stock for five observations are $R_1 = 6\%$, $R_2 = 10\%$, $R_3 = 15\%$, $R_4 = 20\%$ and $R_5 = 10\%$. Calculate AR and CAR over this five-year period.

16.8 Five firms announce an increase in dividends. On the announcement date the daily rate of return on these five stocks was $R_1 = 1\%$, $R_2 = 0\%$, $R_3 = 10\%$, $R_4 = 5\%$ and $R_5 = 3\%$, where the index $i = 1, 2, 3, 4$ and 5 denotes the different firms. We are given the following additional information:

| Firm | Beta | Daily rates of return on the announcement date | |
		Market portfolio	Risk-free rate
1	1	1%	0.013%
2	0.5	0.5	0.014
3	2	0.02	0.012
4	0.8	−1	0.009
5	1	2	0.010

Are there any abnormal returns on the dividend announcement date? Explain.

16.9 Four firms announce major stock repurchases. On the announcement date the daily rate of return on these four stocks was as follows: $R_1 = -3\%$, $R_2 = 2\%$, $R_3 = 12\%$ and $R_4 = -5\%$, where the index $i = 1, 2, 3$ and 4 denotes the different firms. We are given the additional following information:

| Firm | Beta | Daily rates of return on the announcement date | |
		Market portfolio	Risk-free rate
1	1.2	1.5%	0.01%
2	0.4	0.5	0.014
3	2	0.02	0.009
4	0.8	3	0.015

Are there an abnormal returns on the stock repurchase announcement date? Explain.

16.10 IBM announced a loss of more than $2 billion in the third quarter of 1992. On the announcement date, IBM's stock price fell by 10%. Suppose that after the announcement date, the rate of return on IBM was as follows:

Days after announcement	+1	+2	+3	+4	+5	+6
Rate of return adjusted for risk	−1%	−0.5%	−2%	−1%	−3%	−6%

Does this result support the notion of the efficient market theory?

16.11 Suppose five firms announce they are going to split their stocks. On the announcement date you have the following *abnormal* returns:

Firm	Abnormal return
1	−1%
2	2
3	3
4	0.5
5	4

(a) Calculate the average abnormal return.
(b) 'Because Firm 1 has a negative return, we cannot conclude that a stock split announcement positively affects a particular stock's price.' Evaluate this statement.

16.12 You observe the following abnormal returns on McDonnell Douglas, Inc., stock:

	Day	Abnormal return
	1	0%
	2	0.02
	3	3
	4	4
Announcement date —→	5	6
	6	0.1
	7	−0.1
	8	0.5
	9	−0.5
	10	0

On Day 5 the firm announces that a big contract has been signed with the Department of Defense.

(a) Calculate the cumulative abnormal return for Days 1 through 10.

(b) What can we conclude from this price behaviour?

16.13 Many investment analysts expect Xerox, Inc., to have earnings of $10 per share. The firm announced $12 earnings per share. What is the standardized unexpected earnings if the standard error of the estimate was 0.05?

16.14 Firm A announces an EPS of $10, whereas Firm B announces an EPS of $8 per share. The stock price of Firm A fell by 2%, and the stock price of Firm B went up by 4% on the announcement date. From this fact it is concluded that the lower the profit, the more positive is the market reaction. Do you agree?

16.15 There are two groups of firms. The first group consists of 100 small firms with an average size of $100 million, and the second group consists of 100 large firms with an average size of $1 billion. The average rate of return and beta of these groups are as follows:

	Small firms	Large firms
Average annual return	18%	12%
Beta	1.3	0.9

The average rate of return on the market portfolio is $\overline{R}_m = 13\%$, and the risk-free interest rate is 3%. Are there abnormal returns to the small firms? Are there abnormal returns to the large firms? Discuss.

16.16 Using cumulative abnormal rates of return over time, describe the expected behaviour of a stock before a major takeover when the following was true:

(a) There was no insider trading, nor was any insider trading anticipated.

(b) There was insider trading.

(c) Some astute investors rightly viewed the company as being underpriced.

SELECTED REFERENCES

Freund, W.C., and M.S. Pagano. 'Market efficiency in specialist markets before and after automation', *The Financial Review*, Vol. 35, No. 3, August 2000.

Kaiser, Kevin Stouraitis. 'Agency costs and strategic considerations behind sell-offs: The UK evidence', *European Financial Management*, Vol. 7, No. 3, 2001.

Ibbotson Associates, *Stocks, Bonds, Bills, and Inflation 2000 Yearbook*, Ibbotson Associates, Inc, Chicago.

Liu, Pu, Stanley D. Smith, and Azmat A. Syed. 'Stock price reactions to the *Wall Street Journal's* securities recommendations'. *Journal of Financial and Quantitative Analysis*, 25, September 1990, pp. 399–410.

Majnoni, G., and M. Messa. 'Stock exchange reforms and market efficiency: The Italian experience', *European Financial Management*, Vol. 7, 2001.

Malkiel, Burton. 'Efficient market hypothesis', in John Eatwell, Murray Milgate, and Peter Newman (eds.), *The New Palgrave: Finance*. New York: Macmillan Press, 1989.
This book is a concise review of the efficient market hypothesis.

Moy, Ronald L., and Ahyee Lee. 'A bibliography of stock market anomalies'. *Journal of Financial Education*, November 1991, pp. 41–51.
This article is a good place to begin examining the empirical evidence related to market anomalies.

Rendleman, Richard, J., Jr., Charles P. Jones, and Henry A. Latané. 'Empirical anomalies based on unexpected earnings and the importance of risk adjustments'. *Journal of Financial Economics*, 3, 1982, pp. 269–87.
This paper is one of many that address the quarterly earnings surprise anomaly.

Rubinstein, M. 'Rational markets: Yes or no? The affirmative case', *Financial Analysts Journal*, May/June 2001.

Tumarkin, R., and R.F. White Law. 'News or noise? Internet postings and stock prices', *Financial Analysts Journal*, May/June 2001.

SUPPLEMENTARY REFERENCES

Ariel, Robert A. 'A monthly effect in stock returns'. *Journal of Financial Economics*, 18, March 1987, pp. 161–74.

Bachelier, L. *Theorie de la speculation: Annales de l'Ecole Normale Superieure*, translated by A.J. Boness in P.H. Cootner (ed.), *The Random Character of Stock Market Prices*. Cambridge, MA: MIT Press, 1967.

Ball, R. 'Anomalies in relationships between securities' yields and yield-surrogates'. *Journal of Financial Economics*, 6, June–September 1978, pp. 103–26.

Bernard, Victor L. and Jacob K. Thomas. 'Evidence that stock prices do not fully reflect the implications of current warnings for future earnings'. *Journal of Accounting and Economics*, 13, December 1990, pp. 305–40.

Bhardwaj, R.K., and Brooks, L.D. 'The January anomaly: Effects of low share price, transaction costs and bid-ask bias', *Journal of Finance*, 47, January 1992, pp. 553–75.

Chan, K.C., and Nai-fu Chen. 'Structural and return characteristics of small and large firms'. *Journal of Finance*, 46, September 1991, pp. 1467–84.

Cochrane, John H. 'Volatility tests and efficient markets: A review essay'. *Journal of Monetary Economics*, 27, June 1991, pp. 463–85.

Connolly, Robert A. 'An examination of the robustness of the weekend effect'. *Journal of Financial and Quantitative Analysis*, 24, June 1989, pp. 133–69.

Cowles, A., and H.E. Jones. 'Some posteriori probabilities in stock market action', *Econometrica*, 5, No. 3, 1937, pp. 280–94.

Fama, E. 'The behavior of stock market prices'. *Journal of Business*, 38, No. 1, 1956, pp. 34–105.

Fama, Eugene F. 'Efficient capital markets: 2'. *Journal of Finance*, December 1991, pp. 1575–617.

Fama, Eugene F., and Kenneth R. French. 'The cross-section of expected stock returns'. *Journal of Finance*, 47, June 1992, pp. 427–65.

Fama, E., L. Fisher, M. Jensen, and R. Roll. 'The adjustment of stock prices to new information'. *International Economic Review*, 10, No. 1, 1969, pp. 1–21.

Granger, D., and O. Morgenstern. 'Spectral analysis of New York stock market prices'. *Kyklos*, 16, 1963, pp. 1–27.

Haugen, Robert A., and Jorion Philippe. 'The January effect: Still there after all these years'. *Financial Analysts Journal*, January–February 1996, pp. 27–31.

Huberman, Gur, and Shmuel Kandal. 'Market efficiency and Value Line's record'. *Journal of Business*, 63, April 1990, pp. 187–216.

Jegadeesh, Narashimham. 'Evidence of predictable behavior of security returns'. *Journal of Finance*, 45, July 1990, pp. 881–98.

Jersen, Gerald, Robert R. Johnson, and Jeffrey M. Mercer. 'New evidence on size and price to book effects'. *Financial Analysts Journal*, November–December 1997, pp. 37–42.

Kendall, M. 'The analysis of economic time series, 1: Prices'. *Journal of Royal Statistical Society*, 96, No. 1, 1953, pp. 11–25.

Lakonishok, Josef, and Edwin Maberly. 'The weekend effect: Trading patterns of individual and institutional investors'. *Journal of Finance*, 45, March 1990, pp. 231–43.

Merton, R. 'On estimating the expected return on the market: An exploratory investigation'. *Journal of Financial Economics*, 8, No. 4, 1980, pp. 323–61.

Ogden, J.P. 'Turn-of-month evaluations of liquid profits and stock returns: A common explanation for the monthly and January effects'. *Journal of Finance*, 45, September 1990, pp. 1259–72.

Roll, R. 'Orange juice and weather'. *American Economic Review*, 74, No. 5, 1974, pp. 861–80.

Seyhun, H.N. 'Can omitted risk factors explain the January effect? A stochastic dominance approach'. *Journal of Financial and Quantitative Analysis*, 28, June 1993, pp. 195–212.

Index